CRIME

AND

MR.

CAMPION

Three of Margery Allingham's finest studies in suspense have been collected in this long-awaited omnibus. Starring Miss Allingham's charming,
bespectacled sleuth Albert Campion, the three novels gathered here are:

DEATH OF A GHOST (1934)—The death of the great painter John
Lafcadio introduces Albert Campion to the strange world of high art and
low intentions.

FLOWERS FOR THE JUDGE (1936)—Albert Campion investigates
the scandal-plagued publishing house of Barnabas, Ltd. and discovers the
author of a murder.

DANCERS IN MOURNING (1937)—The theatre and its personalities
have never presented as vicious and evil a face as in this brilliant novel
about the world of the ballet.

Scene: England

Margery Allingham

CRIME
AND
MR.
CAMPION

Doubleday & Company, Inc.
GARDEN CITY, NEW YORK

*All of the characters in this book are fictitious,
and any resemblance to actual persons,
living or dead,
is purely coincidental.*

DEATH
OF
A
GHOST

LAFCADIO, John Sebastian, R.A., b. 1845, d. 1912. Painter. Entered studio of William Pakenham, R.A., 1861. Lived in Italy, 1865–1878. First exhibited Royal Academy, 1871; A.R.A., 1881; R.A., 1900; m. 1880, Arabella Theodora, d. of Sir J. and Lady Reid of Wendon Parva, Sussex. One son, John Sebastian, b. 1890. Killed in action, 1916. Best known works include: "The Girl at the Pool" (Nat. Gallery), "Group in Sunlight" (Tate), "Belle Darling" (Louvre), "Portraits of Three Young Men" (Boston), "Meeting of the Magi" and "Satirical Portrait" (Yokohama), etc., etc., also Loan Collection of forty works destroyed in Moscow, 1918. Cf. *The Life and Work of Lafcadio*, Vols. 1, 2, & 3, Max Fustian; *The Victorian Iconoclast*, Mrs. Betsy Fragonard; *The Moscow Tragedy*, Max Fustian; *Lafcadio the Man*, Max Fustian; *Biographie d'un maître de peinture à l'huile*, Ulysses Lafourchardière; *Weitere Bemerkungen zur Wahl der Bilder von John Lafcadio*, Gunther Wagner.

—Weber's *Who's Who in Art*

LAFCADIO, J., see *Charles Tanqueray, Letters to* (Phelps, 15/—)
—Dent's *Dictionary of Authors*

"LAFCADIO, . . . the man who saw himself the first painter in Europe and whom we who are left recognize as the last."
—K.J.R. in *The Times*, April 16, 1912

1 : *Interior with Figures*

There are, fortunately, very few people who can say that they have actually attended a murder.

The assassination of another by any person of reasonable caution must, in a civilized world, tend to be a private affair.

Perhaps it is this particular which accounts for the remarkable public interest in the details of even the most sordid and unintellectual examples of this crime, suggesting that it is the secret rather than the deed which constitutes the appeal.

If only in view of the extreme rarity of the experience, therefore, it seems a pity that Brigadier General Sir Walter Fyvie, a brilliant raconteur and a man who would have genuinely appreciated so odd a distinction, should have left the reception at Little Venice at twenty minutes past six, passing his old acquaintance Bernard, bishop of Mould, in the doorway, and thus missing the extraordinary murder which took place there by a little under seven minutes.

As the general afterwards pointed out, it was all the more irritating since the bishop, a specialist upon the more subtle varieties of sin, did not appreciate his fortune in the least.

At twenty minutes past six on the preceding day, that is to say exactly twenty-four hours before the general passed the bishop in the doorway, the lights in the drawing room on the first floor of Little Venice were up and Belle herself (the original "Belle Darling" of the picture in the Louvre) was seated by the fire talking to her old friend Mr. Campion, who had come to tea.

The house of a famous man who has been dead for any length of time, if it is still preserved in the condition in which he left it, is almost certain to have a museum-like quality if it has not achieved the withered wreaths and ragged garlands of a deserted shrine. It is perhaps the principal key to Belle's character that Little Venice in 1930 was as much John Lafcadio's home as if he were still down in the studio in the garden fighting and swearing and sweating over his pigments until he had thrashed them into another of his tempestuous pictures, which had so fascinated and annoyed his gentle and gentlemanly contemporaries.

If Belle Lafcadio was no longer the Belle of the pictures, she was still Belle Darling. She had, so she said, never had the disadvantage of being beautiful, and now, at two months off seventy, ample, creased, and startlingly reminiscent of Rembrandt's portrait of his mother, she had the bright quick smile and the vivacity of one who never has been anything but at her best.

At the moment she was wearing one of those crisp white muslin bonnets in which Normandy peasants delighted until fifty years ago. She wore it with the assurance that it was unfashionable, unconventional, and devastatingly becoming. Her black gown was finished with a little white filet round the neck, and her slippers were adorned with shameless marquisite buckles.

The room in which she sat had the same lack of conformity to any period or scheme. It was a personal room, quite evidently a part of someone's home, a place of strange curios but comfortable chairs.

L-shaped, it took up the entire first floor of the old house on the canal, and although nothing in it had been renewed since the war, it had escaped the elegant banalities of Morris and the horrors of the Edwardian convention. It was Belle's boast that she and Johnnie had never bought anything unless they had liked it, with the result that the deep Venetian red damask curtains, although faded, were still lovely, the Persian carpet had worn silky, and the immense overmantel which took up all one narrow end of the room and which was part of a reredos from a Flemish church had grown mellow and at one with the buff walls, as things do when accustomed to living together.

What was odd was that the sketch of Réjane by Fantin-Latour, the casual plaster study of a foot by Rodin and the stuffed polar bear presented to Lafcadio by Jensen after the 1894 portrait should also live together in equal harmony, or for that matter the hundred and one other curios with which the room was littered: yet they did, and the effect was satisfying and curiously exciting.

Mrs. Lafcadio's visitor sat opposite her, an unexpected person to find in such a room or in such company. He was a lank, pale-faced young man with sleek fair hair and horn-rimmed spectacles. His lounge suit was a little masterpiece, and the general impression one received of him was that he was well bred and a trifle absent-minded. He sat blinking at his hostess, his elbows resting upon the arms of his chair and his long hands folded in his lap.

The two were friends of long standing, and the conversation had waned into silence for some moments when Belle looked up.

"Well," she said with the chuckle which had been famous in the 'nineties, "here we are, my dear, two celebrities. Isn't it fun?"

He glanced at her. "I'm no celebrity," he protested fervently. "Heaven forbid. I leave that to disgraceful old ladies who enjoy it."

Mrs. Lafcadio's brown eyes, whose irises were beginning to fade a little, smiled at some huge inward joke.

"Johnnie loved it," she said. "At the time of Gladstone's unpopularity after the Gordon business Johnnie was approached to make a portrait of him. He refused the commission, and he wrote to Salmon, his agent: 'I see no reason to save Mr. Gladstone's face for posterity.'"

Campion eyed her contemplatively. "There's always a new Lafcadio story about this time of year," he said. "Do you invent them?"

The old lady looked demurely at the handkerchief in her hand.

"No," she said. "But I sometimes improve on them—just a little." She became suddenly alert. "Albert," she said, "you haven't come here on business, have you? You don't think someone's going to steal the picture?"

"I sincerely hope not," he said in some alarm. "Unless, of course, that supersalesman Max is planning a sensation."

"Max!" said Mrs. Lafcadio and laughed. "Oh, my dear, I've had a sweet thought about him. His first book about Johnnie, which came out after the Loan Collection in Moscow was lost, was called *The Art of John Lafcadio*, 'by one who knew him.' His eighth book on Johnnie came out yesterday. It's called *Max Fustian Looks at Art*—'a critical survey of the works of John Lafcadio by Europe's foremost critic.'"

"Do you mind?" said Mr. Campion.

"Mind? Of course not. Johnnie would have loved it. It would have struck him as being so funny. Besides, think of the compliment. Max made himself quite famous by just writing about Johnnie. I'm quite famous, just being Johnnie's wife. Poor dear Beatrice considers herself famous just being Johnnie's 'Inspiration,' and my blessed Lisa, who cares less about it than any of us, really is famous as Clytemnestra and the Girl at the Pool." She sighed. "I think that probably pleases Johnnie more than anything." She looked at her visitor with a half-apologetic grimace. "I always feel he's watching us from somewhere, you know."

Mr. Campion nodded gravely. "He had the quality of fame about him," he said. "It's amazing how persistent it is. If I may say so, regarded from the vulgar standpoint of publicity, this remarkable will of his was a stroke of genius. I mean, what other artist in the world ever produced twelve new pictures ten years after his death and persuaded half London to come and see them one after the other for twelve years?"

Belle considered his remark gravely. "I suppose it was," she agreed. "But you know, really, Johnnie didn't think of it that way. I'm perfectly certain his one idea was to fire a Parthian shot at poor Charles Tanqueray. In a way," she went on, "it was a sort of bet. Johnnie believed in his work, and he guessed that it would boom just after his death and then go completely out of favour—as of course it did. But he realized that as it was really good it would be bound to be recognized again eventually, and he guessed that ten years was about the time public opinion would take."

"It was a wonderful idea," the young man repeated.

"It wasn't in his will, you know," said the old woman. "It was a letter. Didn't you ever see it? I've got it here in the desk."

She rose with surprising agility and hurried across the room to a big serpentine escritoire, and, after pulling out one untidy drawer after another, finally produced an envelope which she carried back in triumph to the fireplace. Mr. Campion took the curio reverently and spread out a sheet of flimsy paper scribbled over in Lafcadio's beautiful hand.

The old lady stood beside him and peered over his shoulder. "He wrote it some time before he died," she said. "He was always writing letters. Read it aloud. It makes me laugh."

"Belle darling," read Mr. Campion. *"When you return a sorrowing widow from the Abbey, where ten thousand cretins will (I hope) be lamenting over some marble Valentine inscribed to their hero (don't let old Ffolliot do it—I will not be commemorated by nigger-bellied putti or unibreasted angels)—when you return, I want you to read this and help me once again as you have ever done. The oaf Tanqueray, to whom I have just been talking, is, I discover, looking forward to my death—he has the advantage of me by ten years—to bask in a clear field, to vaunt his execrable taste and milk-pudding mind unhampered by comparison with me. Not that the man can't paint; we Academicians are as good as beach photographers any day of the week. It's the mind of the man, with his train of long-drawered village children, humanized dogs, and sailors lost at sea, that I deplore. I've told him that I'll outlive him if I have to die to do it, and it has occurred to me that there is a way of making him see the point of my remark for once.*

"In the cellar I shall leave twelve canvases, boxed and sealed. In with them is a letter to old Salmon, with full particulars. You are not to let them out of your hands for five years after the date of my death. Then I want them sent to Salmon as they are. He will unpack them and frame them. One at a time. They are all numbered. And on Show Sunday in the eleventh year after my death I want you to open up the studio, send round invitations as usual, and show the first picture. And so on for twelve years. Salmon will do all the dirty work, i.e., selling, etc. My stuff will probably have gained in value by that time, so you'll get the crowd out of mere curiosity. (Should I be forgotten, my dear, have the shows for my sake and attend them yourself.)

"In any case old Tanqueray will have an extra twenty-two years of me hanging over his head, and if he outlives that, good luck to him.

"Many people will try to persuade you to open the packages before the date appointed, urging that I was not of sound mind when I wrote

this letter. You, who know that I have never been of sound mind in the accepted sense of the term, will know how to treat any such suggestion.

"All my love, my dear. If you see a strange old lady not at all unlike the late Queen, God bless her, mingling with the guests on the first of these occasions—it will be my ghost in disguise. Treat it with the respect it will deserve.

> Your husband, Madame,
> John Lafcadio.
> "(Probably the greatest painter since Rembrandt.)"

Mr. Campion refolded the letter. "Did you really see this for the first time when you returned from his funeral?" he demanded.

"Oh, dear me, no," said Mrs. Lafcadio, tucking the envelope back into the drawer. "I helped him write it. We sat up one night after Charles Tanqueray and the Meynells had been to dinner. He did all the rest, though. I mean, I never saw the pictures packed, and this letter was sent to me from the bank with the rest of his papers."

"And this is the eighth year a picture has been shown," said Mr. Campion.

She nodded, and for the first time a hint of sadness came into her faded brown eyes. "Yes," she said. "And of course there were many things we couldn't foresee. Poor old Salmon died within three years of Johnnie, and some time later Max took over the Bond Street business from his executors. And as for Tanqueray, he barely lasted eighteen months longer than Johnnie."

Mr. Campion looked curious. "What sort of man was Tanqueray?" he said.

Mrs. Lafcadio wrinkled her nose. "A clever man," she said. "And his work sold more than anyone else's in the 'nineties. But he had no sense of humour at all. A literal-minded person and distressingly sentimental about children. I often think that Johnnie's work was unspoilt by the conventions of the period largely because he had a wholly unwarrantable dislike of children. Would you like to come down and see the picture? All's ready for the great day tomorrow."

Mr. Campion rose to his feet.

As she tucked her arm through his and they descended the staircase she looked up at him with a delightfully confidential smile.

"It's like the mantelpiece in the Andersen story, isn't it?" she whispered. "We are the china figures. We come alive on one evening of the year. Tomorrow afternoon we shall retaste our former glory. I shall be the hostess, Donna Beatrice will supply the decorative note, and Lisa will wander about looking miserable, as she always did, poor creature. And then the guests will go, the picture will be sold—Liverpool Art Gallery this time, perhaps, my dear—and we shall all go to sleep again for another year."

She sighed and stepped down onto the tiled floor of the hall a little wearily.

From where they stood they could see the half-glass door to the garden, in which stood the great studio which John Lafcadio had built in 'eighty-eight.

The door was open, and the famous view of the "master's chair," which was said to be visible to the incoming guest once he stepped inside the front door of the house, was very clear.

Belle raised her eyebrows. "A light?" she said, and added immediately, "Oh, of course, that's Tennyson Potter. You know him, don't you?"

Mr. Campion hesitated. "I've heard of him, and I've seen him at past private views, but I don't think I've ever actually met him," he said.

"Oh, well, then—" She drew him aside as she spoke, and lowered her voice although there was not the remotest chance of her being overheard. "My dear, he's *difficult*. He lives in the garden with his wife—such a *sweet* little soul. I mean, Johnnie told them they could build a studio in the garden years ago when we first came here—he was sorry for the man—and so they did. Build a studio, I mean, and they've been here ever since. He's an artist; an engraver on red sandstone. He invented the process, and of course it never caught on—the coarse-screen block is so like it—and it blighted the poor man's life." She paused for breath and then rushed on again in her soft voice, which had never lost the excited tone of youth. "He's having a little show of his engravings, as he calls them —they're really lithographs—in a corner of the studio as usual. Max is angry about it, but Johnnie always let him have that show when an opportunity occurred, and so I've put my foot down."

"I can't imagine it," said her escort.

A gleam came into Mrs. Lafcadio's eyes. "Oh, but I have," she said. "I told Max not to be greedy and to behave as though he was properly brought up. He needs his knuckles rapped occasionally."

Campion laughed. "What did he do? Hurl himself at your feet in an agony of passionate self-reproach?"

Mrs. Lafcadio smiled with a touch of the most innocent malice in the world.

"*Isn't* he affected?" she said. "I'm afraid Johnnie would have made his life unbearable for him. He reminds me of my good grandmother: so covered with frills and furbelows that there's no way of telling where they leave off. As a child I wondered if they ever did, or if she was just purple bombazine all the way through. Well, here we are. It's a darling studio, isn't it?"

They had crossed the narrow draughty strip of covered way between the garden door of the house and the studio, and now entered the huge outside room in which John Lafcadio had worked and still entertained. Like most buildings of its kind it was an unprepossessing structure from the outside, being largely composed of corrugated iron, but inside it still reflected a great deal of the magnificent personality of its owner.

It was a huge airy place with a polished wood floor, a glass roof, and two enormous fireplaces, one at either end. It was also bounded on the northern side by a low balcony, filled in below with cupboards composed of linenfold panelling rescued from a reconstructed farmhouse in the 'nineties. Above the balcony were five long windows, each about twelve feet high, through which was a magnificent view of the Regent's Canal. Behind the fireplace nearest the door was a models' room and lavatory, approached by a small archway at the extreme western corner below the balcony.

The skeleton of the room, which is always in evidence in a building of the kind, was far more massive than is usual and effectually removed the temporary air of church hall or army hut.

At the moment when Belle and Campion entered, only one of the big hanging electric lamps was lit, so that the corners of the room were in shadow. There was no fire in the grate opposite the door, but the big old-fashioned stove in the other fireplace at the near end of the room was going, and the place was warm and comforting after the chilly garden.

Out of the shadows the famous portrait of Lafcadio by Sargent loomed from its place of honour over the carved mantel. Of heroic size, it had all the force, truth, and dignity of the painter's best work, but there was an unexpected element of swashbuckling which took the spectator some time to realize as a peculiarity of the sitter rather than of the artist. In his portrait John Lafcadio appeared a personage. Here was no paint-ennobled nonentity; rather the captured distinction of a man great in his time.

It is undeniably true, as many critics have pointed out, that he looked like a big brother of the Laughing Cavalier, even to the swagger. He was fifty when the portrait was painted, but there was very little grey in the dark red hair which galloped back from his forehead, and the contours of his face were youthful. He was smiling, his lips drawn back over very white teeth, and his moustache was the moustache of the Cavalier. His studio coat of white linen was unbuttoned and hung in a careless bravura of folds, and his quick dark eyes, although laughing, were arrogant. The picture has of course become almost hackneyed, and to describe it further would be superfluous.

Belle kissed her hand to it. She always did so, and her friends and acquaintances put the gesture down to affectation, sentimentality, or sweet wifely affection according to their several temperaments.

The picture of the moment, however, stood on an easel on the left of the fireplace, covered by a shawl.

Mr. Campion had taken in all this before he realized that they were not alone in the room. Over in the far corner by the stove a tall thin figure in shirtsleeves was hovering before a dozen or so whitewood frames arranged on a curtain hung over the panelling of the balcony cupboards.

He turned as Mr. Campion glanced at him, and the young man caught a glimpse of a thin red melancholy face whose wet pale eyes were set too close together above the pinched bridge of an enormous nose.

"Mr. Potter," said Belle, "here's Mr. Campion. You two know each other, don't you? I've brought him down to see the picture."

Mr. Potter put a thin cold hand in Mr. Campion's. "It's very fine this year—very fine," he said, revealing a hollow voice of unutterable sadness, "and yet—I don't know: 'fine,' perhaps, is hardly the word. 'Strong,' perhaps; 'dominating'; 'significant.' I don't know—quite. 'Fine,' I think. Art's a hard master. I've been all the last week arranging my little things. It's very difficult. One thing kills another, you know." He sent a despairing glance into the corner whence he had come.

Belle coughed softly. "This is *the* Mr. Campion, you know, Mr. Potter," she said.

The man looked up, and his eyes livened for an instant. "Not the— Oh, really? Indeed?" he said and shook hands again. His interest faded immediately, however, and once more he glanced in misery towards the corner.

Campion heard the ghost of a sigh at his elbow, and Belle spoke.

"You must show your prints to Mr. Campion," she said. "He's a privileged visitor, and we must take him behind the scenes."

"Oh, they're nothing, absolutely nothing," said Mr. Potter, in agony; but he turned quite brightly and led them over to his work.

At first sight of the array Mr. Campion began to share Mr. Potter's depression.

Red sandstone does not lend itself to lithography, and it seemed unfortunate that Mr. Potter, who evidently experienced great difficulty in drawing upon anything, should have chosen so unsympathetic a medium. There was, too, a distressing sameness about the prints, most of which appeared to be rather inaccurate and indefinite botanical studies.

Mr. Potter pointed out one small picture depicting a bowl of narcissi and an inverted wineglass.

"The Duke of Caith bought a copy of that, once," he said. "It was the second year we started this posthumous-show idea of Lafcadio's. That was 1923. It's now 1930: it must be seven years ago. That one has never gone again. I've put in a copy every year since. The picture business is very bad."

"It's an interesting medium," said Mr. Campion, feeling he was called upon to say something.

"I like it," said Mr. Potter simply. "I like it. It's a strain, though," he went on, striking his thin palms together like cymbals. "The stones are so heavy. Difficult to print, you know—and shifting them in and out of the acid is a strain. That one over there weighed thirty-seven pounds in the stone, and that's quite light compared with some of them. I get so tired. Well, let's go and look at Lafcadio's picture. It's very fine; perhaps a bit hot—a bit hot in tone, but very fine."

They turned and walked down the room to where Belle, who had removed the shawl from the picture, was fiddling with an indirect-lighting device round the frame.

"This is Max's idea," she said, shaking herself free from the tangle of flex. "People stay so late, and it gets so dark. Ah, here it is."

Immediately the picture sprang into prominence. It was a big canvas, the subject the trial of Joan of Arc. The foreground was taken up with the dark backs of the judges, and between their crimson sleeves one caught a vision of the girl.

"That's my wife," said Mr. Potter unexpectedly. "He often painted her, you know. Rather fine work, don't you think? All that massing of colour. That's typical. Great quantities of paint, too. I used to say to him—in joke, you know—'It's lucky you make it yourself, John, or you'd never be able to afford it.' See that blue on her scarf? That's the Lafcadio blue. No one's got that secret yet. The secret of the crimson had to go to help pay the death duties. Balmoral and Huxley bought it. Now any Tom, Dick, or Harry can get a tube for a few shillings."

Belle laughed. "Both you and Linda do so begrudge anyone having the secret of his colours. After all, the world's got his pictures; why shouldn't it have his paint? Then they'll have the copy and the materials, and if they can't do it, too, then all the more honour to Johnnie."

"Ah," said Mr. Potter, "remember Columbus and the egg. They could all make it stand up after he'd shown them how to crack it at one end. The secret was simple, you see, but Columbus thought of it first."

Belle grinned. "Albert," she said, "as one of the busiest investigators of our time, has the real significance of the Columbus story ever dawned on you?"

Mr. Campion indicated that it had not.

"That the egg was boiled, of course," said Belle and went off laughing, the white frills of her bonnet trembling.

Mr. Potter looked after her. "She doesn't change," he remarked. "She doesn't change at all." He turned back to the picture. "I'll cover it up," he said. "Lafcadio was a chap you didn't mind waiting upon. He was a great man, a great painter. I got on with him. Some people didn't. I remember him saying to me, 'Potter, you've got more sense in your gluteus maximus than old Charles Tanqueray has in the whole of his own and his damned art committee's heads put together.' Tanqueray was more popular than Lafcadio, you know, with the public; but Lafcadio was the

man. They all see it now. His work is fine—very fine. A bit hot in tone—
a bit hot. But very, very fine."

He was still muttering this magic formula when Mr. Campion left him
to rejoin Belle in the doorway. She took his arm again as they went into
the house.

"Poor Tennyson Potter," she murmured. "He's so depressing. There's
only one thing worse than an artist who can't draw and who thinks he
can, and that's one who can't draw and knows he can't. No one gets anything out of it then. But Johnnie liked him. I think it was all the stones
he uses. Johnnie was rather proud of his strength. He used to enjoy heav-
ing them about."

Her remarks were brought to a sudden end, as they came into the hall,
by the appearance at the top of the stairs of an apparition in what Mr.
Campion at first took to be fancy dress.

"Belle!" said a feminine voice tragically. "You really must exert your
authority. Lisa— Oh, is that someone with you?" The vision came down
the stairs, and Campion had time to look at her. He recognized her as
Donna Beatrice, a lady who had caused a certain amount of flutter in
artistic circles in 1900.

In 1900, at the age of thirty, she had possessed that tall beauty which
seems to have been a peculiarity of the period, and she had descended
upon the coterie which surrounded Lafcadio, a widow with a small income and an infinite capacity for sitting still and looking lovely. Lafcadio,
who could put up with anything provided it was really beautiful, had
been vastly taken by her, and she was referred to as "his Inspiration"
by those romantic feather-brained people who were loath to be uncharitable and at the same time incapable of understanding the facts.

There were two superstitions connected with Donna Beatrice. One was
that in the days when everyone was chatting about the beautiful peacock
strutting so proudly about the studio, she had approached Mrs. Lafcadio
and, in that sweet vacant voice of hers, had murmured: "Belle darling,
you must be Big. When a man is as great as the Master, no one woman
can expect to fill his life. Let us share him, dear, and work together in
the immortal cause of Art." And Belle, plump and smiling, had patted
one of the beautiful shoulders and whispered close to one of the lovely
ears: "Of course, my dear, of course. But let us keep it a secret from
Johnnie."

The other superstition was that Lafcadio had never allowed her to speak
in his presence; or, rather, had persuaded her not to by the simple expedient of telling her that her pinnacle of beauty was achieved when her
face was in repose.

For the rest, she was an Englishwoman with no pretension at all to
the "Donna" or the "Beatrice," which she pronounced Italian fashion,
sounding the final e. Very few knew her real name; it was a secret she

guarded passionately. But if in Lafcadio's lifetime she had been content to remain beautiful but dumb, on his death she had developed an unexpected force of character inasmuch as she had shown very plainly that she had no intention of giving up the position of reflected glory which she had held so long. No one knew what arguments she had used to prevail upon Belle to permit her to take up her residence in the house, but at any rate she had succeeded, and now occupied two rooms on the second floor, where she continued her hobby of manufacturing "art" jewelry and practising various forms of semi-religious mysticism to which she had lately become addicted.

At the moment she was dressed in a long Florentine gown of old-rose brocade, strongly reminiscent of Burne-Jones but cut with a curtsey to Modernity, so that the true character of the frock was lost and it became an odd nondescript garment covering her thin figure from throat to ankle. To complete her toilet she had draped a long pink-and-silver scarf across her shoulders, and the two ends rippled behind her with the untidy grace of a nymph on the cover of *Punch*.

Her hair was frankly 1900. Its coarse gold strands had faded, and there were wide silver ribbons amongst them, but the dressing was still that of the Gibson Girl, odd in a convention not old enough to be romantic.

An incongruous note was struck by a black cord running from beneath her hair to a battery on her chest, for her hearing, never good, had declined with the years, and she was now practically stone deaf except when equipped with this affront to her vanity.

Round her neck was a beaten-silver chain of her own making, hanging to her knees and weighted by a baroque enamel cross. She was a figure of faintly uncomfortable pathos, reminding the young man irresistibly of a pressed rose, a little brown about the edges and scarcely even of sentimental value.

"Mr. Campion?" A surprisingly hard bony hand was thrust into his. "You've been seeing the picture, of course?" The voice was soft and intentionally vibrant. "I was so thrilled when I saw it again after all these years. I remember lying on the chaise-longue in the studio while the Master painted it."

She dropped her eyes on the name, and he had the uncomfortable impression that she was about to cross herself.

"He liked to have me near whilst he was painting, you know. I know now that I always had a blue aura in those days, and that's what inspired him. I do think there's such a lot in Colour, don't you? Of course, he told me it was to be a secret—even from Belle. But Belle never minds. Dear Belle." She smiled at the other woman with a mixture of affection and contempt.

"Do you know, I was discussing Belle with Dr. Hilda Bayman, the

Mystic. She says Belle must be an old soul—meaning, you understand, that she's been on the earth many times before."

Campion gave way to the embarrassment which Donna Beatrice's mystic revelations invariably produced upon her more acute acquaintances. Pampered vanity and the cult of the Higher Selfishness he found slightly nauseating.

Belle laughed. "I love to hear that," she said. "A dear old soul, I always hope. A sort of Old Queen Cole. Has Linda come in yet? She went to see Tommy Dacre," she continued, turning to Campion. "He came back from Florence last night, after three years at mural work. Isn't it tragic? The students used to paint cathedral ceilings; now they paint cinema roofs."

Donna Beatrice's still beautiful face adopted a petulant expression.

"I really don't know anything about Linda," she said. "It's Lisa I'm worrying about. That's why I wanted to see you. The creature simply refuses to wear the Clytemnestra robe tomorrow. I've had it let out. She ought to defer a little to the occasion. As it is, she simply looks like an Italian cook. We always look like our minds in the end—Belle, what are you laughing at?"

Mrs. Lafcadio squeezed Mr. Campion's arm. "Poor Lisa," she said and chuckled again.

Two bright spots of colour appeared on Donna Beatrice's cheekbones. "Really, Belle, I hardly expect you to appreciate the sacredness of the occasion," she said, "but at least don't make my task more difficult. We've got to serve the Master tomorrow. We've got to keep his name green, to keep the torch alight."

"And so poor Lisa's got to put on a tight purple dress and leave her beloved kitchen. It seems a little severe. You be careful, Beatrice. Lisa's descended from the Borgias on her mother's side. You'll get arsenic in your minestrone if you tease her."

"Belle, how can you! In front of a detective, too." The two bright spots in Donna Beatrice's cheeks deepened. "Besides, although Mr. Campion knows it, I thought we'd agreed to keep Lisa's position here a secret. It seems so terrible," she went on, "that the Master's favourite model should degenerate into a cook in his household."

Belle looked discomfited, and an awkward moment was ended by a peal on the front-door bell and the almost instantaneous appearance of Lisa herself at the kitchen door.

Lisa Capella, discovered by Lafcadio on the slopes outside Veccia one morning in 1884, had been brought by him to England, where she occupied the position of principal model until her beauty passed, when she took up the household duties for Belle, to whom she was deeply attached. Now, at the age of sixty-five, she looked much older, a withered, rather terrible old woman with a wrinkled brown face, quick, dark, angry eyes, and very white hair scraped back from her forehead. She was dressed completely in black, the dead and clinging folds which enveloped her only relieved by a gold chain and brooch.

She shot a sullen, vicious glance at Beatrice, sped past her on noiseless, felt-slippered feet over the coloured tiles, and swung the front door open.

A rush of cool air, a little dank from the canal, sped down the hall to meet them, and instantly a new personality pervaded the whole place as vividly and tangibly as if it had been an odour.

Max Fustian surged into the house, not crudely or noisily, but irresistibly, and with the same conscious power with which a successful actor-manager makes his appearance in the first act of a new play. They heard his voice, deep, drawling, impossibly affected, from the doorway.

"Lisa, you look deliriously macabre this evening. When Hecate opens the door of Hell to me she will look like you. Ah, Belle darling! Are we prepared? And Donna Beatrice! And the sleuth! My salutations, all of you."

He came up out of the shadow to lay one very white hand affectionately on Belle's arm, while the other, outstretched, suggested an embrace which included Mr. Campion, Donna Beatrice, and the stealthily retreating Lisa.

When one considered Max Fustian's appearance it was all the more extraordinary that his personality, exotic and fantastic as it was, should never have overstepped the verge into the ridiculous. He was small, dark, pale, with a blue jowl and a big nose. His eyes, which were bright and simian, peered out from cavernous sockets, so dark as to appear painted. His black hair was ungreased and cut into a conventional shock which had just sufficient length to look like a wig. He was dressed, too, with the same mixture of care and unconventionality. His double-breasted black coat was slightly loose, and his soft black tie flowed from beneath his white silk collar.

He had thrown his wide black hat and black raincoat onto the hall chest as he passed and now stood beaming at them, holding the gesture of welcome as one who realizes he has made an entrance.

He was forty, but looked younger and appreciated his good fortune.

"Is everything ready?" The indolent weariness of his voice had a soporific quality, and he swept them down to the studio again before they had realized it.

Potter had gone, and the place was in darkness. Max switched on the lights and looked round with the quick, all-seeing glance of a conjuror surveying his paraphernalia. A frown spread over his forehead, and he returned to his hostess.

"Dear Belle, why do you insist on those nauseating lithographs? It degrades the occasion into a church bazaar." He pointed contemptuously to the unfortunate Mr. Potter's display. "The fancywork stall."

"Really, Belle, I think he's right." Donna Beatrice's low singsong voice was plaintive. "There'll be my little table over here with the Guild's jewelry upon it, and really I think that's enough. I mean—other people's pictures in *his* studio—it's sacrilege, isn't it? The vibrations won't be right."

Looking back upon that evening in the light of after events, Mr. Campion frequently cursed himself for his lack of detachment. Seen in retrospect, after the tragedy, it seemed to him impossible that he could have spent so long in the very heart of the dormant volcano without hearing the rumblings of the eruption to come. But on that evening he noticed nothing save that which passed upon the surface.

Max had disregarded his ally's efforts and continued to look interrogatively at Mrs. Lafcadio.

Belle shook her head at him as though he had been a naughty dog, and glanced round the studio.

"The floor looks very nice, don't you think?" she said. "Fred Rennie scrubbed it, and Lisa polished it."

Max shrugged his shoulders, a gesture almost contortionate, but having made his protest he gave way gracefully. Next instant he was himself again, and Campion, watching him, realized how he had managed to insinuate himself into the position of Lafcadio's entrepreneur.

He strode down the room, flipped the shawl from the painting, and stood back enraptured.

"Sometimes Beauty's like the Gorgon's head. One's spirit turns to stone, beholding it," he said. His voice was startlingly unaffected, and the contrast lent the extravagant phrase a passionate sincerity which startled everyone, including, it would seem, Max Fustian. To Mr. Campion's amazement the little dark eyes suddenly suffused with tears.

"We must all vibrate to green when we think of the picture," said Donna Beatrice with paralyzing idiocy. "Beautiful apple green, the colour of the earth. That shawl is so helpful, I think."

Max Fustian laughed softly. "Green is the colour for money, isn't it?" he murmured. "Suffuse the picture with a green light and it'll sell. Well, I have done my part. Tomorrow everyone will be here: soldiers, poets, fat mayors buying for their cities, the intelligentsia, diplomats—the ambassadors are coming, I heard tonight—and of course the Church." He flung out his hand. "The Church, big-bellied, purple-gowned."

"The bishop always comes," ventured Belle mildly. "Dear man, he used to come before there were any pictures."

"The press," Max Fustian swept on, "and the critics, my colleagues."

"Leashed in like hounds, no doubt," said Belle, who was growing restive. "Don't let me forget to put a shilling in the meter or the whole place will be in darkness after six. I wish we'd never had it put in for that wretched dancing class during the war."

Donna Beatrice caught her breath noisily. "Belle, you promised never to mention that again. That was almost blasphemy."

Belle sniffed quite definitely. "Johnnie's stock was down, we were very short, and the money was useful," she said. "And if I hadn't had the meter put in we should never have been able to pay the electric-light bills so soon. And now—" She broke off abruptly. "Oh, Linda! My dear, how pale you look!"

They turned round immediately as John Lafcadio's granddaughter strode down the room towards them. The daughter of Belle's only son, killed at Gallipoli in 1916, was, according to Donna Beatrice, "definitely Aries."

Upon expansion this term proved to mean something uncomplimentary, a daughter of the Sun, a young soul and pertaining to some lowly plane in the astrological cosmos. To the unenlightened eye she was a strongly made, tempestuous young woman of twenty-five who bore a notable resemblance to her grandfather.

She had the same coarse tawny hair, the same wide mouth and high cheekbones. She was beautiful only by the most modern standards, and her restless violent personality was apparent in every movement. She and Belle understood one another, and a tremendous affection existed between the two. The others were all a little afraid of her, save perhaps Mr. Campion, who had many strange friends.

At the moment her pallor was almost startling, and her eyes beneath her thick brows were burning with nothing less than ferocity. She nodded to Campion and shot a frosty, barely civil glance at Max and Donna Beatrice.

"Tom is in the hall," she said. "He's just coming. He's brought some photographs of his stuff for the Puccini library. They're very fine. I suppose you didn't think so, Max?"

The challenge was gratuitous, and Belle's old eyes flickered anxiously as they had done on private-view days long ago.

Max smiled. "Dacre has all the elements of a great man," he said. "But he should stick to his medium. In tempera he can express himself. There are times when he reminds me of Angelica Kaufmann."

"The panels for the library are in tempera."

"Oh? Really? I saw a photograph of a figure piece. I thought it was a poster for a mineral water." Max's tone had a leisurely spitefulness that was masterly. "I saw the model, too. He brought her back from Italy with him. In imitation of Lafcadio, I suppose."

The girl swung round on him, unconsciously adopting the odd angular posture, with one hip thrown out, so beloved by the moderns. Her pallor had increased. It was evident that an explosion was imminent, and Belle interposed.

"Where is the man, anyway?" she demanded. "I haven't seen him for three years, and he's a very old friend of mine. I remember when he came in here as a little boy, so prim, so solemn. He told Johnnie just what he thought of one of his pictures, and Johnnie put him across his knee and spanked him for his impudence—his mother was so angry. But Johnnie altered the picture afterwards."

Donna Beatrice tittered politely at this reminiscence of John Lafcadio's disgraceful behaviour as the victim of it came into the room.

Thomas Dacre, a man of great ability, thirty-seven years old, unrecognized and obsessed by his own shortcomings, resembled a battered, careworn edition of the Apollo Belvedere in horn-rimmed spectacles. He was one of that vast army of young men who had had five all-important years cut out of their lives by the war, and who bitterly resented the fact without altogether realizing it. Dacre's natural disbelief in himself had been enhanced by severe shell-shock, which had left him capable of making any sacrifice to the furtherance of his creature comforts. His engagement to the tempestuous Linda had surprised everyone at its announcement just before his departure for Italy, but it was supposed that these two unhappy spirits had found mutual solace in each other's charity.

He came up to Belle, who greeted him with that delight which was half her charm.

"My dear, I am glad to see you. I hear you've done so well. Have you brought the photographs? Johnnie always predicted you'd be a great man."

He flushed: Belle was irresistible. But, immediately ashamed of his pleasure, he shrugged his shoulders and spoke ungraciously.

"I'm a cinema-house decorator," he said. "Ask Max. He knows good commercial work when he sees it."

But Belle was indefatigable. She slipped her arm through the newcomer's.

"Tell me all about it," she said. "Did you stay at the old studio in San Gimignano? And is poor old Theodora still alive? Isn't her cooking atrocious? Do you know, Johnnie made one of her children eat up every bit of the omelette she once sent up for our supper. And of course the wicked old thing had to nurse the poor little mite all the next day."

This unconventional sidelight on the character of a great man was suitably received, but Max was not willing to lose command of the stage for long. With his little dark eyes flickering mischievously, he glanced at the girl, who had lit a cigarette and was surveying her grandfather's picture with the critical but unbiased gaze of a fellow craftsman, and turned again to Dacre.

"How does the lovely Rosa-Rosa take to London?" he enquired. "Such a romantic name, madame. Rosa-Rosa."

"Your new model?" said Belle, still concentrating on the younger man.

He nodded. "One of the Rosinis. Do you remember them? She's a bastard, I think, by a German. Extremely modern in shape. The Teutonic streak gives her an extraordinary flatness. I've used her for nearly a year now. Her feet are ugly."

Belle, who had listened to this somewhat technical description with complete understanding, nodded her white headdress sagely.

"All the Rosinis have little, stubby feet. You don't remember Lucrezia? There was a great fuss about her thirty years ago. She claimed to be descended from Del Sarto's model, but she grew tired very easily and wouldn't work."

"You must have found the girl very useful," drawled Max with another glance at Linda, "since you bring her home despite the official business of permits and so on."

Dacre looked at him with lazy surprise. "Of course the girl's very useful," he said stiffly. "A reliable model who isn't hideous or temperamental is the most difficult thing in the world to get hold of. This girl sits like a rock."

"What an extraordinary addition to the ménage in Drury Lane. How does the estimable D'Urfey respond to the lady's charms?" Max seemed to be deliberately offensive, and again he shot that sidelong glance at Linda.

Suddenly she seemed to become aware of it.

"Rosa-Rosa is the most beautiful creature I ever saw," she said with dangerous quietness. "She's got the figure of a John gipsy and the face of a fiend. Both Matt and Tom are hysterical about the things she says. *And you're a nasty little sneaking, trouble-mongering mongrel.*"

She strode over to him and caught him a savage blow with the back of her hand which brought out a red mark on his sallow cheek. The attack was so sudden and unwarranted, and betrayed her so utterly, that the shocked silence in the great room lasted until she had disappeared through the doorway.

It was then and only then that Mr. Campion caught a glimpse of something dangerous beneath the surface of this odd pantomime rehearsal performed in such solemn deference to the fancy of a dead man.

Max laughed sulkily and pulled the cover over the painting so that his back was turned to the company. Dacre looked after the girl, his forehead knotted with fury. Donna Beatrice remarked "Aries, Aries" with that sublime complacency known only to those who have the happy conviction that they are not as other men, and Belle, her lips pursed into a little grimace of pity and her faded brown eyes shiny with tears, murmured deprecatingly, "My dear—oh, my *dear!*"

2 : *Show Sunday*

In the great days of the 'nineties, when Art and the Academy were synonymous in the public mind, the Sunday before sending-in day was a festival. In every studio in the kingdom was held a solemn exhibition of those works intended for the Selection Committee's delectation. Since it was so often the first and last time that the pictures were ever exhibited anywhere, the gatherings served a useful purpose, and while much tea and sherry was consumed many technical mysteries were discussed.

The death of this pleasant custom marked the end of an era, and it says much for Max Fustian's powers of showmanship that he managed to turn the annual affair at Lafcadio's studio into a minor social event and to create in it one of the little ceremonies which mark the very beginning of the Season.

To the press it was a yearly blessing, provoking the first fanfare before that hardy set piece, the opening of the Royal Academy's Summer Exhibition. Lafcadio, always in advance of his time, was still a good deal too modern for "Constant Reader" and "Paterfamilias," and the element of surprise connected with the yearly picture and its subsequent purchase by the inevitable public body or philanthropist made it one of those sure-fire newspage-column headings comparable with the arrival of the Cambridge crew at Putney or the Birthday Honours List.

On a Sunday in March 1930, therefore, the dusty windows of the dusty yellow houses of Swallow Crescent reflected some of the glories of their past in the parade of automobiles parked against the plump stone balustrade of the canal.

Little Venice ceased to look merely shabby and became interestingly Bohemian, as in its doorway Fred Rennie, magnificently unself-conscious in his leather apron and crimson shirtsleeves, stood to receive the guests.

Fred Rennie was yet another denizen of Lafcadio's remarkable garden. Rescued as a child from a fever-infested canal boat by the painter, he had been taken into the household as a colour mixer. His somewhat sketchy education he had received from Lafcadio himself, and he served the great man devotedly, grinding up the colour and experimenting with new mediums in the grand manner of centuries before. The old coach house at the end of the garden had been turned into a little laboratory, and in the room above it Fred Rennie lived and slept.

When Lafcadio died, disdaining the offers from several paint firms, he had remained with Lisa to form the domestic staff of Little Venice.

Even his service in the war had not uprooted him. For female society he depended upon the canal boats, so that his attachments were necessarily of a transitory nature. His life was peaceful, and it is probable that he enjoyed these annual ceremonies more than anyone save Max Fustian himself.

His costume was Donna Beatrice's idea, since the picturesque rags he had worn in Lafcadio's studio as a child were scarcely suitable for state occasions.

For the rest, he was a little, wiry person with thick dark hair, quick eyes, and hands stained and bitten with acid.

He greeted Mr. Campion as a friend. "We're very full now, sir," he murmured deferentially. "A good many more than last year, I should say."

Campion passed on down the wide hall and would have gone on to the studio had not someone plucked at his arm in the dark corner by the basement stairs.

"Mr. Campion. Just a minute, sir."

It was Lisa, Lisa bad-tempered and uncomfortable in a shiny purple gown only too evidently let out at the seams. In the shadow, with her dark eyes glittering at him, he caught a glimpse of her as she must have appeared that morning on the slopes of Veccia. But the next moment she was the old wrinkled Italian woman again.

"You come up to see Miss Linda?" The foreign intonation turned the remark into a question. "Mrs. Potter's with her in her room. Mrs. Lafcadio told me to look out for you and to ask you to persuade her to come down. There are not enough people to greet. Donna Beatrice cannot leave her little jewelry table."

The contempt in the last words was indescribable. Lisa's opinion of Donna Beatrice defied thought, much less print.

Mr. Campion, whose rôle of universal uncle brought him many strange commissions, accepted this one without a thought, and with a word to Lisa he hurried up the six flights of stairs to the third floor, where, in one of the little attics under the slates, Linda had her studio.

The uncarpeted room with its uncurtained windows smelt vilely of oil paint, and the usual paraphernalia of a work studio as opposed to the show variety was heaped about the floor.

Linda Lafcadio was leaning on her elbows at one of the windows looking down at the canal.

Mrs. Potter stood in the centre of the disordered room. She was a little, dowdy woman with iron-grey bobbed hair, capable hands, and an air of brisk practicalness which stamped her at once as one of those efficient handmaids-of-all-work to the arts who are capable of undertaking any little commission from the discovery of a Currier & Ives to the chaperoning of a party of society-girl students across Europe. She was an expert embroideress, a connoisseur of bookbinding, and supported herself and, it was said, her husband by sundry art classes at fashionable day schools and a few private students.

She looked at Mr. Campion uncertainly, and he introduced himself.

"I know what you've come to say. You want me to come down," she said, before he could get in a word of explanation. "Belle wants me. I was the model for this picture, you know—I don't like to think how many years ago. Well, I'll leave you to talk to Linda. Try and persuade her to come down. After all, we don't want to let anything spoil today, do we? So grateful to you, Mr. Campion."

She bustled off, leaving a tang of schoolmistress in the air.

As Linda did not move, Mr. Campion looked for somewhere to sit down.

Displacing a heap of paint rags, an ashtray, a bottle of glue, and a small plaster cast, he spread a handkerchief over the seat of the only chair the room contained and settled himself. He sat there for some time looking inoffensive but hopelessly out of place. As the owner of the room did not move he took a wallet from his breast pocket and extracted a newspaper cutting. Adjusting his spectacles, he began to read aloud:

"*DEAD HAND SPEAKS AGAIN. Today, in a little old forgotten corner of our wonderful London, the ghost of a great artist, thought by some to be the greatest artist of our time, entertains the glass of fashion and the mould of form for the eighth time in a twelve-year programme. Ambassadors, prelates, society matrons will all vie with one another in discussing John Lafcadio's new picture, which comes to us across the gulf of the years.*

"*Are you embarrassed when you meet a duchess? It may be your lot to rub shoulders with the nobility, or yours may be a humbler station, but, in whatever circle you move, you should be prepared at any moment to meet the most trying of social ordeals. What would you say if Royalty spoke to you, for instance? Would you stand tongue-tied, or break into hysterical laughter, thus wasting for ever a golden opportunity never to be* —Oh, I beg your pardon; I'm in the wrong column. This is all about a free booklet. Let me see; where were we? *Peeking in at a certain hotel in the Strand, I found Lady Gurney laughing heartily over her husband's adventures in the East.*"

There was still no sign from the figure in the window. He threw the cutting away disgustedly.

"There's nothing else on that," he said. "Should I sing, perhaps?"

There was a long silence after he had spoken, and presently she turned round and came towards him. He was startled by her appearance. Her pallor of the preceding night had gone, and a livid hue had taken its place. Her eyes looked dangerous, her mouth unnaturally firm, and her whole body stiffened and unnatural.

"Oh, it's you," she said. "What are you here for?"

She did not wait for his answer, but walked across the room, and, taking up a palette knife, began to chip little flecks of colour off a partially finished canvas on the easel. She paid minute attention to the damage she was doing, her face very close to the knife.

Mr. Campion, who recognized this symptom, bounded to his feet and caught her by the shoulders.

"Don't be a fool," he said sharply. "And for heaven's sake don't make an exhibition of yourself."

The unexpected vigour of this attack had the desired effect. Her hands dropped to her sides.

"What's up?" he said, more kindly. "Tommy?"

She nodded, and for an instant her eyes were honestly angry and contemptuous.

Mr. Campion sat down again. "Serious?"

"It wouldn't be, if I wasn't such a fool."

She spoke savagely, and her despair was evident.

"You haven't seen her," she said, after a pause, "have you?"

"Who? The model?" Mr. Campion felt he was coming to the root of the matter.

Her next remark startled him.

"It's the hopeless interference of people who don't even understand the facts which is making me hysterical," she said. "Claire Potter has been trying to explain for the last half hour that in her opinion models are barely human and it doesn't follow that just because a man brings one back from Italy he's in love with her. As if that came into it! If Tommy had fallen in love with Rosa-Rosa the situation would be very simple, and I shouldn't feel so much like murdering him as I do now."

She walked over to a cupboard and, after rummaging in its untidy depths, returned with a sketchbook.

"Look at that," she said.

Mr. Campion turned over the pages, and his casual interest suddenly deepened. He sat up and readjusted his spectacles. "I say, these are very fine," he said. "Where did you get them?"

She jerked the book from his hand. "Tommy," she said, "before he went away. And now he's doing stuff that would disgrace a magazine cover. Do you realize he's brought that girl over here to make wrappers for patent medicines? Don't you see, he's thrown everything away. It looked like madness when he gave up oils to go in for tempera. *Now* it's just suicidal, turning to this sort of thing."

Mr. Campion, who had been impressed by the sketches, could see this point of view, but could not work himself up into the quivering state of indignation which she had achieved. After all, in a cold world it seemed that if the fires of high art had died down in a man's heart a taste for commerce was not to be deplored. He said as much.

She turned on him, blazing. "Quite," she said. "I've got nothing against commercialism. But it puts a man on a different plane. It's insufferable of him to expect the same sacrifices. If he hadn't brought Rosa-Rosa over, the whole thing would probably never have arisen—at least, not violently."

"If I may say so," said Mr. Campion quietly, "I don't quite see how Rosa-Rosa comes into this."

"You're extraordinarily dense," said the girl. "He married her first, of course. How d'you think he got her into England for keeps otherwise? That's what Max was getting at last night. That's why I hit him. As I say, if Tommy had been in love with her it wouldn't have been so bad."

Here was a grievance that even Mr. Campion could understand.

"I see," he said weakly.

She came towards him, looking for an instant like a passionate untidy child.

"Can't you understand that if he'd gone on doing his own sort of stuff it wouldn't have mattered? I wouldn't have been insulted last night when he suggested that we should all three set up house together. The trouble of getting this girl into England permanently would have been a sufficient reason for his marriage, but if he simply needs her for commercial work he's not worth it. Oh, I wish to God he was dead!"

Campion felt that it was impossible not to sympathize with her, even if her point of view was not altogether his own. One thing remained clear: her grievance was not imagined.

"Don't mention it to Belle," she said quickly. "She'd be furious, and it wouldn't do any good. Belle's very conventional."

"So am I," said Campion, and a long pause ensued. "Look here, I'd better go down," he said at length. "I don't see that there's anything I can say about this bad business, but if there's anything I can do you've only got to point it out."

She nodded absently, and he thought she had returned to the window, but before he had reached the first landing she caught up with him, and they went down together.

As they reached the hall the constant stream of incoming visitors had thinned and was now jostled by a secondary stream coming out. Mr. Campion and the girl were held up on the staircase by two old gentlemen who had taken possession of the bottom stair for a moment of conversation.

Noticing the young people hovering behind them, the acquaintances shook hands hastily, and Brigadier General Sir Walter Fyvie hurried out while Bernard, bishop of Mould, strode down the hall into the studio.

3 : *Murder at the Reception*

The evening mist rising up from the canal had grown perceptibly thicker, Campion noticed as he walked behind the bishop down the asphalt path, and the studio lights were blazing. Lisa had drawn the curtains over the tall windows to shut out the melancholy yellow sky, and the grateful heat and scented air of the crowded studio was comforting after the dankness of the garden.

The reception was drawing slowly to a close. The majority of the guests had gone, but the big studio was still alive with chatter and polite laughter.

Max had every reason to be satisfied with his organization. The gathering had been the most brilliant of its kind. The ambassador and his satellites were still hovering about the picture, which dominated the room, and there was a fair sprinkling of personages among the lesser social and artistic fry.

No one could doubt that the gathering was an Occasion. It seemed impossible that Lafcadio himself should not be there striding about, welcoming his friends, overwhelming in his size and magnificence.

But if it was a triumph for Max, it was also one for Belle. She stood in the centre of the studio greeting her guests, her black velvet frock severe and simple as ever, but her peasant bonnet of crisp organdie sewn with Valenciennes.

The bishop went up to her with outstretched hands. They were very old friends.

"My dear lady," he said, his famous voice rumbling like the organ in his own cathedral in his efforts to lower it a little. "My dear lady, what a triumph! What a triumph!"

Mr. Campion gazed round the room. It was evident that he would not be able to get near Belle for some time. He caught sight of Donna Beatrice, a startling vision in green and gold, talking psychomancy to a bewildered-looking old gentleman whom he recognized as a scientist of world-wide distinction.

In the background, unnoticed and forlorn, he espied the melancholy Mr. Potter, whose eyes turned ever and again with shuddering agony to the dismal display of prints upon the curtain.

He heard Linda catch her breath, and he turned to see her gazing across the room. He followed her glance and caught sight of Tommy Dacre leaning by the table where the jewelry made by Donna Beatrice's protégées, the Guild of Women Workers in Precious Metals, was displayed. He was standing with his back to the table, half sitting on the edge of it, in fact. He was carelessly dressed, but had taken the precaution of conforming to the costume permitted by popular superstition to the artist.

By his side was a girl, a girl so striking, even startling, in her appearance that Campion recognized her immediately as the cause of the passionate resentment in the breast of the elemental young woman at his side. Rosa-Rosa looked less like an Italian than one would have thought possible. She had a curious angular figure whose remarkably well-developed muscles showed through her thin grey dress.

Rosa-Rosa's frizzy yellow hair was parted in the centre and hung obliquely round her head. Her face was beautiful but fantastic. She had the dark mournful eyes and arched brows of a Florentine Madonna, but her nose was long and sharp and her lips thin and finely curled. Like all natural models she moved very little and then only to drop from one attitude into another, which she held with remarkable faithfulness.

At the moment she was listening to Dacre, who was chatting to her in Italian, his head thrown back, his hands thrust deep into his pockets, and his black hat crushed under one arm.

She was leaning forward, her chin tilted slightly, her weight supported on one foot, her arms hanging at her sides. It was an arrested movement, perfect in its way and utterly unexpected and striking.

She looked, Campion thought, less like a human animal than an example of decorative art.

Linda walked across the room towards them, and Campion followed her. Dacre's smile vanished as he caught sight of the girl, but he did not look embarrassed, and as a layman Campion wondered afresh at the oddities of the artistic temperament.

He was introduced to Rosa-Rosa, and as he spoke to her he understood some of Linda's fury. Rosa-Rosa had another of the perfect model's peculiarities; she was unbelievably stupid. She had been trained not to think, lest her roving fancy should destroy the expression she was holding. For the best part of her life, therefore, her mind remained a complete blank.

"I've brought Mr. Campion to admire the exhibits," said Linda.

Dacre slipped off the table and turned round lazily to survey its display.

"I'm minding them for Donna Beatrice," he said. "She wanted to toddle off and chat to her friends. I don't know if she's afraid someone'll walk off with this junk—kleptomaniacs, and that sort of thing. Pretty terrible stuff, isn't it?"

They stood looking down at the handiwork of the industrious Guild of Women Workers in Precious Metals, and the depression induced by the contemplation of the useless and the unlovely descended upon them.

"Modern design approached from the outside by the eighteen-ninety mentality can be rather terrible, can't it?" said Dacre, indicating a pair of table-napkin rings in enamelled silver.

Rosa-Rosa pointed to a pair of lapis lazuli earrings.

"Attractif," she said.

"Don't touch," said the man, pushing her away as though she were an overeager child.

She rewarded him with a blank stare and relapsed into a pose, indicating respectful submission.

Mr. Campion felt Linda quivering at his side. The situation was very trying.

"What do you think of the pièce-de-résistance?" said the girl. She indicated a pair of scissors with slender blue blades some nine inches long and handles so encrusted with chunks of coral and cornelian that it seemed impossible they could ever be used.

"Toys," said a voice behind them. "Rather stupid toys."

Max hovered for an instant behind Campion. "You should be looking at the picture, my friend. I am afraid it is going out of the country. I cannot say any more just now—you understand? But—in your ear—the sum was fantastic."

He sped off again, and they had the satisfaction of seeing him waylaid and captured by Donna Beatrice.

"Flatulent little tuft hunter," said Dacre, looking after him.

Rosa-Rosa endorsed this remark with a gesture of startling and violent vulgarity which took them all completely by surprise.

Dacre reddened and admonished her sharply in her own language. She did not look crestfallen but merely bewildered, and stepped back a little.

Linda was still looking at the scissors. "It's a pity to waste steel like that," she said. "The blades are beautiful."

Again the young man in the horn-rimmed spectacles had an inkling of danger in the wind. It was nothing in the girl's tone—of that he was certain; but a wave of alarm passed over him for no apparent reason. Mr. Campion was not a person given to psychic experiences, and the phenomenon irritated him, so that he put it hastily from his mind. But the impression had been there, and it had been very strong.

His thoughts were diverted at this point by a guffaw from Dacre.

"Max is in the toils," he said. "Look."

The scene he indicated was amusing. Donna Beatrice was talking volubly to Max Fustian. Knowing her, Mr. Campion shuddered to think of the matter of her discourse. It was evident that her victim could not escape.

Linda, who had been watching them steadily, laughed contemptuously.

"She's telling him all about the time in the Turkish bath when she was likened to the Rokeby Venus. That's all there is to it, but it goes on for hours. Once she's on the subject you can't stop her, and today Max can't even be rude to her to any good purpose because she's taken off her ear thing. She always does on state occasions, so that she's as deaf as an egg and about as intelligent."

"I think," said Rosa-Rosa with the naïveté of a child, "I shall now go to the water closet," and went off, leaving them all a little embarrassed.

Mr. Campion caught sight of Belle standing in the middle of the room unattended for the moment, and seized the opportunity to pay his respects.

"Oh, my dear," she said, clutching at his arm and speaking with that charming trick of hers which gave each newcomer the impression that he and he alone was the reason for the gathering, "I'm so glad you've come. Isn't it a crush? I'm so tired. Wouldn't Johnnie have loved it? Look at him up there, smiling all over his face." She nodded her bonnet at the Sargent portrait. "I do hope he's not tormenting Charles Tanqueray at some heavenly peephole."

She paused for breath and, leaning heavily on his arm, gazed round anxiously at the visitors.

"There's whisky and soda on the balcony," she murmured. "I think Max has got a cocktail bar there, too. I'm not supposed to approve. I don't know whether I do or not. I can't get over the feeling that gin's so vulgar. It always was when we were young. But now, since it's come into money, as it were, I suppose it's all right. Look at the dear old bishop," she continued practically in the same breath, "standing over there. Doesn't he look a dear? Don't breathe a word to a soul—but his bootmaker pads his gaiters just a little bit. I know, because he came to dinner here one night and got his feet so wet I made him take them off. He sat in front of my fire with a quilt over his knees. We talked about sin, I remember."

"John Lafcadio should be very grateful to you," said Mr. Campion. "It's a very brilliant gathering."

She sighed, a little murmur of satisfaction, and her faded brown eyes twinkled.

"It's wonderful," she said. "It makes me feel thirty-five again. Everyone here—everyone admiring Johnnie. It's all going smoothly; everyone being polite, very silly, and very flattering."

As the last word left her lips there was a faint whir over their heads and every light in the studio went out, leaving the brilliant assembly in complete darkness save for the faint glow from each fire. Belle's grip on Mr. Campion's arm tightened involuntarily.

"The shilling in the meter!" she murmured huskily. "Oh, Albert, I forgot it!"

The immediate effect of the sudden darkness was such as is usual in such emergencies: there was the familiar pause in the conversation, the startled giggle of some half-wit female; somebody whispered and someone else stumbled over something. And then politeness reasserted itself and conversation went on only a little more quietly than before.

Mr. Campion felt in his pockets. "I've got one," he said. "Leave it to me."

He set off, crossing the room cautiously. The majority of people had the intelligence to stand still, but there were a few who moved about, aimlessly it seemed.

Campion found his way to the little doorway under the balcony with some difficulty; he also experienced some delay because Mr. Potter, who had grown tired of standing beside his "lithographs," had placed a chair for himself with its back against the door.

It was while Campion was removing this obstruction that he noticed some commotion on the far side of the room, somewhere near the jewelry table. He thought nothing of it then and hurried into the cold concrete passage within, where, with the aid of his cigarette lighter, he located the meter and inserted the shilling.

As he came up into the once more brilliantly lighted room he became aware again of the disturbance near the table, and for an instant the wild notion came to him that some sort of smash-and-grab raid had taken place. The next moment he saw that it was a case of faintness. One or two people had gathered round a figure doubled up beside the table. The rest of the guests were studiously taking no notice of the incident, and, miraculously, it seemed, a long queue had already formed to take leave of Belle.

Max, flustered a little by the incident but keeping his head admirably, was assisting the old lady, and Donna Beatrice was making her way towards the door to shake hands with her acquaintances after they had parted from Belle.

Lisa and Fred Rennie were among the group by the table, and even as Mr. Campion looked he saw Rennie bend down and hoist a figure up before taking him out to the models' room through the little door from which Campion had just emerged. That young man, seeing nothing else that he could do, joined the queue.

The business of saying farewell seemed to be an interminable affair, and the queue moved very slowly.

He had allowed his attention to wander, and it must have been a good seven minutes later, when he had moved up some six feet or so in the line, that he became aware of Lisa staring at him intently as though she would force his attention by sheer personal magnetism. As soon as she caught his eye she beckoned to him furiously.

He stepped out of the line and hurried over to her. She led him over to the little door under the balcony, her bony fingers biting into his arm. Once they were out of sight he turned to her enquiringly and was startled by her appearance. The little woman in the tight purple dress was staring at him, her yellow face a mask of horror. When she spoke, her lips moved stiffly and her voice was strangled.

"It was young Mr. Dacre," she said. "He's dead. And the scissors—oh, Mr. Campion, the scissors!" The young man put his arm about her as she tottered towards him.

4 : *"Not I!"*

The steady stream of departing guests flowed slowly out of the studio. A gloom had descended upon the gathering, although the majority had no idea at all that anything unusual had happened; much less that one of their number now lay dead in the little models' room behind the panelling, surrounded by a terrified group and guarded by a bewildered doctor.

The atmosphere was rather one of cold inhospitality than horror, as though the lights had never regained their former brilliance and the occasion had been disappointing.

Nevertheless probably everyone save the immediate members of the household and Mr. Campion might have left the house without being aware of the tragedy at all had it not been for Rosa-Rosa, who suddenly burst through the little doorway under the balcony, screaming.

The noise she made attracted everyone's attention, and her appearance did the rest.

Her training had made her face expressive, and now she presented a picture of such exquisite terror that it was impossible to disregard it. Her yellow hair, crimped like a Botticelli angel's, hung stiffly round her face; her eyes, widened to their utmost, were black pits of fear, and her wide mouth was drawn up into a blue O in her pallid face.

"*Santa Maria! Madri di Dio! È morto! Cosa posso fare? Il mio marito è morto—ucciso!*"

The shrill Italian ended and she began to shout in English: "Murdered! Murdered! Right through the stomach. They did it with the scissors."

It took Max just those three seconds to get across the room and seize the girl by the arms, while the shocked silence in the room deepened into a growing perception of horror.

Max spoke to the girl softly and volubly in her own language. She began to sob noisily, great gulping animal sounds which whipped the already jolted nerves of the company to the point of agony.

A few of the die-hard school of manners clung to their standards and talked together quietly, affecting not to have noticed this second disturbance, while they edged as unobtrusively as possible towards the exit.

But the majority forgot themselves sufficiently to stand silent and agape, watching the girl as Max led her firmly back to the door under the balcony.

These were rewarded by the unusual spectacle of Sir Gordon Woodthorpe, that eminent society physician who had been present at the reception, hurrying out of the little concrete passage, his elegant white hair dishevelled and two patches of crimson burning in the sides of his throat, while he licked his lips feverishly, a nervous habit that had persisted since childhood.

He hurried over to Belle, who was standing in her place by the door, superbly gallant and unruffled in the nightmare crisis. He spoke to her for some moments, and even the die-hards looked curiously in their direction.

After the first few moments Sir Gordon appeared to be arguing with the old lady, offering, it appeared, to take a duty from her shoulders, but she repulsed him gently. Taking his arm, she leant heavily upon it and raised her voice, which was still clear and soft in spite of her age and emotion.

"Ladies and gentlemen," she began, and then her voice quivered and she stood looking at them, her old mouth trembling slightly.

There was silence instantly. The moment was one of drama, and those minds which had hastily dismissed Rosa-Rosa's outburst as a regrettable, hysterical, or drunken incident suddenly wheeled round to face the half-formed fear which had secretly assailed them all.

"My dears," said Belle piteously, "something very terrible has happened. There has been—well—there has been an accident."

Her voice was trembling unashamedly, and her unconscious use of the endearment made her announcement very real and her appeal very personal. She went on, still leaning heavily on the doctor's arm, while they listened to her breathlessly with that sinking of the heart and faint sense of nausea which always comes just before the worst is told.

"A young man who was with us here a few minutes ago is now dead. He died in here when the lights were out. Sir Gordon feels that—that no one should leave until the police have come."

She looked round her appealingly, as though imploring them to understand. It was odd what an impressive figure she was, this plump old lady in the high white bonnet and the long black dress.

"Of course I can't order you to stay if you want to go," she went on. "That would be absurd. In the circumstances I can only appeal to you. I can't tell you any more. This is all I know myself."

She finished, and Sir Gordon, very conscious of his responsibility and the position in which he stood as Belle's champion, escorted her to a chair on the far side of the room.

Another old woman, Lady Brain, a friend of Belle's of long standing, hurried over to her, and Sir Gordon, forgetting to excuse himself, turned with a sigh of relief to the door under the balcony, skilfully avoiding the eye of acquaintances who would have waylaid him.

There were many peculiarities about the murder at Little Venice. Not the least of these lay in the quality and variety of intelligences who shared its first shock.

There are in England an average of about one hundred and fifty murders a year. The majority of these are of a simple and sordid nature, and the aggregate brain power of those present at their discovery is as a rule something less than normal.

But here in Little Venice at the time of the crime was gathered together a collection of people all notable in varying degrees, the majority recruited from the successful professional classes. Once the existence of the tragedy had percolated and the shock had been assimilated, the reaction was ordinary enough inasmuch as the male half of the gathering formed itself into a group of grave-faced important-voiced personages anxious to cling together and protect their womenfolk, while the said womenfolk hung back and, with the natural secrecy of their kind, chattered in little groups with lowered eyes and voices.

As soon as it was established that the victim of the tragedy was a young man scarcely known, even by sight, to anyone, the peculiarities of this particular gathering began to assert themselves.

In ninety-nine cases out of a hundred Belle's hearers had taken the sense of her words rather than their literal meaning; that is to say, they realized that a murder had taken place, moreover a mysterious murder and in their own immediate proximity, and with the exception of two or three rare and somewhat unnatural souls each man and woman began to consider the affair as it most nearly touched himself.

Some were appalled by the thought of the notoriety entailed, others were shamefacedly excited by it, and immediately wires were jerked, wheels began to turn, and fifty little comedies were enacted.

The sturdy, brown-skinned, and rather stupid young equerry to the ambassador, whose eyes had snapped while Belle was speaking and whose brain was quick to seize the possibilities of any situation, permitted himself the thought that if only some foolish policeman could be persuaded to forget himself for a moment and offer an ill-advised question to His Excellency, quite a little insult could be worked up and an unpleasant incident averted only by the brilliance and tact of His Excellency's equerry.

Meanwhile, on the other side of the room a soldierly man whose unobtrusive polish and sharp intelligence had made him invaluable to the Foreign Office stood watching the ambassador's equerry and reflecting that a timely telephone call to headquarters must certainly be arranged somehow, and that meanwhile every conceivable means must be employed to get the ambassador and his equerry out of the house before any fool policeman had a chance to put his foot in it. He began therefore to move unobtrusively towards the door.

At the far end of the narrow concrete passage, standing beneath the very meter into which he had so lightheartedly dropped a shilling only fifteen minutes before, Mr. Campion hesitated. On his right was the door of the models' room from which he had just come, and the recollection of the scene within was still clear in his mind. It had been very stuffy and dusty. The dressing table was dismantled, and the green-covered couch had looked dingy, like the furniture in a secondhand shop. It was upon this couch that the body still lay.

Mr. Campion, in spite of his long association with crime, was not callous enough to be entirely unmoved by the spectacle of a young man suddenly dead.

He was human enough also to consider his own position. Very few people knew much about Mr. Campion. In the first place, that was not his name. The majority of his friends and acquaintances knew vaguely that he was the younger son of some personage, who had taken up the adventurous calling of an unofficial investigator and universal uncle at first as a hobby and finally as a career. His successes were numerous, but for the best reasons in the world he remained in the background and avoided publicity like the plague.

There were some who insisted that he was in reality a member of Scotland Yard's vast army of unobtrusive agents whose work is done entirely behind the scenes, but Mr. Campion himself would have denied this vigorously. The fact remained, however, that he had many friends at Scotland Yard.

At the moment he was in a quandary. He was in the house of friends. Obviously it was his duty to do what he could. He knew enough of English law and English justice to realize that in a case of murder the pursuit is relentless and the punishment unavoidable.

He had no doubt in his mind concerning the author of the crime. He could see Linda now in his mind's eye as she had turned from the window and come towards him. Temporary insanity, of course.

Rapidly he considered the chances of there being insufficient proof. The handles of the long narrow-bladed scissors still protruded from the grey pull-over. Sir Gordon Woodthorpe had been intelligent enough not to attempt to remove the weapon before the arrival of the official doctor.

The useless ornate handles presented no flat surface, so that the chances of their retaining fingerprints were remote. Nevertheless it would all be very difficult.

He was shocked when he thought of Linda. She was just the wild emotional type who might easily succumb to a sudden impulse. It was amazing that she had waited until the darkness.

Of course, even if the best happened and the matter were dropped for lack of evidence, she would have to be put under restraint.

He passed his hand over his forehead. It was damp, and he felt cold. God, what a terrible thing to have happened! Poor Belle. Poor Linda. Poor tragic, insufferable young blackguard lying dead in the next room.

There was the model, too, who had probably been in love with him. Lisa was quietening her now, speaking harshly in her own language, bright startled tears on her withered cheeks.

Mr. Campion checked himself. Something must be done immediately before some bobby off the beat made matters even more difficult. He remembered that the telephone was on the landing and that the door on his left led into the garden. Inspector Stanislaus Oates was the man to get hold of; the shrewdest and at the same time most kindly member of the Yard.

It was Sunday afternoon; therefore he would probably be at home. Campion remembered the number as he ran: Norwood 4380.

Within the studio the atmosphere was becoming unbearable. There were sporadic silences which hung heavily over the great room. One or two people were becoming hysterical. No one complained openly, largely out of deference to Belle, who with remarkable fortitude and typical good sense remained where she was, knowing that her presence alone prevented an open demonstration.

Mr. Campion came in so unobtrusively that his reappearance was not noticed, and he spoke to Belle for some moments unobserved.

"I've been on to Inspector Oates of Scotland Yard," he murmured. "It's quite all right. He says he's coming round right away, but that meanwhile there's no point in keeping this crowd here. After all, everybody came by invitation, and anyone who was particularly anxious to escape after—well—after the lights were turned on again could easily have done so. I saw twenty or thirty people go myself."

He did not look at her as he spoke. He could not bring himself to face her warm brown eyes swimming in tears.

She took his arm and drew herself up.

"I'll tell them," she said.

She moved over towards the door, a solitary figure, very brave and very lonely standing beneath the portrait of her smiling husband.

Gradually the whispered talk died away and all eyes were turned to her enquiringly. She opened her mouth to speak, but words failed her, and, stepping to the door, she pulled it open and stood clinging to the handle, waiting.

The steady stream began again, moving a little more quickly than before.

The old woman stood erect, shaking hands mechanically, smiling wanly at the murmured words of commiseration and regret, looking exactly what she was, a very gallant old lady.

Mr. Campion conquered his impulse to remain by her side. There were other things to be done. He disappeared through the door under the balcony, slipped out into the garden by the back way, and by entering the kitchen door in the basement escaped collision with the departing guests.

He guessed there must be a back staircase, and he found it and reached the landing outside Linda's studio without encountering a soul. He stood listening outside the door. Everything within was silent.

Campion was no fool. Linda had been in an unbalanced nervous condition that afternoon, and he had no illusions concerning her probable state of mind at the present moment. He went in prepared to meet a lunatic.

He knocked, and, receiving no response, opened the door quietly and stepped into the darkness.

"Linda," he said softly.

There was no reply, and he felt round the door for the switch. As the room leapt into sight he realized that, save for himself, it was empty.

He was just going out again when a door on the other side of the room opened and the girl came out. She was still pale, but seemed remarkably composed. She laid a finger on her lips when she saw him.

"Hush," she whispered. "Rosa-Rosa's here in my room, asleep. I've given her an enormous bromide. She won't wake for a long time."

Mr. Campion was prepared for the worst, and her words sent a thrill of horror down his spine.

"Good God, Linda! What have you done?"

The words were forced from him, and he shot past the girl into the little bedroom beyond.

Rosa-Rosa, her face red and swollen with tears, lay on the bed sleeping naturally enough. Campion went over to her, scrutinized her face, and touched her wrist as it lay upon the coverlet. When finally he straightened himself and turned, Linda was standing in the doorway regarding him, a puzzled expression gradually deepening to horror in her eyes.

When he went out into the little studio she followed him and touched his arm.

"What did you mean?" she demanded breathlessly.

Campion looked down at her, and his pale eyes behind his spectacles were troubled.

"What did you mean?" the girl insisted.

He passed his hand over his forehead. "I don't know what I thought, Linda."

She caught hold of the cupboard door to steady herself.

"Albert," she said, "you don't think that I killed Tommy, do you?"

When he did not answer she drew back from him, her eyes starting with terror.

"Albert, you don't think I'm insane!"

When he remained silent, she put her hand up to her mouth as though to stifle a cry.

"What shall I do?" she said huskily. "What shall I do?"

She suddenly stepped forward and caught him by the shoulders.

"I loved Tommy—at least I suppose I did. And I was angry with him. But not as angry as that—not mad. I'd moved away from him when the lights went out. I was at the other end of the table. I heard someone moving in the darkness, and I heard him go down, though I didn't realize what had happened then, of course. Oh, Albert, you do believe me, don't you? You do—you *do* believe me?"

Campion looked down at her. The world was reeling. This was the last development he had expected, the last eventuality for which he had been prepared. He looked down into her face, saw the agonized appeal in her eyes, and spoke truthfully.

"I do, old dear," he said. "Heaven help me, I do."

5 : *Inspector Oates*

Inspector Oates, sitting in the library at Little Venice, a pad of scribbling paper in front of him, bore a gloomy expression upon his cold, rather weary face. He had spent a trying three hours. There may be Scotland Yard detectives who enjoy wringing secrets from unwilling witnesses and placing their fingers unerringly upon the most likely suspect late on a Sunday evening, but Stanislaus Oates was not among them. He had found the whole business very tedious, very distressing, and probably auguring a lot of trouble.

His last witness was now on his way from the drawing room, where the family had assembled, and Mr. Oates was quite anxious to see him, so that when the door opened and a uniformed constable put his head in to say that Mr. Campion was outside he pushed the pad away from him and looked up with interest.

Albert Campion wandered into the room looking his usual vacant, affable self. If there was a hint of anxiety in his eyes it was hidden by the spectacles.

The inspector regarded him solemnly, and Campion was reminded of very much the same scene in a headmaster's study many years before. There had been the same feeling of apprehension, the same air of calamity.

"Well?" said Oates, using very much the same inflection that old "Buggy" had chosen, and very nearly the same words. "How did you manage to get mixed up in all this? You've got a nose for crime. Sit down, won't you?"

The fact that Mr. Campion and Inspector Oates were old friends never obtruded itself when there were business matters at hand.

For the first two or three minutes the proceedings were positively formal, and Campion's alarm increased.

"Oates," he said, "you're behaving as though it were all over, bar the arrest. Is it?"

Oates shrugged his shoulders.

"I'm afraid so," he said. "It seems very clear, doesn't it? I'm afraid it's going to be awkward for you, a friend of the family and that sort of thing. Still," he went on more cheerfully, "we've got to collect the evidence. I don't think we've got anything conclusive enough for a conviction. No one saw her do it, you know."

Mr. Campion blinked. The sudden fulfilment of a fear, however much expected, always comes as something of a shock. He leant back in his chair and regarded the inspector gravely. "Oates," he said, "you're on the wrong horse."

The inspector looked at him incredulously.

"And you've known me all these years!" he said. "You've known me all these years, and you make a deliberate attempt to impede me in the course of my whatever it is."

"Duty," said Mr. Campion helpfully. "No. You've known me long enough," he went on, "to realize, I hope, that I have no conscience in these matters at all. Conscience doesn't come into it. If I believed that Linda Lafcadio killed her fiancé and I thought any good purpose could be served by throwing dust in your eyes, I should do so if I could."

The inspector grunted. "Well, we know where we are, don't we?" he said pleasantly. "How did you know I'd found out that the girl did it?"

"Well, it's the easiest theory," said Campion. "Not wishing to give offense, Stanislaus. You're always hot on the easiest scent."

"You won't offend me," said the inspector, bridling. "But because you've been lucky enough to come across a few really interesting cases you expect to have the same experience every time."

Something in Mr. Campion's manner had made him slightly uncomfortable, however. In the last case they had worked on together, Mr. Campion's fantastic theory had been correct, and the inspector, who was a superstitious man in spite of his calling, had begun to regard his friend as a sort of voodoo who by his mere presence transformed the most straightforward cases into tortuous labyrinths of unexpected events.

"Look here," he said persuasively, dropping entirely the headmaster manner, "a passionate, slightly unbalanced girl goes to meet her fiancé off a boat train. She finds he's brought a beautiful young Italian home with him and afterwards discovers that they are married. The young blackguard cheerfully proposes that they shall set up a ménage-à-trois, which she very properly refuses. The young man comes to a party. She happens to be standing by him, driven insane by jealousy, when the lights go out. Those damned scissors are near her hand. What a filthy weapon, Campion! Did you see 'em? They opened a bit in the heart itself. Killed him instantly, of course. Let me see, where was I? Oh, yes. Well, she was in the dark. She sees her weapon, sees her opportunity. Then she just loses her head and there you are. What could be plainer, what could be clearer than that? It's so simple. In France, you know, she might get off. It'll be insanity as it is, I expect."

Mr. Campion regarded his friend steadily. "You know you'd never get a conviction on that," he said. "It isn't even circumstantial. You've got a possible motive, but that's all."

The inspector looked at him uncomfortably. "I told you I didn't think there was enough evidence," he said. "I did say that, didn't I?"

Mr. Campion leant forward. "Leaving the girl out of it for the moment," he said, "what do you actually know? Have you got any fingerprints on the scissors? Could the blow have been driven home by a woman? Wasn't it very clever of the murderer to take a single shot in the dark and drive the scissors straight into the man's heart?"

Stanislaus Oates rose to his feet. "If you're going to set up as counsel for the defense—" he began.

"I should be doing you a singular service, my dear peeler. Why take an unprofitable theory to your heart just because it happens to be the first one you think of?—or you knew a case once where the same sort of thing happened? Were there any fingerprints?"

"Did you see the scissors?" countered the inspector, and as Mr. Campion nodded he shrugged his shoulders. "Oh, well, then, you know. Of course there weren't. I never saw such stupid things in my life. Absolute waste of good steel."

Mr. Campion blinked. He had heard a phrase very much like that before, and the scene when Linda and he had stood talking to Dacre and his amazing wife returned to him vividly. Just for an instant his belief in Linda wavered, but, as he recalled the episode in her little studio only a few hours before, his conviction returned.

"Well, that's disposed of," he said cheerfully. "How about the blow? Could it have been struck by a woman?"

"I've had all that out with Sir Gordon Woodthorpe and old Benson, our man." The inspector's gloom was returning. "It was a most extraordinary blow, Campion. How anybody struck it in the dark, I don't know. It's practically the only sort of knife wound that would kill a man instantly —that is, before he had time to make any sound. It entered the body just under the point of the breastbone and went straight up, skewering the heart completely. The scissors were broad enough and thick enough to destroy the organ at once. I don't see how anyone could have done it intentionally. I mean, I don't see how anyone could have been sure that it would come off just like that. Both doctors admitted they wouldn't have been anywhere near certain of bringing it off themselves. I suppose artists know a good deal about anatomy, but even so she had diabolical luck."

"Are you sure a woman could have done it?" ventured the younger man.

"Well"—the inspector spread out his hands—"my mother couldn't have done it, and I don't suppose yours could. But these modern kids are as muscular as boys. The blow was a hefty one—I admit that—but it wasn't in the kick-of-a-horse class. And you know, Campion"—he lowered his voice—"there's insanity in the family, isn't there?"

"Insanity? Certainly not. I've never heard of any. You're on the wrong tack here completely, Stanislaus."

The inspector considered a moment before continuing. He sat down at the table and rubbed his moustache the wrong way, an irritating habit he possessed.

"That woman who lives in the house, is she an aunt or something?"

He consulted his notes. "Here you are: Harriet Pickering, alias Donna Beatrice. I realized she was going to keep me up half the night if I was going to get even the more ordinary facts from her, so I left it till later. Well, she's a perfectly ordinary hysterical type, there's no doubt about that. Very near the edge of mania, too, I should say. You must know the woman I mean—wears an acoustic device," he went on testily, catching sight of Campion's blank face. "I couldn't manage her, so I turned her over to the doctors. She told me a cock-and-bull story about seeing lights round my head. Seeing lights round the victim's head. Something to do with indigo and the viler emotions. She seemed to be in fancy dress, too. She may not be certifiable, but—well, she's not quite *compos mentis*, poor soul. That was one of the things I wanted to ask you. Who is she? And what is she doing here?"

Mr. Campion did his best to give the inspector a brief outline of Donna Beatrice's career as he knew it, during which Oates's eyes widened and his moustache seemed to be in danger of being rubbed off altogether.

"Really!" he said at last. "Lafcadio's Inspiration? I didn't know he was that sort of man at all."

"He wasn't," said Mr. Campion. "I doubt if he ever treated the lady with anything but the utmost propriety."

"Oh, well, then, there's your insanity," said the inspector easily. "The whole household is definitely queer. There's that cook who used to be a model, and those funny people who live in a shed in the garden. Bohemia's one thing, but this has a respectable veneer. I think you'll find that there's insanity somewhere. All round, if you ask me."

"What about Mrs. Lafcadio?" Campion ventured.

The inspector smiled. "I wasn't counting her," he said. "There's something very attractive about the real McCoy when you meet it. I told her she ought to go and lie down. It's been a shock, I'm afraid. I want you to go and prepare her for something worse soon. I think we shall have to detain the girl."

"You'll be making a very silly mistake if you do, on a par with the time when you nearly arrested Uncle William in Cambridge."

The inspector was silent for a little while.

"If you want to get rid of that moustache, why don't you shave it?" said Campion.

The inspector laughed and dropped his hand.

"Oh, well," he said, "it all falls back on routine in the end. That man Rennie seems an intelligent sort of person. I'm getting a list of the guests from him. We shall take a statement from each of them, and you never know, something may turn up. But I'm afraid there's no doubt about it this time. The girl had the motive, and she had the opportunity. I know that's not conclusive, but it's nine points out of the ten. Will you go to the old lady, Campion, while I see Rennie? Oh, by the way, you didn't see anything, did you? I haven't had a statement from you. Where were you when it happened?"

"In the passage, putting a shilling in the meter."

"Of course!" said the inspector bitterly. "Probably the one trained observer in the party out of the room at the psychological moment."

He walked over to the door with Campion.

"You see, that meter is another thing," he said. "No one could have arranged for that light to go out just then. It all points to an impulsive, insane gesture that happened to come off. You work on the line of insanity; you'll find it there somewhere."

"If you detain that girl you'll never prove anything against her," said Campion, his hand on the door knob.

"That's the trouble," said the inspector. "Without conclusive evidence we shouldn't be able to get a conviction, but the whole world would believe she's guilty."

"That's what I'm afraid of," said Mr. Campion and went out.

6 : *The Gesture*

Mr. Campion went slowly upstairs to the drawing room reflecting that the situation was impossible. He dreaded the meeting with the family. Belle, he knew, looked to him for comfort, and in the circumstances he had very little to offer her.

The cold air of calamity had permeated the whole household. The atmosphere of the hall was chill and yet curiously stuffy.

They would have to be warned of the inspector's intention—he realized that—and there was the question of insanity, too. The longer he considered his task the less he was attracted by it.

He pushed open the door of the drawing room and went in. They were all there save Linda and Rosa-Rosa. Belle sat in her usual chair by the fire just as she had done on the evening before, when she had been chatting so happily to Campion. She was very grave now, but there was no sign of weakness on her face. Her hands were folded in her lap, and she stared down into the fire, her mouth screwed into a small grimace of pity.

Lisa was crying softly, huddled up on a low chair by Belle's side. At least it seemed that she was crying, for she dabbed her little black eyes with a big white handkerchief from time to time.

On the opposite side of the hearth, Donna Beatrice, the only one of the party who had changed her dress, sat swathed in black georgette, a silver chatelaine hanging from her girdle and a great silver cross round her neck.

Max strode up and down the room impatiently. Like Donna Beatrice he had been quick to see the dramatic possibilities of the affair, and whereas he did not actually "make copy" out of them he obviously got a modicum of satisfaction out of the drama. At worst it seemed to mean that something else was happening on the little stage which he made his life. The vital question whether the scandal would affect Lafcadio's reputation advantageously or adversely also confronted him.

As the young man came in he glanced at Campion carelessly and made him a helpless gesture. If he had said, "It's too terribly trying, isn't it? But emergencies do occur," he could not have conveyed his thought more clearly.

Donna Beatrice's greeting was more sensational, and Campion remembered with sudden satisfaction that her real name was Harriet Pickering. She rose from her chair.

"Your aura," she said. "Your aura . . . You looked like a flame coming into the room, a vigorous cosmic flame."

Lisa made some muttered protest in her own language, and Belle put out a hand to soothe her.

Donna Beatrice sank down again.

"The vibrations in this house are terrible," she continued. "The air is full of evil spirits crowding upon one another. I can feel them oppressing me, wearing me down. It's all very well for you, Lisa. They pass you by. But I'm attuned to the higher consciousness, and I know we're all in danger. The evil act has set millions of vibrations going. We must be very strong. I must be very brave."

Belle dragged her eyes from the fire and let her mild gaze rest upon the other woman.

"Harriet," she said, "*don't* enjoy it."

It was the first ill-natured remark any of them had ever heard her make, and the rebuke was all the more effective.

Max permitted a smile to pass over his face, Lisa ceased to sniff, and Donna Beatrice herself made a noise like a startled hen. Then with tremendous conscious dignity she reasserted herself.

"Belle darling, you should lie down. This terrible thing is getting on all our nerves. I can stand it because I'm an old spirit. I've probably gone through this sort of experience in other incarnations many times before."

Belle, who realized that for chronic hysteria there is no cure, ignored her and stretched out a hand to Campion.

"Come and sit down, my dear," she said. "Tell me, whom are they going to arrest?"

Campion looked at her sharply. Her shrewdness was always surprising him. He saw that they were all looking at him, waiting for his news. He realized that he was their only friend, their only personal link with that terrifying organ of justice, the Police.

Mr. Campion had faced many dangers in his time and had come unscathed through many adventures, but at this moment he was desperately uncomfortable. He cleared his throat.

"Look here, Belle," he said, still holding her hand, "this is rather an awkward question, but do you know anyone who was at the reception or—" he hesitated—"anyone in the house who is liable to uncontrollable fits of fury? I mean, have there ever been violent incidents in the past? Not verbally violent, you know, but—well, has anybody ever done anything almost dangerous?"

Whatever reply he expected, the immediate results of his question were startling in the extreme. A wail of mingled anguish and terror sounded in his very ear, and Lisa, her face ashen, rose from her seat and stumbled blindly out of the room. There was a blast of chilly air as the door swung open and the little click which the catch made as it closed to echoed forlornly in the silent room.

"Lisa also appears to be a recipient of the higher consciousness," Max drawled, nettled into impoliteness, while Donna Beatrice caught her breath sharply and Belle's hand tightened over Mr. Campion's.

Donna Beatrice shrugged her shoulders.

"So it's come out at last," she said. "When I first saw the scissors I knew there was something strange about them. Something repelled me slightly when I touched them. I might have known—I might have known!"

Campion looked at Belle. His eyes were sharp behind his spectacles, and his manner had authority.

"I think you ought to tell me," he said. "What is it?"

Belle seemed loath to speak, but Donna Beatrice sailed in with an eagerness that was frankly uncharitable.

"Some years ago," she said, "Lisa made a wholly unwarrantable attack on me down in the studio. It was the outcome of ungovernable fury."

"Beatrice!"

Belle stretched out her hand.

"Oh, nonsense! You can't hide things like that. Mr. Campion's asked for the truth, and now he shall have it. After all, it's only fair to ourselves. If you get a young, unbalanced soul to deal with, you must protect yourself in a practical manner."

Mr. Campion was listening patiently, and even Max had paused in his perambulations and now stood behind Belle's chair watching Donna Beatrice's placid face wearing its smug expression. She was very conscious of her audience and told her story with a simulation of hesitancy which they found unbearably irritating.

"It was when the Master was alive," she began, dropping her eyes as usual on the name. "Lisa was just beginning to lose her beauty—all traces of beauty, I mean. She confided to me that she was worried about it, and I tried to help her by telling her of the beauty of the spirit. Of course,

I was inexperienced then or I should have recognized her as the young soul she is, incapable of benefiting in that way. Anyhow, the poor creature lost her temper and made an attack upon me. I've had to remind her of it since, several times. I made no complaint at the time because the Master was anxious that I shouldn't, but I've never forgotten it. I put up my arms to shield my face, and I had a cut quite a quarter of an inch deep right across both my forearms. I can show you the scar on my left arm now. She was trying to disfigure me, you see."

Mr. Campion looked at her in amazement. It seemed impossible that she could realize the full gravity of the accusation she made.

"That's what she was thinking of when she ran out of the room," the woman continued. "It's understandable, isn't it?"

Belle peered at Mr. Campion anxiously.

"It's twenty-five years ago," she said. "Quite twenty-five years ago. I thought we'd all forgotten it. Johnnie was so upset at the time, and poor Lisa was so penitent. Need it all be brought up again now?"

Mr. Campion looked reassuring. "I don't think so," he said. "After all, it is rather different, isn't it?"

Donna Beatrice pointed a long, white finger at him.

"I know we must be charitable," she said. "And I realize that we must do the right thing. But there's something Belle hasn't told you, something that I consider very significant. You see, Lisa happened to have attacked me with a pair of scissors. She had them in her hand at the time."

"Oh, Beatrice!" The reproach in Belle's voice was bitter. "How could you!"

Mr. Campion remained unimpressed. He thought he could imagine almost any woman in the situation which Donna Beatrice had described being moved to stop that excruciatingly stupid voice with whatever weapon came to hand. He shook his head decidedly.

"No," he said. "Inspector Oates is not particularly interested in Lisa."

"Of course he's not," said Donna Beatrice. "He's not interested in anyone, I hope. It's perfectly obvious that poor misguided Dacre committed suicide. I told the inspector there were angry dull brown and indigo rays round the boy's head last night. Read what all the authorities say about dull brown and indigo rays. I don't suppose even the inspector is going to question the authority of men like Kunst and Higgins. Dull brown and indigo rays mean violence, depression, and a lowering of the cosmic tone. A perfectly simple case of suicide. After all, that's the only charitable way to look at it."

"You saw the rays?" said Max, fixing her with a dark, unwavering eye. "Are you prepared to swear in court that you actually saw coloured rays of light encircling young Dacre's head any time in your life?"

Donna Beatrice's gaze wavered for an instant, but not for long.

"Yes," she said exasperatingly. "I can see rays round all your heads now. There are too many dark colours in your own aura, Max."

He continued to look at her with gloomy irritation. Then he bowed ironically.

"Dear lady, you are superb," he murmured and turned away with an exaggerated gesture of exasperation.

But Donna Beatrice was equal to any treatment of this sort. "Don't flounce, Max," she said.

Belle seemed to be oblivious of the exchange. Her old brown eyes had grown introspective, and her lips moved ruminatively. Suddenly she turned to Campion.

"My dear," she said, "I've got to be told some time or other, haven't I? What is it? Whom do they suspect? Linda?"

Mr. Campion squeezed the hand which still rested in his own.

"It's only some batty idea Stanislaus has," he said lamely. "There's nothing to worry about, of course."

Belle nodded. She was not listening to him. "Oh, dear," she said piteously. "Oh, dear."

Both Max and Donna Beatrice were startled out of their respective poses by this development.

"Linda?" ejaculated Lafcadio's Inspiration. "Oh, how wicked! How dreadful! Oh, Belle, we must do something. Oh, oh, how wicked!"

Max confronted Campion. He looked less affected and more human than the young man ever remembered seeing him before.

"Another Scotland Yard blunder?" he enquired bitterly.

Having plunged into the trouble, Mr. Campion struck out.

"Well," he said, "there's the motive, you know. It's ridiculous, of course, but Dacre having married Rosa-Rosa like that did suggest to the inspector—" He paused without finishing the sentence.

"Dacre married to the little model?" exploded Donna Beatrice. "Oh, how dreadful! Oh, poor Linda! I understand how she felt. Poor girl! Ought I to go to her?"

Both Max and Campion seemed to be moved by a single thought, for they started simultaneously as though they would detain the good woman by force if necessary.

Belle allowed a stern expression to creep into the lines of her face.

"Don't be a fool, Harriet," she said. "We must pull ourselves together and think what's best to be done. Of course, there's no question that the poor child is innocent, but not everyone knows her as well as we do. Albert, my dear, what shall we do?"

Donna Beatrice began to sob. The refined sniffing which is perhaps the most irritating sound in the world heightened the tension in the room until it was unbearable. Belle was trembling. Campion could see her struggling to keep back her tears and forcing herself to think consecutively.

Max had been temporarily forgotten, so that when he spoke, his exaggerated drawl startled them all.

"My dear people," he said, "don't disturb yourselves. I see this matter must be cleared up immediately, and if you'll permit me to use the phone, Belle, I think everything will be satisfactorily arranged."

He moved over to the instrument, an extension from the hall, with his old self-conscious swagger, and, sitting down before it, dialled a number.

They listened to him as people always do listen to telephone conversations, that half-permitted eavesdropping which is irresistible.

"Hullo, is that you, Mrs. Levy? This is Max Fustian. Could I have just a word with Isidore?"

He paused and glanced back at them with a reassuring smile.

Campion recollected that Isidore Levy was the astute, thickset gentleman who assisted in the management of Max Fustian's Bond Street business.

"Hullo, is that you, my dear boy? Listen. I haven't much time. You must send Miss Fischer to the Picasso show. She knows my views. She must do my article this week. Now listen . . ."

He went on, evidently ignoring some muffled question from the other end of the wire.

"The American—you know who I mean—will probably come in tomorrow. Show him the Degas only. You understand? Nothing else. Only the Degas. You must attend the Leamington Castle sale without me. Our top price is fifteen thousand; not a penny more. . . . We shouldn't get it back—don't argue—we shouldn't get it back."

He paused, listening, and when he spoke again his tone was so casual that the words were barely formed, and it occurred to Campion that the man was labouring under some tremendous excitement.

"Yes," said Max Fustian into the telephone. "Yes, I shall be away. For two or three days; perhaps longer. . . . What? Something important? Yes, in a way. I suppose so."

He lifted the phone and looked over it at the puzzled group round the fire. When he was satisfied that he held their attention he devoted himself once more to the instrument. His hand was shaking, and his little dark eyes danced.

"My friend, my friend, why so importunate? . . . Very well, then; I don't know when I shall come back. . . . I say my return is problematic. . . . Yes. You see, I'm just going down to a lugubrious policeman in Lafcadio's dining room."

He looked up and spoke half to the room, half to the phone. "I'm going to confess to a murder. That's all."

7 : *Confession*

"So you killed the deceased deliberately, Mr. Fustian? Well, now, perhaps you wouldn't mind sitting down and telling us clearly and concisely in your own words just exactly how you did it and why."

The inspector's slow voice sounded startlingly matter-of-fact in the room, which still tingled and vibrated with the dramatic eloquence of Max Fustian's announcement. Oddly enough the drama became more intense, more serious, the difference between the real thing and a play, and the constable sitting at one end of the long mahogany table, his helmet placed carefully in front of him, breathed heavily as he waited, pencil poised, to take down from dictation.

Apart from the inspector and the self-accused man the room also contained Mr. Campion, lounging carelessly against the bookcase, his fair head bent and his hands thrust deep in his pockets.

The light seemed irritatingly bad and the atmosphere of the room cold and unventilated.

Max was excited, not to say exalted. There were feverish spots of colour in his sallow cheeks, and his eyes were unusually bright.

"You wish me to make a formal confession, I take it, Inspector? Well, that's perfectly in order. My name is Max Nagelblatt Fustian. I am forty years of age—"

"That's all right, Mr. Fustian."

Once again the inspector's patient, unemotional voice supplied a genuine note in Max's histrionics.

"We know all that. I shan't cast this into statement form until after we've got the facts. It's very important to take a thing like this quietly. We don't want any mistakes at the beginning. If you start off right it's easier for everybody in the end. Don't go too fast, because Bainbridge here will be taking it down. Think before you speak. What happens afterwards is nearly always based on what you said at the beginning, and a word spoken now will carry more weight than a dozen tomorrow morning. Now then, just start from where you made up your mind to kill the other gentleman."

Max regarded the grave-faced, slow-speaking policeman with contempt and exasperation. As an appreciative audience the inspector was a failure.

"I resent this official attitude," he burst out. "Can't you see I'm trying to help you? If I hadn't chosen to come forward you'd still be floundering. I made up my mind to kill young Dacre last night. I was not sure when or how, but last night when I heard that insufferable young idiot had married the girl Rosa-Rosa and had insulted Miss Lafcadio I decided that the man should be done away with. My motive was purely altruistic. I am one of those people who are blessed, or cursed, with a nature which has to interfere. If I see a thing that needs doing I do it."

He was striding up and down the room as he spoke, throwing off the short, explosive sentences with the transparent conceit of a child.

The inspector watched him gravely, and the constable scribbled without once lifting his head. Mr. Campion appeared to be lost in thought.

"I had no time to lay my plans carefully. The opportunity came and I took it. From the beginning the scissors fascinated me. When the lights went out I saw my opportunity. The rest was simple. I went quietly across the room, picked up the scissors, struck the blow. The boy grunted and went down like a pig. The dagger was still in my hand. I wiped the handle, dropped it on the body and moved away. It was really very simple. I think that's all I can tell you. Would you like me to come with you at once? There's a cab rank on the corner. Perhaps Mr. Campion would be so kind as to tell Rennie to fetch one."

The inspector grunted.

"All in good time, Mr. Fustian," he said mildly. "You must let us have our own way a little, you know. There's just one or two things we shall have to ask. Just read what the gentleman said about the actual stabbing, Bainbridge."

The constable, looking undignified and very young without his helmet, cleared his throat and read the sentences without punctuation or expression:

" 'I went quietly across the room picked up the scissors struck the blow the boy granted and went down like a pig the dagger was still in my hand I wiped the handle and dropped it on the body.' "

"Ah," said the inspector. "The word's 'grunted,' Bainbridge, in the second line. 'Grunted and went down like a pig.' "

"Thank you, sir," said the constable and made the correction.

"Yes, well," said the inspector, "that's all right as far as it goes. Now, Mr. Fustian, supposing this was the scissors. Would you hold it, please?"

He picked up a long, round ruler from the inkstand and handed it gravely to the man.

"Now you, Mr. Campion, would you come and be the deceased, please? The man Dacre was sitting on the edge of the table where the jewelry was exhibited; leaning on it, I take it, supported partly by his hands. Now would you take up that position, please, Mr. Campion?"

Mr. Campion came forward obligingly and took up the position the inspector indicated. It was some moments before the inspector was satisfied, but at length he stepped back and returned to Max.

"Now, Mr. Fustian, would you demonstrate with the ruler, please, exactly how you struck the blow?"

"But this is ridiculous—insufferable." Max's voice was high-pitched with exasperation. "I've confessed. I stand before you self-accused. What more do you want?"

"Just a matter of routine, sir. We want to do everything right. It saves a lot of trouble in the end. Now, just go over it exactly as you did it in the studio in the dark. You walked over to him. We'll assume you've picked up the scissors."

Max was staring at the man, his eyes glittering. He was trembling with excitement and uncontrolled temper, and for a moment it seemed as if he would forget himself entirely and resort to physical violence. However, he pulled himself together and with a superb shrug of his shoulders permitted himself his famous crooked smile.

"Oh, well," he said, "if you want to play games, why not? Look very closely and I'll show you just how the horrid murder was done."

He gripped the ruler, raised his arm above his head, and brought it down within an inch of Campion's waistcoat.

"There you are," he said. "Perfectly simple. Straight through the ribs and into the heart. Very pretty blow, really. I think I'm rather pleased with it."

The inspector's nod was noncommittal.

"Just once again, please," he said.

Max complied, all his old contemptuous amusement returning. "I raised my hand, thus, and brought it down with all my strength."

"Did you feel any resistance?" said Oates unexpectedly.

Max raised his eyebrows. "Well, I—I felt the slight resistance of the waistcoat cloth, and I think I touched a bone, but really it happened so quickly . . . I'm afraid I haven't your prosaic mind, Inspector."

"Very likely not, Mr. Fustian."

There was no underlying tartness in Oates's tone.

"What did you do then—after you felt the resistance of the bone, I mean?"

"Then I felt the man fall. Then—oh, let me see—then I wiped the handle of the scissors on my handkerchief and dropped them on the body. Then I moved away. Anything else I can tell you?"

Oates considered. "No," he said at last. "No, I think that's all, Mr. Fustian. Perhaps you will sit down."

"Really, is all this hanging about necessary?" Max's drawl was becoming plaintive. "After all, this is a nerve-racking business for me, Inspector, and I should like to get it over."

"So would we all, Mr. Fustian." Oates was gently reproving. "But then it's a serious business. Murder's a capital charge, remember, and, as I say, we don't want to make any mistakes at the beginning. Hand me that note, will you, Bainbridge? Thank you. Now, you went across the room in the dark and picked up the scissors. The failure of the lights was a complete accident. It came as a surprise to everyone. There's no question on that point. We have evidence to show that you were standing talking to Miss Harriet Pickering when the lights failed, at approximately a distance of fifteen feet from the table where the deceased was leaning. We have three separate statements to show that. According to your story you went over and picked up the scissors.

"Well, we won't question that. Wait a minute, sir," he continued, waving aside Max's excited outburst. "You then tell us—and we've been very careful over this point; you've shown us and you've described it—that you raised your hand above your head and brought the weapon down, noticing the resistance of the tough cloth of the deceased's waistcoat and a slight resistance which you thought must be caused by the blades glancing off a bone.

"Now that brings us to another point. The blow which killed Thomas Dacre was an upward thrust delivered very scientifically. As the deceased was wearing a woollen pull-over and not a waistcoat, there was very little resistance offered to the blow by the clothing. The weapon entered the body just below the lower rib and went straight up into the heart, causing almost instantaneous death."

Max was sitting very stiff and white in his chair, his bright eyes fixed upon the inspector's face. Oates remained slightly preoccupied and perfectly grave.

"Now, to return to your statement, sir. You then removed the weapon, wiped the handle, and dropped it on the body. I query this because the weapon remained in Dacre's body until the police surgeon took it out. Also, the handle was not wiped.

"I think that's all, except for the matter of the motive. We have a great many murders every year, most of them committed for obvious reasons, some of them very sound reasons. The altruistic murderer is rare, and of course I couldn't say what the chances of your being one were until we have the evidence of the police doctor as to the state of your mind. But I'm prepared to forego the trouble of instituting an enquiry of that sort in the present instance. I don't think it's necessary in view of the discrepancies I've already mentioned."

Max regarded him narrowly. "Do I understand that you are refusing to accept my confession?" he said icily.

Oates folded the constable's notes and fitted them into his pocketbook before he replied. Then he glanced up. His rather tired eyes were as mild as ever.

"Yes, Mr. Fustian," he said. "That's about it."

Max said nothing, and after an interval the inspector went on speaking. He was very quiet, very friendly, and unexpectedly authoritative.

"Now look here, Mr. Fustian," he said, "you may as well understand our position. We've got to get at the truth. No doubt you did what you did for the best reasons in the world. You thought a young lady was about to be arrested, and you thought you'd do her a good turn. Very likely you thought we were making a silly mistake and didn't care what you did to stop us giving unnecessary pain. I appreciate your motives, and I think you've done a very nice thing, in a way, but you must see that you're only wasting our time and your own and not really helping things forward at all.

"Oh, I may as well mention, too, before you go, that in Miss Harriet Pickering's evidence she states that she was talking to you throughout the entire time that the lights were out, so you see your gesture was doomed to failure from the beginning. Good evening. I'm sorry this should have happened like this, but you see how it is."

There was a moment or two of silence after the inspector had finished speaking, and then Max rose slowly to his feet and went out of the room without uttering a word. They heard his brisk pattering footsteps disappearing down the corridor.

The inspector nodded to the constable, who picked up his helmet and went out.

Mr. Campion and his friend exchanged glances.

"A bad show," ventured the younger man.

The inspector grunted.

"There's one born every minute," he said. "I don't like that type, though. Exhibitionists they're called, aren't they? It leaves us with our original problem. There isn't anything to be gained from it at all. I shall give the girl twenty-four hours yet, in case something turns up. Now I think I'd better get back and make my report. A nice thing to happen in the middle of a Sunday afternoon!"

Mr. Campion lit a cigarette.

"It's an incomprehensible business," he said. "As you say, the only person in the world who could have had any conceivable reason for killing so insignificant a person as young Dacre was the girl, and I assure you she's innocent. I'd stake my last bob on it.

"Of course," he added hopefully, "the whole thing might have been an accident. I mean, there's always the possibility that Dacre was not the man the murderer intended to kill. After all, there's an element of chance about the whole affair; the blow being struck in the dark and going straight home and that sort of thing."

"Oh, it's a stunner," said the inspector gloomily. "I knew that as soon as I heard the telephone bell going this afternoon." He spoke savagely and as one who believed in premonitions. He tapped the papers in his hand.

"From the statements here you'd think we'd come to a lunatic asylum. There's only two or three concise stories among the lot. That woman Potter was as good as anyone. She seemed to have her wits about her. But her husband was the vaguest thing on earth. D'you know, Campion, I sometimes wonder how some of these fellows manage to keep alive. God knows it's hard enough to earn a living when you've got all your wits about you. But these blokes don't die. Someone looks after 'em."

Campion accompanied the inspector to the front door, and as they passed through the hall the object of Oates's gloomy conjectures hurried out of the dining room to meet them. Mr. Potter's red unhappy face wore an even more wretched expression than usual, and his eyes were frightened.

"Oh, I say, you know, I would like to go back to my studio," he said. "I don't see any point in hanging about here any longer. It's all very sad and awkward, I know, but we must live. I mean, life's got to go on, hasn't it? I can't do any good here."

He was half in and half out of the dining-room doorway as he spoke, and twice he glanced apprehensively over his shoulder back into the room during his short speech. He was so palpably alarmed and preoccupied that both men instinctively glanced past him.

What they saw was completely unexpected. Lying upon the hearth rug and cutting into the picture made by the angle of the door was a pair of feet encased in sensible brown shoes.

The inspector walked into the room, sweeping aside Mr. Potter's tentative and ineffectual gestures of protest.

"That's all right, Mr. Potter," he said. "I see no reason why you shouldn't go back to your studio now. It's only in the garden, isn't it?"

"Yes, yes, that's right." Mr. Potter was still dancing in front of the policeman in an attempt to screen the object on the floor.

His efforts were completely fruitless, however, and Campion, who had followed Oates, found himself looking down at Mrs. Potter lying upon her back, her face crimson and her sleek hair disordered. She was breathing stertorously, and her eyes were closed.

Mr. Potter gave up all attempts at deception with a rather pathetic little shrug of his shoulders, and then, as the silence became oppressive, "It's my wife," he said apologetically. "The shock's been too much for her, you know. She feels things very deeply. These—these masterful women sometimes do."

"You'd better get her to bed," said the inspector casually. "Can you manage?"

"Oh, yes, yes. It's nothing." Mr. Potter was already motioning them towards the door. "Good night."

"Good night," said Oates. "Are you coming, Campion?"

As they walked down the steps to the street, the older man glanced at his friend.

"Did you see that?" he said. "That was a funny thing, wasn't it? Now I wonder what that means."

The younger man's friendly face wore a faintly puzzled expression. "I didn't go very near her," he said, "but it looked to me as if—"

"Oh, she was drunk, all right," said Oates. "Didn't you see the decanter on the sideboard? She must have taken pretty well a tumblerful neat to put her out like that. Some people do, you know. It's a form of drugging. But what for, I'd like to know? What's she got on her mind that she can't bear to think about? There's something very odd about all this, Campion. Well, well, I wonder now."

8 : *Little Things*

The affair at Little Venice might have lingered on at this stage in its development until it became a tabooed subject at Scotland Yard and a worn-out scandal in Bayswater, had it not been for the conversation which the grave-faced man from the Foreign Office held with his department.

The dictates of diplomacy being of considerable importance in those days of conferences, the Home Secretary took action, and the press became oddly disinterested in the murder. A discreet inquest was followed by a quiet funeral, and the remains of Thomas Dacre were deposited in Willesden Cemetery without further attention from the police.

Lafcadio's household quietened down and might never again have emerged from its seclusion had it not been for the startling, utterly unexpected tragedy which was the second murder.

A little over three weeks after Dacre's death, when Inspector Oates had ceased to sigh with relief for the intervention of the powers that be, Mr. Campion was seated in his own room in the flat at Bottle Street when Linda called.

She came in hurriedly, her coat clinging to her lean young figure. She looked modern and distinctive, and once again he was reminded that the tempestuous Lafcadio was her grandfather. There was the same faint air of rebellion about her, the same nonchalance, the same frank consciousness that she was a privileged person.

She was not alone. Her companion was a young man of her own age. Campion found himself liking him even before the introductions had been effected.

He was not unlike the girl herself, loosely but strongly built, wide of shoulder and narrow of hip, with faded hair, a big characterful nose, and shy dancing blue eyes.

He seemed delighted to see Campion and favoured the room with the frankly approving stare of a friendly child.

"This is Matt D'Urfey," said Linda. "He used to share a hovel with Tommy."

"Yes, of course. I've seen your pen drawings about, haven't I?" Campion turned to the visitor.

"Very likely," said D'Urfey without pride. "I must live. I say, I like your flat."

He wandered across the room to look at a small Cameron over the bookshelf, leaving Linda to continue the conversation. She did this at once, plunging immediately into the matter on her mind with her usual directness.

"Look here, Albert," she said, "about Tommy. There's something very queer going on."

Campion glanced up at her shrewdly, his pale eyes suddenly grave behind his spectacles.

"Still?" he enquired, adding, "I mean, anything fresh?"

"Well, I think so." Linda's tone kept a touch of its old defiance. "Of course you may pooh-pooh the whole thing, but you can't get away from the facts. That's why I've brought Matt along. I mean, look at Matt; he's not the person to imagine anything."

The recipient of this somewhat doubtful compliment glanced over his shoulder and smiled delightfully, returning immediately to the etching, which he evidently enjoyed.

"My dear girl,"—Campion's tone was soothing—"I haven't heard the facts yet. What's up?"

"There aren't any actual facts. That's what's so infuriating." Her big grey-green eyes above the wide cheekbones were suddenly suffused with helpless tears.

Campion sat down. "Suppose you tell the sleuth all about it," he suggested.

"I want to. That's why I've come. Albert, whoever killed Tommy is not content with stealing his life. They're just obliterating him as well, that's all."

Mr. Campion had a gentle, kindly personality and was possessed of infinite patience. Gradually he calmed the girl and got her to tell her rather curious story.

"The first things that disappeared were those drawings of Tommy's that I showed you on the day of the private view," she said. "You remember them. They were in that cupboard in the studio. About a dozen or fourteen. Just sketches, most of them, but I'd kept them because they were good. I went to get them out last week because I wanted to have a little show of Tommy's work somewhere—nothing ambitious, you know, just a few things of his in one of the small galleries. I didn't want him to just fade away utterly, you see, because he—he—well, he had *something*, didn't he?"

Her voice, never very steady, threatened to break, but she controlled herself and went on:

"First of all I found my drawings had gone. I turned the place out and raised hell generally, but they'd just vanished. They've gone as completely as if they'd never existed. And then, of course, I couldn't get a gallery."

She paused and regarded Campion earnestly.

"Can you believe that there isn't a single small gallery in London to be had for love or money to exhibit Tommy's work? It isn't even as though times were good and money was floating around. It's a conspiracy, Albert, a wretched, measly, mean effort to stamp Tommy out of the public mind for ever."

Mr. Campion looked uncomfortable.

"My dear girl," he said at last, "don't you think the—well, the unfortunate circumstances of young Dacre's death may have something to do with it? After all, I know the good gallery folk aren't all renowned for good taste, but don't you think they feel they don't want to lay themselves open to any accusation of sensation-mongering? Why not leave it for a year or so and let him burst on the world without any unpleasant associations?"

The girl shrugged her shoulders.

"Perhaps so," she said. "That's what that little beast Max says. Still, that's only a half, only a quarter, of the whole thing. You see, Albert, it isn't only my drawings that have vanished. All his work, everything he ever did, is going. Someone hated him so much that they don't want anything he possessed to remain."

Matt, who had given up contemplating the walls, lounged back to Linda's side.

"I thought it was rather odd that anyone should burgle the hovel," he remarked. "I mean, what had Tommy got? Nothing but his paints and a spare shirt. Nothing of mine was touched. Thank God," he added piously.

"Burglary?" enquired Campion.

"Good Lord, yes. Hasn't Linda told you? I thought that's why we came." Mr. D'Urfey seemed astonished. "The night before last, when I was down at the Fitzroy, some lunatic walked into the hovel and removed every single thing Tommy possessed. His clothes, one or two old canvases, all his paints, brushes, and other paraphernalia. Rather queer, wasn't it? I was glad to get rid of the stuff in a way—other people's junk, you know —but I thought it was odd, so I mentioned it to Linda, and since all the poor chap's stuff is vanishing she thought we'd better come along."

Mr. Campion listened to this somewhat extraordinary announcement with interest. "When you say all his stuff is vanishing, what do you mean?" he enquired.

"Just that," said Linda. "Seigal's in Duke Street had a few of his drawings, and just after he died they displayed them in that small box case on the left of the door. You know they haven't much window space. Well, the whole box was taken, stolen, some time in the lunch hour when the street was pretty well deserted. No one saw them go. Then there were the contents of his studio in Florence. Someone bought the lot within twenty-four hours of his death. I wrote the people last week and got their reply yesterday."

She hesitated and went on awkwardly:

"He owed quite a lot, and they were glad to accept any offer for the stuff he left behind. They didn't seem to know who the man was. I've wired them for full particulars, but I haven't had any reply yet."

Mr. Campion sat on the arm of his chair, his long, thin legs stretched out in front of him.

"This is very odd," he said. "About the—er—hovel burglary. You say nothing but Dacre's stuff was taken?"

"Oh, well, they lifted an old overall of mine," said D'Urfey casually, "but the rest was all his. That wasn't so difficult, as a matter of fact," he went on frankly. "Dacre was a tidy bloke anyway, and he'd only just returned, so most of his stuff was stacked up in a corner of the studio, hardly any of it unpacked. What made me think it was a bit queer," he continued, evidently making a much longer speech than was his wont, "was why anyone should come to the hovel. It's perfectly simple to walk into, of course, but why should anyone do it?"

"Where," enquired Mr. Campion, "is the hovel?"

"Christian Street. It turns off the wrong end of Shaftesbury Avenue," said Mr. D'Urfey promptly. "It's that smelly little road on the right, opposite the Princess Theatre and parallel with Drury Lane. The hovel is two top rooms in the house over the rag-and-bone shop. The stink has worn off by the time you get to the top, or you've grown used to it—I've never been sure which," he added frankly. "It's not bad. No sanitation, but central and all that. Anyone could walk in and move out my entire estate at any time, of course, but no one ever does. Why should they?"

"No one saw any stranger go up, I suppose, on the day of your burglary? The people underneath, for instance?"

"No. Mrs. Stiff lives on the floor below. She's a flower girl in Piccadilly, and she was out all the evening. The rag-and-bone shop closes at five, and the place is pitch dark after eight. We're not very hot on street lamps in our district—the kids smash 'em—so anyone could have come in. Still, it doesn't matter, but it's funny, isn't it?"

Mr. Campion considered. Linda was regarding him sombrely, but Mr. D'Urfey's dancing eyes had already strayed to a Currier & Ives which had taken his fancy, and he moved over to get a closer view.

Campion framed a delicate question.

"There is Dacre's wife," he ventured at last. "Might not she have felt that his things were her property?"

"Wife?" Matt left his print unwillingly. "Oh, Rosa-Rosa. I forgot. Yes, we thought of her at once. I looked her up, but she doesn't know a thing about it. In fact she's livid about his trunk going. Apparently there's a pair of stays in it that he refused to let her wear. She was very fond of them. She's very dense, you know, but these things were heirlooms as far as I could make out. Did you understand her, Linda?"

"Rosa-Rosa did not take Tommy's things." The girl spoke with the quiet conviction which quenches all argument. There was a pause. "I don't know why I've come to you, Albert. I don't know what I expect you to do," she burst out suddenly. "But something queer is happening; something I don't understand."

Her strong brown hands fluttered in an odd, helpless gesture. "Do you know, I can't think of anything in the world I can lay my fingers on that he ever possessed—not a scrap of drawing, not a paintbrush."

Campion rose to his feet and patted her shoulder.

"I think I can alter that for you," he said, a tinge of satisfaction in his voice. "I've got a drawing of Dacre's in the next room. You can have it if you like."

He hurried out, to return almost immediately with a big flat brown-paper parcel which he set down on the desk.

"I'm afraid I ought to confess that I did a bit of sharp buying myself," he said, snipping the string. "I phoned Max Fustian at his office on the day after the—er—private view and told him that I'd seen some of Dacre's work and was very impressed with it. He went round to Seigal's, I suppose, for when I got to his gallery he had half a dozen to show me. I bought one, and as I was off to Paris that afternoon they kept it and didn't send it round until yesterday. I haven't opened it yet. I like it immensely. It's the head of a boy, a Spaniard, I think."

On the last word he brushed back the brown paper and revealed a strip of plywood packing within.

"Here we are," he went on, lifting it up and removing the layers of tissue, "all mounted and everything—"

His voice trailed away on the last word, and a startled exclamation escaped the girl, for the pristine mount was empty, and, although they searched the parcel again and again, of the "Head of a Boy" by Thomas Dacre there was no sign whatever.

9 : *Salesmanship*

"My dear fellow, fantastic! Positively fantastic!"

Max Fustian strode up and down the luxurious carpet which covered the floor of the principal salon of his exquisite little gallery and offered this opinion with a wealth of gesture.

The Salmon Galleries in Bond Street had been redecorated when he took them over, and now they were a fitting tribute to his taste and his business acumen. Save for a few carefully displayed pictures, Mr. Fustian's stock-in-trade was kept delicately in the background, and the unwary visitor might imagine that he had inadvertently strayed into the private house of some fabulously wealthy personage whose taste was so elegantly refined that it had almost reached the point of negation.

The soundproof walls shut out all noise from the street, and, in the hushed atmosphere common to art galleries, cathedrals, and banks, Max's melodious drawl sounded less out of place than it had done in Belle's drawing room.

Mr. Campion leant upon his stick and watched the man with interest.

"Well, I thought I'd tell you, you know," he said half apologetically, since it seemed to be committing sacrilege to mention anything so vulgar as the contents of a brown-paper parcel in such a rarefied atmosphere.

"My dear Campion, of course." Max was magnificently condescending. "I've sent for the man who does our packing. No drawing in the mount, you say? It's fantastic. But then, you know, extraordinary things are happening in connection with that wretched boy's death; the wildest things. I had an amazing experience myself. I'll tell you about it. If you've seen Linda—poor child! how decorative she is in her grief—you know about Seigal's case of drawings. Really, until this morning I thought you were the last man in London, possibly in the world, to have a specimen of Dacre's work."

With the movement of a ballet dancer he swooped down upon a beautifully chased steel box, the only object on an exquisitely figured walnut table, which in turn shared with two William and Mary chairs the privilege of being the only furniture in the room.

Mr. Campion refused an Egyptian cigarette which looked odd, unpleasant, and possibly of enormous value.

"You agree with Linda, then, that someone's trying to stamp Dacre's work out of existence?" he ventured.

Max raised his eyebrows and spread out his long white hands.

"Who can tell?" he said. "Nothing's impossible, you know, Campion. Personally, I'm not inclined to bother about it. Dacre had talent, you know, but then who hasn't in these days? He was one of thousands—

thousands! Talent is not enough, Campion. The modern connoisseur wants genius. Poor Dacre! Poor, mediocre Dacre! Only his death made him interesting."

Mr. Campion grinned. "That's a distinction he shares with quite a lot of painters," he ventured.

The other man's little bright black eyes flickered for an instant.

"How exquisitely true," he said. "But I suppose we ought to be grateful to Dacre that at least his death was genuinely interesting. All his work vanishing like this, it's quite romantic. My own experience was interesting. I didn't admire Dacre's work, you know, but there was a little thing—just a study of a hand—a little thing of no value at all, but it pleased me. There was something in the line, something—how shall I say?—enlightened, you understand. I had it framed rather charmingly. A new idea of my own: the moulding was carved from stone. It's exceptionally right for certain pencil drawings. The greys blend. I had it hanging in my dining room just above a rather lovely stripped Stuart bread cupboard."

He paused and held a gesture which Mr. Campion took to indicate that he was visualizing a pleasing scene.

"It was a conceit of mine," he went on, sublimely unconscious of any impression but the one he intended, "to keep a certain coloured rose in a pewter jar a little to the left of the picture. It formed a little group, broke the line, and pleased me. The other night when I came into my flat I realized at once that someone had been there. Just little things altered, you know—a chair not quite in alignment, a cushion on the wrong end of the sofa—just little things that offend one's eye. Although nothing was actually in disorder, you understand, I knew at once that someone had been through the place, and I hurried into my bedroom.

"There was the same story. Just little things altered. The moment I entered the dining room the thing hit me in the eye. The pewter jar with the rose was set directly beneath the picture. I hurried over, and there was the empty frame. The drawing had been taken out quite skilfully.

"I don't mind admitting to you, Campion, that at first I was inclined to suspect Linda, although how she could have got into my flat, I don't know. But after seeing her and talking to her I realized, of course, that she didn't know anything and was just as puzzled as I was. The whole thing's absurd, isn't it?"

"The drawing had gone?" said Mr. Campion, who seemed to be afflicted with a sudden stupidity.

"Completely." Max waved his hands in the air. "Just like that. Ridiculous, isn't it?"

"Amazing," said Mr. Campion bluntly.

The conversation was interrupted by the arrival of a sallow, somewhat scared-looking child in a travesty of one of Max's own suits.

"This is Mr. Green, who packs our pictures," said Max with the air of one introducing a rare and privileged creature. "You've heard of our difficulty, Mr. Green?"

The boy looked bewildered. "I can't understand it, Mr. Fustian. The drawing was all right when I packed it."

"You're sure it was there?" Max fixed the young man with a bright, beady eye.

"There, sir? Where, sir?"

"I mean," said Max with gentle force, "I mean, my dear Mr. Green, that you're certain there was a drawing in the mount which you so carefully packed and sent to Mr. Campion?"

The boy's sallow cheeks flushed. "Well, naturally, sir. I'm not barm— I mean, I'm sure it was there, Mr. Fustian."

"There you are, Campion." Max turned to his visitor with the gesture of a conjuror removing the black cloth.

Campion turned to the boy.

"What happened to the parcel after you had packed it? Was it delivered straightway?"

"No, sir. I understood you didn't want it delivered at once, and so it stood on the rack in the room downstairs where we make tea for about a week."

"The room where you make tea, Mr. Green?" asked Max coldly.

The child, who, Campion decided, could not be more than fourteen, wriggled painfully. "Well, the room where we wash our hands, sir," he muttered.

"In the staff cloakroom?" said Max in cold astonishment. "Mr. Campion's beautiful drawing stood on the rack in the staff cloakroom for almost a week? Surely, Mr. Green, that was a mistake?"

"Well, it had to stand somewhere," said the wretched Mr. Green, goaded into revolt by this mixture of injustice and the inexplicable.

"I see," said Max coldly. "Then at any time during the week anyone could have tampered with Mr. Campion's beautiful drawing. That will do, Mr. Green."

Mr. Green departed miserably, and Max returned to Mr. Campion with a rueful gesture.

"One's staff!" he said. "One's staff!"

Mr. Campion smiled politely, but his pale eyes behind his spectacles were thoughtful. On the face of it this new development in the affair at Little Venice was frankly bewildering. At first he had been inclined to suspect Linda of a disordered imagination. Then the thought had occurred to him that some price-forcing conspiracy might be afoot. But although there are many collectors who will buy up all the pictures of a painter tragically dead, there were surely few who would go to the lengths of committing burglary and appropriating old clothes.

On the other hand, in his own surroundings Max was inclined to be a more comprehensible person than he had appeared in Lafcadio's home. His somewhat extraordinary line of conversation sounded less bizarre in the gallery.

Mr. Campion, who had the wit to make a study of men without considering himself a connoisseur of humanity, began to regard him with new interest. The inspector, he felt, had not done him justice.

It was at this point in his reflections that Mr. Isidore Levy, plump and intelligent, came hurrying up to murmur a few words to Max.

Campion saw the little black eyes light up.

"He's come, has he?" he said. "I'll be with you immediately."

Mr. Campion hurried to make his excuses. In the past few moments he had become aware of a suppressed excitement in the gallery, an air of momentous happening.

"I'll come back later," he said. "Or perhaps you'd phone me?"

"My dear fellow, don't go." Max's tone was obviously genuine. "I have a client." He lowered his voice. "Sir Edgar Berwick—yes, the politician. He rather fancies himself as an authority on Flemish art."

He slipped his arm through Campion's and led him down the room away from the door, talking softly.

"It's really rather amusing. He wants to make a presentation to his local art gallery, and I think I have something that will interest him. Come along; you must hear it. It's part of your education. I insist. And besides," he added with sudden naïveté, "I'm better with an audience. You're a student of psychology, aren't you? Here's an interesting example for you."

When he followed Max into the smaller salon which formed the other showroom of the gallery, Campion saw at once that salesmanship had already begun. The high narrow room with its top lights and stripped-pine panelling had been prepared for the contest. The picture stood at the far end of the room on an easel, and the only other touch of pure colour was provided by a long velvet curtain draped graciously over a second doorway. By happy chance or ingenious design, the vivid blue in the picture was echoed in this hanging. The effect was very pleasant.

When Mr. Campion entered unobtrusively behind Max, Sir Edgar was already standing before the picture, his grey head bent. He was an oldish man, large and remarkably dignified. His skin was pink and his natural expression belligerent. At the moment he looked important and extremely wise. He also appeared to be aware of the fact.

Mr. Campion, while feigning interest in a screenful of early German engravings, had leisure to observe the greeting. Max, he reflected, was superb. He approached his somewhat pompous client with just the right mixture of deference and friendliness and then stood beside him in silence, looking at the picture with somewhat self-conscious satisfaction, patently aware that he saw it as an expert and as no ordinary man.

Sir Edgar remained so long in contemplation that Mr. Campion had time to get a glimpse of the picture itself and all the others in the gallery before the interview continued.

He was not a judge of oils, but he could see from where he stood that the piece was a Flemish interior in the Jan Steen manner. It represented a christening party in a pleasant, clean-looking room where many little comedies were taking place. The painting seemed to be in good condition apart from a rather serious crack straggling across one corner.

At length, when Mr. Campion had completed his circle of the gallery and was back again at the colour prints, Sir Edgar stirred and turned to Max.

"Interesting," he pronounced. "Definitely interesting."

Max seemed to shake himself out of a trance. He dragged his eyes away from the canvas and permitted a faint enigmatic smile to pass over his countenance.

"Yes," he said softly. "Yes."

The superb noncommittal of this opening gambit over, silence again ensued. Sir Edgar squatted down on his august heels and peered through a small glass at the texture of the paint on the very bottom of the canvas.

Presently he rose to his feet and spoke brusquely:

"Can we have it out of the frame?"

"Of course." Max raised a hand, and magically two assistants in baize aprons, one of them the ubiquitous Mr. Green, appeared, the beautiful old frame was removed, and the picture, looking surprisingly less important, relinquished naked to Sir Edgar's little glass.

Then followed a minute examination of the canvas, back and front, interspersed by little grunts and muttered technicalities from the two combatants.

Presently the frame was restored and they took up their old positions in front of the easel, Sir Edgar a little pinker and a trifle dishevelled from his exertions, Max quieter, more enigmatic, than ever.

"No signature and no date," said the amateur.

"No," said Max. "Only internal evidence."

"Of course," the other agreed hastily. "Of course."

And once again there was silence.

"There's no mention of this christening piece in the catalogue of Steen's work," Sir Edgar ventured at last.

Max shrugged his shoulders. "In that case there'd hardly be a question," he said and laughed a little.

Sir Edgar echoed his laugh. "Quite," he agreed. "It's indubitably the right period."

Max nodded. "We have only the picture to go upon," he said, "and of course doubts naturally crowd into the mind. But there are little touches which you as an expert must recognize, Sir Edgar; that curious cross-grained canvas, that sitting figure in the foreground. Very like Steen himself. Interesting how those men went in for self-portraiture.

"Of course," he added, shrugging his shoulders, "I know no more than you. As I told you, it came into my hands in a perfectly orthodox way. I bought it at Theobald's in January. I paid fourteen hundred and fifty for it. I bought it after examining it very closely, you understand, and I backed my own judgment. I can't tell you whether it's a genuine Steen. I don't know. I'm inclined to think not. After all, a piece of luck like that doesn't happen these days. Not to me, at any rate. A signed Steen was sold in the same sale for two thousand seven hundred pounds, and A. T. Johnson, who bought that picture, ran me up to fourteen-fifty for this.

"But of course," he went on with a sudden gesture which swept aside anything so uninteresting as money, "there's the picture itself. This little group here, for instance"—his long fingers described an airy circle—"there's spirit and jollity there. There's something quite indescribable. Don't you notice it?"

"Oh, I do." Sir Edgar was plainly impressed. "I do. In fact I'm inclined to go further than you, Fustian. You were always overcautious. The drawing of the child, that little piece of drapery, that suggests Steen to me."

"Yes," said Max casually. "Yes. Or a pupil."

"A pupil?" Sir Edgar considered this contingency and shook his head. "But," he went on, feeling perhaps that he had gone too far, "as you say, we can't be sure."

"No," said Max. "No. There's a mention in the first catalogue of a picture called 'The First Birthday.' If the child were older—but no. Even supposing the early chroniclers had not been too accurate, I fancy the production of a new find of that name would call into question a picture of that name in the Viennese collection."

Sir Edgar produced his glass once again and peered long and thoughtfully at the child.

"Well, Fustian," he said, "I'll let you know definitely. Fifteen hundred, you say? In the meantime I'll get you to put it on one side for me."

Max hesitated and then, with the air of one making a decision, produced what Mr. Campion suddenly felt must be the master stroke of this ordeal by innuendo.

"Sir Edgar," he said, "I'm sorry to disappoint you, but I've been thinking this matter over while we've been standing here, and I tell you frankly that I do not think it is a Steen. On the face of it I can't sell it with any kind of guarantee. It's charming, it's like—it's very like—but in the absence of external evidence I don't think I can commit myself to such a pronouncement. No, no. Leave it at that. I don't think it is a Steen."

Sir Edgar's bright, rather greedy blue eyes smiled.

"Officially," he murmured.

Max permitted himself a deprecatory grimace.

"No, I won't even say that," he said. "I'm afraid you must let me make it quite definite. I don't think it is a Steen. But I shall sell it to you for fifteen hundred, or I shall put it back in the sale room with that reserve."

Sir Edgar laughed and polished his glass carefully with his handkerchief before replacing it in his pocket.

"Cautious," he said. "Too cautious, Fustian. You ought to stand for Parliament. Put it on one side for me."

Mr. Campion drifted into the other salon. The interview, he understood, was at an end.

Max returned after some minutes, quietly elated. His small black eyes were supremely happy, and although he did not directly refer to the interview which had passed, Campion felt that he was to understand that it had been a triumph.

They parted with many protestations of regret on Max's part and a reckless promise that the "Head of a Boy" should be recovered though it lay at the end of the earth.

Mr. Campion wandered off down Bond Street. His mind was uneasy. The affair of the Dacre drawings was odd and irritating, but he was aware that the root of the uncomfortable impression chipping at his mind lay not here. Rather, it was something that had happened during the last few minutes, something which his unconscious mind had seized and was trying to point out to him.

In sheer annoyance he forced himself to think of something else.

10 : *The Key*

When Mr. Campion went to call on Belle three days after his visit to the Salmon Galleries his interest in the murder was still mainly academic.

The police, embodied by the inspector and his sergeant, had their own cut-and-dried views of the case. These had become crystallized in their minds by the cessation of the investigation, and their curiosity was appeased.

Campion, on the other hand, was convinced afresh every time he saw Linda that she had had nothing to do with the killing of Dacre and also that she was not hiding anything.

For him the question remained, and as he walked up the staircase to the drawing room he felt strange in the old house. It was as though he were visiting it for the first time and noticing something uncanny about it, something inhospitable, as though the very walls were hugging themselves away from him with jealous secrecy.

The drawing room looked much the same as usual, however. A fire had been lighted against the chilly spring weather, and Belle sat in her low chair beside it, her plump hands held out to the blaze. As soon as Campion saw her he experienced his first feeling of animosity towards the murderer.

In the few weeks since the affair Belle had aged. She looked thinner and more fragile than before. There was a droop in the muslin of her bonnet and another at the corner of her mouth. Her brown eyes were more faded, and her welcome, although warm, was a trifle tremulous.

They were careful not to mention the business in those first minutes when they sat together by the hearth and waited for Lisa to bring tea, but its presence was very obvious, and even the grand bravura of John Lafcadio's trophies scattered round the room seemed to have lost its magic beside the piece of violent, sordid reality which had invaded their fastness.

When Lisa, the tea, and the inevitable Donna Beatrice arrived together, the skeleton could be kept decently in the cupboard no longer. Indeed, Donna Beatrice drew it forth with a flourish and the same air of self-righteous courage with which some people disclose the more disgusting details of their ailments.

"Mr. Campion," she said, thrusting her surprisingly strong hand into his own, "you don't regard us as social lepers, at any rate. As soon as I came into the room I was aware of a strong blue aura over here in the corner by Belle, and I said to myself, 'Well, here's a *friend* at any rate.'"

Mr. Campion, who had forgotten her rainbow complex, was taken aback.

"Not at all," he murmured unsuitably and rose to assist Lisa in the matter of the tea table. The old Italian woman shot him a sly, grateful smile from under her yellow lids, an expression immediately followed by a most expressive glare of hatred directed at the unsuspecting "Inspiration," who had seated herself in the high Stuart chair across the hearth.

Donna Beatrice was still dramatizing the situation on National Theatre lines. Her heavy black velvet, chased silver cross, and fine lace handkerchief were almost traditional. Belle's kind brown eyes rested on her a little wearily.

"No news, no developments. The secret grows oppressive," Donna Beatrice remarked with relish as she accepted a cup of tea. "Tell me, Mr. Campion, have the police really dropped the case, or are they just crouching, watching, waiting to spring?"

Mr. Campion glanced at Belle for support, which she gave him generously.

"I don't want to talk about it, Beatrice, if you don't mind," she said plaintively. "I'm growing old. I don't want to think of unpleasant things."

"Always a weakness, Belle dear," said the irrepressible Inspiration with intentional gentleness. "But if you say so, we'll change the subject. Tell me, Mr. Campion, do you think the trend of modern art shows degeneracy or a leaning towards the primitive?"

Half an hour later, when Campion was wondering why, with a murderer at large in Little Venice, Donna Beatrice should have escaped killing, Max arrived.

He made his usual entrance, kissed Belle's hand, bowed to the younger lady, all but chucked Lisa under the chin, and seemed a little put out to see Campion.

"Tea, Lisa," he said. "Tea, that vulgar little stimulant we sip to soothe our afternoons. Bring me tea."

With his arrival the talk steered onto more general subjects, and Donna Beatrice was eclipsed.

"Linda spends a great deal of her time with the boy D'Urfey," Max remarked suddenly. "I met them going out together just now when I came in from my call on Claire Potter."

"He seemed a nice boy," said Belle. "He reminds me of poor Will Fitzsimmons before he became famous."

Donna Beatrice made a gesture. "Isn't that typical of Belle?" she said. "I'm afraid I'm more squeamish. Linda's infatuation for the friend of her murdered fiancé seems too much like morbidity for me."

Belle's eyes hardened.

"My granddaughter is neither morbid nor infatuated," she said with sudden vigour, and Max, who had opened his mouth, shut it again with the words unspoken.

Mr. Campion found himself growing more interested in Max. The man was not merely an empty poseur, and he felt he could begin to understand how he had carved a niche for himself in contemporary letters without having any especial gift. His was a tortuous, subtle brain, unexpectedly mobile and adroit.

Glancing at him now, lounging gracefully on a settee, his small dark face with its blue jowl and lively eyes turned towards the fire, Campion found him a most arresting personality.

"I trust the outcome of your masterly piece of salesmanship was successful the other afternoon?" he enquired.

Max turned to him lazily, but his smile showed him to be pleased.

"Eminently, thank you," he said. "The deal went through without another word."

Campion turned to Belle. "I had the privilege of seeing Fustian sell an old master the other afternoon," he said. "A most exciting experience. Tell me," he added, glancing back at the indolent figure on the settee, "how much doubt was there about the authenticity of that thing?"

"None whatever." The drawl was very pronounced. "None in the world." Belle looked up sharply.

"What picture was it?" she enquired.

"Nothing to interest you, dear lady." Max seemed anxious to let the question drop. "A conversation piece in the Steen manner, that's all."

His casualness had not deceived the old woman, however. She leant forward, her eyes fixed upon him.

"Not a christening scene?"

Max avoided her glance at first, but presently he laughed and looked into her eyes.

"There was a child in it," he admitted.

"And a lot of blue and a kneeling figure in the foreground?" Belle persisted.

Max shot a glance at Campion.

"I confess to all these," he said, laughing.

Mrs. Lafcadio sat back in her chair, her eyes round, and reproachful, a flush in her wrinkled cheeks.

"Max, that's very disgraceful," she said. "Very disgraceful indeed. Poor old Salmon would turn in his grave if he knew about it—he's probably doing it now. Really, my dear, that's dishonest!"

"But my adorable Mrs. Lafcadio,"—Max was still smiling—"you don't understand. I never for one moment suggested that the christening scene was a genuine Steen. Campion must bear me out—I told my client very definitely that in my opinion it was not a Steen. I sold it on the strict understanding that I could give no guarantee of any kind. I said that in front of witnesses, didn't I, Campion?"

Mr. Campion was spared replying by Belle, who continued in the same impulsive way.

"That picture," she said, "as you must know very well, Max, was painted by old Cornelius van Pipjer. Surely you remember his widow? She used to live in the Cromwell Road. Johnnie and I were so sorry for her. I remember her dying quite well. It's some years ago, of course, because Linda's father wasn't born."

Max smiled faintly. "It's an old picture, then, anyway," he said.

For a moment Belle's eyes clouded, and then she too smiled.

"I forget how old I am," she said. "Yes, of course, poor Hester van Pipjer was before any of your time. But I remember that picture. There were half a dozen of them, and Johnnie made Salmon buy them. Van Pipjer was a copyist, but that one picture was an original in the Steen manner. Van Pipjer himself would never part with it, but when he died and his widow was so desperately poor, Johnnie made Salmon buy the pictures. I remember, poor dear, he was very cross at having to pay as much for the original as the copies. He could sell the copies, you see, for what they were, but a single picture by an unknown artist in the manner of a master was hardly worth anything at all. Still, Mrs. van Pipjer was very glad of the money. I remember how she cried when she saw it, poor thing."

Max continued to smile, mischievously now, his eyes dancing.

"Dear Belle—what a gift!" he said. "You touch everything with the fairy finger of Romance. Can't you see her, Campion? The old Dutch widow weeping, the corner of her apron held to her eye, while my portly predecessor in the frock coat of munificence slips the golden guineas into the bosom of her dress!"

"Max, you won't get out of it that way." Belle shook her head at him angrily. "Besides, old Salmon would never think of slipping guineas into anyone's dress, although he certainly did wear a frock coat. But Mrs. van Pipjer never wore an apron, and if she had and was weeping into it, it would have been impossible to put money down her chest. But that's not the point. How much did you get for that picture?"

Mr. Campion looked the other way.

Max closed his eyes. "Fifteen," he said.

"Guineas?" demanded Belle, a little mollified.

"Hundreds," said Max.

"Fifteen hundred? Oh, Max, I won't have you here. I'm disgusted."

Donna Beatrice laughed a little enviously. "Very clever of Max, I think," she said.

"Don't encourage him." Belle was furious. "Oh," she added inconsequentially, "what a boon that money would have been to Hester! She had such a pretty daughter—in consumption, I remember."

Max burst out laughing. "Belle, you exquisite period piece," he said. "You do me wrong. I told my client that in my opinion the picture was not a Steen."

"Then why did he pay fifteen hundred pounds for it?"

"Because," said Max superbly, "the man was a pompous inbecile who imagined that I could be wrong."

"I suppose you suggested that it was a contemporary picture?" persisted Belle.

"I suggested nothing," said Max. "He did all the talking. Isn't that so, Campion? He certainly said it was painted on canvas contemporary with Steen, and I agreed with him. So it was. Your friend Van Pipjer must have had a stock of old canvases. Very useful."

Belle's muslin bonnet quivered in the warm air.

"You're very clever, Max," she said, "but you're not good."

Max's reply to this summing up of his character was typical. He slipped onto one knee at her side and burst into a torrent of words.

"Let me explain, dear lady. You're judging me unheard. If you had seen the man, you'd have agreed with me. You would have been my ally. You'd have convinced him it was a Steen, sold it for three thousand pounds, and spent the money on Hester van Pipjer's descendants. And you'd have been right."

He threw out his arm.

"There was this man, an overfed, self-important ignoramus with a ridiculous little glass—the sort of thing the detective in a farce might use— crawling about on my floor talking about the texture and the pigment as though he knew what the words meant. Why was he doing it?"

He sprang to his feet and strode down the room, working himself into a passion of eloquence, his eyes blazing with righteous fire.

"He was attempting to get an important picture cheap to present to the Art Gallery in a beastly town whose underfed millions he hopes to represent in Parliament. By this ostentatious gift he intends to impress the undereducated snobs on the local town council while the shivering children of the poor who subscribe to the rates and taxes are not interested in pictures at all. They want food. Do you know what I intend to do with that fifteen hundred pounds, Belle? I shall buy a motorcar. This fellow's rival candidate owns a factory which employs hundreds and thousands of men. I shall buy one of his cars, and the money which my idiot client should have spent on the poor children of his constituency will go back to them after all, with the picture thrown in."

He finished his peroration, one hand thrown out expressively.

The silence which followed this somewhat extraordinary argument was broken by a ladylike and ridiculous "Hear, hear, Max!" from Donna Beatrice.

"I agree with Max entirely," she said. "Too many people imagine they know something about Art."

Belle raised her eyebrows. "It seems to me," she said, "that two blacks make a white and there's a very expensive motorcar thrown in somewhere."

Mr. Campion alone was silent. He was assimilating the facts he had just heard and comparing them with the interview he had witnessed in the Salmon Gallery. It seemed to him that he was on the verge of a very startling and important idea.

He and Max left together soon afterwards and walked through the Crescent to a taxi rank on the railway bridge. It was raining and unusually dark for the time of year. Max appeared to be in high spirits. He strode along jauntily, his immense black hat set at an angle. Its brim was so wide that Campion, who towered above him, could not see his face beneath its shadow.

"The memory of the old!" Max remarked. "The coincidence, too! Extraordinary, wasn't it? Quite an instructive afternoon."

Campion was thinking furiously. The idea which had been nibbling at the back of his mind ever since he had turned out of the Salmon Gallery and walked down Bond Street suddenly became clear, and its significance sent an unaccustomed thrill down his spine.

What he had noticed subconsciously at the Salmon Gallery was an unmistakable family likeness between Max's story to the politician and his confession to Inspector Oates.

Apart from the obvious difference of emotional tone, the points of resemblance were striking: the apparent frankness, the flamboyancy, the whole-hearted courage, the completeness of the job. The other side of the picture-selling episode he had heard, and now a thought seized and bewildered him. What if there was another side to the confession? What if that, too, had been an essay in the second degree of subtlety?

He glanced down at the figure at his side, walking down the deserted London street, and experienced the odd physical phenomenon so aptly described as "the blood running cold." The more he thought about it the more clear it became. Max's confession had been altogether too easily discounted by the inspector. It was the confession of the hysterical and affected egotist Max appeared to be at first sight, and which the inspector still supposed him.

Mr. Campion now knew more than the inspector. He knew that Max was not a negligible idiot; moreover there seemed a reasonable chance that he was one of those strange, slightly crooked brains who not only take the courageous path but blind themselves to danger and truth alike. As Campion saw it now, Max's confession might very well have been a doubly ingenious lie, and if so the truth was terrifying.

He was aroused at this point in his reflections by a taxi pulling up beside them and Fustian's solicitous enquiry if he desired a lift.

Campion made his excuses, and Max entered the vehicle and was driven away. Mr. Campion stood in the rain looking after the cab until it disappeared from sight, momentarily stricken by what he could only regard as a species of revelation.

In the taxi Max removed his hat and lay back and laughed a little.

For some time he remained content in the contemplation of his own cleverness, but after a while he frowned and his bright black eyes narrowed. He was thinking of Mrs. Potter.

11 : *Before the Fact*

On the morning of the Thursday on which she died, Mrs. Potter rose a trifle earlier than was her wont because there was so much to do.

She climbed out of the bed, which was a divan by day, and stood for a moment thinking. Her nightdress, copied from a figure on a Grecian plate, was surmounted by a pathetically warm and ugly bed jacket, comforting her throat and arms which the linen draperies neglected.

Her iron-grey hair was tousled and her face very pale. She had slept badly.

Mr. Potter had already risen and had retired to the lean-to shed behind the scullery in which he bit and printed his lithographs. He was safe for another hour at least.

His wife dressed mechanically, nervous lines wrinkling her forehead.

The studio was draughty and not very comfortable, so that its air of careful unconventionality was a little sad. The Chianti-bottle and Roman-shawl school of decoration now suggested less of the *vie-de-bohème* than the set for an amateur production of *Trilby*, and the romantic makeshifts and picturesque squalor so brave in youth were in the middle age merely disheartening.

Claire Potter hurried, arraying herself in a Russian overall for housework. It was William's day at Blakenham, the school in Chelmsford which was optimistic enough to employ him as a visiting art master. He had to be "got off" in time.

In her efforts to set aside the one vital and terrible thought which had haunted her nights and days for the past three weeks, Mrs. Potter forced herself to consider the duties of the day. There were the tickets for the Roman Guild's water-colour show to be sent up to the committee for distribution. Then the efforts of the Gipsy Sketch Club had to be marked and a hurried criticism scribbled on the back of each; arch little criticisms they would be: "Tone values! Careful!"—or "That broken wash again! Avoid viridian."

Claire Potter took them very seriously, which, since she was paid for them, was to her credit and very nearly constituted an excuse.

When the bed had been draped into its striped homespun blanket and the pillows thrust into their daytime slips and piled into one corner to give a "touch of colour" to the room, Mrs. Potter made her toilet at the scullery sink.

She had never identified herself with the unwashed movement and performed her ablutions carefully, finishing off her face with rice powder, which she packed herself and sometimes sold in pretty, hand-painted boxes.

She moved deftly and methodically, the only way of doing anything in the face of so many domestic inconveniences, although on this particular morning much of her wonted brisk efficiency was absent.

She paused for a time, a wave of sudden heat sweeping up her backbone and over her head, leaving her scalp tingling and her eyes feeling sticky and uncomfortable. She had lived in a world of small things for so long

that the intrusion of something really large hardly registered on her conscious mind, but it had a curious physical effect upon her.

She took her brushes out of the turpentine, cleaned them carefully
before preparing breakfast, but she dropped the whole handful of them
and upset the jar at the sound of a footstep outside the studio door.

She was angry when she remembered it was probably Lisa or Fred
Rennie leaving the *Morning Post*, which came to the Lafcadio front door.

It was some time before she could bring herself to look at the paper.
She was the last person in the world to indulge in premonitions, but the
restless, terrified feeling which had been slowly increasing all through the
week seemed to have become insupportable this morning. It was as though
she felt the breath of disaster on her cheek.

She snatched up the paper at last and scanned the news columns, an
ever-growing sense of relief spreading over her as no familiar name caught
her eye.

She turned back resolutely to the work of the day. There was so much
to do and so little time. It was a terrible life. When one was really artistic,
it did seem a pity that one should have to spend one's whole time working.

She began to think of Italy, of a little village up in the hills behind
San Remo, where one could prop up one's easel beside the church and
sit in the shadow and enjoy the lighting. It was all so clean and clear
and courageous; the colours straight out of the tube.

She repeated this to herself aloud as though she found a particular
comfort in it. If it weren't for William, and their dreadful poverty, and
the never-ending round of things to do, she would go back to that village.

Just for an instant, when she was spreading the peasant cloth over the
old English gate-legged table, an impulse seized her to go, to go at once,
to leave everything and fly precipitately. But this outcome of an instinct
for self-preservation was unfortunately hastily set aside.

She would think about it, perhaps. If her nerve failed her she might
try it in the autumn. As it was, she must see Fred Rennie about some
paint. And there was Miss Cunninghame coming at half past three for
her lesson. The day was going to be a rush.

There had been times when Mrs. Potter had enjoyed Thursday. She
liked being busy, she liked the air of importance which being secretary
to the Roman Guild gave her, and she enjoyed pointing out to the refined and wealthy Miss Cunninghame exactly where that good lady's
rather dated taste had let her down.

But today it was different.

Mr. Potter returned from the shed at the moment when the kippers
were set on the table.

Mrs. Potter looked at him as though she were seeing him for the first
time as he came in at the doorway, and it occurred to her forcibly that
he was of no possible help to her in her terrible situation. She had never

had a great opinion of him and, looking at him now in this new cold light, she wondered how on earth they had ever come to marry. Surely it must have been obvious in those halcyon days thirty years ago at St. Ives that the burden which that sad-faced youth had carried in his soul was not genius but a gloomy conviction of his lack of it.

All this was particularly sad because Mr. Potter was very happy. He was collarless, his old canvas trousers bagged at knee and seat, and his feet thrust into heelless Turkish slippers were bare. But he was joyful. The wretchedness had almost completely vanished from his face, and he waved a damp piece of jap paper at his wife in something akin to triumph.

"A beauty," he said. "A beauty. Claire, my dear, that last stone is a corker. I'm afraid I'm a little dirty. The ink, you know. But look at it! You couldn't get that feeling on ordinary stone. Sandstone's a new and important medium. I've always said so, and this is going to prove it."

He pushed the crockery out of the way and set the print down upon the tablecloth, leaving an inky thumb smear upon the linen.

The sight of this blemish was the first blot on Mr. Potter's morning, and he dropped his hand over it hastily, glancing at his wife out of the corners of his eyes.

Somewhat to his relief, she was not looking at him but staring out of the window, an expression on her face that he did not remember having seen there before. She looked almost afraid, almost gentle.

For some reason which he did not understand, this phenomenon delighted him. He plucked at her sleeve.

"Look," he said. "It's good, isn't it? I was going to call it 'A Bit of Old Bayswater,' but I think I might have something a bit more modern than that, since it's come off. There's the railway bridge, you see. It's come out beautifully, hasn't it? Those nice shadows there."

She still did not speak, and he continued to gloat over the lithograph.

"I thought I'd frame it and hang it over there, instead of the Medici print. After all, an original's better than a reproduction any day."

"Oh, William, don't be silly. Get on with your breakfast. I've got such a lot to do."

Mrs. Potter flicked the print onto the divan and put the food back in front of her husband.

"Oh, be careful, my dear. It's not dry. Such a beautiful print. It's taken me all the morning."

Despair was creeping back into Mr. Potter's tone, and as he sat down meekly now and pecked at his kipper, which had grown cold and unappetizing, he looked old and neglected and rather dirty.

Mrs. Potter ate her breakfast as though she would have disliked it had she thought about it. Once again the frightened expression which made her look gentle deceived her husband, and, after a sly glance to see that his print was all right, he leant forward.

"Are you well, Claire? You've seemed nervous and not quite the thing ever since the reception."

To his surprise she turned on him with quite unwarranted vigour.

"That's not true. I'm perfectly all right. The reception has got nothing to do with it, anyway. Hurry. You've got to catch the ten-thirty at Liverpool Street."

"All right." Mr. Potter's gloom had completely returned. "I'm sorry I've got to go today," he said. "I would have liked to make one or two more prints. Mrs. Lafcadio would like one, I know. It's deadly work, teaching," he went on. "It's difficult enough teaching people who want to learn, but those boys aren't a bit keen. It makes it very difficult."

Mrs. Potter made no reply, but sipped her coffee from the *filtre* glasses they had brought from Belgium and quite evidently did not think of him at all.

Mr. Potter's glance stole round again to the lithograph.

"It'd look very nice over there," he said. "The light's good and it's interesting. I think I shall frame it and hang it up if you don't mind, my dear."

"I don't want it there, William. I've taken a lot of trouble over this room. I receive my pupils here, and it's important to me that it should be kept just so."

Mrs. Potter found that it relieved her feelings to be so definite. Moreover, this question of the decoration of the room was an old bone of contention between them, and she always prided herself upon never permitting her personality to be overshadowed by her husband's. The fact that this was a rather superfluous precaution never seemed to occur to her.

In the ordinary way Mr. Potter gave up without a struggle, but today he was flushed with triumph, emboldened by success.

"But, my dear," he said gently, "there *are* people who like my pictures. Someone might come in and see it and want to buy a copy. The Duke of Caith bought one once, remember. He liked it."

"William, be quiet. I can't stand it."

Mrs. Potter's tone was so hysterical and so unlike herself that her husband was silenced and sat regarding her in open-mouthed bewilderment.

The rest of the meal passed in silence, and after it Mr. Potter shambled back to his shed with his precious print, his old despondent self again.

At a quarter to ten he departed for his school, and as his wife saw his untidy, unhappy figure wandering out of the garden gate, his lank hair tufting under his hat and his brown-paper parcels of drawings flapping under his arm, she knew that she would not see him again until seven o'clock. She waved to him perfunctorily.

Had she realized that she would never see him again it is doubtful whether her adieu would have been much more cordial. From his wife's point of view, Mr. Potter was an impossible person.

The Roman Guild tickets and the Gipsy sketches, combined with a modicum of housework, kept Mrs. Potter busy until just on one o'clock, when she went over to Fred Rennie's for a tube of flake white.

The lower part of the converted coach house, where the Lafcadio secret colours were still prepared, had much of the alchemist's laboratory about it. Fred Rennie was no chemist, and he did his work in the curious elementary fashion which he had learnt from the painter.

The whole place was indescribably untidy, and the chances of any thief stealing the process were ludicrous. Only Rennie knew his way about the littered benches where poisons, food, and quite valuable pure colour were littered in small screws of dirty brown paper. Rows of old jam jars contained valuable mixtures, and the smell of medium was overpowering.

Fred Rennie was at work, and he looked up and smiled at her as she came in.

Rennie did not like Mrs. Potter. He considered her nosy and officious and suspected her of trying to buy paint from him at less than cost price, which was in point of fact quite justified. He had an elementary sense of humour, and Mrs. Potter disliked him because he had no deference as far as she was concerned and was inclined to treat her as an equal.

Getting out the flake white entailed a certain amount of furniture-shifting before he could reach the great press at the far end of the room where his completed products were kept.

While his back was turned, Mrs. Potter moved to the bench on which he had been working and peered at the paraphernalia spread out upon it, not because she was particularly interested but because it was her habit to peer at other people's work. Indeed, the movement was mechanical and her mind very far away, still obsessed by its stupefying secret, so that she came to herself with a start to find Fred Rennie holding out a great brown-paper bag full of white powder. She saw his leering cockney face behind it.

"Take a pinch," he said.

Somewhat taken aback by this familiarity, she spoke sharply: "What is it?"

"Arsenic," said Fred Rennie and laughed till he was nearly sick. He was an uncouth person.

He gave her the flake white, was firm in their usual argument about the price, and when she went off he congratulated himself for having snubbed her for her curiosity.

Mrs. Potter had very little time for lunch. The shop in Church Street which sold her pen paintings phoned her when she came in from Rennie's shed, and she spent a busy hour packing up, pricing, and getting off a consignment of table centres.

When she came in again and took in the parcel of wood blocks from Salmon's which had been left with Rennie, there was only fifteen minutes to spare before Miss Cunninghame was due. She made herself a cup of Bovril in the scullery and settled down by the window in the studio to drink it. It was the first quiet time she had had since breakfast. Yet she found herself thinking it was too long.

In the ordinary way she could keep her mind happily occupied by thinking of little things, but lately she had been forced not to think at all. Whenever she let her mind loose it reverted to the one subject which was taboo, the one thing she dared not consider, this impossible and awful thing which had descended upon her and made everything in which she was interested seem negligible by comparison.

It was with a sense of relief that she heard the latch of the garden gate and Miss Florence Cunninghame's soft heavy feet on the brick.

She thrust the empty cup out of sight and rose to meet her visitor with a travesty of her bright professional smile.

Miss Cunninghame was a very fair specimen of her type. She was plump, ladylike, elderly, and quite remarkably without talent. Her tweed coat and skirt, silk blouse and pull-on hat might have belonged to any provincial schoolmistress. She had money of her own and an insatiable passion for painting water-colours.

As a person she was not very nice. Her blue eyes were set a little too closely together, and her mouth had small vertical creases round it which made it look as though it drew up on a string. It was her habit to bring her sketches every fortnight to Mrs. Potter for criticism and advice. She had a great portfolio of them now, having just returned from an orgy of painting near Rye.

"Glorious weather," she said in a faint, rather affected voice. "I painted the whole time. The colouring is so beautiful down there. There was quite a crowd of us."

Mrs. Potter felt suddenly helpless, an experience she never remembered knowing before in a similar situation, but the fine weather and colour near Rye and Miss Cunninghame's sketches seemed to have become inexplicably silly.

Her visitor stripped off her brown kid gloves and set about unpacking the portfolio with the eagerness of a child preparing a surprise.

Mrs. Potter felt her eyes glazing as she watched, and when the dozen or so green landscapes, horrible in their wet similarity, were spread out in front of her on the table she could hardly force herself to say the right things, to remember the well-worn words and phrases, the right inflections of surprise and gratification for which her visitor waited and would eventually pay her.

When the first excitement of showing her drawings had passed, Miss

Cunninghame's blue eyes took on a more determined light and she sat down, quite frankly preparing to gossip.

"No more *news?*" she said, lowering her voice and leaning forward confidentially. "I mean," she went on hastily, "last time I was here it was just after the—the affair. Don't you remember? You were very upset, and I only stayed for ten minutes or so. You poor thing, you did look ill. You don't look very much better now," she went on, eyeing her victim appraisingly. "I've been away, so I haven't heard much. The newspapers have been very quiet, haven't they? But my friend Miss Richards, whose brother is in the Foreign Office, tells me that the police have dropped the whole affair. Is that true?"

Mrs. Potter sank down in a chair opposite Miss Cunninghame, not because she wanted to talk but because her knees would no longer support her. She knew her forehead was damp under her fringe, and wondered how long this dreadful physical reaction to the thoughts she would not permit herself to face would last.

Miss Cunninghame went on with the dreadful eagerness of one who has broken the ice of a difficult subject.

"You haven't heard, I suppose? The police are very inconsiderate, aren't they? I've always understood that. It must have been very terrible for you," she added in a blatant attempt to flatter her hearer into a confidence. "You knew him quite well, didn't you? Was he ever a pupil of yours?"

"Dacre?" said Mrs. Potter. "Oh, no. No, I never taught him anything." She might have added that that would have been impossible, but her instinct was to keep very quiet, to say nothing. It was as though she were standing in the middle of a stream of traffic and her only hope was to remain still.

Something that was almost a smile of satisfaction broke through Miss Cunninghame's imperfect mask of sympathy.

"I mean, the inquest was so *funny,* wasn't it?" she said. "I didn't go, of course, but the reports in the newspapers were so vague. There was one thing I was going to ask you. They said he was married. *I* always understood that he was engaged to Miss Lafcadio. But perhaps I was mistaken."

Mrs. Potter forced herself to speak. "They were engaged once," she said, "but it all blew over. Before he went to Italy, you know."

"Oh, I see." Miss Cunninghame nodded and pursed the lips which pursed so easily. "Of course," she went on suddenly, her mild blue eyes widening alarmingly, "he *was* murdered, wasn't he? Oh, forgive me for using that word, but I mean he was stabbed. But I see that perhaps you don't want to talk about it. Perhaps it's too painful."

The mild eyes seemed to have become positively devilish. Mrs. Potter wondered if the beads of sweat had rolled down under her fringe. The chattering old gossip seemed to have become a fiend possessed of super-human insight in the power to wrest truth from its well.

Mrs. Potter defended herself weakly. "It was a great shock," she said. "I know nothing about it."

"But of course you don't," laughed Miss Cunninghame, a little nettled. "Of course you don't, my dear, or else you wouldn't be sitting here, would you? I only wondered. Of course I did hear—or at least I gathered from something Miss Richards let slip—that there was some business about an ambassador.

"Not that he had done it, you know, but that—well, that he was there. Miss Richards thought," she went on, lowering her voice, "that it might be —well, Bolshevists, you know. Not quite intentionally, you know, but for propaganda, like the suffragettes. One does hear such extraordinary things.

"I suppose," she went on in a last attempt to get something intelligent out of her informant, who had become wooden-faced and dumb with sheer, unmixed, stultifying fear, "I suppose you haven't any idea?"

"No," said Mrs. Potter dully. "I haven't any idea."

When Miss Cunninghame had packed up her drawings and stood ready to go, having already stayed a little over her time, she made a final effort.

"Poor Mrs. Lafcadio!" she said. "She's so old. What a shock for her! It's so terrible, it being left like this with nobody really knowing."

Mrs. Potter gripped the door handle.

"Yes," she said unsteadily. "Nobody *really* knowing. That's the awful part."

"That's what I say," said Miss Cunninghame brightly and went.

Left to herself, Mrs. Potter glanced at the clock. It was half past four. William would not return until seven, and until then she was free. There was no need to prepare a meal. At a quarter to seven Belle would come down the garden path and ask them both to dinner: "As you're so busy on Thursdays, my dear, I'm sure you haven't had time to get anything ready."

Belle had done this every Thursday for nearly six years now. The invitation sounded spontaneous every time, but it had become a tradition, and there was no reason to suppose that this day would be unlike any of the others, were it not for that awful feeling of impending danger pressing down upon her.

As she stood irresolute, her eyes wandered across the room and rested on something standing there, but she drew them away from it. That was not the way. She must pull herself together and not think.

Suddenly everything in the room became startlingly clear. She saw it as though she had never seen any of it before. The fact that it was the last time that she would ever stand and look round this little room, so full of its pathetic mementos of past affectations, was, of course, unknown to her, but the fact remained that she saw it all in relief. Every piece of furniture, every picture, every drapery stood out clear from its neighbour.

It was while she remained there wondering at this phenomenon that the telephone bell began to ring.

12 : *What Shall We Do?*

It was Belle who found the body; sweet, friendly old Belle with her white Breton cap aflutter from the breeze in the garden and her skirts held up a little to escape the dewy grasses on the sides of the path.

She paused for a moment on the Potter step to break off a dead rose hip left over from the autumn on the rather straggly seven-sister tree which grew over the porch.

Then, mildly surprised at receiving no answer to her knock, she went round to the scullery door, which stood open. "Claire, my dear," she called. "Claire, are you busy? May I come in?"

Her voice fluttered round the little building and was silent, and after waiting expectantly for a moment or so she went in and passed through to the studio.

Claire Potter lay face downward on the divan, her arms limp and her features mercifully covered by the cushions. Her small compact figure in its art overall mingled so well with the homespun blanket that for a moment Belle's eyes failed to distinguish it, and she stood looking round the room, faintly disappointed to find it deserted.

She had decided to sit down to wait, avoiding the exertion of a second visit, when the body on the divan caught her eye, and her whole attention was focused upon it, as if its shape had been defined by thick black lines.

A quick intake of breath preceded her sharp exclamation: "Claire! I didn't see you, my dear. What's the matter?"

Claire Potter's body lay limp and flat, like a heap of clothes. Belle went over to it, her puckered face colouring with motherly concern.

"Aren't you well, child? Claire!"

She laid a hand upon the flaccid, unresisting shoulder and attempted to rouse the piteous thing in the art overall.

"Come, dear. Come, Claire. Sit up."

Beneath the old woman's frail strength the body lifted a little, and for an instant the face which had once been Mrs. Potter's was exposed. Blue skin, distended eyes, and terrible, parted lips, they all showed clearly against the raucous orange of the cushions.

Belle's old fingers released their hold, and the face disappeared again in the pillows.

The woman standing in the studio straightened herself. The movement

was very slow. Her face was pale and her gentle brown eyes oddly expressionless. For some seconds she remained irresolute. Then she began
to move with remarkable determination and agility.

She glanced round the studio, noted that the place seemed to be in
normal good order, and then, stepping gently out of deference to that
odd superstition that the dead sleep lightly and so must be preserved
from noise, she went out into the scullery again.

The small mirror over the sink shocked her with its reflection of a
tottering, white-lipped old woman in a dishevelled bonnet of lawn, and
she stopped resolutely to compose herself.

At all costs, for everyone's sake, there must be no fuss, no painful scene.
No one else must be subjected to the shock of seeing unexpectedly that
terrible, terrible face. Poor Claire! Poor, clever, practical Claire!

In a moment or so she imagined she had forced herself to look more
or less normal, and she continued steadily about the things she had to do.

From the scullery door she could see down the path to Rennie's shed.
"Fred," she called softly. "Fred, come here a moment."

She had fancied that her voice was normal, but the man shot up from
his bench and came hurrying towards her, the liveliest concern in his face.

"Why, ma'am, what is it?" he demanded, catching her arm to support
her.

Belle looked up at him and remembered disconcertingly in the midst
of the crowding fears and sorrows in her mind that the first time she
had seen him he had been a ragged, dirty child of five crying for his
mother at her knee.

"What is it, ma'am?" he repeated urgently. "Are you ill at all?"

His concern for herself at such a time irritated the old lady, and she
became briskly practical.

"Come in here, where we can't be seen from the house," she said, stepping back into the scullery, and continued as he followed her in wonderingly, "Mrs. Potter is in the studio. I've just found her. She's dead."

"Dead?" said the man, his jaw dropping open. "Are you sure, ma'am?"

Belle shuddered and was ashamed of herself for the reaction. "Yes," she
said simply. "Go in, but don't disturb her, poor soul."

Fred Rennie returned, his dark face grave and his forehead puckered.

"You must come into the house, ma'am," he said. "It's not right for
you to have had to see that. Not at all right. You must lie down. Put
your feet up," he added rather helplessly.

"Rennie, don't be a fool." Belle's authority returned. "There are several
things to be done. Poor Potter will be home at seven, and we can't let him
go in there. First of all we must get a doctor."

"That's right, ma'am. We must tell someone. No need for Miss Beatrice to know at once."

"Certainly not," said Belle, adding involuntarily, "Fred, I'm glad your master's not alive."

The man nodded gravely. "It would have worried him," he said and went on after a pause. "Better have her own doctor. He lives down in the Crescent. Shall I phone him?"

Belle hesitated. "No, I don't think so. Donna Beatrice might hear you, and I don't want the household alarmed."

"There's Mrs. Potter's own phone in the studio."

Belle shook her head. "No. It's not quite respectful in front of the dead. Besides, I think nothing in that room ought to be disturbed, not even in the slightest."

"Not disturbed?" he began and broke off abruptly as the significance of her words sank into his mind. "Why, ma'am, you don't mean to say that you think she . . . that is, you don't mean that her death wasn't natural, that there's been another . . ."

He stopped, not caring to use the word.

"I don't know what I think," said Belle. "You'd better go and fetch the doctor. Bring him back with you."

"But I can't leave you here, ma'am."

"Rubbish!" she said. "Do as you're told."

But when Rennie had departed, walking with suspicious nonchalance until he was once past the garden gate and then taking to his heels like the proverbial bringer of bad news, Belle thought of Mr. Campion.

She went quietly down the garden path and called to Lisa.

"Lisa," she said, "I want you to stand on Mrs. Potter's doorstep. Don't let anyone go in until I come back."

On the phone in her own house Belle was studiously noncommittal, but to Mr. Campion, sitting up in his flat in Bottle Street, her message came like a frantic appeal for help.

"Albert," she said, "is that you, my dear? I've had such trouble getting on to you. I wonder if you could come over and see me? Yes, now. At once. No, no, nothing is exactly wrong. Nothing to get alarmed about, actually. But I should be very grateful if you could come soon. Albert, listen. Take a taxi."

It was the last three words which convinced Mr. Campion that something was seriously amiss. Like many people of her generation, Belle regarded taxicabs as telegrams, measures of emergency.

"I'll be over right away," he said and heard her gentle sigh of relief.

As Belle hung up the receiver, Donna Beatrice came to the top of the stairs.

"Whom were you talking to?" she asked suspiciously.

"Campion," said Belle truthfully. "He's coming over to talk to me."

Miraculously, Donna Beatrice was satisfied, and Belle went down the staircase to the garden again.

Lisa came out of the porch as her mistress appeared. Her skin was very yellow, and her bright black eyes looked scared. "I went in," she said without preamble.

"Oh, Lisa!"

One old woman eyed the other.

"How did she die?"

"I don't know. I'm waiting for the doctor."

"I will wait also," said Lisa, and they were both in the little scullery when Rennie returned with assistance.

Young Dr. Fettes was a quiet, square young man with bushy black hair growing low down over his forehead and the gift of looking blank without appearing foolish. During his seven or eight years of general practice he had not quite grown used to the amazing complacency with which the relations of his patients put their responsibilities gratefully onto his shoulders, as if his medical degrees carried with them a species of omnipotence together with a thorough knowledge of the world.

He surveyed the three anxious people in the scullery now, their frightened eyes resting on him trustingly, and wondered regretfully what past generation of supermedicos had engendered the superstition. Mercifully they saw nothing on his face but the comforting stamp of authority. He was a doctor.

He knew them all slightly, which made it easier, and when Belle explained that Potter was down at his school and would not return until seven he went in to see that which had once been Mrs. Potter.

Lisa accompanied him. She was firm on this point, and Belle relinquished the unpleasant duty gratefully.

Rennie brought a chair from the shed for his mistress and stood by her side like a sentinel throughout the gruesome business.

From the scullery doorway a bright corner of the studio was visible. Its brightness was intentional, with heaped shawls and Chianti bottles and painted poppy heads. Belle could not look at it, but sat like a girl and twisted her wedding ring round and round to keep herself from crying.

Campion found her like that, sitting on the kitchen chair, her head bent and her old fingers turning in her lap. She lifted her head as he came up, and he stopped and kissed her involuntarily and slipped his hand over hers.

"What is it?"

She told him in a soft hushed voice which sounded old and pathetic, and he listened with horror creeping up his backbone.

"You found her first?"

"Yes."

"You're sure she was dead?"

"Oh—oh, yes. Yes, my dear. Quite dead. Poor, poor, busy Claire!" She swayed forward a little as she spoke, and he caught her.

She refused to go into the house, however.

"The doctor will want to see me," she said. "He told me to stay."

Dr. Fettes came into the scullery at last, was introduced to Campion, whose name he recognized, and began to ask questions.

"Mrs. Lafcadio," he said, betraying a very faint Scots accent, "when you went into the studio and found the—the lady, did you move anything at all?"

"No." The old woman spoke unhesitatingly. "Nothing at all, except—her. I lifted her up, saw her face, and came out here."

"I see. You didn't by any chance open the windows? Or the doors maybe?"

"No." Belle was puzzled. "No, I didn't."

"How long would it be after you found Mrs. Potter that this fellow here came round for me?"

"Five minutes . . . ten at the outside."

"Really!" The young doctor frowned and finally gave up the indirect method of enquiry for one better suited to his temperament.

"I'll be frank with you, Mrs. Lafcadio. You didn't notice a smell of gas when you came in?"

Belle looked bewildered.

"Gas? Why, Doctor, you don't think that she . . . I mean . . ."

"You didn't notice a smell of gas in the room, did you?"

"No." She shook her head. "No. I didn't notice anything in the least unusual. The windows were just like they are now, I think; I didn't notice."

The young doctor sighed.

"Well," he said at last, "it's half after six now. Maybe I'd better wait and see Mr. Potter."

Belle touched his sleeve. "That poor man won't be able to help you much," she said. "He's been out all the day, and this shock will unnerve him terribly."

Dr. Fettes considered. He knew Mr. Potter and had no illusions concerning that gentleman's capabilities whether under nervous strain or no. He also knew that the Potters lived as it were under Lafcadio patronage, and being uncertain of the exact path which etiquette dictated wisely chose the easier.

"Frankly, Mrs. Lafcadio," he said, "I can't give a certificate in this case. There'll have to be an inquest."

Belle nodded. She made no other comment.

Campion took the situation in hand, and Fettes, who knew his name and had heard all the gossip concerning the first mysterious death at Little Venice, was glad enough to permit him to do so.

Belle was persuaded to return to the house with Lisa to look after her, and Campion phoned Inspector Oates.

He made the call from the house, leaving the doctor to keep an eye on the studio where the body lay.

"The room is practically untouched," he said. "I thought you'd probably like to come along right away. Yes, I've got the doctor here. . . . He doesn't seem to know . . . talks about gas."

Stanislaus's usually weary voice sounded brisk, almost excited.

"Good for you, Campion. Hold everything till I get there. I knew something like this would happen. Is the girl about?"

Mr. Campion passed a hand over his forehead.

"Look here," he said, "I can't argue over the phone."

"You don't have to," said Oates, who seemed to be positively elated by the gruesome news. "I'll be over in ten minutes."

He rang off.

13 : *Police Work*

While the discovery that Linda was away in Paris and had been there for several days pursuing her own line of investigation shook the inspector's conviction of her guilt in the second outrage at Little Venice, it did not completely dispel it by any means. He was set back rather than defeated, and retained an official reticence until the facts should be assembled and his theory triumphantly proved.

Dr. Fettes repeated his opinion that Mrs. Potter's death was due to asphyxia and refused to say more until after the post-mortem.

Belle retired to the house with Lisa, and the forlorn little studio was left in charge of the police.

Mr. Campion was there, silent, observant, and marvellously unobtrusive, while the dreadful formalities were accomplished.

In the beginning Oates was nearly as cheerful as his personality permitted. Here, experience told him, was an example of premeditated crime, which was nearly always handled successfully by police machinery.

The murder—for he had already made up his mind it was a murder—was going to be subjected to the fullest floodlight of police scrutiny, and Inspector Oates considered that without undue optimism he could count on its success.

As the details sorted themselves out, however, there was born in his mind the faint beginnings of that bewilderment and irritation which so exasperated him afterwards.

He was compelled to agree with the doctor that Mrs. Potter had been asphyxiated without signs of violence, without a foreign body in the throat, and apparently without gas.

For perhaps half an hour, while the photographers and fingerprint experts were at work, things were at a deadlock.

Into the inspector's optimism crept a note of truculence, and as each ordinary avenue of enquiry proved barren in turn, his expression of hearty self-assurance became more rigidly fixed and less convincing.

Fred Rennie came in for a careful cross-examination as one of the last people to have seen Mrs. Potter alive, but beyond a careful and fairly accurate account of the purchase of the flake white they could get nothing from him.

The first light on what was fast becoming the inexplicable arrived when plain-clothesman Downing, who had been left on guard outside the studio, caught Lisa in the act of rinsing out the cup from which Mrs. Potter had drunk her midday Bovril, after he had observed the old Italian woman retrieve it surreptitiously from a clump of spear grass in the flower bed.

He brought the woman and the suspected vessel, now practically clean and of no use whatever as evidence, triumphantly before the inspector.

Lisa stood just inside the doorway, the light from the hanging bulbs shining on her face. She made an extraordinary, unforgettable picture, the flushed policeman standing at her side. Her bright black eyes glowed from out the network of yellow wrinkles which formed her face and succeeded in giving her the appearance of incalculable guile, whereas acute alarm was probably her only emotion.

The inspector surveyed her black-clad funereal figure with mistrust. When he spoke, however, his tone was friendly.

"Miss Capella and I know one another," he said. "We met before—some weeks back."

Lisa nodded, and her misleading black eyes flickered with something which might have been malignant satisfaction but which was in point of fact mere recognition.

"Yes," she said. "At the other murder."

"Murder?" Oates pounced on the word. But Lisa seemed unaware of any admission. She stood looking at him, helplessness and stupidity alike masked by that baffling exterior.

"What makes you think Mrs. Potter was murdered?"

"I saw her face. She did not die naturally. Dead people do not look like that when they die naturally."

"Oh, you saw her face, did you?" said the inspector, sighing. "That was when you came in for the cup, I suppose? That cup."

He pointed to the rather ridiculous pottery mug which P. C. Downing still held so confidently, but if he hoped for any dramatic collapse from the old woman, Lisa was a disappointment.

"Yes, when I got the cup," she agreed, moistening her lips with the tip of her tongue, her eyes flickering maddeningly.

"Ah!" The inspector was almost embarrassed by such a wealth of admission. "You don't deny, then, that you took the cup from this room after Mrs. Potter was dead and attempted to wash it out?"

The triumphant note in his voice seemed suddenly to warn Lisa that the conversation was not merely an idle chat. She shut her mouth hard, and her eyes became dull and completely expressionless.

The inspector repeated his question.

Lisa threw out her hands expressively.

"I do not talk any more," she said.

After several hopeless attempts to make this statement untrue, Oates turned to Campion.

"You know her," he said. "Make her understand she can't go as far as this without explaining more fully."

But, once alarmed, Lisa was not easily soothed, and it was not until fifteen minutes later that she showed any further signs of being able to speak at all.

At last, however, she conceded a few hesitating replies:

"I came in when Mrs. Lafcadio went indoors to phone. It was then I saw Claire Potter's face. . . . Yes, I saw the cup, too. . . . Yes, it was then I put it in the flower bed."

"Why?" the inspector demanded.

"Because I did not wish to go into the house then. Mrs. Lafcadio had told me to wait by the studio. I did not want anyone else to go in the studio."

"Why?"

"Because Mrs. Potter was dead."

Inspector Oates sighed. Campion intervened.

"Why did you take the cup away, Lisa?"

The old woman hesitated. Her eyes were alive again, darting painfully from side to side.

"I saw it there," she said unexpectedly, pointing to the occasional table beneath the window on the lower shelf of which Claire had thrust her cup when Miss Cunninghame arrived. "And I took it to clean."

"But why, Lisa? You must have had a reason for doing such a thing at such an extraordinary time."

The old woman turned upon him.

"I had," she said with totally unexpected vigour. "I thought perhaps there was poison in the cup and that she had died from it and that there would be trouble. So I washed the cup that there might not be any more unhappiness in the house."

The inspector was regarding her with fascinated eyes, while upon the face of P. C. Downing there was something approaching wonderment and joy.

Mr. Campion persisted anxiously.

"You must explain."

"I do not talk any more."

"But you must. Don't you see, if you don't explain, these gentlemen will naturally think it was you who put the poison in the cup if any was there?"

"I?" Lisa was plainly horrified. "Why should I?"

Oates took a step forward.

"That's what we want to know."

Lisa began to cry. She sank down on the nearest chair and wept unrestrainedly. It was all very uncomfortable.

The task of persuading the truth out of her seemed to have devolved upon Campion, and he tried again.

"Who do you think would poison Mrs. Potter, Lisa?"

"No one. No one. I only washed out the cup in case."

"Oh, but come, Lisa, that's not true. You were fond of Mrs. Potter—"

"I was not." The tearful vehemence was alarming. "She was a fool. A domineering woman. A great fool."

"Well, then,"—Mr. Campion mopped his forehead—"you liked her, you knew her well. If any—any outsider had poisoned her, you would like him to be caught. Is that true?"

"Yes,"—grudgingly.

"Well, then, you must tell us who you thought had poisoned the cup."

"I didn't think he had done it . . . I didn't . . . I didn't . . . I only washed out the cup in case. When I saw her dead I remembered him coming in and I thought . . ." Her sobs increased, and she became speechless.

Campion and Oates exchanged glances, and the inspector snorted with relief. It was coming at last, then.

"There, there," he said foolishly, patting her shoulder. "You'd better tell us the truth, you know. There's no use hiding anything in a business like this. Whom did you see coming in?"

Lisa's sobbing became hysterical.

"I don't know. I didn't see anyone. I won't speak."

Oates's grip on her shoulder tightened, and he shook her gently. "You pull yourself together. Come on, out with it. Whom did you see coming into this studio?"

The voice of authority had its effect. Lisa began to mutter tearfully:

"I don't know anything. I only saw him come in and go out again, and afterwards when I saw her dead I wondered . . ."

"Yes, yes, we know." The inspector spoke impatiently. "But who?"

Lisa raised her drowned eyes to his.

"Mr.—Mr. Potter," she said. "Her husband. For six years now he's caught the five-thirty from Chelmsford, arrived at Liverpool Street at a little before half past six and come home by seven, and so when today

I saw him come in at five and go out again in a minute or two I guessed something was going to happen."

The inspector, who had been jotting down facts in a small, untidy notebook, nodded to his subordinate.

"Get on to Enquiries, and find out the number of the school at Chelmsford, and ask if Mr. Potter left early today. Don't say who you are, of course."

While this operation was in progress, Lisa was questioned closely in the matter of times. She was inclined to be sullen and unhelpful at first, but Oates revealed himself the soul of tact and patience and presently almost succeeded in pinning her down.

"It was a quarter to five by the kitchen clock when I saw Miss Cunninghame go," she said slowly. "The clock is fifteen minutes fast, so that would be half past four. Then I heard the gate go again, and I looked out to see if it was the fishmonger, and I saw that it was Mr. Potter. It was five o'clock then, because I looked at the clock. I was afraid for a moment, you see, that it was seven o'clock and I had got muddled with the time."

"Then if the clock said five it was really a quarter to, since the clock was fast?" said Oates, writing.

"No. It was five then, because when Miss Cunninghame went I knew it must be half past four, so I altered the clock. It was then I might have got muddled in the time."

"Quite," said Oates dryly and altered his notes. "How long was Mr. Potter in the studio here?"

"I don't know. I didn't look at the clock again, but I think about ten minutes."

"Ten minutes. How did he go out? Was he in a hurry?"

Lisa began to weep again. Finally, however, she nodded.

"Yes," she said. "That was what I noticed. He crept like he was afraid of being seen. That's why I washed the cup."

Downing returned from the telephone, his manner betraying respectfully suppressed excitement.

"Mr. Potter has not been at Blakenham all today, sir," he said. "They received a telegram at ten o'clock this morning to say he was confined to his bed."

The inspector grimaced.

"I see," he said slowly. "I see."

There was a silence after he had spoken, and it was in that silence that Mr. Potter opened the garden gate and, striving to step naturally and with carefree decision, crossed the path and entered the studio.

He stood in the doorway and blinked at the astonishing sight of so many people in his home, as yet not distinguishing the separate personalities and the possible significance of their presence.

He looked much as Mr. Campion first remembered seeing him. His thin red face with its enormous nose and watery eyes was melancholy even in its surprise. Also he was quite startlingly untidy. His tufty hair burst from beneath his hat, his hastily gathered papers were in painful imminence of descending to his feet in chaos, and one long refractory shoelace straggled behind him dangerously.

Yet, Campion noticed with growing concern, there was a new note in the general air of frustration and despair which was his general atmosphere: the high thin note of alarm.

It became more and more insistent as he looked from one face to another: the weeping Lisa, staring at him like a dog beseeching forgiveness, the stolid doctor, the excited plain-clothesman, Campion, and the curious inspector.

They waited for him to make the first movement, and when it came it was so natural, so utterly typical and in character, but at the same time so horrible in the circumstances, that they all felt the chill.

Mr. Potter, having taken in each face, looked beyond them to the scullery.

"Claire," he called. "Claire, we have visitors." He returned to the stricken company. "Sorry no one here," he said, relapsing into his habitual helpless mumble. "Very awkward for you . . . awkward all round. I suppose you want to see my wife? She'll be here in a moment . . ."

The plain-clothesman shifted his position, and as his bulk moved, the sheet-covered form on the bed came into view.

Mr. Potter stared at it. All the watery redness of his face seemed to rush into his huge nose, making it grotesque and absurd. His small eyes, which were set so closely beside the pinched bridge, grew round and foolish like a frightened child's.

He started across the room towards it, and Campion caught his arm. "No," he said. "No, not yet. Wait."

Mr. Potter turned to him, the incredulity in his eyes growing until it seemed they must become blank.

"Is that my wife?"

The words were whispered. Campion felt some of the choking horror of nightmare.

Is that my wife?

He had not repeated the question, but the piteous, affected little room seemed to vibrate with it.

Campion nodded.

Mr. Potter glanced at the others. Lisa's unbridled weeping was the only sound.

"Claire?" said Mr. Potter in a voice in which amazement, disbelief, and despair were all inextricably mingled. "Claire?"

He broke away from Campion and went to the divan. To their unutterable relief he did not try to pull back the sheet. He bent down and felt the cold arm through the linen.

"Dead," he said suddenly and stepped back. "Claire dead."

He moved round the room and stood with his back to them. They saw him tall and oddly held in the yellow light.

"Dead," he said again in the most matter-of-fact tone they had ever heard him use.

Then the mass of papers and his battered hat slipped to the ground, and Dr. Fettes leapt forward to catch the man as he toppled over.

"It's the shock," said the young doctor, tugging at the limp collar. "It's the shock."

14 : *Ravellings*

"I really don't know when I've been so upset."

Miss Cunninghame, pink with excitement and an underlying sense of outrage at tragedy treading so near, made the announcement as though it were an important confidence.

"I really don't know when."

Inspector Oates sat forward on the broad Chippendale chair, his head on one side like a terrier at a rabbit hole. Mr. Campion was stationed a little behind him. The inspector never knew quite why he always invited the pale young man to accompany him on this sort of expedition in defiance of edict and etiquette alike, but the fact remained and so did Mr. Campion.

The small front suburban room in which they talked was a reflection of Miss Cunninghame's gentility and modestly sufficient means. Its white paint, shining brass, Morris chintz, and good furniture were tasteful, old-maidish, and intensely ordinary. Only the appalling water-colours in the narrow gilt frames were individual.

Miss Cunninghame went on talking.

"Of course," she said, the light of self-preservation creeping into her eyes, "Mrs. Potter was not a *friend* of mine. I mean, we were never *intimate*, we never *talked*. I took a few lessons from her from time to time because she seemed such a capable person, and then her *background* attracted me. John Lafcadio still lives in that little colony—or did," she added dubiously, as though even that eminent ghost would hardly survive this last upheaval.

The inspector remained quiet and alert, and Miss Cunninghame was shamed into further speech.

"So you see," she finished lamely, "I hardly knew her . . . Poor soul!"

"She didn't confide in you?" Oates seemed disappointed.

"Oh, no . . ." It seemed for a moment that Miss Cunninghame would leave well alone, but the inspector's air of expectancy had its reward. "I thought she seemed very odd this afternoon," she said suddenly. "But if she was going to meet her death so soon afterwards, poor creature, that's hardly to be wondered at."

"Odd?" enquired Oates, ignoring his informant's somewhat confused deductions.

Having committed herself, Miss Cunninghame did not draw back.

"Definitely odd," she declared. "I told her she looked ill, and she was almost angry. Also she was stupid."

The inspector's head straightened. It almost seemed to Campion that his ears pricked forward.

"When you say stupid, did it seem to you that she was dazed—drugged, I mean?"

Miss Cunninghame's eyes opened very wide.

"Drugs?" she said. "You don't say that she . . . Well, really, if I had ever guessed—"

"Oh, no, no." The inspector was very patient. "No. I'm only trying to get at the probable cause of Mrs. Potter's death. The doctors have not yet decided the actual cause, and as you were the last person to see her alive, as far as we know, we are naturally anxious to hear how she seemed to you."

"I was the *last* person? Was I really? Oh!" Miss Cunninghame's momentary thrill of importance was suddenly damped by a new and disturbing thought. "An inquest! I shan't be called—oh, Inspector, I shan't be called to give evidence? I couldn't—I didn't know her—"

"We're not sure of anything yet," said Oates mendaciously. "Suppose you tell me all you can now."

"Yes, yes, of course. Anything." Campion found Miss Cunninghame's pathetic terror a little nauseating. "Well, she was odd. Distinctly vague. Not herself at all. I tried to get her to talk to me about the—the other trouble—crime, I mean. I was sorry for her, and I thought she might be comforted."

Miss Cunninghame glanced guiltily at the inspector, but the omnipotent, all-seeing powers with which she credited the police were not evinced, and she hurried on:

"It was then that she seemed stupid. She heard what I said—just a few leading, quite kindly questions, but she was quite, quite blank. I left her at half past four. She didn't come to the door. I went out alone, but she was all right because I heard the phone ring."

The inspector, who had relapsed into melancholy as he realized there was nothing really definite here, suddenly revived.

"You heard her phone ring at half past four?" he said, getting out his notebook.

At the sight of this evidence of officialdom Miss Cunninghame grew visibly flustered, but she repeated the fact slowly, as though she were dictating to a spelling bee.

"I heard her phone bell ring at half past four as I was going out . . . I also had the impression that she went to answer it," she went on more quickly, "but I couldn't be sure. I didn't stop to listen, of course."

"Of course," agreed the inspector.

"But I would have done," said Miss Cunninghame with deliberate moral courage, "had I known what was going to happen." Oates, rather nonplussed at this announcement, paused awkwardly.

"But there, I couldn't know, could I?" said Miss Cunninghame. "I only saw she was worried. And now, Inspector, I needn't give evidence, need I? I'm really very upset. After all, if we weren't friends I've visited her for several years, and I was only talking to her about my paintings this afternoon. Death," she added, with the satisfaction of one who knows herself to be right, "is a very dreadful thing."

"Yes," said the inspector. "Yes, it is."

Mr. Campion and the policeman walked back together through the dusty squares of stolid mansions now reduced to tenements which streak their dreary way from Maida Vale to Bayswater. Oates seemed anxious to talk, a most unusual circumstance, and Campion was more than ready to listen.

"Funny type, that old woman," he remarked. "I only seem to meet 'em in murder cases. They manage to wriggle out of everything else. The world's full of uncharitable people," he said irrelevantly.

"She has told us two things," said Campion.

Oates nodded. "(A) Mrs. Potter was worried to the point of being uninterested in the old cat, and (B) she had a telephone call about half past four. The first may or may not mean a thing. The other we may be able to follow up, which may lead us a step further."

He turned to Campion. "It's funny, isn't it?"

"What's funny?"

"The whole darn thing. The two cases one after the other like this. When you phoned me this afternoon I thought we should have it straight in an hour. Homicidal mania on the girl's part. These descendants of famous men are often a bit unbalanced. But now, d'you know, I'm not so sure."

Campion forbore to comment, and the inspector went on, his grey face with its shrewd, kindly eyes grave and absorbed: "Did that woman strike you as an exaggerator or the reverse? I mean, how worried do you think Mrs. Potter was?"

"Suicide?" enquired Campion dubiously.

"Well, I wondered. There's no evidence either way yet, of course. We don't even know the cause of death. I hate theorizing. It's always silly. Still, it's as well to keep an open mind."

"Ah," said Mr. Campion, and his eyes became foolish as the idea which had been rankling in the back of his head ever since the tragedy stood out in all its absurdity.

"Of course," muttered the inspector, striking viciously at some railings with his folded evening paper, "there's that chap Potter. It was nice of Mrs. Lafcadio to take him in and pop him into bed like that. He'll be ready to talk in the morning. We ought not to think, even, until we've heard what he has to say."

"Both Lisa and the school can't be lying," said Mr. Campion.

"No," said Oates. "No, that's right. I'm not losing sight of that. He was up to something." He paused and eyed his friend. "If that first remark of his when he came in was fake," he said, "I'll resign."

This promise, as it happened, was never carried out because, of course, Mr. Potter had been acting at the time, which was certainly remarkable.

The inspector idled on.

"That Italian woman Lisa," he said. "A bad witness, but honest, I should say, although you can't ever be sure. She's probably right when she talks of poison. If the P.M. doesn't tell us about that, though, the Home Office analyst will. Amazing chaps, Campion. They bob up in court and swear to the millionth of a grain. Often right, too."

Campion shrugged with distaste.

"Poison," he said. "Bad method at the best."

"Um," said the inspector, eyeing him. "A knifing and maybe a poisoning. Italians about. It's worth considering."

"Lisa?" Mr. Campion's expression was of complete incredulity.

"No, no, I'm not saying anything. I'm not even thinking. I'm just letting my mind run on. I find it pays sometimes. There's that wife of Dacre's—an extraordinary kid. D'you know who she is?"

"Who? Rosa-Rosa?"

"Yes. One of the Rosinis, my boy. She's a niece or something of old Guido himself. She's staying at the store now in Saffron Hill. What do you know about that!"

"I don't see how being first cousin to a race gang connects one with the death of a respectable lady in Bayswater," said Campion.

"Nor do I," said the inspector, sniffing, "but it's worth bearing in mind."

Mr. Campion opened his mouth to speak, changed his mind, sighed, and walked on in silence.

"Out with it," said the inspector without looking round.

Campion shook his head.

"It's wild," he said, "and yet—"

"Oh, let's have it. We're having an orgy of idiocy, anyway. We're here, or rather I'm here, to investigate facts, not to daydream, yet we've been happily speculating for the last half hour like a couple of amateurs. So why not go the whole hog? What's on your mind?"

Mr. Campion considered Max Fustian and the ideas which had crossed his mind concerning him.

"No," he said at last. "It's too vague for anything. It was a sort of odour of an idea I had concerning the murder of Dacre, but it doesn't fit in with this new affair at all."

"Motive," said Oates vehemently. "That's the only way to connect these two affairs. Find the motive and you find the man—or woman."

"Murder and suicide, then?" suggested Campion.

Oates shrugged.

"Maybe. I hardly think so, though. Then again, what's the motive for the murder? I tell you what, though," he went on, brightening suddenly. "If this is a poisoning we'll get our bird. The Dacre business was spontaneous—impulsive. Anyone could or might have done it. But this is a different caper. This, if it is murder, is premeditated and thought out. It's not natural for there to be two killers running loose in one family at a time, therefore the odds are on it being the same person, and I don't believe there's a man alive to pull off the two."

That was the inspector's second mistake.

Campion said nothing, and Oates strode on faster.

"Motive," he repeated. "We'll get at her—or him—whoever it is, that way."

They reached the canal and turned into the Crescent. The mock stone planes of Little Venice looked sad and shabby in the lamplight. The splendours of Show Sunday had gone, leaving it melancholy. The blinds were drawn, contrary to custom, and the front door was closed. The house was in trouble.

A flashy little car outside gleaming expensively enhanced the shabbiness of the house.

"Whose?" enquired the inspector, nodding towards the shining toy.

"Max Fustian's." Campion's tone was wondering.

Oates laughed shortly. "Come to confess again, no doubt."

"I . . . I wonder," said Mr. Campion.

15 : *As It Happened*

Mr. Campion knew that Max Fustian had killed Mrs. Potter as soon as he saw him that evening.

He did not arrive at this conclusion by the decent process of quiet, logical deduction, nor yet by the blinding flash of glorious intuition, but by the shoddy, untidy process halfway between the two by which one usually gets to know things.

When he saw the man standing on Belle's hearth rug, his swarthy face pale to blueness, his quick eyes exultant and his breath a little short, Campion regarded him and thought, "Well, he did it." And afterwards, "God knows why . . . or how."

The other occupant of the room at the moment was Donna Beatrice. The inspector was conferring with the harassed Dr. Fettes downstairs while Belle was in the kitchen comforting the conscience-stricken Lisa.

The Chosen Apostle of the Higher Urge was dramatizing this new situation but halfheartedly. She sat far back in her chair, her shoulders hunched and her cold eyes stupid.

"Claire!" she repeated to herself. "Claire!" And at intervals, "So practical. So utterly the *last* person."

Max met Campion's eyes and nodded to him with superb condescension.

"How extremely lucky you were able to come to Belle's assistance so soon, my dear Campion," he said.

The liquid affectation in his voice sounded a little more pronounced to the young man's sensitive ear.

"When I dropped in myself about an hour ago she told me you had been very kind," Max continued with the same new, insufferable superiority. "I've been congratulating myself that I obeyed the impulse to come on here from Meyer's. One dare not ignore these presentiments."

For the first time Campion noticed that Max was in gala dress. His morning clothes were miraculously cut; the broadcloth gleamed with silky elegance.

"Meyer's?" he enquired.

"Private view of the Duchess of Swayne's pastels," said Max briefly. "Delicate, you know. Genuine feeling. Selling like hot cakes."

Campion sat down and looked at him. For the first time in his life he felt unequal to the situation and afraid of giving himself away.

Max was more than merely confident; he was elated. Triumph and something that was surely satisfaction glowed beneath his decent veil of sympathetic grief. Campion felt at a loss.

"He's got away with it. He knows he's safe." The thought which was no more than a nebulous irritant at first slowly grew to a certainty in his mind.

Max went on to talk about the tragedy.

"Terrible," he said. "Terrible. One of the most useful of women. One cannot assimilate it somehow."

He sighed with genuine regret.

Campion raised his eyes to find the man regarding him impudently. There was no hiding it; Max was the master of the hour.

"Useful!" said Donna Beatrice, sitting up. "Through all the horror, that's the word I've been searching for. Claire was useful."

"Poor Potter," said Campion lamely. "He's badly cut up, I'm afraid." He broke off awkwardly. Max was looking at him and smiling. His head was a little on one side, and his heavily drawn mouth drooped at one end with what was, unmistakably, tolerant amusement.

Outrage, combining as it does shock, anger, reproach, and helplessness, is perhaps the most unmanageable, the most demoralizing, of all the emotions. Campion pulled himself together with difficulty and strove consciously to survey the man in front of him with true impartiality, but the thought which stuck most obstinately in his mind was that Max was very sure of himself and must consider himself absolutely safe.

Donna Beatrice copied Max's smile, but without meaning, and the effect was rather horrible.

Voices on the stairs ended the nightmare, and Campion rose as the inspector and Belle came in.

It was a tottery little old woman who peered round the room from under her white bonnet. The Belle Darling whom Lafcadio had loved, protected, and leant upon was beaten to her knees by the deluge of horror poured down upon her. Campion looked at her, and there rose up in his heart genuine ruthless hatred which took possession of him and gave him back the poise and confidence which had temporarily deserted him. Belle was leaning on the inspector, who looked as nearly humanly concerned as Campion had ever seen him.

"Sit down, ma'am," he said, using the old-fashioned form of address. "Don't worry. Leave that to us. We'll see to everything."

He caught sight of his friend with relief.

"I've got to go down to the mor— I've got to go with Dr. Fettes," he said. "He's waiting for me. I'll leave Mrs. Lafcadio with you. See you tomorrow."

He nodded casually to Max, ignored Donna Beatrice, and was gone.

Belle permitted herself to be led to her chair by the fire. Max did not move from the hearth, and Campion was shocked to find that it required an absurdly vigorous effort to prevent himself from kicking the exquisite little figure out of the way. From that moment, however, Belle required all his attention.

"Albert," she whispered, beckoning him to come closer, "listen."

He dropped down beside her chair, and she laid a little plump hand on his shoulder.

"I'm worried for Linda. If that child comes home to—to *this*, after the other shock . . . you see what I mean? See she stays in Paris or else is told before she comes to the house."

He put up his hand and held hers where it was on his shoulder. "I will," he said. "Leave everything to us. You heard what the inspector said. Leave everything to us."

Belle's brown eyes grew slowly blurred, and the tears rolled down her cheeks.

"Oh, my dear, if I could. If only I could."

"Well, why not, Belle?" Campion was as earnest as he had ever been. The vacuity had vanished from his face, leaving him unexpectedly capable.

Her grip on his shoulder tightened.

"Albert," she whispered. "Oh, my dear, for pity's sake find out and *stop it.*"

His eyes met hers through her tears.

"I will," he said quietly. "I will. I promise, Belle."

Max did not seem to hear this conversation, or if he did he was not interested. He had moved over to the corner cupboard and was examining the useless ivory baton once presented to Wagner.

The following morning, when the inspector came, Campion was still in the house, having taken up his quarters in Linda's little suite.

Oates sat down on the window ledge, gathering the skirts of his raincoat about him. He was brisk and practical.

"The inquest is fixed for twelve o'clock," he said. "Only formal evidence, and a postponement. There's no need for either of us to turn up. I'm waiting for Fettes to see Potter before I put him through it. Care to come?"

Campion signified his grateful acceptance of the favour and enquired after Belle.

"In bed, I hope," said the inspector. "I got Fettes to insist on it. Then he can trot down to the court and swear that neither she nor Potter is in a fit state to give evidence. There's no point in dragging that poor old lady through the tiresome business again. What's the matter with you, by the way? You look all het up."

To Campion the night had brought no counsel. He was still undecided on his course of action and never remembered finding himself in a similar quandary. The situation in which he was at once so certain in his mind and so utterly devoid of concrete evidence was mercifully new. Of one thing alone he was sure: the time to confide in the inspector had not yet arrived.

"I'm all right," he said. "A bit puzzled, that's all."

"You should worry!" Oates spoke grimly. "There's hell blowing up in the department. Orders are to get it all cleared up and over quickly. Imagination is a wonderful thing. I wish that darn doctor would turn up."

In the end Dr. Fettes phoned to say that the P.M. had taken him all night and if he was to get to the inquest on time he could not visit

Little Venice first. However, his assistant, Dr. Derrick, a sandy-haired young man with a blue suspicious eye, arrived and pronounced Mr. Potter fit for examination.

Campion and the inspector went into the faded spare bedroom which had housed so many famous folk in the great days when Lafcadio was a lion.

Campion was prepared for a painful experience, but even so the sight which Mr. Potter presented as he sat up in the big Italian bed, propped by the glistening pillows, had in it that element of the unexpectedly shocking which is the very essence of embarrassment.

The natural redness of his face had gone, leaving it a network of tiny red veins, so that his skin looked like crackleware. His eyes had shrunk and become paler, as if they threatened to disappear altogether, and his mouth was loose and piteous. He looked old and frightened to stupidity.

The inspector stood regarding him gravely, and for some seconds it seemed that the man in the bed had not noticed the intrusion. Suddenly he glanced up.

"The suggestion that I killed my wife is absurd," he said. He spoke without vehemence or, it seemed, much personal feeling.

Oates cleared his throat. "What put such an idea into your head, Mr. Potter?" he began cautiously.

For a moment the washed-out eyes rested on the policeman's grey face with contempt.

"I've been listening to Lisa," he said shortly. "No point now in beating about the bush. No time for conventions, manners, affectations. Too many affectations in my life, anyway. Too many in everybody's life. It's all no good—rotten stuff."

The inspector shot a sidelong glance at Campion.

"It's very unfortunate that Miss Capella should have been able to get in to you," he said sternly. "She will probably get into serious trouble."

If he hoped to shake the man in the bed out of his uncompromising mood by this threat he was disappointed. Mr. Potter, normally the kindest of men, shrugged his shoulders. "I really can't help it," he said. "I can't help anything. I should like to be left alone."

"Now, Mr. Potter,"—Oates's tone became conciliatory—"I do realize that it must be most painful for you to talk now, but the matter is urgent. There are several questions I want to put to you and an explanation I must have. In trying to help you yesterday Miss Capella raised a question which must be cleared up—do you understand?"

The question was an afterthought, for Mr. Potter had turned away and was staring out of the window at the speeding sky.

Oates repeated the words, and the figure in the bed moved. He looked at his tormentors and with an obvious effort strove to concentrate.

"I am alone," he said suddenly. "I am quite free. I can go where I like, do what I like. I wish I were dead."

There was complete silence after he had spoken. Campion felt breathless, and the inspector's eyes contracted. It was very terrible.

Oates deliberated. Finally he shook his head.

"I must know," he said. "Why did you send a telegram yesterday morning to the headmaster of Blakenham to say you were in bed, ill?"

Mr. Potter looked at him vaguely for a full minute before replying.

"Other things were important," he said at last, and then very painstakingly, as though he were treading on new ground: "Nothing that was important then is important now. Nothing at all is very important now. It was for some trifling reason—I had a lithograph print I was pleased about." Mr. Potter seemed astonished as he remembered. "I wanted to show it to someone. I was mad."

"Where did you go?" Oates prompted.

"To Bill Fenner's studio in Putney. We spent all day talking and looking at stuff. I was playing truant, like a child. As if it mattered!"

"When did you come back?" demanded Oates, making a mental note of the name and district. "When you saw me—all of us?"

"Yes—yes, I think so." The effort of recollection was clearly difficult, and Mr. Potter's forehead was furrowed for a moment until his eyes suddenly widened and he looked at the inspector blankly.

"No, of course," he said. "Of course, it was yesterday. I came back before, that's how it happened. I understand now."

"You came back before?"

"Yes. About five o'clock. Does it matter?"

The inspector sat down on the edge of the bed.

"Try to remember it exactly, sir," he said. "I know it's difficult."

"No," said Mr. Potter unexpectedly. "No, it's very clear, although it seems a long time ago." He sat very still, and his face worked helplessly. "I saw her and I didn't know," he said. "My poor Claire, I didn't know."

"You saw her?" The inspector's quiet voice gently forced the man to keep to the story.

"She must have been dead then," whispered Mr. Potter. "When I came in the first time, I saw her lying there, the glass at her feet, and I didn't know. Even then . . ." His voice trailed away.

The inspector's eyes snapped.

"The glass at her feet? We found no glass."

"I washed it out and put it back in the cupboard," said Mr. Potter simply.

"Why?" There was something very like stupefaction in the inspector's face.

"More affectation," said Mr. Potter. "Another thing that didn't matter. Polite fiction. It's all silly trumpery stuff . . . no real point in it."

"Why did you wash out the glass?" the inspector persisted.

"It was Thursday," said Mr. Potter. "At a quarter to seven on Thursdays, Mrs. Lafcadio always comes . . . came . . . down to the studio to ask my wife and me to dinner. I knew it was no use trying to rouse poor Claire, but I thought if Mrs. Lafcadio did not see the glass the evidences of—of my wife's condition would not be so apparent. So I sluiced it out and replaced it in the cupboard. Then, as there seemed nothing else I could do, I hurried out, hoping no one had seen me. I see now how idiotic it was. It didn't matter what I did."

The inspector, who had taken out his notebook now, sat, his pencil poised and an odd expression in his eyes. Campion caught his thought, and the recollection of the curious scene in the dining room after the reception came back to him.

He saw the bright interior, the straight brown legs in the sensible shoes sticking out across the picture framed by the doorway, and Mr. Potter's nervous attempts to keep the inspector and himself outside. The whole mystery concerning the man's early visit to the studio became suddenly clear.

The inspector braced himself. To officials facts are facts and must be treated as such.

"When you saw Mrs. Potter how did she look? Where was she?"

"She was lying face downward on the divan, half sitting, her body twisted so that her face was hidden." Mr. Potter spoke with a sort of wonder, as though his mind were concerned with essential things far removed from the trivial matters he related.

"Weren't you surprised to see her like that?"

Mr. Potter roused himself with an effort.

"I couldn't have told you this yesterday," he said, "because yesterday it seemed a serious matter, but now it seems so small. My wife frequently drank enough alcohol in one draught to render her completely unconscious for some time. I think it took effect very quickly. It was a form of drugging, I suppose. If anything upset her too much . . . I mean, if she suddenly found she could not bear anything . . . she used to do that. I remember it worried me. I was frightened by it and . . . God forgive me . . . shocked. It seems ridiculous now. Why shouldn't she?"

"So when you saw Mrs. Potter lying on the divan you thought she was . . . you thought that was what had happened and were not alarmed?"

Oates was speaking with unexpected gentleness, and it occurred to Campion that he must share his own curious feeling that Mr. Potter was living in a new stark world in which there were very few familiar landmarks.

"Yes," said Mr. Potter. "I thought she was drunk."

"So you took the glass away so that Mrs. Lafcadio should not see it, possibly examine it, and guess what was the matter?"

The man in the bed laughed. It was a strange sound, having in it nothing of the melodramatic but a percentage of pure derision.

"Yes. Asinine."

"Why did you wash the glass?"

"I—" Mr. Potter looked at his persecutor, and unexpectedly his eyes brimmed over with tears. "We had an arrangement about the incidental housework. We each washed up and tidied up as it occurred. I rinsed out the glass naturally and stood it on the shelf to drain. I couldn't put it away dirty."

"I see," said the inspector hastily and busied himself with his notebook. "Well," he said at last, "where was the bottle?"

"I don't know."

"Oh, come, Mr. Potter, where was it usually kept?"

"I don't know." The inspector's victim had the disconcerting air of speaking the literal truth about something in which he was not interested. "I never found out. It used to worry me. Good God, the things that used to worry me! I've been mad. I used to hunt when she was out. It was all so tidy—it should have been easy. I never found anything. Yet whenever she wanted it I used to find her like that. It's gone on for years."

"Years?" Campion and the inspector felt they were peering in at a secret. The vision of the tragic, ineffectual husband protecting his masterful wife in his small, worried way seemed indecent, sad, and to be covered.

"Not so much at first, of course, but often lately."

"She did it only when she was upset?"

"Oh, yes. She was very strong. She never let it take hold of her. It was only when things got too bad."

"I see." The inspector rose. "Thank you for your information, Mr. Potter. It has been very valuable. I shall try not to bother you any more than I can help. By the way, did your wife ever consult a doctor about this—er—habit of hers?"

"A doctor? No, I don't think so." Mr. Potter seemed mildly surprised. "She and I were the only people who knew about it, I think, although the others must have guessed, and she did not consider it important at all. I used to worry."

"What was it?" enquired Oates. "Whisky?"

"I don't know, I never saw it. I told you."

"Most extraordinary," commented the inspector. "Where did she buy it?"

"I don't think she did buy it."

Mr. Potter made this extraordinary announcement with the same air of detachment which had characterized him throughout the interview.

Inspector Oates paused halfway across the room.

"Where did it come from, then?"

"I told you, I don't know," said Mr. Potter with patient disinterest.

"Lately, whenever my wife was distressed I used to find her unconscious, usually with a glass by her side, but although I hunted everywhere I never found any supply. On one occasion I found her in the dining room at this house—you were there, I remember—but that was the only time. Apart from that it was always in the studio. I don't think she bought any alcohol, because it is expensive, you know, and our resources were so very small that it would have been impossible for her to spend even a few shillings without my knowing. We were impossibly poor. That seemed to matter very much, too. Oh, dear God, I am tired." He lay back and closed his eyes.

Campion and the inspector went out. The younger man wiped his forehead and stretched as though his clothes had become tight.

The inspector sighed.

"It's things like that that make me believe in capital punishment," he said briefly. "We'll get this bird, Campion, and we'll string him up."

16 : *That Was on the Sunday*

"Nicotine," said the inspector, displaying his copy of the analyst's report, "one of the most pernickety poisons in the world, specially prepared by Providence, no doubt, to delay police officers in the execution of their duty."

Campion and the inspector were in the library at Little Venice. It was the morning of the Sunday following the Friday on which they had interviewed Mr. Potter.

In the circumstances it seemed to Mr. Campion that the Home Office chemists had been unusually expeditious, and he said so.

"I thought they were liable to take six weeks on a job like this," he remarked.

"Not when the whole department is up in the air." The inspector spoke succinctly. "We all want this thing cleared up before the press decides to scream itself into a fit. Unfortunately all we seem to be able to do is to create a lot of excitement all round. In this instance it's done a bit of good. Those beggars can do with a bit of hustling. Still, it's interesting, isn't it? The nicotine, I mean. It's getting fashionable just now, yet up to a few years ago there was only one known instance of it being used criminally.* Know anything about it?"

"Not much," said Campion. "A small dose is fatal, isn't it?"

* Tardieu records a case in which Count Bocarmé and his wife were convicted of murdering M. Fougnies by administering the alkaloid which Bocarmé manufactured himself. Vide: *L'Étude Méd. Lect. sur l'Empoisonment.*

"Ten to twenty milligrams of the alkaloid does the trick in three to five minutes—paralyzes the respiratory system among other things." Oates spoke savagely. "I saw the stuff in the lab last night—I always sweat these things up as I go along. You'd be surprised how much I know about arsenic," he added with apparent irrelevance. "Criminals ought to stick to arsenic. These fancy poisons let us in for no end of trouble. Still, this nicotine is colourless, volatile stuff which goes yellow if you leave the cork out, and if you keep it long enough it goes solid. That's practically all I learnt on the subject from our boys."

Campion was looking at the report.

"By applying the Stas-Otto process to the contents of the stomach we isolated 14.80 milligrams Alkaloid Nicotiana Tabacum," he read. "Yes, well, that's clear enough. It ought to be simple to trace the source, once you get your lists of suspects. You can't go and buy this muck by the pint, I take it."

The inspector glanced at the younger man curiously, and when he spoke his voice was weary.

"Anyone can buy a box of cigars," he said.

"A box of cigars?" Mr. Campion's pale eyes widened. "Can the alkaloid be extracted easily?"

"As far as I can see, yes." Oates was very grave. "In fact, I gather that either of us with very little knowledge and practically no unusual paraphernalia could get enough trouble out of a box of Havanas to keep the analysts busy for months, so, although we shall consider the question of source with our customary thoroughness, I don't expect much help in that direction. We're up against brains, Campion. It may make it more interesting, but it's putting years on my age."

Mr. Campion hesitated and opened his mouth as though to speak, but thought better of it, and Oates did not notice him.

"Come on," he said. "We'll go down to that damn studio. We've got no business here, anyway. I seem to have been using this room as an office ever since the crime. Mrs. Lafcadio doesn't resent it, either. Bless her! Now and again she sends me a cup of tea!"

The two men went through the hall and down the staircase to the garden door.

The Potter studio was forlorn and deserted save for the plainclothesman encamped in the tiny porch.

The inspector unlocked the door and they went in.

Without the dignity of tragedy the room looked smaller than when Campion had first seen it. The atmosphere was close and smelt abominably of damp, although the place had been unoccupied so short a time. While it was not actually untidy, the bookshelves and the side tables had a slightly ruffled appearance, betraying a recent search amongst their contents.

Oates stood looking round him in mild exasperation.

"There you are," he said. "Nothing at all. Not a sign of a bottle or a flask in the whole outfit. Not a trace of alcohol in the place."

"Could she have got it from the house in a glass?" Campion spoke without much enthusiasm, and the elder man shrugged his shoulders.

"And put the stuff in herself? Well, she might, but I don't think so. Hang it all, what did she get the nicotine out of? There's not a phial, not a pill bottle, nothing that might have contained it. Besides, someone must have seen her go into the house—Lisa, for instance, whose window looks straight out on this doorway."

Campion nodded absently. "You've made a thorough job of it, I suppose?"

"Well, I had Richardson and Miss Peters. You know 'em, don't you?"

Campion had a vision of the stout, lazy-looking man with the delicate hands and the sharp, inquisitive eyes, followed by the tiny, birdlike woman whose hands moved so quickly yet so methodically through drawers and tableloads of litter. The legend concerning them was that they were relations of the Recording Angel whom nothing ever escapes.

"That settles it, then," he said. "There's nothing here."

"I know that."

"They found no alcohol and no poison?"

"Poison!" The inspector spoke explosively. "My good boy, this garden is lousy with poison. Rennie has about two stone of pure white arsenic to start with. There's a quart and a half of dilute hydrochloric acid in the shed behind the scullery—Dutch mordant. Potter used it in his lithography. Then we found spirits of salt over the sink, to say nothing of a small chemist's shop of patent medicines, all of which seemed pretty dangerous to me. But not a sign of the sort of stuff we were looking for."

"It's the choice of poisons that makes it so obviously murder, I suppose?" said Campion slowly. "Now you've spotted it."

"Exactly," Oates cut in. "If that young doctor hadn't been particularly honest, or even if he hadn't had his suspicions aroused by the Dacre business, it's a hundred to one he'd have called it heart failure—which is always true up to a point, when you come to think of it—issued a certificate and left it at that. Someone was being clever, darn clever, let's hope a bit too clever by half."

Campion sat down in the chair by the window table. He was so much more thoughtful than usual that Oates glanced at him sharply. He did not press for confidences, however, but contented himself by observing that the fingerprint people had found nothing of interest.

"The deceased's own prints were all over the phone," he observed. "By the way, that woman Cunninghame stuck to her tale about the phone bell she heard as she left that afternoon, so as a matter of routine I traced the call. It's hardly evidence. These exchange folk aren't reliable.

How can they be? But apparently this number was called from a public box somewhere about that time. There was some hitch in the connection at first, and the supervisor was called. She got through to this exchange—that's how I was able to trace it at all. I saw both girls, but they couldn't help me much. They fixed the time, though. Four thirty-one. It bears out Miss Cunninghame but gets us no further."

"Where was the callbox?"

"Clifford Street.—What's the matter? Tell you anything?"

Campion was sitting up in his chair staring ahead of him. Presently he took off his spectacles. "Look here, Stanislaus," he said, "I'd better tell you. Max Fustian killed Mrs. Potter."

The inspector regarded him for a full twenty seconds.

"Think so?" he said at last.

"I'm sure of it."

"Got any proof?"

"Not a trace."

Oates hurled his cigarette stub into the empty fireplace.

"What's the good of that?" he demanded.

"It's a comfort to me," said Mr. Campion.

The inspector lit another cigarette. "Let's have the whole thing," he said. "It's mainly second sight, I suppose?"

Campion rose to his feet and, without hesitating to lay himself open to a charge of disordered imagination, related to the listening policeman all the little details and scraps of suspicion which have been here set down. When he had finished, Oates rubbed his moustache dubiously.

"I like you, Campion," he said at last. "You've got nerve. I follow you, all right, but if I may say so it's rather a case of an angel treading where even the fools fear to rush in. You've got no evidence at all."

"I know."

"Precious little in the way of definite suspicion."

Mr. Campion paused halfway across the room.

"That's what's so infuriating, Oates. Yet I'm sure. Don't you see it's only the cold facts themselves which point away from him?"

"I don't know what more you want," said the inspector glumly. "Still, I see what you mean. There's nothing more deceptive than facts. You find that out in the witness box, God knows. However, let's consider your yarn about the first murder. I concede your point that for an intelligent man Max Fustian's confession was suspiciously ridiculous if he wanted it to be believed. But the facts, my boy, the facts! What about his alibi?"

Campion glanced shrewdly at his friend.

"I wonder," he said. "When you interviewed Donna Beatrice did you ask her what they were talking about when the lights went out?"

Oates scowled. "I did, and I got a full account for my pains. Some

awful interminable anecdote about a loony in a Turkish bath who mistook Miss Beatrice for a picture—that woman's mental, Campion."

"It was a long story?" the young man suggested.

"It was."

"Did Donna Beatrice strike you as a person who would let anyone else
get a word in edgeways?"

The inspector shook his head.

"It's no good, Campion," he said. "If you're trying to tell me that
Fustian slipped off as soon as the lights went out and left the woman
talking, and came back again without her twigging, you're wasting your
time and mine."

"Why?"

"Because it's not possible. Think of it. You're holding forth to me in
the dark. Wouldn't you know if I was there or not?"

"How could I tell?"

"Well, damn it, man, you'd hear me breathing for one thing, shifting
about, coughing perhaps or grunting as I tried to get a word in. If I moved
off, even if I crept away, you'd hear me. Of course you would."

Campion nodded. "I know," he said awkwardly. "But she wouldn't. I
only remembered the other day. She's as deaf as an egg without that
contraption she wears, and she took it off for the party. Don't you see,
she wouldn't hear a thing and it was very dark."

The inspector sat up. "Took it off? What for?"

"Vanity, I suppose."

"Well, I'm damned!" Oates leant back in his chair, and for a moment
he was silent.

"There's no solid evidence, though," he said at last. "No case—nothing
we could have taken to court even if that business was reopened. As I
said at the time, it was the impulsive, spontaneous nature of that knifing
which licked us at the outset. The luck was all on his side. This, thank
God, is premeditated. That gives us an equal chance."

"You agree with me, then?"

"I? Good heavens, no. I've got an open mind. I suspect everyone and
no one until I get proof." Oates grinned as he spoke. "The old official
attitude is a great stand-by. Got any more revelations up your sleeve?"

Campion remained serious.

"I can't guess at the motive," he said slowly. "In Max Fustian's life
young Dacre and Mrs. Potter were surely the most unimportant people
on earth."

"To get back to facts," said Oates without rudeness, "where was Fus—
this suspect of yours between four-thirty and five o'clock last Thursday?"

"Where he took the trouble to tell me he was," said Campion. "At
Meyer's Art Gallery, enthusing over a duchess's pastels. Old Meyer is by
way of being a friend of mine, and I dropped in to see him yesterday.

He was very full of his private view and told me all I wanted to know without any prompting. Max came into the gallery about five-and-twenty to five. Meyer noticed the time because it was so late. He'd been expecting him all the afternoon. The exhibition shut at half past six, but Max stayed on chatting to Meyer until nearly seven. Then they both went out and had a drink. Meyer was very gratified but a trifle surprised by the great man's condescension, I fancy. Max does not usually behave so graciously."

"Miss Cunninghame left here at four-thirty," observed the inspector. "Fustian entered Meyer's at five-and-twenty to five and stayed there for a couple of hours, by which time Mrs. Potter was dead, discovered, and we had arrived. That only gives him the five minutes between four-thirty and four thirty-five to get busy in. Not long enough to do anything, my boy."

"Long enough to phone," said Campion.

"How d'you mean?"

Campion sat forward in the chair he had resumed.

"When Miss Cunninghame left here at four-thirty she heard the phone bell ring. You traced that call and found that it came from a box in Clifford Street. Max entered Meyer's gallery at four thirty-five. Meyer's gallery is in Clifford Street, and there's a callbox twenty yards down the road—the only one in the street."

"That's not evidence."

"I know it's not, but it's suspicion. Dozens of people may have seen him in the callbox. He was looking pretty conspicuous, you remember. Besides, practically everyone round there knows him by sight. It ought not to be difficult to find witnesses."

"What's this leading to?" The inspector's interest was genuinely aroused. "Suppose we do prove that the phone call she had came from him—which won't be easy, by the way—what then? Did he poison her over the telephone? You've been reading thrillers again."

The pale young man in the horn-rimmed spectacles remained unusually serious.

"This bit is pure theory," he said, "but I'm open to bet anything you like it's true. Look here, we know from our own observation and from Potter himself that when Mrs. Potter was suddenly confronted by a crisis she used to pour a tumblerful of neat whisky down her throat and pass out. We know that Potter thought that had happened this time. He said so. Suppose it had happened."

"But her usual supply of liquor had the addition of a small quantity of alkaloid nicotine?"

"Yes."

"It's worth thinking about," Oates conceded cautiously. "She received her shock, or whatever it was, over the phone, the telephoner relying upon her to react to it in the usual way and so fix the moment of the murder at a time when the murderer had a watertight alibi. It's not bad, Campion."

"I think that's how it happened." Campion spoke softly. "After all, think of it. It all worked out so neatly. Mrs. Potter was bound to be in at four-thirty because Miss Cunninghame was due to leave at four-fifteen and always stayed over her time by ten minutes or so. Then Potter was away—the only day in the week he was always out—so the woman could take the stuff and die alone. Of course he couldn't hope for Potter to come in early and wash out the glass, but he could expect that Fettes would diagnose heart failure or acute alcohol poisoning."

"It's neat," said the inspector. "Very neat. And it sounds feasible. But it's too full of holes, and pure hypothesis anyway. How did he get the nicotine into the spirit, or, having done so, how did he know that she wouldn't take the stuff before he rang up?"

Campion considered.

"I think the answer to that last question is that the poisoned spirit had not been in her possession very long," he said at last. "Even Max, who's the most optimistic soul on earth, wouldn't risk her taking it too soon. Therefore the answer to the first question is that he got the stuff here some time on Thursday."

"Was he here on Thursday?"

"No."

"Or during the week?"

"No. I admit all this, but after all she was a secretive woman. It might have come by post. He might almost have given it to her in town. There are so many possibilities here that we can't work 'em all out. That's why I join with you in feeling that our only hope is to find the container, the thing that originally held the stuff."

The inspector glanced round the little room.

"We'll find it," he said with sudden decision. "We'll find it. Until then I reserve judgment. But it's a glimmer, my boy, it's a definite glimmer. Come on. We'll search this darn place ourselves."

The inspector revealed a thoroughness which surprised Campion, although he had not the neatness of the trained police searchers. Every piece of furniture in the overcrowded room was carefully examined, every loose floorboard prized up, every conceivable corner where a hidden cupboard might have been concealed laid bare.

The living room, the scullery, and the shed without all went through this gruelling examination by turns. Again and again Campion found himself confronted by little domestic secrets of the Potter household, little economies, little slovenlinesses which he felt were private and which brought home unbearably the pathos of the tragedy. However unlovable a character Mrs. Potter had been, her destroyer had also annihilated a home which without her became a desolate collection of rubbish.

They refused Belle's kindly offer of lunch and worked on until half past three in the afternoon, when their work ended. Hot, dishevelled, and defeated, they smoked a cigarette in the untidy room.

"We're sunk," said the inspector. "I'm glad I made sure myself, though. You can see for yourself that Richardson and Miss Peters were right. There's nothing here."

Regretfully Campion agreed, and they were still sitting in despairing silence when Lisa knocked at the door.

"Mrs. Lafcadio says you must have some tea," she said, planting a tray on the table. "As you wouldn't come in, I've brought it down."

She stayed to pour out for them, and Campion was acutely aware of her bright inquisitive eyes peering first at the disordered room and then at themselves.

Idly he went over ground already explored.

"After Mrs. Potter died and before I arrived, no one but you and Mrs. Lafcadio and Fred Rennie came in here at all?" he enquired.

"I have told you, no," said Lisa with some dignity. "I have also told *you*," she added, nodding to the inspector.

He smiled at her wearily as he returned his teacup to the tray. "You have, Miss Capella," he said. "Until you're tired, I'm afraid."

Campion frowned. "Someone must have come," he said. "Someone must have come—to the door only, perhaps. That's it, Lisa. Did someone come to fetch anything at that time? Anything at all?"

"I have told you," the old woman began brusquely. "No one came except the boy from the art gallery."

Both men sat staring at her. The inspector's hand was halfway to his lips, the cigarette hanging from his fingers, while Campion sat up stiffly, his face completely expressionless. Not unnaturally Lisa was taken aback by the sensation she had created. Two spots of colour appeared in her yellow cheeks.

"It was nothing," she said. "He often comes at that time. I gave him the blocks and he went. I didn't let him see inside the studio, of course. It was when Mrs. Lafcadio had gone to telephone."

The inspector pulled himself together. His eyes were hard and concentrated on the woman's face.

"I ought to have heard of this before," he said. "But it doesn't matter. When exactly did the boy come?"

Lisa's dark eyes were frightened.

"Mrs. Lafcadio had gone to telephone," she repeated. "I had just come in here and seen Mrs. Potter. There was a knock. I was startled, I think. I went to the door. When I saw who it was I was glad it was only the boy. I told him to wait. I shut the door so he wouldn't see anything.

Then I got the blocks. They were wrapped up in their cloth, and I gave them to him and he went away. That is all."

"All right," said Oates soothingly. "All right. What were the blocks?"

"Wood blocks—wood engravings." Lisa found the inspector's ignorance very disconcerting. She began to speak very clearly, as though to a foreigner, which indeed he was. "Big heavy squares of wood. She cleaned and printed them for him."

"For whom?"

"For Mr. Max. I am telling you. His boy came for them. I gave them to him."

The inspector looked at Campion, his face twisted into a travesty of a smile. "She gave them to him," he said.

17 : *The Slack Cord*

"Sebastiano Quirini? Why, my dear, his engravings were quite lovely."

Belle looked up as she spoke, and for a moment her eyes lost the dull, weary expression which Campion had grown to dread in them.

They were in the drawing room again, sitting by the fire, whose comfort had become a necessity since the second tragedy although the spring was not a cold one.

Campion and the inspector, having decided that Mr. Potter was better not disturbed unless it became absolutely necessary, had come to Belle for information.

"I believe it was a sort of secret," she said, "so you mustn't let anyone know. Max discovered nearly fifty of Quirini's old wood blocks in Paris when the Société des Arts Anciens was sold up. It was a very old business, you know. They dealt in antiques as well as pictures, and their warehouse in the Centre had not been cleared for years. When they started to turn it out before the building was pulled down, they found all sorts of things, I believe. Anyway, there was quite a sensation at the time. It's very long ago.

"However, that's all beside the point. Max picked up these Quirinis, all quite black and clotted with ink, some of them nearly ruined. He had one or two cleaned and found out what they were."

Oates was still looking puzzled, and Campion explained.

"They're the solid chunks of boxwood on which the artist engraved the picture," he said. "They'd vary in size and thickness considerably. The picture was made by pressing a piece of fine paper, or silk sometimes, on the inky surface of the graved wood. Mrs. Potter melted the old ink out and reprinted them, I suppose, Belle?"

The old lady nodded. "Claire was very clever at that sort of thing," she said, her eyes softening. "Very patient and painstaking. Wood engraving is not difficult to print, you know, but it takes time and a lot of care. Max will miss poor Claire."

The inspector's eyelids flickered.

"Did she do much for him, ma'am?"

"Oh, so many things." Belle shook her head at the recollection of Claire Potter's many activities. "She worked much too hard. There are quite a number of little confidential jobs in the picture world," she went on, smiling faintly at the inspector. "Little things like this that require absolute integrity as well as skill. You see, Max wanted to get the Quirinis all ready at once, so that he could have a show of them all together and perhaps start a little fashion for them. So much depends on fashion: it seems very silly, but there it is.

"Claire had nearly finished them. She had been at work for two years."

"Two years?" The inspector was startled.

"Oh, yes. It was a long job, you know, and some of the blocks were in very bad condition. She did so many other things, too."

Oates glanced at Campion.

"She didn't keep these things in the studio, then?"

"All of them?" said Belle. "Oh, dear, no. They were much too bulky and too precious. Max used to send them down to her—one or two at a time—his boy would fetch one lot and bring another. I remember seeing him often—such a funny little grown-up boy. I wish children never had to work. The blocks were always wrapped up in a green cloth. Claire always had the second lot waiting for him, all packed and ready. She was most particular about them. No one was allowed to touch them except herself. I remember once being in the studio when they arrived, and I offered to unpack them for her, but she quite snapped at me. Poor Claire! It was so unlike her that I was quite surprised. She was most conscientious. The blocks were always kept packed up. They used to stand on the bookshelf in their cloth. Max paid her very badly, I'm afraid, but she never complained."

She sighed and looked down at her plump little hands. "She was very kind to me always," she said, and added unexpectedly, "that poor, helpless, silly man, too. No one to look after him now. She took care of him. The pity of it! The dreadful, wasteful pity of it!"

They were silent, and the moment was relieved by the arrival of Lisa with a message from Donna Beatrice.

That good lady, finding herself temporarily eclipsed by other, more important matters, had promptly taken to her bed on the ancient principle that if one cannot command attention by one's admirable qualities at least one can be a nuisance.

Somewhat grudgingly Lisa announced that Donna Beatrice was asking for Belle.

"She has not eaten," she said. "She refuses to take anything unless you are there. Shall I leave her until tonight?"

"Oh, no," said Belle, getting up. "I'll come. Poor soul," she remarked apologetically to Campion, "she's hysterical. It's very naughty of her. She makes herself so unpopular."

She went out, and Lisa followed. Campion and the inspector were left alone.

"She never let anyone unpack those wood blocks except herself," said Oates, taking out his notebook. "Max paid her very badly but she never complained. She did a great deal for him, confidential work. What are you thinking?"

"I was thinking," said Campion slowly, "that it is more than possible that Max had been in the habit of aiding and abetting Mrs. Potter in her unfortunate weakness for some time—months, perhaps even years. Under-paying her and keeping her happy that way. When the occasion arose, it was simplicity itself to poison her. It was probably so easy that he couldn't resist the temptation."

Oates sighed. "It looks like it," he agreed, "and if so we'll never get him. If the corpse conspires to shield the murderer, where are you! A couple of these wood blocks wrapped in tissue and baize would make a parcel large enough to hold, say, a flat half pint, I take it?"

"Oh, quite, I should say. It's ingenious, Oates."

"Darn ingenious," agreed the inspector. "But all conjecture, Campion. Based on strong suspicion, but all conjecture. Not a ha'porth of evidence in the lot. I'll see the boy, of course. That reminds me: Rennie says that when Mrs. Potter was out on the afternoon of the crime he took in a green-baize parcel secured by a strap from Salmon's and left it in her porch. Why did the boy call again in the evening? There's a chance I may get something out of the kid without disturbing Fustian, which is the last thing to be done at this juncture. Come on, Campion, we'll get on with it. Nothing more here at the moment."

Campion next saw the inspector at noon on the following day in his own chilly room at Scotland Yard.

Oates looked up as the young man came in, and he hailed Campion with even more enthusiasm than usual.

"I've seen the boy," he said, plunging into the business without pre-amble. "Caught him at the gallery first thing before anyone else arrived. He's an odd little object—name of Green."

"I think I've seen him at the shop."

"Have you? Oh, well, then, you know him. That's him—funny kid. Not too happy in his job, I fancy. Still, he didn't say so. Campion . . ."

"Yes?"

"I think you're right."

"Really? What did you get?"

Oates flipped over the pages of the ragged little book in which he kept his notes.

"The boy bears out all the other evidence, of course. He used to take those green-baize parcels backwards and forwards at irregular intervals. He usually got out to Bayswater in the evening because it was the last thing he had to do and it was a long way. There were two of them, by the way—two bits of baize and two straps, I mean—so that one parcel was always waiting for him when he brought the other."

"Did he ever see them packed at the gallery end?" said Campion.

"No. I particularly enquired about that. He was not even sure what they contained. Apparently Fustian has a habit of cooking up minor mysteries in the firm. He seems to have impressed the kid with the idea that he's a sort of art-world genius, a great financier pulling strings and starting hares and all the rest of it. These parcels were simply given to Green by Fustian, who packed them himself and who told him that they were very valuable and to be treated with great care. The boy seems to have felt that he was a privileged person to be allowed to touch the things at all. He's a simple-minded little beggar."

"Is that all?" Campion sounded disappointed.

"No, not quite. I explained to him, of course, that I was just checking up on all the people who had been to the studio during the day—you must tell 'em something, you know—and he volunteered the information that it was most unusual for him to call at the studio twice on one day and that it had happened because of a mistake of Fustian's. Apparently Green came down with one parcel on the lunch hour, and collected the other, which had been left with Rennie. This alteration in the usual time was because that evening he had to meet the five fifty-eight train at Victoria to collect some prints from Paris. The prints were on silk, and they had to be seen through the customs.

"When he arrived back at the gallery after the lunch hour, Max sent for him and explained that he had put the wrong contents in the parcel, and therefore when the kid had completed his mission at Victoria he was to go straight on to the studio and ask for the parcel back. Are you following?"

Campion nodded. His eyes were half closed behind his spectacles.

"When the kid got to Victoria the prints had not come. It took him some little time to discover this—about twenty minutes in all, he thinks. Then he went to the studio, arriving there about seven. Lisa gave him the parcel and he took it back to the gallery."

The inspector paused and regarded his friend.

"When he got there Max was waiting for him. The boy was surprised to see him and more surprised still when, after enquiring if he saw Mrs.

Potter and receiving the reply that he had not but that Lisa had given him what he wanted, Max gave him a couple of bob. Then the kid went home, and that's all he knows."

"Extraordinary," said Campion.

"Interesting," said the inspector, still consulting his notes. "Oh, by the way, one other little thing: I asked the kid if he knew what was in the parcels. He said no, but after a while, as we got matey, I could see there was something on his mind, and presently he came out with it. About three weeks ago he dropped one of those darn parcels he was taking to Mrs. Potter on the tube stairs. He didn't like to open it to see if any damage was done, and in fear and trembling he took it on. He said he didn't get into any trouble, as he expected to, but when he handed the thing in he noticed the green cloth was quite wet. I pressed him, but he hadn't noticed anything else."

Campion sat up. "So we were right," he said.

"Yes," said Oates. "As far as we're concerned, the mystery's solved, but we can't say so. Exasperating, isn't it?"

"There's not enough evidence for an arrest?"

"Enough! There's none at all."

The inspector rose to his feet and stood looking out of the window. "Another unsolved mystery, that's what the papers say," he remarked. "In all my experience I remember only one murder case in which the police didn't know whom they wanted. We haven't got enough here even to have him up and question him. He's licked us. While we were deciding if the corpse was poisoned or not, he was downstairs in the cloakroom of his gallery washing out the bottle."

"If only Potter hadn't washed out the glass," said Campion.

Oates considered. "I'm not sure about that," he said at last. "On the face of it I admit it looks as though that were the intervention of Providence on the wrong side, but was it? Suppose Potter had behaved like any ordinary sane person on finding his wife. Had a look at her, found she was dead, sent for the doctor and told him the whole story about the whisky drugging. It's ninety-nine to a hundred he'd have diagnosed heart failure and alcohol poisoning and we shouldn't have come into it. It was only the mystery at the beginning that put us onto it at all."

Mr. Campion was still digesting these reflections when Oates spoke again.

"Nothing," he said. "Not a thing on him. He's got away with it."

"What are you going to do? Drop it?"

"Good Lord, no!" The inspector looked shocked. "You ought to know more about police procedure than that. We shall go on snuffling about like an old terrier on a stale scent. We shall write each other coldly disapproving letters from department to department. We shall tell each other the facts in confidence and go on worrying round a little less week by week. Then something else will turn up and we shall all be very busy and this will get crowded out."

The young unhappy face of Dacre as he lay in the little robing room in Lafcadio's studio; Mr. Potter standing with his back to the shrouded figure of his wife; Belle sitting in the scullery twisting her fingers; these things passed in front of Mr. Campion's eyes, and he looked up.

"At least you can find the motive," he said bitterly. "Couldn't you get him on that?"

"Motive and doubtful circumstantial evidence isn't enough," said the inspector gloomily, "much less the mixture of conjecture and suspicion we've cooked up. Besides, there may not be a motive."

"What d'you mean?" The words had crystallized a fear which Campion had been fiercely refusing to recognize.

The inspector met his eyes for an instant. "You know what I mean. Nothing sufficient, not a *sane* motive."

Mr. Campion studied the carpet. "You suggest—"

"Look here," cut in the inspector, "I admit it's a disturbing thought, but you know as well as I do that when a chap of that age and type suddenly becomes a killer it means something's gone radically wrong with his sense of proportion. The cleverer he is the later we get him."

"Then you don't think we can do anything now?" Campion's tone was lifeless.

"No," said the inspector. "No, my boy, he's been too neat. We must wait."

"Wait? Good God, what for?"

"Next time," said Oates. "He won't stop at this. They never do. The question is, who is going to annoy him next?"

18 : *Dangerous Business*

The coroner was an honourable man, but he was also sensible, with a natural distaste for publicity.

When the court resumed after the postponement, Mrs. Potter's sad little corpse was sat upon by a dozen interested but busy people who, after all the available evidence had been placed before them, brought in a sane but not very satisfactory open verdict.

They found that the deceased had met her death by poisoning by nicotine, but that there was insufficient evidence to show if it were self-administered or no.

The testimony of the tremulous Miss Cunninghame concerning her friend's behaviour on the last afternoon of her life did much to dispel the jury's doubt from the public mind at least, and, as there is hardly anything which the average man finds so dull and depressing as a tale of suicide, the whole business faded gently into obscurity.

The press, which has a gift amounting to second sight for detecting an unsatisfactory story when the first ripe buds are laid upon the editorial table, had relegated the yarn to the final news columns as soon as the customary outcry against police inefficiency had grown stale, and the authorities counted themselves blessed.

Campion and the inspector alone recognized the situation for what it was, and as the sensation died away and the atmosphere of Little Venice subsided once more into a false peace the younger man at any rate experienced the sensations of a maiden lady who sees the burglar's boots below the curtain as the last of the neighbours troop back to their homes after the false alarm.

He haunted the house for the next few weeks, drifting in on every conceivable excuse. Belle was always pleased to see him, while Donna Beatrice welcomed him with the thirsty affection of a performer for her audience. Mr. Potter remained in his room most of the time, a new uncouth creature with a secret life. Dr. Fettes shook his head over him.

The optimism of a healthy mind is indefatigable, however, and, as time went on, even Campion began to see the events here recorded from that detached distance so often miscalled true perspective.

The gentle procession of ordinary life swept them all along, and it began to seem as unlikely that violence would ever again assail Lafcadio's household as it had done on that Saturday evening when he and Belle had discussed the morrow's reception.

When the first trumpet of alarm came so crudely, therefore, it carried with it an element of shock.

Max put forward his ingenuous suggestion to the Lafcadio legatees with all the elaboration and hot air with which he usually invested business matters.

He phoned one morning, made an appointment for three o'clock, arrived at a quarter to four, and addressed the little gathering as if they had been a board meeting.

Donna Beatrice, Lisa, Belle, and the impatient Linda sat and listened to him in the drawing room. Mr. Potter, the only other member of the household, and D'Urfey, who was almost one, were excluded at Max's own suggestion.

The old room, with its comfortable decorations and faded curios, was very gracious and mellow in the afternoon sunlight streaming in from over the canal. Belle sat in her usual chair by the fire, Lisa at her side and Linda hunched up on the rug, while Donna Beatrice took the chaise-longue and prepared to enjoy herself.

Max took the floor, his small, graceful figure heightened by importance.

His naturally picturesque appearance was considerably exaggerated by his latest sartorial fad, consisting somewhat astonishingly of a fully coloured Victorian fancy waistcoat. This gallant vestment was without question a thing of beauty. Its shades of mauve, old gold, and green were elegantly blended, and its workmanship lovely enough to account for its preservation, but on Max's attentuated form, beneath his flowing tie and in conjunction with his magnificently cut if somewhat loose new spring suit, it smacked altogether too much of affectation and the very peculiar, and even Belle, who took a childish pleasure in bright things, regarded its exuberance with doubt.

Linda, contemplating him sombrely from beneath her tawny brows, reflected that during the past month or so Max's conceit and overemphasis had become noticeably worse. Now and again there was a distinct touch of well-simulated foreign accent in his drawling utterances, and his swagger was becoming Irvingesque.

Looking at him posturing in the dusty sunlight, it occurred to her that it was really remarkable that he should not appear very ridiculous. She thought also that this was certainly not the case. Max Fustian's old strength, a passionate belief in his own magnificence and a force of personality which thrust this illusion upon all he met, had increased with the other eccentricities until the electric atmosphere which emanated from him was frankly disturbing. His opening remark was typical of this new super-affectation.

"My dear ladies," he said, regarding them as though they were at least partial strangers and not people he had known for twenty years, "we have something to face. John Lafcadio's great memory, which I myself have done so much to preserve, has been desecrated. It will take all my powers, all my skill, to put him back where he belongs. To do this I shall require your co-operation."

"Ah!" said Donna Beatrice with gratified idiocy.

Max shot a patronizing smile in her direction and continued in the same oratorical vein.

"Lafcadio was a great painter," he said. "Let us never forget that. A great painter. This calamity, this petty blot upon his household, this little smirch across his memory, must not be allowed to make any one of his admirers forget that. A great painter."

Lisa was listening, her quick dark eyes fixed upon his face in the fascinated stare of imperfect comprehension.

Linda, on the other hand, showed signs of restiveness and would have spoken had not Belle's plump hand upon her shoulder counselled her to be still.

Max continued, his head thrown back, the phrases falling lazily from his lips.

He had perched himself upon the arm of the great chair which Lafcadio had always pronounced, without any foundation at all, a part of the belongings of Voltaire. The faded crimson tapestry made a background for Max's eccentric figure and lent it some of its own gracious magnificence.

"Of course," he said easily, "you all realize that it will be impossible to continue the pretty Show Sunday conceit in future years. That amusing little idea has ended unfortunately. Lafcadio's beautiful work must never enter that tainted studio again. You will probably leave this house, Belle. The name must be preserved from notoriety. That is most important."

Belle sat upon her chair and regarded her visitor in mild astonishment. Waving her unuttered comment aside, Max went on with supreme confidence.

"I have given the matter quite a considerable amount of thought," he confessed, with a little condescending smile at the group on the rug. "As I am undoubtedly mainly responsible for bringing Lafcadio before the public, I naturally feel it my duty to do what I can to save the rest of his work from any contamination by this wretched little scandal."

"Quite," said Donna Beatrice faintly.

Max nodded briefly at that portion of the room in which she sat. He appeared to be enjoying himself.

As she sat looking at him, Belle's brown eyes seemed to grow larger and more dense in colour, but she made no sound, and only the gentle pressure of her hand on Linda's shoulder increased slightly.

"My plans are these," said Max briefly. "My name has been too long linked to John Lafcadio's for me to allow any private considerations to deter me from coming to his rescue at a time like this."

He had dropped the impossible artificiality of manner with which his opening remarks had been made, but a new matter-of-fact didacticism was if anything even more offensive. "At considerable personal inconvenience, therefore, I shall take the remaining four Lafcadio canvases to New York this autumn."

He made the announcement bluntly and continued without waiting to see if his audience agreed with him.

"Although times are bad, I think with my powers of salesmanship I can expect to sell one or perhaps even two canvases. The echoes of the distressing affairs in this house will have died down over there by that time, if they ever reach so far. After New York I shall take the remaining works to Yokohama, perhaps returning to Edinburgh with any that are left. I realize, of course, that I am taking a risk, but I am willing to do this as a last tribute to the man whose genius I have established."

He paused triumphantly with a wave of his long hands.

Belle remained perfectly silent, but Donna Beatrice leant forward, her thin face flushed, her necklace jangling.

"Dear Max," she said, her voice shaking with self-conscious sweetness, "keep his name green. Keep the Master's torch alight."

Max returned the pressure of her thin fingers and released them perfunctorily.

"The only reason I come to you at all," he remarked, slipping gracefully into the great chair, "is that written consent to break the terms of the present arrangement must be given by you, Belle, before I can take the canvases abroad. I have the documents with me. You sign them and I'll make all the necessary arrangements."

Donna Beatrice rose with a rustle and glided gracefully to the serpentine bureau in the corner.

"Sit here, Belle dear," she said. "*His* desk."

Mrs. Lafcadio did not seem to have heard her, and Max laughed softly and went over to her.

"Dear Belle!" he said. "Aren't you going to thank me? I wouldn't do so much for any other painter in the world."

When the habitually even-tempered suddenly fly into a passion, that explosion is apt to be more impressive than the outburst of the most violent amongst us.

Belle Lafcadio rose in the full dignity of her seventy years. Bright spots of colour burned in her crumpled cheeks.

"You preposterous little puppy," she said. "Sit down!"

The use of the old term of contempt was unexpectedly effective, and if Max did not obey her at least he slipped back involuntarily, his brows contracting.

"My dear lady—" he protested, but Belle was aroused, and Lisa and Donna Beatrice, who both remembered the last time Belle lost her temper some twenty years before, were silent.

"Listen to me, my boy," she said, and her voice was the vigorous, resonant thing it had been in her thirties. "Your conceit is turning your head. This is not a subject we talk about as a rule because politeness and kindness forbid it, but I see that the time has come for a little truth. You are in the position you occupy now because you have had the intelligence to cling to Johnnie's coat tails. I admire your intelligence in clinging, but don't forget the motive power is his, not yours. *You'll* do what you can to save his pictures! *You've* been mainly responsible for bringing his name before the public! Upon my soul, Max Fustian, you want your ears boxed.

"Johnnie left instructions about his pictures. For eight years I've obeyed those instructions, and for the remaining four I shall do the same, please God. If no one buys them, if no one comes to the parties, it doesn't matter. I know what Johnnie wanted, and I shall do it. Now go away, and don't let me see you for at least six weeks or I'll take the whole thing out of your hands. Be off with you."

She remained standing, breathing a little faster than usual and the colour still burning in her cheeks.

Max gaped at her. Her resistance was a thing he had obviously never considered. Gradually, however, his equanimity returned.

"My dear Belle," he began stiffly, "I make every allowance for your age and the disturbing time through which you have passed, but—"

"Really!" said the old lady, her brown eyes positively flashing. "I never heard such monstrous impudence in all my life. Will you be quiet, sir! I have told you, no. The present arrangement holds. My husband's pictures remain in this country."

"Oh, Belle dear, is this wise? That angry red cloud in your aura! Max is so clever about business, don't you think—" Donna Beatrice's mild protest from the chaise-longue ceased abruptly as Belle ganced at her.

Mrs. Lafcadio smiled politely.

"Beatrice dear," she said, "I wonder if you'd mind going to another room for a moment. I see this is to be a business talk. Lisa, my child, you can go downstairs now. Bring tea, in fifteen minutes. Mr. Fustian will not be staying."

"Vivid crimson and indigo," muttered Donna Beatrice maddeningly. "So dangerous. So harmful to the Higher Consciousness!"

But she went all the same, rustling from the room like a startled bird. Lisa followed her, and as the door closed after them Belle glanced down at her granddaughter.

"I want to do what Johnnie told me to, Linda," she said. "You and I are the only people concerned. What do you think? If we lose a little money, does it matter?"

The girl smiled.

"They're your pictures, sweet," she said. "You do what you like. You know how I feel. Somehow I don't really care very much. If you don't want them to go away, that settles it as far as I'm concerned."

"Then not in my lifetime," said Belle. "While I live I shall do what we arranged all those years ago."

"Criminally absurd," Max declared. "Sheer stupidity. My dear Belle, even though you are Lafcadio's widow you mustn't presume on your position too much. Those pictures belong, not to you, but to the world. As Lafcadio's executor in Art I insist: they must be sold as soon as possible, and our only hope is in the other great capitals. Don't let obstinate sentimentality degrade the work of a man you obviously never appreciated."

His voice had risen, and in his anger his movements had lost their studied grace and become oddly childish.

Belle sat down in her chair. The old room which still breathed the presence of the turbulent Lafcadio seemed to range itself around her. She looked at the man coldly. Her anger had passed and taken with it all that radiating warmth and friendliness which made her what she was.

In its place a new and unexpected Belle was revealed: a woman still strong enough to set her face implacably at anything of which she disapproved, still shrewd enough to see flattery for its tawdry self, and still sufficiently rich in friends to be able to choose.

"Max," she observed unexpectedly, "you must be over forty. I am over seventy. If we were both thirty years younger, as I feel we ought to be to make this disgraceful exhibition even faintly excusable, I should send for Lisa to put you in a cab and send you home. You mustn't come to people's houses and be rude. You make yourself ridiculous in the first place. Also they dislike it. You may go now. I want the remaining four cases which my husband left sent back here unopened within a week."

He stood looking at her.

"Are you really going to make that colossal blunder?"

Belle laughed. "Silly, pompous little man," she said. "Go away now and send the pictures back, and don't behave as if I were a Lyceum audience."

Max was angry now. His skin was very sallow, and the little muscle at the point of his jaw twitched ominously.

"I have to warn you, you are making a very serious mistake. To take the works out of our hands is a serious step."

"Bless the man!" said Belle in exasperation. "If Johnnie were here I don't like to think what would happen to you. I remember a man coming here once and behaving about as badly as you have done this afternoon, and Johnnie and McNeill Whistler threw him in the canal. If you don't go this instant I'll send for Rennie and have it done again."

Max retreated. He was livid, and his small eyes snapped dangerously. Halfway across the room he paused and looked back. "This is your last chance, Mrs. Lafcadio," he said. "Shall I take the pictures abroad?"

"No."

"Nothing will make any difference?"

"Only my death," said Belle Lafcadio. "When I'm dead you can all do what you like."

The words were spoken with peculiar spirit, and Mr. Campion, arriving on one of his many visits, heard them with all their significance as he came up the stairs.

He hurried forward to see who their recipient might be and was confronted by Max striding out of the doorway, his face contorted with uncontrollable rage.

19 : *The End of the Thread*

"My dear, I must be getting old."

Belle patted her muslin headdress into position as she spoke. She was standing in front of the small oval mirror with its frame of white Dresden flowers which hung over the gilt console table between the two windows. She remained surveying herself, while the roar of Max's acceleration died away in the street below.

In actual fact she looked considerably younger than of late. The clash had brought out some of her old fire, and there was a trace of the "Belle Darling" of the Louvre in her quick smile as she turned to nod at Campion, who had just entered.

After the greeting she returned to the mirror.

"I like these bonnets," she remarked. "They make me look so clean, don't you think? Old women often look so mothy, put away for the summer without being brushed. That little whippersnapper, my dear! He talked to me as if I were a case of senile decay living on the parish."

Mr. Campion looked apprehensive.

"You behaved like a lady, no doubt?" he ventured.

"Not in the least," said Belle with satisfaction. "I washed my hands of him, absolutely, irrevocably. Johnnie and I never put up with people when we really disliked them, and I'm not going back on the habit of a lifetime. I have taken the rest of the Lafcadio business out of Master Fustian's hands. I've told him he takes those pictures abroad over my dead body."

"Oh, dear," said Mr. Campion.

Belle laughed, but Linda, who had not spoken since Max left, regarded the young man thoughtfully. The old lady reseated herself.

"Now I want a cup of tea," she said. "Touch the bell, Linda, child."

Five minutes later, as they sat round sipping out of the famous crackle-ware cups mentioned in so many books of reminiscence, the sensation of calamity which had returned to Mr. Campion as he came up the staircase burst into his fullest mind.

Max in the drawing room, Max at a reception, or in the gallery, might be a ridiculous, overexaggerated poseur; but there was another Max, a Max as yet unseen, but who, when reconstructed from the facts gathered about him, was certainly no person for a hot-headed old lady to offend.

Altogether it was not a very comfortable meal. Belle was stimulated and frankly pleased with herself. Linda remained unaccountably silent. Donna Beatrice sulked in her room, refusing to appear, and Lisa hovered round the tea tray, a gloomy, nerve-racked ghost.

Yet the presence of John Lafcadio was still apparent.

If he had been forgotten in the storm which had burst over his house, as soon as it had subsided he had returned to his former importance.

For the first time in his life Mr. Campion was faintly irritated by that flamboyant, swashbuckling shade. Its presence conveyed an air of confidence and protection which was naturally not genuine. In spiritual dangers and mental pitfalls John Lafcadio's memory might be a tower of strength to his household, but in physical attack it was hardly so effective.

The appearance of Matt D'Urfey was a welcome diversion. He put his head round the door, a picture of mild reproach.

"I've been hiding in your studio," he said to Linda. "I didn't know you were all feeding. Is the conference over?"

"My dear," said Belle, fussing shamelessly, "come and sit down at once. Linda *dear*, you haven't looked after him."

Looking at the newcomer, Mr. Campion felt again a liking for this naïve, friendly spirit who regarded the world as an odd sort of party upon which he had dropped in by mistake.

He sat down by Linda and received the tea which Lisa handed him as his right, like a child or a puppy which has been overlooked and discovered just in time.

Even with his advent Linda did not become talkative. She sat looking into the fire, her elbow resting on her knee and her shabby painter's hand playing idly with her coarse, wild curls.

Suddenly she rose to her feet.

"When you've finished eating, Matt," she said, "come back to my studio. I want to talk to you."

She took a cigarette from the box on the table, lit it, and went off to her room with a nod and a smile at Belle.

D'Urfey stayed until he had finished his repast, neither hurrying nor being deliberately slow, but when he had finished he returned his cup and plate politely to Lisa, smiled engagingly at Mrs. Lafcadio, and rose to his feet.

"I've got to go and talk to Linda now," he said and went off.

Belle looked after him.

"Just like Will Fitzsimmons before he made his name," she said. "Success brought that man down to earth. He began thinking in terms of money and finally died of depression."

Campion grimaced. "What an outlook for D'Urfey!"

The old lady shook her head.

"I don't think so. Have you seen his work?"

"Does Linda like him?"

"Very much, I think." Belle seemed complacent about the suggestion. "They'd have a very happy, untidy sort of existence together, which is after all the main thing. She would have been miserable with poor Dacre. Love so seldom means happiness."

Mr. Campion was still reflecting upon this facet of the tragedy when Linda reappeared.

She looked a little more dishevelled than usual, and there was a note of underlying authority and purpose in her voice which Campion had not heard there before.

"Albert," she said, "I wonder if you'd mind coming upstairs for a moment."

"Anything wrong?"

"Good heavens, no. Why should there be? I only want to show you some drawings."

Her tone, although it was evidently intended to be so, was not particularly reassuring.

Belle nodded in response to Campion's unspoken question.

"Run along, my dear," she said. "I won't come with you. I've grown very tired of pictures. All painters' wives feel like that in the end."

Linda led Campion up to her little studio where he had found her on the day of the reception. It was in much the same state of chaos now, and as he came into the room the recollection of Mrs. Potter, briskly practical, came back vividly to his mind.

Matt D'Urfey was sitting on the window sill, his hands in his pockets, the expression in his china-blue eyes that of the intelligent but detached spectator.

Linda turned to him.

"I think I shall show him," she said.

"Very well," said D'Urfey.

"You think it's an idea, don't you?"

"Yes, I think so." In spite of his words, D'Urfey did not seem particularly convinced either way.

Campion's curiosity was whetted.

"What's up?" he enquired.

Linda went to her famous cupboard, which was believed in the family to contain somewhere in its depths everything which had ever been mislaid in the house, and produced a brown-paper parcel. She brought it to the table, swept aside a miscellaneous collection of paintbrushes, pots of paint, bottles of varnish, odd reels of cotton, and other débris, and proceeded to unpack it.

Campion looked over her shoulder.

What he saw was a careful pencil study of a woman's figure in a ragged blouse, a basket in her arms and a curious, half-horrified, half-eager expression on her face. Apart from the fact that the model had clearly been Mrs. Potter, he saw nothing unusual about it, except that the draughtsmanship was exceptionally fine.

He looked up to find Linda peering at him.

"Notice anything?" she enquired.

"No," said Mr. Campion. "Not particularly, I mean. What is it? A study for an oil?"

Linda sighed. "Wait a minute."

More rummaging in the cupboard produced an old number of *The Gallery*. She turned over the illustrated pages impatiently and finally pounced on the sheet she sought.

This was a full-page reproduction of an oil painting, showing the crowd round the Cross in modern dress. In the foreground was the completed figure from the sketch.

It did not take even Mr. Campion, who was an amateur in these matters, long to decide that.

Linda turned the magazine round so that he could read the descriptive paragraph upon the opposite page:

"We reproduce here the seventh of the Lafcadio pictures, unveiled in London in March last. This work, which is perhaps in some ways the most disappointing of the whole collection of posthumous pictures left by John Lafcadio, R.A., is nevertheless well up to the standard of that brilliant technician's later work. It has been purchased by the Warley Trust for the Easton Art Gallery and Museum."

"Now do you see what I mean?"

Mr. Campion picked up the study.

"Is this your grandfather's? I thought all his stuff was preserved somewhere."

"So it is," said Linda. "Sit down. When I was in Rome this time I came back through Paris. I told you I hadn't been very successful in finding any of Tommy's stuff. Someone had been round before me and cleared off everything. But when I was in Paris for a few days it occurred to me that he might have given a sketch or two to old D'Epernon, who keeps a filthy little café in Montparnasse. I looked him up. He lets lodgings as well, and Tommy used to take a room there whenever he came up from Rome."

Mr. Campion nodded to show that he was still attentive, and she hurried on.

"D'Epernon hadn't got a thing, but the wineshop people over the way were more helpful and finally fished this out. Apparently they had a daughter whom Tommy used to flirt with. He gave her this sketch as a parting present. I bought it and brought it home. Now do you see what I'm driving at?"

Mr. Campion had the uncomfortable sensation that he was being very stupid.

"How did Dacre get hold of it in the first place?" he demanded. "Did you give it to him?"

Linda picked up the magazine.

"You're not very intelligent," she said. "Look here. This picture, Grandfather's seventh posthumous exhibit, was solemnly unpacked at the Salmon Galleries just before Show Sunday last year. It wasn't supposed to have been touched or the original seals broken before that date. By that time Tommy had said good-bye to the wineshop girl for over six months and she herself was safely married and living in Aix with her husband, who's a baker or something. Her parents assured me that they'd had this sketch in the house for over eighteen months."

"Yes," said Mr. Campion, on whom the truth was slowly beginning to dawn. "Where is all this leading?"

"You'll see," said Linda grimly. "Look at the paper this sketch is drawn on." She held it up to the light. "See the watermark? That's Whatman Fashion Surface, slightly rough. That paper wasn't manufactured until about seven years ago. I remember it coming out when I was a student."

"Which would argue," put in D'Urfey from the window sill, "that Daddy Lafcadio didn't make the drawing."

Campion frowned. "You're sure Dacre couldn't have seen your grandfather's picture at some period before it was officially opened?"

"And copied it, you mean? I don't think so. The pictures were kept in the cellar at Salmon's. Max made quite a fetish of them. He'd hardly let a student see them, and no one else. Oh, Albert, don't you see what I'm driving at?"

Mr. Campion regarded her mildly through his enormous spectacles. "You're suggesting, I suppose," he said slowly, "that Dacre painted the picture?"

"I'm not suggesting," said Linda. "I'm telling you."

Mr. Campion rose slowly to his feet and stood looking out at the canal. His face was completely expressionless, and he appeared to be looking at something far away in the mist on the opposite bank.

"If this is true," he said at last, "it explains . . . well, quite a number of things."

Linda shot an appraising glance at him and was clearly about to speak, but a second thought occurred to her and she stood fingering the drawing meditatively.

Mr. Campion roused himself from his reverie.

"It's rather a dangerous yarn, isn't it?" he said with an attempt at his old levity. "I mean, I shouldn't go spreading it around. It might get you into a lot of trouble. There is probably some perfectly innocent explanation, anyway."

"I don't think so."

"But, my dear girl, how can you be sure?" Campion snapped the question intentionally. "I should keep very quiet about it if I were you."

The girl regarded him coolly, and he noticed, as one often notices irrelevant things in times of stress, that her eyes were quite green save for the little flecks of brown in them. She was really astoundingly like Laf-cadio himself.

"I should keep quiet—I have, for two or three weeks—if I didn't think the time had come to talk. You see, Albert, I'm as sure as anybody can be sure that the seventh picture, which the Warley Trust bought last year, was painted by Tommy, and I'm open to bet that if there are any Lafcadios left in the Salmon cellars at least three of them were painted by Tommy, too."

"My dear girl, you mustn't make unfounded suggestions like this." Mr. Campion was shocked.

Matt D'Urfey, who had given up listening to the conversation and had been pottering with some drawings of Linda's in a corner, now returned to it to some purpose.

"Have you told him about Lisa?" he enquired.

Mr. Campion spun round.

"What are you two hiding?" he demanded. "Believe me, it's most dangerous at this stage."

Linda looked up at him.

"So you've guessed, too, have you?" she said. "I did, but not until this afternoon, and that's why I decided to talk to you. We don't want Max getting his teeth into Granny, do we?"

Her remark was so unexpected and echoed his own thoughts so completely that for a moment Mr. Campion was silenced. Finally he took the girl by the arm.

"What do you know about this business?" he said urgently. "What's this yarn about Lisa? That woman runs through this affair like a squib. You never know where she's going to explode next."

"Lisa's all right," said the girl carelessly. "She's very simple, though. People don't seem to realize that. She doesn't think like ordinary people. She's never had occasion to. She was a complete peasant when she came here. I don't suppose she knew more than a hundred words in any language. She doesn't mean to be secretive. She just doesn't know what's important and what isn't. When I came back from Paris I got her up here one night and made her remember quite a lot of things. She told me something which explains everything. You see, Grandfather didn't leave twelve pictures; he left eight. Lisa knows, because she helped him to seal them up."

Mr. Campion took off his spectacles and polished them. An enormous knot in the skein was unravelling before his eyes.

"It was very difficult to get it out of her," the girl went on. "It took endless questioning. But as far as I could gather, this is what happened: The year before Grandfather died—that is, in nineteen-eleven—Belle was very ill. She had rheumatic fever, and when she recovered she went down to stay at San Remo with the Gillimotts. He was a poet, and she painted.

Funny, nervy people, I believe. Belle was down there for about six months, and it was during that period that Grandfather packed up the pictures and put the whole scheme in order. So Belle saw some of the pictures, and some she didn't. Mrs. Potter had seen them, because she was hovering about as usual. Old Potter was away somewhere, teaching, probably, in Scotland, and Lisa remained to look after the house. Grandfather was very secretive about the whole business. Everybody put that down to his age, whereas of course the old boy had a perfectly sound reason for keeping it all so dark."

She paused.

"There's one point you've got to understand," she said at last. "It may strike you as hard to credit, but it seems perfectly logical and natural—to me, at any rate. And it's this: The main reason why Grandfather did the thing at all was to get his own back on Charles Tanqueray. He really hated Tanqueray, and he left the pictures to discourage him. He wanted to leave a lot. He wanted to sound as if he were going to be in the limelight for a long time. He only had eight canvases he could spare, and so he labelled those '1924,' '1925,' and so on. But the last four parcels were fakes. Lisa says, as far as she remembered, one contained a kitchen tray, and one of the others a big cardboard sign advertising beer. Just anything, you see. The Victorians had that sort of humour, you know. It wasn't lunacy. He was that sort of old boy—a buffoon of a person.

"Lisa told me all this quite solemnly," she went on. "Apparently she promised him to keep quiet and helped him nail up the packing cases and couldn't understand what he was so amused about. She said he was in tremendously good humour when they'd finished and made her drink a whole bottle of Lafite with him."

"But the hoax was certain to be found out," said Campion.

"Of course it was," said Linda impatiently.

She seemed to share some of her grandfather's enthusiasm for the scheme.

"But that wasn't the point. Don't you see, Tanqueray was younger than Grandfather, and it had occurred to him that his hated sparring partner was only waiting for the Lafcadio demise to set up unpersecuted as the Grand Old Man of the art world. Grandfather gave him ten years to cool his heels, with the infuriating knowledge that at the end of that time Lafcadio was going to return with a spectacular stunt which would keep him in the public eye not for one year only but for another twelve. The fact that he had only eight canvases and hadn't the energy or the time to paint any more—he was portrait-painting right up to the time of his death, you know—made him slip in the faked packing cases for the last four years. I daresay he reckoned that eighteen years would about see the end of old Tanqueray. He overestimated it, poor darling. Tanqueray didn't live to see the first picture. Have you got that far?"

Mr. Campion signified that he had. The tangle was unravelling fast.

"Well, now," said Linda, "the rest is a sort of guess, I know, but it fits in perfectly. Some years ago someone at Salmon's—and I think it's pretty obvious who—had a peep into the packing cases and hit upon the obvious swindle. After all, as far as the authenticity of a picture is concerned, preconceived ideas are half the battle. If the fake's good enough you'd be surprised at the authorities who get taken in. Here was everything all ready. Everybody knew there were twelve Lafcadio pictures, everybody expected twelve Lafcadio pictures. Even if one of them was howlingly indifferent, why should anyone think that Lafcadio hadn't painted it? Whatever it was like, it was worth its price. Lafcadio's reputation was made. One dud, or even four, couldn't hurt it much."

"Quite," said Mr. Campion, who found these revelations very enlightening.

"Four years ago, before Tommy went to Rome, he took an extraordinary holiday. Matt'll tell you about it. He completely disappeared for about ten months. No one heard from him; no one saw him. At that time he was trying to be a portrait painter, very much in the Lafcadio manner. When he came back he gave up oils suddenly and went to Rome to study tempera."

"He got the Prix de Rome, didn't he?" said Campion.

"No. He didn't. That's the point. He got the other one, the Chesterfield Award, and Max was adjudicating that year."

Mr. Campion was silent for a moment, setting these facts in order in his mind.

"Where was Mrs. Potter when Dacre was on his mysterious holiday?" he enquired.

Linda nodded at him approvingly.

"You're shrewder than I thought," she said without discourtesy. "Quite remarkably, that period corresponds exactly with the time when Mrs. Potter had what was, as far as I can gather, the one stroke of luck in the whole of her life. She got a commission to go curio-hunting in middle Europe and was away for ten months. I never heard of anything she brought back. She was supposed to be moving around the whole time, and so no one wrote to her, nor did she reply. You know how casual people like us do that sort of thing. She did her curio-hunting for Max, of course. So you see she knew all about it, which probably accounts for . . . well, for everything."

"What about the last picture?" said Campion. "The Joan of Arc one."

"Oh, that's genuine. It was clever of Max, wasn't it, mixing the dud in with the others? There was a certain amount of criticism of last year's effort, and so this year out comes the genuine thing again."

"But look here," protested Campion, still bothered by the technicalities, "surely an expert could tell the difference? There's the paint, for one thing. And hang it all, the genius of the man. That couldn't be faked."

"You're talking like an amateur," said Linda. "Don't put too much faith in experts. They're only human. As for the rest, it was perfectly simple for Mrs. Potter to get hold of the Lafcadio paint. She was always begging little tubes of this and that from Rennie, anyway. The question of genius doesn't come into it. I've told you there was a certain amount of criticism of the seventh picture, but nobody thought of questioning its authenticity. It wasn't bad enough for that. As a matter of fact it was very good. Grandfather might easily have painted it. He didn't turn out a masterpiece every time.

"The question of technique is the most difficult of all. That had to be copied, of course. I think Tommy copied it deliberately. I think he was paid to. I've told you he used to imitate—or shall we say be influenced by?—Lafcadio, anyway. And he was particularly clever in oils. Really I don't see why he shouldn't have done it. In fact I'm perfectly certain he did do it."

"It would explain—" began Campion.

"It does explain," the girl corrected him. "One of the things it explains is why Tommy suddenly chucked up oils. It was part of the bargain, you see. If ever the question of authenticity arose in future years, one of the first questions everybody would ask would be who had painted the damn things. And if there was a competent painter very much in Max's pocket, who worked very like Lafcadio, the answer wouldn't be far to seek, would it? So Tommy had to give up oils. I'll never forgive Max for that."

"There are other things that'll take a bit of forgiving," pointed out Mr. Campion.

The girl flushed.

"I know," she said. "I haven't assimilated all that yet. The full explanation of the whole ghastly business only occurred to me when Max and Belle were having that row this afternoon. That was why I decided to tell you all this. I didn't realize you knew already. Something's got to be done before Max takes Belle at her word. He's got four pictures, remember; three duds and one good one. He knows his one real chance to dispose of them—and they're worth anything up to ten thousand pounds apiece—is to take them abroad and sell them before the hoo-ha dies down. It's a good selling tale, you know: 'to be disposed of quietly because of scandal.' 'All hush-hush, but the genuine thing, my dear boy.' "

Mr. Campion pulled himself together.

"You must keep quiet," he said. "That's the main thing. Let one breath of this get about and we may lose him, if nothing else happens."

"You can trust me," said Linda grimly.

"And D'Urfey?"

Linda regarded the affable, blue-clad figure with affection. "It wouldn't occur to him to talk," she said. "He's too lazy, for one thing."

"Not at all," said Mr. D'Urfey with dignity. "It's just not my affair, that's all."

"You'll do something, Albert?" Linda persisted. "You didn't see Max's face when he left Belle this afternoon. I did. He looked insane."

But Mr. Campion had seen and had formed his own opinion.

He went to see the inspector.

20 : *A Nice Little House*

"Yes, well, there you are," said the inspector, kicking the fire, which in spite of its brightness did not take the chill out of his grim little office. "There's the whole story. We know nearly everything now. But what can we do?"

Mr. Campion looked as nearly excited as the inspector had ever seen him. He sat on the visitor's chair set out in the middle of the square of dingy carpet, his hat on the floor by his side and his hands folded across the knob of his stick.

"You can't leave it here, Stanislaus," he said earnestly. "The man's a menace, a sort of malignant germ which may produce an epidemic at any moment."

Oates rubbed his short moustache.

"My dear fellow, I don't want you to think I'm not interested," he said. "I am. We all are here. We've had conference after conference about this case. Your information completes a fascinating story. I can't promise to act upon it immediately because there's not a ha'porth of concrete evidence in the whole yarn. I needn't point that out to you; you know it as well as I do. You're not an amateur in the sense that you're a beginner. You must see the thing as we do here."

Mr. Campion was silent. In his heart he had known that some such answer must meet his demands, but he could not rid himself of the growing conviction that the matter was urgent.

"It would be most unfortunate for all concerned if a scandal about the Lafcadio paintings broke now," he said at last. "But if it meant that you could put that fellow under lock and key, then frankly I shouldn't hesitate."

"Good heavens!"—Oates was inclined to be querulous—"that was the first thing that came into my head, naturally. That's why I've been questioning you so carefully about this latest discovery. But as far as I can see, the only thing you have which looks faintly like proof is the figure study for the picture on recently made paper. What does that amount to in all conscience? Nothing at all. Fustian's only got to say that he gave the boy permission to see the pictures, confessing to a little irregularity, you see, and the mainstay of the whole case is swept away. It's not enough, Campion. There's no one more eager than myself to get an arrest. I'm badgered on all sides to make one. But one blunder now and we should lose him for ever. We've got to be canny. We've got to wait."

Mr. Campion rose to his feet and walked over to the window, where he stood looking down into the yard below.

"I feel it's urgent," he said obstinately.

"I agree." The inspector came and stood beside him. "Can't you persuade the old lady to go away somewhere or make her let the fellow have his own way? Meanwhile we've got our eye on him. Don't make any mistake about that. If he breaks the law in any way whatsoever—if it's only a motoring offense—we shall be down on him. And if he makes any serious attempt upon anyone, we're not unprepared this time and we shall get him."

He hesitated, his brow wrinkling.

"If Mrs. Lafcadio does succeed in getting those four cases from Fustian, I very much suspect that at least three of them will contain the original junk which the old man packed. But if by chance Fustian should be foolish enough to send the three fake pictures, and she can detect them—really detect them, I mean; not just personal-opinion stuff—she might possibly be able to hotch up some sort of case against him, though on what grounds I'm not quite sure. She'd have to go into that with a lawyer. However, in my opinion that'd be a dangerous proceeding in the present situation. As I think I've said before, when a man of that age suddenly takes to murder it means that there's a spanner in his mental machinery and God knows when he's going to stop. But then you know that, and that's probably why you came to me today."

"Yes," said Campion soberly. "That's why I came."

The inspector walked over to the desk, where he stood idly digging a pen into a piece of blotting paper before he spoke again.

"Thinking it over," he said, "I believe our only avenue of attack at the moment is through the pictures. There are one or two blanks we haven't filled in yet, you see. One is why Fustian should choose to kill Dacre when he did and not before the boy went to Rome at all . . . that looks like blackmail to me. And two, why was it, exactly, that Mrs. Potter came in for hers?"

"I don't think we shall ever know that," said Mr. Campion. "I don't think it matters. I think it's fairly obvious that she was with Dacre while he did the work for Max, serving as general factotum, model, and guardian, I should think. But whether he killed her because she guessed he had murdered Dacre or because she had threatened to give the game away about the pictures, I don't see that we can ever tell. Personally I incline to the former."

He looked at his friend helplessly.

"I'm at a dead end, Stanislaus," he said. "Manhunting isn't my métier. It's a job for the police. I do see that you're hampered. If this fellow does it again, you'll get him. You've only got to watch him until he makes the attempt and fails or succeeds. I'm in a slightly different predicament. I want to stop him attempting."

"Then concentrate on the pictures," said Stanislaus Oates. "Concentrate on Dacre. And that reminds me; I meant to mention it, but your story put it clean out of my mind. That Rosini girl, the little Italian he married: early on in this business I got the police of the Saffron Hill district to keep an eye on that bunch and let me know if anything unusual occurred. I had no special reason for this, you understand. It was just part of the ordinary routine. We like to keep an eye on anyone connected with a murder case, however remotely. I'd forgotten all about it, as a matter of fact, but this morning I had word that the erstwhile Mrs. Dacre, who seems to have an odd circle of friends, has been in the habit of going off for week-ends to the country with a whole crowd of them. It says on the report, 'Alleged destination some property left to Mrs. Dacre by her husband.'

"There is nothing remarkable about this, of course," he continued, "and so I didn't hear about it, but last week-end there appears to have been some sort of shindy, for the party returned to London in the small hours of Sunday morning looking as though it had taken part in a pitched battle. That's all the information we have at present. It may be nothing at all, of course, but it sounded odd, so I mentioned it. Did Dacre have any property?"

"None I ever heard of," said Campion.

He picked up his hat.

"I think I shall see Rosa-Rosa," he said. "You've no objection, I suppose, Stanislaus?"

"Oh, Lord, no. Be discreet, of course—but I needn't tell you that. And don't worry, my boy. That man's being watched at every step. I hope for everybody's sake that he doesn't make an attack on the old lady, but if he does we'll get him."

In the doorway Campion paused.

"Stanislaus," he said, "do you think that if you'd known as much as you know now you would have had a chance in ten thousand of saving Mrs. Potter?"

Inspector Oates was an honest man. He shrugged his shoulders.

"Perhaps not. But that was very ingenious," he said.

"Ingenuity seems to be a peculiarity of Mr. Max Fustian's," said Campion and went away uncomforted.

At six o'clock that evening he set out upon his search for Rosa-Rosa. For obvious reasons he did not want to visit her in her uncle's delicatessen store on Saffron Hill, but he had a very shrewd idea where to look for her.

He started off down Charlotte Street with every hope of finding her at the Robespierre, and as soon as he turned into the side entrance of that most odd of all London pubs and pressed through the red-plush curtains which divided the outer bar from the holy of holies within he caught sight of her, seated on one of the shabby leather sofas in the corner by the fire.

The place was not crowded. Barely half a dozen men sat on the high stools round the bar, and the sketch-covered walls and coloured-paper-flecked ceiling were not yet obscured by a haze of tobacco smoke.

The largest party in the room was Rosa-Rosa's own. It consisted of four young men, among whom Campion recognized the sharp-featured Derek Fayre, the cartoonist, whose bitter, slightly obscene drawings appeared occasionally in the more highbrow weeklies. The others were unknown to him, although he was vaguely aware that he had seen the effeminate young man with the side whiskers on the stage at one of the Sunday shows.

The round man with the pointed beard and the real horn spectacles was a stranger, as was also the young Italian with the black eye who sat on Mrs. Dacre's left and held her hand.

Rosa-Rosa had not altered. Even the fact that her head was framed by an enlarged photograph of the 1920 Robespierre children's outing did not lessen the bizarre modernity of her extraordinary appearance.

She wore no hat, her strange immobile features were expressionless, and her yellow hair stuck out flat from the top of her head like the curls in conventional bas-relief.

Campion's immediate problem, which was one of introduction, was settled for him instantly.

As he stood hovering, glass in hand, the girl caught sight of him.

"Hello," she said. "I met you when my husband was murdered. Come and sit here."

This greeting, which was uttered at the top of her harsh, high-pitched voice, made a little stir in the room. The people round the bar paused to glance at her curiously, but the plump, capable woman who was serving did not bat an eyelid. Evidently the tragedy in Rosa-Rosa's home life was no news to her.

The plump young man made room for Campion at the table. Rosa-Rosa evidently regarded him as an old friend, and he settled down with his beer, the legs of his chair almost in the fireplace as he squeezed in on her right.

After her welcome, introductions seemed superfluous, and the conversation went on where it had left off.

"My uncle is taking me to his lawyer," said Rosa-Rosa, who appeared to be in the middle of a story. "When we go to the police court we shall raise hell. I will show that stinker!"

"What will you do, Rosa-Rosa?" said Fayre, smiling. There was something bantering in his tone, as if he were persuading her to perform.

"I will do this."

With one of her lightning changes into electric vivacity Rosa-Rosa did her trick, which consisted of a graphic and vulgar pantomimic display, rendered all the more vivid by the contrast with her natural immobility.

Mr. Campion was a little startled. It was evident that Rosa-Rosa's lack of English was no deterrent to her powers of expression.

"Dirty little beast!" said Fayre, laughing. "I'd like to see you do that all day."

"Get on with the story," commanded the young man with the beard with weary resignation. "I suppose we must hear it."

Rosa-Rosa stuck out a long thin tongue at him and beckoned to the barman.

When the question of further refreshment had been settled, the Italian boy cuffed her gently.

"It's your cottage, isn't it?" he prompted.

Rosa-Rosa choked into her glass.

"My husband who was murdered gave it to me," she declared as soon as she recovered. "Before we came from Italy he told me it was mine. 'We will live there and be happy,' he said."

"You loved your husband, didn't you?" said Fayre, still with the smile and as though he spoke to some clever animal.

Again Rosa-Rosa underwent one of her startling changes. She drooped, she crumpled, her body sagged, even her hair seemed to wilt. Her dejection was not so much exaggerated as epitomized.

She threw her arms out wide and remained very still, her chin resting on her breast.

"I loved him," she said.

It was an extraordinary exhibition; rather horrible, Mr. Campion thought.

Fayre glanced at him.

"Extraordinary, isn't it?" he said. "She does it every time. Carry on, Rosa-Rosa. Nothing's very clear in my mind except that your husband, whom you loved,"—he mimicked her grotesquely—"left you a cottage in his will. You went down once or twice and had a few disgusting parties. The second—or was it the third?—visit was interrupted very naturally by outraged neighbours, who were caretaking for the real landlord. Your uncle —disgraceful old basket—is getting in a shark lawyer, and when you get hold of the landlord, poor beggar, you're going to go like this—" He imitated her first gesture and rose to his feet. "I've got to go," he said. "I met my wife today and she said she might be coming home. If she's there when I get back I'll bring her along."

"Some hopes," said the man with the side whiskers as soon as the cartoonist was out of earshot. "Does he always talk like that to create an impression, or is it genuine?"

"Eve did marry him and did leave him," said the fat man with the beard languidly. "I don't feel his attitude towards it matters very much. Come, Rosa-Rosa, have you finished or is there more of this house-property idyll?"

Mrs. Dacre sat eyeing him sulkily. Then she smiled and began to swear appallingly in Saffron Hill English.

The fat man frowned with distaste.

"Horrible," he said. "Nasty, bad girl. Dirty. The management will throw you out on the street if you talk like that. Your difficulty seems very simple. Prove the will and claim your property."

"Fat beast!" said Rosa-Rosa venomously. She had noticed the cold eye of the lady behind the bar upon her, however, and lowered her voice.

"My husband made no will," she said. "He was murdered."

"Oh, God, how we know that!" said the actor, without bitterness. "Still, if he didn't make a will it's probably not your cottage. Why worry? Come and live in King's Cross. It's much more central and not nearly so insanitary."

Rosa-Rosa looked shocked. "When a husband dies, everything that was his becomes the fortune of his wife," she said. "It is my cottage. My husband and I were going to live there, but he was murdered."

"That's nothing to be proud of," said the fat man.

"Huh?"

"I say it's not clever to be married to a man who was murdered," persisted the young man. "Unless you did it, of course. Did you do it, by the way?"

Rosa-Rosa gave her alibi, and this, too, Mr. Campion felt, was part of a performance which these feckless folk put her through whenever they saw her. His own curiosity about the cottage was thoroughly aroused, however, and he took a hand in the questioning.

"Where is this house?" he enquired.

"At 'Eronhoe. When I have seen my uncle's lawyer you shall come down to a party."

"Don't you go," said the slender young man from the stage. "It's miles away from anywhere, and the neighbours throw bricks at one. Look at that man's eye."

"Is it the Heronhoe in Sussex?" said Campion, making a guess.

The Italian boy answered him.

"No. It's in Essex. Near Halstead. I drove my cousin down there with some of our friends. We went several times. But on Saturday when we arrived the place was all shut up. People from the village were there. They wouldn't let us in."

"Very extraordinary," said Mr. Campion encouragingly.

"Most," said the boy, his solemn face with its one discoloured eye ridiculously solemn. "They said the owner was in London. We were cold, don't you know, and we'd got plenty to drink on board. We had a bit of a fight. Some of the boys got angry, the girls screamed, and the people came for us with sticks and dogs. We drove the car into 'em. Laid one bloke out. I don't think he was hurt. Anyway,"—he smiled engagingly—"we didn't wait to see. We came away. Perhaps they were right. Maybe it's not hers." He laughed at the prospect. "We tore the place up a bit," he said reminiscently. "They were good parties."

Rosa-Rosa had been listening to this recital, her head thrust forward between the two men and every line of her angular body expressing interest.

"It is my cottage," she said vehemently. "My husband gave me a little picture of the house when we were in Italy."

"A snapshot," explained the cousin. "It had the address on the back. That's how we found the place. It was furnished, but no one was there, so we broke in."

"A very stupid thing to do if you didn't know the place was yours," commented the bearded young man, who appeared to be bored to tears by the whole history.

Rosa-Rosa spat at him calmly.

"Stinkin' fat," she said pleasantly. "It is mine because my husband's things are there. All his drawings everywhere. My husband was a great painter. If he had not been murdered we should be very rich. On the day he died he told me so. We were to go down to the cottage and he was to paint four pictures like the others."

"What others?" enquired the man with the side whiskers.

Rosa-Rosa shrugged.

"I don't know. That's what he told me."

Mr. Campion took a deep breath.

"Are you sure they are your husband's drawings—the ones in the cottage?" he enquired.

"Oh, yes, they are my husband's. There are heaps—so high. Two big cupboards full."

"Heronhoe." Mr. Campion did not speak the word aloud, but it was printed indelibly upon his mind. "I wish you luck, Mrs. Dacre," he said. "You won't go down for some time, I suppose?"

"Not till she's seen the lawyer," put in the cousin.

His eyes had strayed to a red-headed girl seated at the side of the room, but he now tore his attention back to the topic which was evidently the principal subject of talk in the Rosini family.

"Afterwards we shall go back and see those country boys. Heh! It was a good fight. Bottles and everything. Not a flattie for miles. When we find out who the wet is who says he owns it there'll be a better fight still." Mr. Campion glanced through the shining window at the murky sky. He rose to his feet. Through the conflicting hopes and alarums in his mind the Italian's soft, thoughtful drawl reached him:

"It's a nice little house."

21 : *A Day in the Country*

It was not so much the prospect of committing a burglary which disturbed Mr. Campion, as he steered his aged Bentley through the winding lanes of that part of Essex which is almost Suffolk, as the problem of the exact address where his project was to take place.

He had located Heronhoe on a survey map, but as he knew neither the name of the cottage nor its owner, its discovery promised a certain amount of difficulty.

It was for this reason that he had chosen to arrive in the daylight and had curbed his impulse to set off at once after hearing Rosa-Rosa's story.

He timed his departure from London at six o'clock the following morning, and it was nearly ten when he arrived at the village, having lost his way several times.

The tidy little main street, as compact and picturesque as the set for a musical comedy, lay fresh and bright in the spring sunlight. The air was chilly but sparkling. There was a crisp, invigorating wind. The fat, bursting buds on the chestnuts were wet and cold and radiant. It was altogether as fine a day for a felony as Mr. Campion had ever known.

He pulled up at the White Lion, a big, straggling hostelry which took up more than its fair share of the southern side of the street, and succeeded in persuading the landlord to admit him at least to the Commercial Room.

Wm. Pudney, according to the minute board over the doorway, was permitted by a gracious government to dispense wines, spirits, and tobacco, and, by immemorial custom, food, to all who should pass, but at ten o'clock in the morning he seemed disinclined to do any of these things for the pale young man with the rakish motorcar.

Mr. Campion was not drawn to Mr. Pudney. He was a spare, pink, youngish man with a masterpiece of an accent which betrayed at once both his ambitions in this direction and his complete lack of the ear by which to attain them.

"Me mother," said Mr. Pudney at last, "will find you somethin' to eat in the pentry. You may sit in the Commercial Lounge."

He led the way to a chamber of horrors on the right of the bar. This room smelt faintly of beer and strongly of oilcloth. The decorative scheme was, properly enough, in keeping with the atmosphere and achieved its devastating effect by lace curtains and vast enlarged photographs of past phases of the Pudney ménage, helped out here and there with cheap mahogany and coloured-glass ornaments.

Mr. Campion felt that the White Lion, commercialism, and Mr. Pudney were not good mixers. He attacked the problem on hand, therefore, without loss of time.

"Many visitors this way?" he enquired artlessly, attacking the limp bacon and anemic egg which Mr. Pudney's mother had found in the pantry.

"Not motorists," said the landlord with disdain. "We're not very keen on motorists litterin' up our beautiful countryside. Trippers lower any place."

In self-defense Mr. Campion ventured the information that he was going to Ipswich to see his father.

"He's in the Church," he added as a grace note to the fable.

"Reely?" Mr. Pudney showed surprising respect. "I thought you was a commercial. You'll pardon me, sir, but we get so many persons round here takin' orders for this and that and demoralizing the cottage people."

Mr. Campion graciously accepted the apology, and Mr. Pudney became chatty.

"We have the cycle club 'ere in the summer," he said modestly. "Me mother does quite a lot of caterin' then. Toppin' chaps they are; nothin' tripperish about them. Very tidy fellows. Never leave so much as a bottle about."

"Good," said Mr. Campion absently.

"We had a party of hikers once," continued Mr. Pudney. "Very intellectual persons, all of them—and there's the hunt, of course, in winter. That's very nice, but we don't tolerate common trippers from London. The village boys set the dogs on them."

It was borne in on Mr. Campion that Heronhoe was eminently unsuitable as a site for a week-end cottage for Rosa-Rosa.

"Really? Have they ever actually set the dogs on anyone?" he enquired.

Mr. Pudney eyed him sharply.

"There was very unregular behaviour at Spendpenny last Saturday night, I 'ear," he said at last. "Quite a fracas."

"Oh? Is Spendpenny a house?"

"Oh, dear me, no." Mr. Pudney's contempt was magnificent. "It's a dirty little old place, a labourer's dwelling. Some people came down and behaved shockin'ly—very common persons. The caretakers in the next cottage couldn't do anything with them, so they got some villagers down there on Saturday and when the persons came there was quite a fight."

"Where is this dreadful place?" enquired Mr. Campion with ghoulish interest.

"Down Pope's Lane. That little path on the left just through the village. It's never had a nice name. An artist had it once."

Campion raised his eyebrows.

"Very lowerin' to the locality," said Mr. Pudney, adding darkly, "artists mean models."

"Quite," said Mr. Campion sagely, and paying his exorbitant bill he went away in his car to turn down Pope's Lane.

The cottage Spendpenny, named after some improvident past owner, lay a good half mile down a steep lane whose banks were heightened by great walls of elder and ash. It was a postcard cottage with a roof like the back of a camel, and boarded walls which had once been tarred but were now mellowed by thirty years' weather to the comfortable greenness of the country verger's frock coat.

As far as Mr. Campion could see, as he drew up in the lane, there were no other houses round about. Spendpenny lay under a fold in a green meadow. The wild patch of garden before the door was still brown with the dead spears of last year's weeds, but the perennial polyanthi and an occasional tulip showed among the ruin.

He had no doubt that this was the cottage he sought. The small wooden gate to the lane was smashed, the newly splintered wood showing yellow against the grey-green of its surface. Moreover, the place itself had an air of desertion, while there were yet ragged curtains at the small square windows, and the grass-grown path was tramped flat.

The loneliness of the countryside descended upon him as he stepped over the ruin of the gate, for like many travellers used to much wilder country he could recognize the peculiar emptiness of the green meadows and the tiny hidden lanes; an emptiness different from the cold freshness of virgin soil, since it is the emptiness of desertion, of the unfurnished room or the forsaken camp.

He stood for a moment looking at the cottage and then stepped forward, his lank figure casting a very small shadow in the bright cold sunlight.

When he was halfway down the path he stopped abruptly. The cottage door had opened with a clatter. For an instant the figure within was indistinct in the shadow. Then it moved out onto the cobbled step.

"My dear fellow," said Max Fustian, "but how delightful!"

The immediate thought which came into Mr. Campion's mind was typical of him. It occurred to him that the emotion of pure surprise was rare, and that when it did come it cleared the consciousness of everything else. But this was obviously no time for introspection. Max was coming to meet him.

Max in tweeds, with his hands dirty and shreds of cobweb in his hair, was in many ways a more fantastic figure than Max in his black hat and fancy waistcoat. The crofters' cottages produce many opulent, not to say exotic, weaves, and Max in heather pink and green plus-fours looked as though he were in fancy dress.

"How nice of you to drop in," he said. "Come inside. The house is obscenely dirty, and I'm afraid there's nothing to drink, but at least there's a chair."

It occurred to Mr. Campion that he ought to say something.

"Are you the landlord?" he enquired, somewhat baldly, since they were the first words he had spoken.

"Of such as it is, yes," said Max lightly as he led the way into the main room of the dwelling, a low, brick-floored apartment sparsely furnished and incredibly dusty. Much of the furniture was broken, and there were quantities of beer bottles about.

"I'm looking for a cottage," said Campion, without hope or even particular intention of sounding convincing. "They told me in the village that this was empty, so I came along."

"Naturally," said Max happily. "Do sit down."

He was evidently tremendously pleased with himself, and his visitor had the impression that his own unexpected arrival was not of the least consequence to him. Campion experienced a sense of futility. He looked at the man and wondered what on earth he could possibly be thinking.

Anyone less like the popular conception of the murderer some weeks after the crime, it was difficult to imagine, yet he experienced the uncomfortable conviction that if he should suddenly say: "Look here, Fustian, you killed Dacre and Mrs. Potter, didn't you?" Max would smile and reply airily: "Yes, I know I did. My dear fellow, what can you do about it? Think about something else."

It was an impossible situation.

Max had produced a case of yellow Cyprian cigarettes, and when Campion begged leave to stick to Virginian he shrugged his regret and lit one himself.

"I don't know if this place would suit you, my dear boy," he said. "It's very remote and quite devastatingly insanitary. But come and look over it. Look in every hole and cranny."

Campion raised his eyes without turning his head, and for a dizzy moment he thought Max had given himself away, but the bickering smile had vanished from the wide mouth and Max was his elated self again.

"I keep this place to lend to artists," he said. "It's so fantastically lonely the beggars simply have to work. There's a wash house out at the back that I converted into a studio. Come along. There's just this one room down here and a scullery. What a hovel, Campion, what a hovel!"

He led the way to a cupboard staircase and clambered up the awkward way to the two small rooms above, Campion following.

Here the disorder was incredible, and Max shuddered.

"I've had uninvited visitors," he explained. "I lent this place to Dacre years ago, and that monstrous little slut of his, Rosa-Rosa Rosini, seemed to imagine it belonged to him. Anyway, I heard from the Ravens, the good peasants who keep an eye on the house for me, that someone had been here, and I came down to find out that 'Mrs. Dacre had come to take possession.' She seems to have brought half the rabble of Clerkenwell with her. However, you can see the rooms."

He turned, and they went down again. Crossing through the minute scullery, they went out into the weed-grown yard and entered the studio.

The fine old wash house had been very simply converted. The warm rose brick floor, coppers, and big open fireplace had been left, and the big north light let into the tiles and a wooden platform at one end of the place were the only alterations as far as Campion could see.

There were two great presses, part of Victorian giant wardrobes, on either side of the fireplace, and the doors of these hung open, revealing them to be empty.

"Charming, isn't it?"

The elaborate drawl at his side drew Campion's attention from the tragic cupboards.

"Very nice," agreed Campion.

"Not cold," said Max unexpectedly. "Not a bit cold. Look at the fireplace."

Mr. Campion's eyes followed the sweep of the graceful hand and rested upon the ruin of his hopes.

The immense fireplace was of the early cavern variety, consisting of a square hole cut at the base of the chimney and furnished with a huge iron basket for the fire itself.

The whole square was a mass of fluttering grey and black paper ashes, still warm, it would seem from the faint heat exuded by the chimney.

"Destroying something?" enquired Campion.

Max met his eyes. He was frankly happy.

"Everything," he said. And then, dropping his voice so that he spoke in a stage whisper, half serious, half bantering, "All my sins, my friend. All my sins.

"When would you like to take possession of the place?" he went on more normally. "Five shillings a week. You pay the Ravens. You can't grumble at that, my dear boy. If you take up painting I'll lend it to you. Come along and give me a lift to the Ravens' cottage down the lane. I left my car there and came over by the fields."

Mr. Campion went meekly.

On the London Road Max's new sports car shot away from the old Bentley at something over eighty, for Mr. Campion drove soberly, almost cautiously. As he sat he thought.

The last straw of evidence which might possibly have led to Fustian's arrest had been destroyed, possibly less than an hour before he himself had arrived. Moreover, he had undertaken to rent a white elephant. The honours of the day lay with Max.

That evening, however, he received a note from Fustian making what seemed to Campion an astoundingly naïve suggestion. He said he had been thinking it would be nice if they should drink a cocktail together some time.

22 : *Invitation*

"I've told Belle, Mr. Campion, I've told Belle over and over again that she must compose her Higher Consciousness, bring herself in tune with the Cosmic Universe, and then her aura will return to its natural blue and rose and everything will be quite all right."

Donna Beatrice delivered herself of this somewhat remarkable confession of imbecility and sat back in the high brocade chair before Belle's bedroom window and smiled up into the strong sunlight as if she placed herself on an equal footing with it as a human comforter.

Belle sat up in her small Dutch bed, a shawl round her shoulders and a crisp muslin bonnet on her head. The coverlet was strewn with letters.

Campion, who sat in the doctor's chair, shook his head at her flaming cheeks and overbright eyes.

"You get some sleep," he said. "Clear the room of all visitors and refuse to see anyone. Wash your hands of the whole business. Forget it."

Belle glowered at him like a fat, rebellious baby.

"Not you, too, Albert!" she said. "I did think I'd get a little intelligence from you. Old Dr. Pye has been here talking like that—silly prim little man! We always call him Mince Pye, and I nearly told him so this morning, only I thought he probably wouldn't have enough French to see the joke, even if his humour rose to the occasion. I don't want to stay in bed. What's a temperature? We never bothered about them when I was a girl. I want to go down to that gallery and fetch those pictures. I won't be treated like a doddering, drooling old half-wit by a posturing little ninny who ought to be spanked."

"I can't stay in the room with such an aura," said Donna Beatrice faintly. "It stifles me."

She made a dignified exit, sighing heavily just before she closed the door behind her.

"Thank God for that!" said Mrs. Lafcadio truculently. "The woman's a fool."

"Why don't you get rid of her?" enquired Campion not unreasonably.

"For good?"

"Yes. Send her right away. It must be very trying to live with a lady of—er—her convictions."

"Oh, no, I couldn't do that." For a moment it was the old Belle who peered out from beneath the organdie. "She's old, poor darling. This is her life. Johnnie gave her a false conception of herself, and she's been living up to it rather misguidedly ever since. When he died he said, 'Belle, darling, look after that damn fool Beatrice for me. She was so lovely once.' No, I mustn't send her away, but I'm glad she's gone out of the room. Now, Albert, you tell them that I'm quite all right and bring your car and we'll go down to Bond Street and take those canvases away. Johnnie wouldn't have hesitated."

"No, Belle, you can't do that." Mr. Campion was embarrassed. "Look here, you leave it to the lawyers and meanwhile get some sleep. If not, you know, you'll die."

"Rubbish," said Mrs. Lafcadio. "If Johnnie were here we'd get the pictures, sell them for what we could, and go away to Capri until the money was spent. I should lie in the sun and listen to him telling the story and improving it."

She was silent for a moment or two, and then she laughed.

"Second childhood, my dear. I do know how different it is now I'm old, but I forget when I get cross. Now, Albert, advise me. What shall I do?"

She leant back among the pillows, and the colour gradually faded from her cheeks, leaving her pale and exhausted.

"I can't leave everything to the lawyers," she said plaintively, "because they say leave it alone. You see, the whole thing is in such a muddle. Johnnie thought I should be dealing with old Salmon, who was a pet, so he didn't bother much about the legal aspect of the business, and now they've come to examine it they find that Max and I are both responsible for the things. He can't do anything without me, and I can't do anything without him. It's all so annoying."

"You're still very angry with Max?"

Mrs. Lafcadio was silent for a moment while her lips moved ruminatively and her eyes grew dark again.

"Yes, I am," she said. "Yes, definitely. Very, very cross."

"What are you thinking of doing?"

"Well, I don't know. I don't know at all. If he takes the pictures out of the country I shall have to proceed against him, I suppose, and that's such a lengthy business and such a nuisance."

"You just want things to go on as they are, then?" said Campion. "I mean, you're really only anxious that the pictures should stay in England and be shown every year as Lafcadio wished?"

"Yes." She nodded emphatically. "Albert, my dear, you see to it. You speak to Max. You make him do what I want. I never want to see the man's hideous little face again, but I give you full powers to act for me. You see to it. Linda is worse than useless. She advises me to let him have his own way."

In view of everything, this was a somewhat awkward mission, and Mr. Campion could hardly fail to recognize it.

There is an optimistic belief widespread among the generous-hearted that the average human being has only to become sufficiently acquainted with another's trouble or danger to transfer it to his own shoulders not merely unhesitatingly but gladly. The fact remains, of course, that the people who say to themselves, "There is real danger here, and I think it had better confront me rather than this helpless soul before me" are roughly divided into three groups.

There are the relatives, and it is extraordinary how the oft-derided blood tie decides the issue, who, moved by that cross between affection and duty, perform incredible feats of self-sacrifice.

Then there are those misguided folk, half hero, half busybody, who leap into danger as if it were the elixir of life.

And finally there is a small group of mortals who are moved partly by pity and partly by a passionate horror of seeing tragedy slowly unfolded before their eyes, and who act principally through a desire to bring things to a head and get the play over, at whatever cost.

Mr. Campion belonged to the last category.

"All right," he said slowly. "All right, I'll see to everything."

"Oh, my dear! Thank you so much. I can just go to sleep then and know that everything will be all right and the pictures will stay here in England?"

He nodded. Having reached a decision, he felt much easier in his mind about the whole business. He rose.

"You go to sleep now and I'll see to things. It may take a day or two, so don't worry."

"Of course I won't."

Belle was very weary, but there was still a gleam of amusement in her eyes.

"He is an odious little beast, isn't he, though?" she said coaxingly.

"I think you underestimate him, at that."

"Do you? Oh, I'm so glad. I didn't like to feel I'd made a fuss about nothing, especially after so much dreadful trouble in the house."

As he reached the door she called after him:

"Did you read his evidence in the Stoddart case yesterday? He was an expert witness for the defense, you know."

He had read the case—everyone in London seemed to have done so—but he let her repeat the story.

"The prosecution said: 'Mr. Fustian, you were called in, I understand, by the defendant to give, as it were, a counsel's opinion,' " came the faint voice from the pillows. "And the little mannikin smiled and said: 'I'm afraid you underrate me, Sir James. I was called in as a judge.' I think he's mad, don't you?"

"Very likely," said Campion absently. "Very likely. Good-bye, Belle. Sleep well."

Mr. Campion sat before the telephone in his own room in Bottle Street for some time, considering, before he drew the instrument towards him and called Max Fustian.

It was now a full week since he had visited Spendpenny, and he had not yet replied to the note he had received on reaching home after that excursion.

As he had hoped, Max was in the Gallery, and, after giving his name to a minion and waiting for some considerable time, he heard the famous voice, rendered, it would seem, even more soft and liquid by the phone.

"My dear Campion, how nice to hear from you! What can I do?"

Campion gave Belle's message simply and without excuse.

There was silence from the other end of the wire until he had finished. Then a soft, affected laugh reached him.

"My dear fellow," said Max Fustian, "must you mix yourself up in that musty business? It's really a matter for experts, don't you think?"

"I don't know that I have any opinion," said Campion cautiously. "I only know that I have been commissioned by Mrs. Lafcadio to prevent the pictures leaving the country."

"Such a charming, stupid woman," sighed the voice over the wire. "I suppose that in your new capacity you take up the same uncompromising attitude that she affects?"

"Yes," said Campion, adding with unnecessary deliberation, "over my dead body."

"I beg your pardon?"

"I say you take them out of England over my dead body."

There was an infinitesimal pause. Then the gentle laugh reached him again.

"How conscientious, Campion! We must meet."

"I should like it."

"Of course. Well, we shall see each other at the Cellini Society's party tomorrow. We can fix something then."

"The Cellini Society?" enquired Campion.

"But of course—the cocktail party to celebrate the new life by Lady du Vallon. Urquhart has done the illustrations, and the White Hart Press have turned out an exquisite book. Haven't you had your card? I'll send you one at once. I shall get there about six-thirty."

"Fine," said Campion, and added with intentional deliberation, "By the way, Fustian, you needn't trouble about the Dacre drawing. The 'Head of a Boy,' you know. I have one."

"Really?" The voice was plainly cautious now, and Campion persisted:

"Yes. A most interesting little thing. A study for a big oil. There's a sketch of the whole picture in the corner—a crowd round the Cross. I recognized it at once."

"I should like to see it."

"You shall," promised Campion airily. "You shall. See you tomorrow."

23 : *Night Out*

Campion left the inspector and went down to Brook Street for the cocktail party.

It had been in full swing for some time when he arrived, and it was a weary servant who led him up the marble stairs with the wrought-iron balustrade and jettisoned him into the green-panelled double drawing room with the exquisite ceiling and the Georgian sconces.

The noise was terrific.

The theory that the art of conversation has died out in modern times is either a gross misrepresentation of the facts or an Olympian criticism of quality alone. Three quarters of the gathering seemed to be talking loudly, not so much with the strain of one trying to capture an audience, but with the superb flow of the man who knows all creation is trying to hear him.

Lady du Vallon, a crisp little woman with sharp eyes and red elf-locks, rustled across in her burnt-sienna tea gown to shake hands perfunctorily and pass him on with a murmur which might have been his name or a good-natured "Look after this" to a lonely-looking man who happened to be standing near.

This individual did not speak at all, but contented himself by looking gratified and leading the way through the gesticulating throng to the cocktail bar.

Mr. Campion accepted a dry Martini from a scowling barman and looked about for Max. His guide, having accomplished his duty, had disappeared, and the next time Campion saw him he was at the entrance again, and it occurred to him that he was probably his host.

Fustian did not seem to have arrived, and he was looking about for a convenient corner in which to stand, for the eddying mass about him was a trifle tempestuous for a lone rock, when he saw Sir Gervaise Pelley, the Cellini authority, standing a few feet away behind a bank of famous stage folk.

The great man looked a little pensive, but his eye flickered as he sighted his acquaintance, and they waded towards each other.

"In an awful hole," he muttered as he came up. "Look."

He half opened his hand, held surreptitiously low at his side, and Campion caught sight of a handkerchief loosely enwrapping a mass of sticky broken glass.

"Ice cream plate," he muttered. "Don't know what to do with it."

"Put it in someone's pocket," Campion suggested helpfully.

Sir Gervaise looked round gloomily.

"There seem to be only women near enough," he said.

In the end it was Campion who took the handkerchief and handed it to the barman in exchange for a couple of cocktails.

Disembarrassed, Sir Gervaise became his old truculent self again.

"Don't know who everybody is," he said, staring with unconscious offense at the nearest celebrity. "This isn't much like the usual Cellini Society show. Very different. I want to see a copy of the book, by the way, and I hear there are some very fine exhibits downstairs. Shall we go along?"

Campion excused himself on the plea that he was waiting for Fustian, and the announcement seemed to dismiss for ever any claims he might have had to Sir Gervaise's interest.

Once more he was left alone. He observed several acquaintances in the crowd but did not go out of his way to speak to them, since he was concentrating on the interview ahead.

The talk continued at fever pitch all round him. Old Brigadier General Fyvie was bellowing his latest *mot*, which seemed to be something about a daring escape from the British Legion; and a little rhyme, "God in His loving arms enfold us—Contrary to the belief of the Huxleys, Julian and Aldous," was going the rounds.

No one seemed to be mentioning the book, and he never discovered its title, but he saw at least two famous publishers and one rather sad-looking critic.

Unexpectedly, he came upon Rosa-Rosa clinging to the arm of a very famous painter whose tongue was quite as much paragraphed as his brush. He was exhibiting the girl as though she were an unusual type of pet and obtaining the same sort of notice for her. She did not see Campion, but swept on, large-eyed and strange-looking in her bright clothes.

The amount of energy, vivacity, and sheer personal force discharged in a single room impressed Campion again, as it always did at these functions, and he wondered idly how long the walls and ceiling and battered carpets would tingle after everyone had gone.

He found himself waiting for Max in very much the same mood as one waits for a train to an unknown destination: with doubts and impatience. There was too much gin in the cocktails, he decided, and reflected that the fault was a common one among unprofessional mixers, the outcome, no doubt, of a horror of appearing economical.

It was very late, and although one or two people seemed to be leaving they did not keep pace with the late arrivals, and the crowd was growing thicker than ever.

Max came at last, pausing to speak to the servant in the passage so that he should make his entrance alone and not in the midstream of a file of guests.

He stood for a moment framed by the great doorway with its beautiful moulding and sculptured cornice.

A number of people turned to look at him, and for an instant something like a hush swept that portion of the room. If it was not quite the silence of delighted or respectful recognition, at least it showed a momentary interest and curiosity, for he was a picturesque figure.

Campion, who had taken up a position by the far window where he could command the door, had a clear view of him.

He was wearing a grey lounge suit, rather light for the season, and a new and dazzling waistcoat. The MacDonald tartan in silk, a little faded, mercifully, but still brave and gay enough in all conscience, was fastened across Mr. Fustian's slender middle with onyx buttons. His dark face, long hair, and mercurial bearing saved him, perhaps, from looking an ordinary bounder, but they increased his oddity considerably.

His hostess recognized him and fluttered over, and Max, enjoying his little sensation, made the most of it.

Their conversation seemed to be common property, and Campion listened, as did most other people within earshot.

Lady du Vallon had not struck him as being a fool when he first saw her, and now, as she went up to Max, hand outstretched, he had no reason to change his opinion. Only the informed seemed to take Max seriously.

"How very very nice of you to come!" she said, allowing him to kiss her hand without embarrassment.

"Absurd, my dear Erica." Max waved away her gratitude self-consciously and added, with the air of one announcing a delightful surprise: "I've read the book!"

The lady's expression was suitably humble and shyly glad.

"Really? Oh, Mr. Fustian, that's too nice of you. I really didn't expect that. I do hope you weren't too disappointed."

"Not at all." The Fustian drawl had reached the point of becoming indistinct. "I found it quite adequate. Even more—dignified. I congratulate you. You have only to work to be a second Vasari. I think I may say that."

"Vasari? The historian? Er—do you think so?"

For a moment something approaching polite bewilderment flickered in Lady du Vallon's bright grey eyes.

"I've said so," said Max grandly.

The conceit of the man was never more apparent, and someone who felt it must be intentionally exaggerated laughed audibly, only to look uncomfortable when no one else smiled.

Lady du Vallon, who knew that she had only written a monograph on the goldsmith to knit some fifty or sixty woodcuts into a book, clearly felt a little at sea, but she was a woman of courage.

"I always saw you in that rôle, Mr. Fustian," she said, taking the bull by the horns. "As Vasari, you know."

"I? Oh, no, dear lady. Not Vasari." Max smiled.

In his tartan waistcoat the man looked like a barrel-organ monkey, Campion reflected.

"I see myself more as a patron of the arts—a Medici, shall we say. Lorenzo de' Medici."

He laughed, and his embarrassed audience were glad to join in with him and turn back to their own more human and more interesting conversations.

"And yet the damn feller gets away with it!" muttered old Fyvie to Campion as he passed. "Can't understand it. Something fishy somewhere."

Max was still chattering to his hostess with a wealth of gesture but in a lower tone and not so publicly as before, while a thin, shy young man had joined the group. This was Urquhart, the cutter of the woods, and Max was evidently much employed.

As Campion waited he watched the exotic little figure and considered him.

He was puny, ridiculously dressed, insufferably or laughably conceited according to one's temper, and yet there was hardly a soul in the crowded room who would willingly offend him. Moreover, he had murdered two human beings in the past three months; one impulsively in an insane fit of hatred, and one in cold blood after considerable preparation. Also he had got clean away with both crimes. Looking at him now, it seemed quite impossible.

Mr. Campion considered murder.

The chief deterrent to private killing, he reflected, was probably the ingrained superstitious fear of the responsibility of ending a human life, but in a man of Max's inordinate conceit this objection could no doubt be swept away by being decided a necessity.

Then, nearly if not quite as strong a deterrent was the fear of apprehension, but here again sufficient conceit and belief in one's powers might easily make one insensible to this second terror also.

The third difficulty, of course, was the practical side of the business. Concerning the murder of Dacre, Mr. Campion was inclined to think that the astonishing luck attending that affair was one of those tragic chances whose results are even more far-reaching than might be at first supposed. If ever a beginner received encouragement, he thought grimly, Max had certainly not lacked it. The impulsive stab in the dark had come off with fantastic ease, and in the consequent enquiries not even suspicion had ever really touched the killer.

Fustian's second essay, on the other hand, the murder of Mrs. Potter, had been ingeniously carried through, ruthlessly and without a slip, but, Campion realized suddenly, the actual details had been no more neat and ingenious than those of a hundred delicate business intrigues which Max must have carried out in his time.

In fact, once the two main objections to murder had been overcome the rest required merely that subtlety and lightness of touch of which Max was admittedly a master.

Campion frowned. As a possible third victim he found the subject extraordinarily interesting.

It was at this moment that he noticed that Max had left his hostess. He went over to join him.

Fustian greeted him effusively.

"My dear fellow!" he murmured. "My dear fellow, what an impossible crush! No room to breathe or move or talk. Why do we come to these herdings of the little brains!"

He spoke affably and loud enough to be heard by all his more immediate neighbours, who shot him resentful or contemptuous glances according to their humour.

At the same time he was forging through the throng. Mr. Campion partook of another cocktail while Max demanded sherry and, after some little delay and trouble all round, obtained it.

He was in excellent spirits, chatting and nodding graciously to everybody whether he knew them or not. Mr. Campion got the impression that he must be almost universally disliked. His affectations seemed to have broadened to the point of farce, and there were people about who laughed at him openly.

He was standing, glass in hand, his head thrown back, surveying the throng and commenting on it as though he were watching it through a microscope, when Bee Birch, the militant painter of athletes, came up with fire in her eye and a magazine in her hand.

She was a picturesque figure herself in her puce stuff dress and outrageous sailor hat lying flat on her soft grey hair. The tales of her battles were many, and her habit of never leaving a thought unsaid was the terror of her hostesses.

She descended upon Max like a very nice war horse and thrust the open magazine at him.

"Fustian, did you write this disgusting piece of effete snobbery?" she demanded.

Campion, who was wedged in by the bar and Max himself, saw that the magazine was the current issue of *Life and Letters*, and the article was headed "The Coarse in Paint, by Max Fustian." Moreover, there was a photograph of him, very dark and dramatic.

It seemed as if a certain amount of unpleasantness must ensue, but Max was unruffled.

"Dear Miss Birch," he murmured. "Of course I shall be delighted."

And then, before anyone realized quite what he was about, he had set down his glass and taken an enormous gold pencil from the pocket of his dreadful waistcoat, signed the photograph with a flourish, and handed the paper back to her with the hint of a bow.

Rendered completely speechless with indignation, Miss Birch stood silent, and, seizing Campion's arm, Max made an unhurried but purposeful getaway.

"We must discuss our business over dinner. I insist," he said as they came down the stairs together. "One can't talk in a bear garden like that. I can't drink a sherry these days without getting a crowd around me."

Campion glanced at him sharply, but he was apparently perfectly serious.

"We must drop in at my flat first," he went on. "Between ourselves, I want to change my waistcoat. Then we'll go on to Savarini's. I have a table there."

Mr. Campion did not demur. He wondered how Max was thinking of killing him. Savarini's sounded safe enough.

The flat in Baker Street proved to be one of those luxury apartments on the top floor of a giant block.

The room into which Max conducted him, with a murmured apology for his absent man and a languid comment on the servant problem generally, had much of the ascetic elegance of the Bond Street gallery: that is to say, it only just escaped being definitely bare. Its lovely stripped-pine walls were decorated by a single Matisse over the fireplace, and the plain pale green carpet was reflected more ethereally still in the slightly domed ceiling.

Campion seated himself in one of the two chairs as big as Austin Sevens on either side of the hearth, while his host slid back a part of the panelling to reveal a small bottle cupboard.

"If you don't mind, my dear fellow, I'll stick to sherry," he said, his fingers moving deftly among the paraphernalia of refreshment. "But I have an excellent cocktail here, my own invention. You must try it."

Mr. Campion felt a fool.

"I don't think I will, if you don't mind," he said. "I've been drinking all the afternoon."

"Really? Oh, but I know you'll change your mind. You needn't be afraid. I know what these home-made concoctions are so often like, but I assure you I'm an expert. I shan't give you the recipe. I guard that most—most jealously."

On the last word he shook a few drops of poisonous-looking green stuff from a bitters bottle into a minute shaker and fastened it up.

"There," he said a moment or so later as he filled a glass and poured out a sherry for himself.

Campion, leaning back in the Gargantuan chair, wondered at himself and his host. The chances of a man poisoning one in his own flat were remote, of course, but in so serious an issue the most unlikely eventualities were worth considering.

Max was still talking. His drawl was less noticeable, his guest thought, and his languor had given place to vivacity.

"Now the cherry," he said. "This is the one cocktail in the world in which the cherry is an integral part."

"I don't like cherries," said Campion feebly.

"You'll adore this one. This cherry," said Max firmly and with an inflection which gave his guest an uncomfortable sensation, "is like no other you have ever tasted—or ever will."

He took a stick with a red blob on the end of it from some recess in the cupboard and dropped it gently into the glass.

"There, my friend," he said, placing the potion in Campion's hand. "If you'll excuse me I'll leave you to enjoy it while I change my waistcoat for something a little less festive."

Campion sat looking at the glass, conviction of the complete unreality of the whole scene creeping over him.

He reproached himself for undue jumpiness, for seeing innuendoes in innocent remarks. Nevertheless, he did not drink from the glass in his hand but, removing the cherry stick with its burden still attached, sniffed the contents cautiously.

It seemed perfectly normal; a little odd in colour, perhaps, but otherwise very much the ordinary flavoured gin which he had been drinking all the evening.

He was about to replace the cherry when a fleck of white upon it caught his attention. He set the glass down and examined the fruit.

Its secret became obvious almost at once. The hole where the stone had been was now filled with a greyish white paste which certainly did not look wholesome.

Campion stared at it, and his emotion was at least half disappointment. The whole ridiculous business was so unbelievably crude. Was this the man who had engineered the death of Mrs. Potter? It seemed hardly credible.

He wondered what exactly the stuff was and what symptoms his host might expect him to show when he returned.

He emptied the contents of the glass in the back of the fire and watched it blaze. Most of it was spirit, anyway, he reflected. The cherry he placed carefully in an old envelope from his pocket and stowed it in his wallet.

Max could hardly be hoping him to die in the flat, he decided, however much his methods might have deteriorated.

He was still contemplating the amazingly puerile attack when it occurred to him that more than likely Max had no conception of the completeness of his own discovery. He must know now that the authenticity of the later Lafcadios was under suspicion, but he probably had no idea that his part in the deaths in the household had been traced.

In this case was the present attempt so childish after all? Campion shuddered to think of the concoctions he had thoughtlessly swallowed down in the houses of acquaintances.

The subtlety might come later—in the disposal of the body, no doubt. Or perhaps it was one of those slow-working things; a culture, even, although that would be difficult for anyone but a doctor to obtain. It would be interesting to see what Max intended to do next.

Max intended to go to Savarini's, that latest love of the moneyed intelligentsia. That was evident as soon as he returned.

He had changed not only his waistcoat, but his whole suit for a set of darker garments, and seemed very happy.

"Did you like it?" he enquired, picking up the glass. "Not very much, perhaps?" he added, as his guest hesitated. "You don't like bitters? I do myself. They seem to give to a drink what minor disappointment gives to life, just that touch of the unsatisfactory which makes it worth one's going on. It's nearly half past eight. I must apologize. You must be positively starving."

Savarini's was crowded, as usual, and at the little tables, under the famous ceiling painted by Du Parc, sat many who had been at the cocktail party. Campion recognized at least a dozen people, including young Farquharson, the shipping heir, dining with a party. He looked hard at his friend and harder at his friend's friend, and raised his eyebrows questioningly. There was a lot of the snob about young Farquharson.

Max himself had something of a royal entry. Preceded by Joseph, the pontifical head waiter with the sabre cut, he strutted among the crowded tables, nodding at every face turned towards him.

Evidently it was to be a special occasion. The table in the alcove of the farthest window was reserved for them, and as they settled down on the upholstered bench they had a complete view of the whole restaurant. Joseph himself superintended their meal, which appeared to have been ordered beforehand. Mr. Campion decided that perhaps after all he was not expected to die at the dinner.

Max was speaking in his new rôle of the perfect host.

"I took the precaution of leaving the food to our good maître, my dear Campion. We're to taste the Cantonetti tonight, and to appreciate it one must eat the right things with it. This is to be a gourmet's meal, a fitting prelude to the discussion of the Lafcadios."

Campion expressed his willingness to enjoy whatever Joseph should set before them and enquired about the Cantonetti. The name was vaguely familiar to him, but he could not place it.

"The Cantonetti?" Max appeared suitably shocked. "My dear Campion, the greatest gastronomic discovery of the age. The one wine our generation has given to the civilized world. Of course in Rumania, the place of its birth, it has been known for generations, but the disastrous effect of old-fashioned transport ruined it completely. The coming of the aëroplane has altered all that."

He beckoned Joseph, who, Campion was grieved to see, was positively hovering.

"Has the Cantonetti arrived?"

"Quite safely, Mr. Fustian, by Monsieur Savarini's private plane."

"And it has been kept at sixty-five?"

"Sixty-five degrees exactly, Mr. Fustian."

Max nodded his gracious approval. "Bring it," he said. "We'll have it with the omelette."

Joseph sped away like one of his own service boys, and Mr. Campion tried to remember. Among the odd information in the back of his mind there was the word "Cantonetti." It was a red wine, he fancied, and the particular possession of a great family, and there was something odd about it, some anecdote, something mildly funny. He gave it up. Whatever it was it had escaped him entirely.

The dinner arrived, and Mr. Campion privately decided that the cherry in his pocket contained some poison with a delayed action; a botulistic culture, no doubt, or one of the fungus poisons. There were mushrooms in the omelette, which strengthened this idea.

Yes, of course, that was it; one of the fungus poisons. How extremely ingenious, and particularly unpleasant. Also, incidentally, how very hard on poor old Savarini.

He eyed Max thoughtfully as a waiter slid the delectable gold-and-black mass onto his plate.

"You like cèpes, I hope?" enquired his host with something that was surely more than ordinary interest.

Campion decided to play.

"Very much indeed," he said, and Max seemed pleased.

The omelette was just in situ, as it were, when a small procession walked up the room to their table.

Joseph came first, dignified and intent, his eye glassy and his bearing superb. Behind him, and in pathetic imitation, strode a small boy bearing a tray on which stood two beautiful glasses. They were fully ten inches high and lily-shaped, with long, slender pedestals and curved lips.

Finally came the Savarini wine waiter, a solemn portly soul, carrying a broad flat basket lined with vine leaves. In the basket reposed the bottle.

Mr. Campion, the most modest of men, was slightly embarrassed by this homage so publicly paid to his stomach.

Joseph made the uncorking an occasion.

The bottle was frankly enormous, and with its dusty sides swatched in a napkin the size of a cot sheet it was probably sufficiently ostentatious even for Max.

"You are prepared for it, Mr. Fustian?" the head waiter murmured, smiling, as he poured a little of the thick crimson stuff into the host's glass and filled his guest's to the lily's brim.

"We've been in training all day," said Max happily. "Haven't we, Campion?"

If four or five cocktails constituted a training for anything, Mr. Campion supposed he had.

He nodded, and Max raised his now full glass.

"Your health, my dear Campion," he said.

The young man smiled. The toast might have been more appropriate, he thought.

They breathed, savoured, and drank, Joseph still standing before them to give the moment its due solemnity.

The wine was remarkable. Campion found himself astonished. So much preparation he had feared could only herald a minor disappointment, but this vintage seemed not only to excuse but even to merit any amount of palaver.

It was heavier than the wines of Bordeaux; deeper in colour and more soft, but without the weight of a Burgundy, and although completely different from either was yet without eccentricity to alarm the palate.

Mr. Campion, who knew the strong vintages of Spain and the odd wines of the East, found himself unable to think of anything with which to compare it. It was really a discovery, and he gave Max due credit.

"Amazing, isn't it?" His host leant back, a gleam of pure pleasure in his little dark eyes. "The secret is to drink it. Don't sip it like Tokay, but drink it like the divine draught it is."

It seemed such excellent advice that Mr. Campion took it, reflecting that the fungus poisoning could hardly be expected to take effect for another two or three hours at least.

The Cantonetti was admirably foiled by the tournedos and afterward by a curious savoury mess of sweetbreads and chicken liver, and it was not until the end of the third glass when Joseph was superintending the presentation of the flat oat biscuits and the little round red cheese of the Danubian plain that Campion noticed anything odd about himself.

His first indication that he was not perfectly normal was the fact that when Max mentioned Lafcadio for a moment he had the greatest difficulty in remembering who that eminent painter might be.

He pulled himself together. The Cantonetti was evidently much more potent than its sisters of France. He felt irritated with himself and glanced at Max, who had drunk considerably more of the stuff. Mr. Fustian was obviously perfectly sober and was surveying the world with the gracious tolerance of one who has dined wisely quite as much as well.

Mr. Campion jibbed at a word and fluffed it badly, and alarm seized that part of his brain which is the last to succumb to alcohol or anesthetic.

He wondered wildly if he had been drugged in the restaurant, but one glance at Joseph reassured him. That monument of dignity would never connive at anything which might harm the prestige of the beloved business in which he was reputed to have a considerable share.

Besides, he decided furiously, he was not drugged: he was drunk, and moreover he was rapidly becoming more and more deeply sunk into that unenviable state.

Cantonetti. He stared at the bottle. Something about Cantonetti was coming back to him. Now it was gone again. Something—something mildly funny. He knocked over his empty lily goblet and laughed to see the little splinters of fine glass sticking in the cheese.

He pointed out the joke to Max, who laughed, too, tolerantly and with graceful good humour.

And then suddenly Campion was ashamed of himself and angry that he had broken the glass, and he put his napkin over the cheese and tried to change the subject and talk about pictures. Only he couldn't think of the names of any artists except a man with an unpronounceable name of whom Max had never heard.

He ate a wheat biscuit, and for an instant his mind cleared. He remembered everything, the cocktail, the cherry in his pocket, and the whole ghastly business. He glanced sharply at Max and saw that he was looking at him narrowly.

He felt suddenly cold. It had dawned on him at last. The second degree of subtlety again. The old trick which had Fustian's characteristic all along. He had meant his ridiculous poisoned cherry to be discovered: he had laid particular stress on it and had gone out of the room so that it would be discovered, and his victim, poor beast, put off the scent for the real attack.

The real attack lay somewhere in the Cantonetti. Campion wished he could remember. The whole of the main restaurant had become indistinct. He was aware of vast planes of misty, chattering ghosts to whom, he supposed fatuously, he was as invisible as they to him.

Max he knew. Max was just beside him. There was something that Max was going to do that he did not like. He could not remember what it was. It was something that he must stop him from doing. It was all very sad and difficult. He ate another biscuit.

Out of the gaily-coloured fog which seemed to have enveloped the table he caught a glimpse of Joseph's face. He felt like laughing at it because it had no body and because it looked so worried. It was saying something to Max to which Campion would have liked to listen but found it difficult because the waiter was speaking so indistinctly. He caught one or two phrases.

"He did not take you seriously, Mr. Fustian—the strongest head cannot stand it if . . ."

Max was saying something now. He seemed to be apologizing.

"Of course I had no idea—he gave me his word . . ."

Once again Mr. Campion became himself, but only for a moment, for the absorbent powers of one small biscuit are not great.

Although his vision was still impaired, the scattered phrases he had heard made sense and awakened his memory.

The Cantonetti.

Old Randall talking about the Cantonetti—most marvellous stuff in the world if you haven't had any spirit within twenty-four hours. If you've had any, though, or especially if you've had any gin—then, oh, my hat!

Campion broke into a sweat. The world was beginning to fade again.

"If you've had any gin—"

Was the mixture a poison? Hardly. Savarini's would hardly risk it.

Confound this idiotic tendency to laugh unreasonably. No—that was it —Randall had said it made one tight but not ordinarily tight. Mr. Campion fancied he had said "gloriously tight," or was it "fantastically tight"? Well, he was fantastically tight now, and Max was going to do something to him. What was it? Oh, what was it? Max was going to— Good God, Max was going to kill him!

He stared at Max now, Max grotesque and misshapen with a yellow haze round him. He looked so ridiculous like that that Mr. Campion could not think of anything else. He laughed uproariously.

Max echoed him, and so did the people behind the curtain of coloured lights. Everybody laughed like anything. It was all very jolly.

Campion flew out of the restaurant, a most exhilarating experience. His feet did not touch the ground, but he hit the top of a chair once with his knee and knocked it over. No one minded. Everyone was so happy, nearly as happy as himself. They were all giggling except Joseph. Joseph's face was gloomy and shocked, and very humorous floating about without its body.

Max was there close beside him, but not flying. Max was walking rather fast, bobbing up and down and knocking into one, but he was happy, too, and did not care.

Only once Campion remembered what it was that Max was going to do, and that was when in the foyer he suddenly saw young Farquharson's face not a foot from his own. The startled expression on the familiar face sobered him, and he clutched at the man's arm as though it were the proverbial straw, and which of course it very well might have been.

"I'm—I'm in danger," he said seriously, and Farquharson's face split into a smile.

"I know you are, old boy," he said. "In danger of falling down if you don't look out."

Then Max was there again, silly Max in his comic clothes. Mr. Campion roared with laughter at him and flew on.

Outside it was lovely.

The wet streets shone as the lamps raced by. All connections with the sordid trappings of earth deserted Mr. Campion. He was a disembodied spirit, and Max was his mortal guide.

Of course there were amusing incidents. There was the time when Max lurched against him and he fell over on a street refuge, and a policeman helped to pick him up and told him to be careful. And there was the man at the embassy who told him he wouldn't like it inside because everyone would be in evening dress and laughed when he offered to take off his waistcoat.

There was the excruciatingly humorous moment when his aunt's butler in Grosvenor Square did not recognize him at first and rushed away and shut the door when he did.

By and by the glory diminished. Campion realized that he was walking, and not walking too well, either. Then he noticed his hands were filthy from the refuge incident and he had lost his gloves.

He became increasingly aware of Max about this time. Max was hurrying, he fancied. He was not talking so much, either. Mr. Campion began to distrust Max. At the back of his mind there was something that warned him not to like Max. Something most unpleasant about the fellow; he couldn't remember at all what it was.

They were in a darker part of the town now. There were not nearly so many lovely dancing lights. It was familiar, though. Very familiar.

Max spoke.

"Now we must go to see that girl in Watford," he said clearly.

"No," said Mr. Campion definitely.

"In Bushey, then."

"In Bushey, but not Watford," agreed Mr. Campion indistinctly and for some reason which he could not bother about. "How will you get to Bushey? You don't know, do you?"

Max's voice was different, more compelling. It seemed to Mr. Campion that it was hardly a voice at all but rather the promptings of his own mind.

"No," he said foolishly. "No, I *don't* know." The remark seemed at the moment to sum up a great tragedy.

"Ask," said the voice again. "Ask at the club."

This wonderful suggestion seemed to solve all Mr. Campion's troubles. Then, marvel of marvels, there was the club right in front of him.

He staggered to the steps and had great difficulty in climbing up them. Max was no longer with him. But the idea was still fixed in his mind: how to get to Bushey? How the hell to get to Bushey?

He put it to old Chatters, sitting in his box, his newspaper on his knee.

But Chatters was stupid and seemed to want him to go away, although he did not say so. Puffins was a rotten club, he decided. A rotten, stuffy club.

He went out again and fell down the steps, and Chatters came and helped him up, but the fool was not clear about the way to Bushey but wanted to call a taxi and send him home.

There were no taxis, though, and Mr. Campion got away from him and wandered down the road into the dark, and then Max was there again.

Mr. Campion did not like him, and said so, and Max suddenly seemed very anxious to hurry. He gave him a drink from his brandy flask, which was kind and generous of him and showed Mr. Campion that he was at heart a decent fellow.

In the hurry Mr. Campion had to think about walking, which had become increasingly difficult because the pavements now gave beneath his feet as if they were mounted on swaying piles.

They came back to the lights, which did not please him so much now, since their motion was giddy rather than the delirious speeding onward which they had affected before. Also, there were more people about. The theatre crowds filled the streets uncomfortably, and they and the unsteady pavements made progress unpleasant.

Suddenly he was aware of a familiar smell. It was the hot used air belching out of a tube station. The vast bright mouth seemed to suck the crowd down and himself and Max along with it.

In the doorway of the lift some inner sense warned him of impending danger, and he stood still, swaying unhappily, but the crowd thrust him on and supported him with its vast sides throughout the descent, which was like the descent into hell.

Afterwards, too, it swept him along giddily down the steep path to the iron trellis which parted wide open before its stream like the gates of a surrendering city.

Max was on his left, holding his arm, and a vast man in a tweed cap fought his way on the other side.

The crowd was so great that they missed the first train, which thundered out of the tunnel. In fact, Max dragging on his arm prevented Mr. Campion from attempting to catch it, and they, with all those in their immediate vicinity, moved forward to the edge of the platform to wait for the next.

Meanwhile, another lift load of homing playgoers had been jettisoned onto the narrow way behind them, and the centre of the long platform was a solid mass of straining people.

In front of the exits, at intervals where the doors of the trains were estimated to pause, were short iron railings made for such occasions, little barriers to prevent outgoing passengers from being forced back into the train by the sheer weight of the incoming mass, but Campion and his guide avoided this protection and stood midway between two barriers on the very edge of the granite. Before them yawned the track with the raised live rail in the centre and the curving poster-covered wall beyond.

Campion was giddy. The world reeled and swayed like a plane in bumpy air. His intense physical discomfort was intensified by the heat and the breathing, rustling crowd like some great weary animal behind him.

Yet his wretchedness was not all of the body. His subconscious mind was struggling to tell him something, to warn him of something. It made him feel futile and afraid.

Max nudged him.

"Look at that poster. Can you see it?"

He raised his heavy eyes from the track at his feet and stared in front of him.

An insurance firm had commissioned an artist to draw a series of rounded doorways, one inside the other, stretching, it seemed, to infinity. An inscription, *The Arches of the Years*, sprawled across the design, but even the lettering had been drawn to heighten the illusion. The first *T* was at least a couple of feet high, and the last *s* only just readable. The curve of the wall increased the oddly inviting effect, and unconsciously the drunken man swayed towards it.

"Can you count the arches?" Max whispered and slipped behind him, the better to indicate what he meant by pointing over his shoulder.

Campion had to move forward a little to make room for him, and Max's place was instantly filled by another traveller forced from behind. He seemed to move instinctively, since he did not take his eyes from the evening paper he held.

Count the arches. Count the arches. Count the arches. Mr. Campion tried.

One, two, three, and three more, and three more and four, and— One and two more and three and six . . . twelve, thirteen, fourteen— One again, one and two—

He stretched out his hand to help him to count. From the distance came the roar of the train.

One and two and five more and . . . One—

People farther down the platform were looking at him, some laughing, some nervous.

One arch again, and two . . . he must get closer.

The train was screaming now; nearer and nearer and nearer.

One and two and three more . . . He was almost amongst them now—

Campion saw the train, saw the great eye in the cab, saw the whole fiendish business, the devilry of the second degree of subtlety; saw the faces in the witness box, Farquharson, the policeman, the butler, old Chatters. *"He was certainly drunk." "He fell down." "He was not himself." "He was trying to get to Bushey."*

He staggered back and met resistance; more than resistance—force.

The man was pushing him. He was falling. Someone screamed . . .

A great weight struck him in the stomach and jerked him up. It was the arm of the man with the newspaper. The train passed him like a monster and screamed and stood still. There was commotion behind him. Max. Max and a screaming crowd. Max in the arms of the man with the cloth cap.

In all his mental vicissitudes Mr. Campion had never remembered the subject of his morning's chat with the inspector—the plain-clothesmen who had been following him patiently ever since he had left Scotland Yard.

24 : *In the Morning*

"Almond paste," said Inspector Oates. "That's what it is, almond paste. What a clever, clever devil!"

He was standing by the desk in the sitting room at Bottle Street, prodding a sticky cherry with a nail file.

It was past two in the afternoon of the following day, and he had already spent half an hour in the flat.

Mr. Campion was himself again in all but one particular: his naturally affable temper had undergone a complete change, and it was a bitterly angry man who confronted his friend.

"Now you know everything," he said shortly. "I've told you my story, and you have your men's reports, I suppose."

A faint smile passed over the inspector's face.

"I have," he said. "One day you shall see them, but not now. You wouldn't appreciate them. In honest P. C. English the history of your night out makes good reading, especially the beginning. There's quite a lot you seem to have missed yourself. You were tight."

"Tight!" said Mr. Campion with disgust.

The inspector did not smile.

"If ever you get nearer to Death than you were last night you'll be able to steal his scythe," he said seriously. "Harris says the train brushed his sleeve when he caught you, and the resistance from behind was extraordinary. For a moment, he says, he thought he must go over with you. That chap Fustian—"

He shook his head as words failed him.

"He beat me," said Mr. Campion briefly. "Beat me with all the cards in my hand. I was taken in by that fake poisoning, taken in by the old second-degree-of-subtlety trick. It didn't dawn on me until I was too hopelessly tight to do anything except make a fool of myself."

"Beat you?" enquired the inspector. "You're alive, aren't you? Harris and Richards were there, weren't they, even if you had forgotten them? You were dragged out from under a train, and Fustian is under arrest. What more do you want?"

"Under arrest, is he?" Mr. Campion brightened. "What charge?"

"Attempted murder. That's enough to go on with."

Campion sat down.

"I'm still a little vague," he said apologetically. "But frankly, on the face of the evidence, I don't see how you dared do that. As far as I can see, the case must resolve into my word against his. The fact that I had a couple of plain-clothesmen trailing me shows that I had the idea in my head all day. It seems to me that his solicitor could make out a very good case against me for attempting to frame him. He's beaten us again, Stanislaus. Don't you see it?"

"Well, he's been charged," said Oates obstinately. "He came up before Mr. Masters this morning, and now he's detained. I want you to come down and see him."

"But damn it, man,"—Mr. Campion was still irritable—"unless you tell the whole story, which is impossible, there won't be any earthly reason apparent to explain why I had the idea he was out after my blood. As for witnesses of the actual pushing, we all know the value of police evidence in a question of that sort, and as for independent testimony I should think practically everyone on that platform was shoving the man in front of him."

The inspector did not comment on this disquieting argument.

He put the remains of the cherry back into its envelope and pocketed it.

"I may as well have this analyzed," he remarked. "But I think there's no doubt about its being non-poisonous, if not particularly wholesome.

Are you coming down to see him? We've got him at the Yard at the moment."

"The Yard? Whatever for?"

"After coming up this morning he wanted to make a statement, and what with one thing and another it seemed the best place to take him."

The inspector seemed to be intentionally uncommunicative.

"A statement! Good heavens, has he made a statement?" Campion was becoming bewildered. "What sort of a statement?"

"A long one."

"Look here, Stanislaus, are you telling me that he's confessed?"

"Not exactly. At least, I don't know."

Mr. Campion's ill temper increased.

"What's the matter with you this morning?" he demanded. "You're as secretive as a green detective on his first case."

Oates remained affable.

"It's afternoon now," he observed. "Come along down and see Fustian."

Campion rang for his hat and gloves.

"I don't want to see him," he said. "It may be childish, but I feel so vicious that I doubt if I shall be able to keep my hands off him."

"We'll risk that," said the inspector. "Come along."

They went out, and ten minutes later, in a long, concrete-lined corridor lined with many small and heavy doors, they passed a little, hurrying man with a hooked nose and gold pince-nez. He looked both pale and startled, and, shooting a glance at Campion, would have passed by with his policeman guide had not Oates stopped him.

He was J. K. Pendle, the solicitor. Campion recognized him and felt resigned. Max had a legal loophole, and it looked as though he had already found it.

"All right, Mr. Pendle." Oates was finishing a murmured conversation. "In my office upstairs in ten minutes."

He returned to Campion. Just before they reached a door near the end of the row, before which a large, helmetless police constable sat on a ridiculously inadequate chair, two men, conversing animatedly but in low tones, came out. Campion thought he recognized one of them, but the name had escaped him.

Oates had a few minutes' chat with the newcomers, and as Campion drew away he heard his own name and the phrase "responsible for bringing the charge."

"I see." The man whose name and calling he had forgotten looked after him with the same half-curious, half-secretive expression which had characterized Mr. Pendle's glance. Then he lowered his voice and went on talking earnestly to the inspector.

"All right, sir." Oates spoke clearly. "I shan't be a moment. In ten minutes, then, in my office. Mr. Pendle is already there."

Mr. Campion turned to the inspector as he came up.

"Do you know, Stanislaus, I don't think I'll see him after all," he said. "I still feel unreasonable. What good can it do, anyway?"

The inspector did not seem to hear.

He signalled to the constable, who had risen at their approach, and the door was unfastened.

Mr. Campion was still angry. The emotion of personal hatred, which is after all practically unknown among sophisticated folk, had descended upon him, making him ashamed. Slowly he went in to his enemy.

Max was the first thing he saw, the first and the only thing. Campion was naturally observant, and training had intensified this attribute so that whole scenes were wont to photograph themselves on his mind in minute detail, but on this occasion he saw but one thing only, one thing lifted out of its surroundings.

He never knew what the room was like. The heavily barred window, the two men in white coats sitting silent in the shadows, the protected light were all lost upon him. He did not see them.

From the floor all that remained of Max Fustian smiled slyly at him with drooling lips.

Mr. Campion stood very still. His anger dropped from him. In its place came the strange horror which is purely instinctive, a primitive terror of that which is not a right thing.

The creature spoke, soft, slurred, meaningless sounds delivered with awful, secret confiding.

The inspector took Campion's arm and led him into the passage again.

"Sorry to spring it on you," he said apologetically. "He's worse than he was when I left. They found him when they took him some food to the cells this morning. He was truculent last night, so they left him there to cool his heels. He was only taken before the magistrate because they thought he was foxing. He wasn't quite like he is now, of course, but pretty bad. He says he's Lorenzo de' Medici. Says he's known it for some time."

Mr. Campion did not speak.

"They're like that, you know," the inspector went on slowly. "As long as all goes smoothly they get away with it, but as soon as they come up against something they can't sweep aside, a police-station cell for instance, they go over the edge and—there you are."

Mr. Campion wiped his face. He had remembered now who the man in the passage was.

"What will happen?" he asked unsteadily.

"Infirmary—Pentonville—remanded until fit to plead. Waiting for the ambulance now," said Oates briefly. "There's his statement, you see. Five thousand words of it. It took them all the morning to get it down. He confesses to everything: your murder, too, incidentally, and also instigating the assassination of Girolamo Riario, a prince of Romagna—but that was in the fifteenth century."

"When he recovers," said Mr. Campion, "will you press the charge?"

Oates shook his head.

"He won't recover. Did you see old Braybridge just now? He's been in to see him. He was very guarded, of course—all these specialists are—but he said 'undoubtedly genuine mania,' and I saw his face. Fustian will get worse and worse and finally curl up and die. I've seen scores of 'em."

"But it's so quick," Campion muttered. "Yesterday—"

"Yesterday he was a genius," put in the inspector, "and today he's a lunatic. Well, there's not all that amount of difference, is there? Besides, it's not so sudden as you seem to think. I've had his partner, Isidore Levy, down here this morning. Poor little chap, he was worried out of his life. He told us Fustian had been growing more and more peculiar for some time. Apparently he used to drop his affectations in private, but lately he kept them up always. There have been other things, too. Only yesterday he went to a party in a scarlet tartan waistcoat. What could be madder than that?"

Campion glanced over his shoulder at the closed door, and there was something very honest in the expression in his eyes.

"He was my dearest enemy," he said gravely, "but I wouldn't have wished that for him."

The inspector smiled.

"No, old boy," he said affectionately. "No, I didn't believe you would."

25 : *Good-bye, Belle*

Some days after Max Fustian died in a prison infirmary, and the Crescent was dusty and littered with autumn leaves, Mr. Campion went to visit Mrs. Lafcadio.

They stood in the great studio and looked at the picture which had been returned from Salmon's and hoisted into position over the fireplace.

It was a cool, dark interior, the figures subdued and the lighting superb.

Belle nodded at it, her white bonnet reflecting the light from the gallery windows.

"Such a nice picture!" she said. "He meant it to be the last to be shown. I remember him painting it quite well, in Spain. I always liked it."

"What will you do with it?" said Campion. "Keep it?"

"I think so." The old lady spoke gently. "There's been such a lot of trouble through this Show Sunday idea of Johnnie's. Poor Johnnie! His ideas always brought trouble. Next year he and I must have our party alone with Lisa and poor Beatrice."

Mr. Campion hesitated. He was on delicate ground.

"Did you see the—the other three?" he enquired at last.

"No," said Belle. "Mr. Levy and Mr. Pendle and Inspector Oates told me about them, and I quite understood. They're still at Salmon's, I suppose."

She paused, her faded brown eyes troubled and her wrinkled lips pursed up.

"I heard he was dead," she said suddenly.

Campion realized that she was deliberately avoiding Max's name and did not mention it himself.

"Yes," he said. "A bad business, Belle. I'm sorry you had to know about it."

She did not seem to hear him, but went on talking in the same quiet voice:

"The inspector hinted that Tommy Dacre was trying to blackmail him, and he lost his temper, saw his chance, and killed the poor boy. I didn't think Tommy would have blackmailed anyone, did you? He was so nice as a child."

Campion shrugged his shoulders.

"I don't suppose he looked upon it as blackmail," he said cautiously. "As far as we can find out from Rosa-Rosa and—and the confession, Dacre had been paid for the four pictures he had done and had finished his scholarship. He needed money and simply announced that he was going to paint another four pictures at the same price and in the same cottage. That's how it happened. If—if his murderer hadn't had an opportunity to hand at that moment, it would never have occurred."

"And Claire?" said Belle, her lips working. "Poor, clever Claire, how did she offend?"

Campion frowned.

"Ah, she was a more serious menace to him," he said. "She knew everything, you see. She had been a confidante in the picture-faking and had taken care of Dacre in the cottage. She guessed and let the man see she guessed, probably on that day he came to see you and told us about the Van Pipjcr. Her nerve seems to have gone to pieces, so when she got a telephone message from him telling her that the police were making dangerous enquiries she did exactly what he hoped she would do, and so she died."

Belle folded her hands over the little cretonne workbag she carried, and for a moment she did not speak.

"Her poor man!" she said at last. "Poor Claire's poor man! He's just beginning to take a little interest in his work again. It's actually a little better, I think; just a little, so that's something for him. But oh, Albert, the wickedness—the dreadful wickedness and the waste!"

She turned away from the picture, but, before they went out, paused before another. The portrait of Lafcadio smiled down at them. "The Laughing Cavalier's Big Brother": again Campion was struck by the resemblance.

There was the same bravura, the same conscious magnificence, the same happy self-confidence.

A thought occurred to him, and he glanced down at Belle, to find her looking up at him.

"I know what you're thinking," she observed.

"No," he said. "I mean, I'm sure you don't."

"I do." Belle was laughing. "You're thinking of the seventh picture, the one the Easton Museum bought, aren't you? None of the facts have been published, and you're wondering what I'm going to do."

The young man looked startled. The thought had been in his mind.

Mrs. Lafcadio opened her cretonne bag.

"This is a secret," she said and handed him a slip of paper. Campion glanced at it curiously.

It was a receipt for four thousand, two hundred pounds, seventeen shillings and ninepence from a very famous artists' charity. The date particularly interested him.

"This is nearly two years old," he said wonderingly. "Oh, Belle, you knew!"

Mrs. Lafcadio hesitated.

"I knew Johnnie hadn't painted the crowd round the Cross," she said. "I didn't see the picture until the party, as it happened, because I was in bed until the very morning, and then I was too busy to look at it closely. When I did see it properly, it had already been sold and everyone was chattering and praising it. I didn't realize what had happened. It never occurred to me to doubt the Gallery."

Mr. Campion was still puzzled.

"Whom did you doubt, then?" he said, not unreasonably.

Mrs. Lafcadio glanced up at the Sargent.

"Johnnie," she said. "My bad old Johnnie. I thought it was a pupil's effort. Johnnie would have laughed so—hoaxing them all like that—all the clever, pompous people."

"So you said nothing?"

"No. I thought perhaps I wouldn't. So I sent every penny I received to a charity, and I made a rule that in future I was to see the pictures before anyone else. Of course the one this year was genuine, so I thought the last was one of Johnnie's naughtinesses and I tried to forget it."

"How did you tell?" enquired Campion curiously.

"That the seventh picture was not genuine?" Mrs. Lafcadio's brown eyes were bright like a bird's.

"Because of the child on the shoulder of the figure in the foreground. I never understood the technique of painting. I'm no expert. But Johnnie never painted a child on a grown-up's shoulder in his life. It was one of his private fetishes. He didn't care even to see it. There's a mention of it in one of his letters to Tanqueray, that dreadful book which everyone said was in such bad taste. He says somewhere: *Your disgusting habit of painting sentimental, elderly yokels supporting their bulbous and probably insanitary offspring on their shoulders repels me. Whenever I see a bloated child carried thus, its head exalted above its father's, I want to tear it down and dust that portion of its anatomy which is always so adequately but unbeautifully covered in your pictures with the sole of my boot.*"

"I see," said Mr. Campion. It seemed the only comment in the face of such irrefutable proof.

"He wasn't altogether a kindly person," Belle remarked.

"Who? Tanqueray?"

"No—noisy old Lafcadio," said the painter's wife. "But he loved my little John. Poor little John."

Campion had never heard her mention Linda's father before, and now she did not dwell upon the subject.

"Never tell about the seventh picture, will you?" she said. "After all, what does it matter? Oh, dear life, what do all these pictures really matter?"

Mr. Campion promised on his oath.

As they walked up the covered way to the house, he looked down at her.

"Well, is everything all right now?" he asked.

She nodded and sighed.

"Yes, my dear," she said. "Yes. And thank you. Come and see me sometimes. I shall be lonely without Linda."

"Linda?"

"She and Matt were married at Southampton on Monday. I had a card yesterday," said Mrs. Lafcadio placidly. "They found that separate cabins on the boat to Majorca would cost so much more than a special license, and they're set on painting down there, so they married. It seems very sensible."

Mr. Campion took his leave. Belle came to the door with him and stood on the steps, plump and smiling, her crisp bonnet flickering in the breeze.

When he turned at the corner to look back, she was still standing there, and she waved a little pocket handkerchief to him.

When he was out of sight she came in and closed the door.

She pulled the mat straight with the heel of her buckled shoe and trotted down the hall. At the kitchen door she paused and looked in.

"Beatrice and Mr. Potter are out tonight, so you and I will have something easy, Lisa," she said.

"Sí, sí," said the old woman, without looking round from the stove. "Sí, sí."

Belle closed the door softly and went up to the drawing room. The yellow evening sun was streaming in, mellowing the faded Persian rugs and caressing the upholstery of the Voltaire chair.

The old lady went over to the bureau and, taking a small key from a chain round her neck, unlocked a narrow drawer under the writing flap.

It slid open easily, and from its green-lined depths she lifted out a small unframed canvas.

She seated herself and propped the little picture up on the desk.

It was a self-portrait of John Lafcadio, painted in the impressionist technique only appreciated in a much later day. It showed the same face which smiled so proudly from Sargent, but there was a great difference.

John Lafcadio's famous beard was here only suggested, and the line of his chin, a little receding, was viciously drawn in. The lips were smiling, their sensuous fullness overemphasized. The flowing locks were shown a little thin and the high cheekbones caricatured.

The eyes were laughing, or at least one of them laughed. The other was completely hidden in a grotesque wink.

It was cruel and revealing, the face of a man who was, if half genius, also half buffoon.

Belle turned it over. Written across the back in the painter's enormous hand was a single phrase:

Your secret, Belle darling.

The old lady returned to the portrait. She touched her lips with her forefinger and pressed it on the painted mouth.

"Oh, Johnnie," she said sadly. "Such a lot of trouble, my dear. Such a lot of trouble."

FLOWERS
FOR
THE
JUDGE

To My Publishers This Book Is Respectfully Dedicated

NOTE

In criminal trials it is not customary for witnesses to remain in court during that part of the hearing which precedes their own testimony, but in Rex v. Wedgwood in 1931 in point of fact they did.

1 : *Damp Dynamite*

The story of the little man, sometimes a stockbroker, sometimes a tea merchant, but always something in the City, who walked out of his suburban house one sunny morning and vanished like a puff of grey smoke in a cloudless sky, can be recalled by nearly everyone who lived in Greater London in the first years of the century.

The details vary. Sometimes it was the inquisitive lady at Number Ten who saw him go by, and the invalid propped up in the window of Number Twelve who did not; while the letter which he was about to post was found lying pathetically upon the pavement between the two houses. Sometimes the road was bounded by two high walls, with a milkman at one end and the unfortunate gentleman's wife on her door-step at the other. In this version the wife was kissed at the garden gate and waved at from halfway down the oddly bordered road, yet the milkman saw neither hide nor hair of his patron then or afterwards.

All the stories have their own circumstantial evidence. Only the main fact and an uncomfortable impression are common to all. A man did disappear and there were reasons for supposing that he did so in no ordinary fashion. Also, of course, he never returned.

Most people know of someone who lived in the next street to the hero or victim of the tale, but the ancient firm of Barnabas and Company, publishers since 1810 at the Sign of the Golden Quiver, never referred to the story because the little man had been their junior partner on that morning in May, nineteen hundred and eleven, when he bade a polite "Good morning" to his housekeeper at his front door in the Streatham Crescent, turned out into a broad suburban road and never passed the tobacconist on the corner, but vanished as neatly and unobtrusively as a raindrop in a pool.

At the time there was a certain excitement in the grand Queen Anne house in the cul-de-sac at the Holborn end of Jockey's Fields which bore the sign of the Golden Quiver, but, when it was discovered that the ledgers were still truthful and that Mr. John Widdowson, the other partner, was quite prepared to carry on while his cousin remained disintegrated or in the fourth dimension, the natural conservatism of the firm reasserted itself and the whole disturbing affair was decently forgotten.

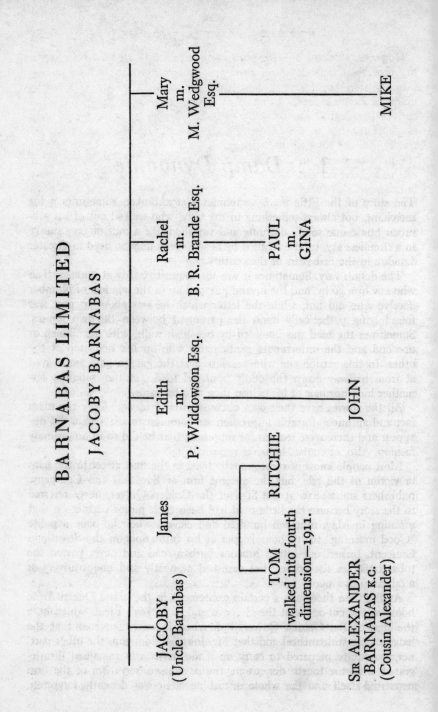

BARNABAS LIMITED

JACOBY BARNABAS

JACOBY (Uncle Barnabas)	James	Edith m. P. Widdowson Esq.	Rachel m. B. R. Brande Esq.	Mary m. M. Wedgwood Esq.

TOM | RITCHIE

walked into fourth
dimension—1911.

Sir ALEXANDER
BARNABAS K.C.
(Cousin Alexander)

JOHN

PAUL
m.
GINA

MIKE

However, although a wonder may degenerate into a funny thing after the proverbial nine days and may well become nothing but an uneasy memory after twenty years, the odd disappearance of Tom Barnabas in nineteen eleven created a sort of precedent in the firm, so that in the curious paradoxical way in which the mind works no one thought very much of it when in nineteen thirty-one Paul R. Brande, one of the directors, did not show up for a couple of days.

Gina Brande sat on the couch before the fire in her big sitting room in the top flat on the Sunday evening after Paul went. "Shop tea" was in progress. This function was part of the Barnabas tradition. On Sunday evenings all through the winter it was the custom of the cousins and Miss Curley to meet together to take tea and hold an inquest on the Sunday papers. Sometimes outsiders were present; perhaps a privileged author or visiting American or, on rare occasions, old Caldecott, that patriarch of agents who had known the Old Man.

When Paul had brought Gina back from New York and the firm had recovered from the shock of having a woman and a foreigner on the doorstep, she had taken over the responsibility of providing the fire and the meal for the gatherings from John's aged housekeeper and the meetings had moved up from the flat below. It was typical of the two principal directors of the firm that they should have snapped up the lease of the house next door to the office, converted its unsuitability into three flats at considerable expense, and had settled down to live in the Holborn backwater, each convinced that they should or could desire no more.

John Widdowson, managing director, senior cousin, and son of the Old Man's eldest sister, took the centre flat as befitted his position, although in size it would have better suited Paul and Gina, who were quartered above.

The ground floor and basement had been more or less wished upon Mike Wedgwood, the youngest cousin and junior director. Barnabas, Limited did things like that in the holy conviction that through minor discomforts their dignity and prestige were upheld.

The tea party was almost at an end, and as yet no one had referred to Paul. The general feeling seemed to be that the gathering was very peaceful without his crimson-faced didacticism.

Gina had folded herself on the big white sofa with its deeply buttoned back and exaggerated curves. As usual, she looked odd and lovely and unexpected amid that sober gathering.

When Pavlov, the décor man, spoke of her as "the young Bernhardt," he did her a little less than justice. Her small-boned figure, tiny hands and feet, and long modern neck would have disappeared into nothingness in the corsets and furbelows of the 'eighties. Her head was modern, too, with its wide mouth, slanting grey eyes and the small straight nose whose severity was belied by the new coxcomb coiffure which Lallé had created for her and which brought her dark chestnut hair forward into a curl faintly and charmingly reminiscent of the "bang" of the last century.

She was wearing one of her own dresses. The firm, or rather John Widdowson in the person of the firm, had not countenanced his cousin's wife continuing her career in England, and she now only designed for herself, and sometimes for Pavlov, in a strictly dignified and semi-amateur way.

The narrow gown, in a heavy dark green and black silk, accentuated her foreignness and her chic, which was so extraordinarily individual. At the moment she looked a little weary. John's weekly diatribe against the firm of Cheshunt, who flooded the book market with third-, fourth- and fifth-rate novels and advertised the figure of their mighty output with bland self-satisfaction, had seemed even a little longer and heavier than usual.

Curley sat in the corner by the fire. Her plump hands were folded on her knee and her very pale blue eyes were quiet and contemplative behind her spectacles.

Miss Florence Curley was easily the least distinguished-looking person in the room. Her iron-grey hair was not even tidy and her black velvet dress was of that variety of ill-cut, over-decorated and disgracefully expensive garments which are made in millions for the undiscerning. Her shoes were smart but looked uncomfortable, and she wore three rings which had obviously been her mother's. But Curley was the firm. Even John, glancing at her from time to time, hoped devoutly that she would outlast him.

Long ago she had been the Old Man's secretary, in the days when a lady typist was still a daring innovation, and, with the tradition of female service and unswerving loyalty to the dominant male still unshattered behind her, she had wedded herself to the firm of Barnabas, Limited as to a lover.

Thirty years later she loved the business as a son and a master. She knew more about its affairs than a roomful of ledgers, and understood its difficulties and cherished its triumphs with the insight of a first nurse.

In the office she was accepted as a benevolent and omniscient intelligence which was one of the firm's more important assets. Outside the firm she was feared, respected and faintly resented. Yet she looked a rather stupid, plain old woman sitting there by the fire.

It was very warm in the room, and John rose to his feet.

"I shall go back to it, I think, Gina," he said. "Tooth's new one is an odd sort of jumble, but I want to finish it. I'm having him up tomorrow."

John always spoke of "having authors up" when he meant that he had invited them to an interview. It was a traditional phrase of the Old Man's.

Miss Curley stirred. "Mr. Tooth is a very self-opinionated young man, Mr. Widdowson," she ventured, and added, with apparent irrelevance:

"I saw him lunching with Phillips of Denver's last week. They were at school together, I think."

John, who followed her line of thought, turned round.

"It's not as good as his first book," he said defensively.

"Oh, no. It's not," Miss Curley agreed. "Second books never are, are they? Still, I think he's got something in him. I shouldn't like to see him leave us. I don't like Denver's."

"Quite," said John, dry to the point of curtness. "I'll finish it," he added. "It may be just possible."

He moved over to the door, an impressive, interesting-looking person with his tall, slender figure, little dried-up yellow face and close-cropped white hair.

On the threshold he paused and looked back.

"Where is Paul? Do you know, Gina? Haven't seen him since Thursday. Off to Paris again, I suppose."

There was a moment's awkward pause, during which Curley smiled involuntarily. Paul, with his hustle methods, his bombast and his energy, while infuriating his cousin contrived to amuse her. John's remark was his first direct reference to the Tourlette biography affair, and everyone in the room recalled Paul's excited, unconvincing voice rising above the din at the September cocktail party:

"I tell you, my dear fellow, I was so thrilled, so absolutely annihilated, that I just rushed off down to Croydon and got a 'plane—didn't even remember to snatch a bag or tell Gina here—simply fled over there and bought it!"

The fact that the Tourlette biography had proved of about the same interest to the British and American publics as the average first book of free verse, and that Barnabas, Limited had dropped a matter of five hundred pounds on the transaction, lent point to the comment.

Gina stirred. All her movements were very slow, and she turned her head with graceful deliberation before speaking.

"I don't know where he is. He hasn't been home since Thursday."

The quiet voice with the unexpected New England accent betrayed no embarrassment or resentment at either the question or the fact.

"Oh, I see." John also did not seem surprised. "If he comes in tonight you might tell him to drop in and see me. I shall be reading all the evening. I've had a most extraordinary letter from Mrs. Carter. I wish Paul would learn not to enthuse to authors. It goes to their heads and then they get spiteful if a book doesn't sell."

His voice died on a plaintive note and the door closed softly behind him.

Ritchie began to laugh, a dry little cackle of which nobody took the least notice. He was out of the circle, leaning back in a chair in the shadows, a quiet, slightly melancholy or, if one felt sentimental, pathetic figure.

Ritchie Barnabas, brother of the transported Tom, was the only cousin who had received no share of the business under the Old Man's will. He had been younger in nineteen hundred and eight, of course, but not so young as Mike, who had been a baby, nor so young as Paul, who was still at school, nor even so very much younger than John himself. His own explanation of this mystery was never sought, but a clause in the will which charged the beneficiary cousins to "look after" Richard Barnabas threw some light on the Old Man's opinion of this nephew.

It was characteristic of the firm, and perhaps of publishing generally, that they fulfilled this charge by supplying Ritchie with a small room at the top of the building, a reasonable salary and the title of "The Reader." He shared the work with some twenty or thirty clergymen, maiden ladies and indigent schoolmasters scattered all over the country, but his was the official post and he lived in a world of battered manuscripts on which he made long and scholarly reports.

Like some thin and dusty ghost he was often seen on the stairs of the office, in the hall, or tramping home with long flapping strides through the network of gusty streets between the sacred cul-de-sac and his lodgings in Red Lion Square.

No one considered him and yet everyone liked him in the half-tolerant, half-condescending way with which one regards someone else's inoffensive pet.

Every year he was granted three weeks' holiday, and on these occasions he was never missed. Only the increasing height of the piles of manuscript in his dusty room bore witness to the genuineness of his absence.

There was a vague notion among the junior members of the staff that he spent these holidays reading in his lodgings, but no one was interested enough to find out. The cousins simply said and thought "Where's Ritchie? Oh, on holiday, of course . . ." and dismissed him for the more important matter that was always on hand.

There had been from time to time sentimental young women, although these were not encouraged in the firm, who saw in Ritchie a romantic and mysterious figure with some secret inner life too delicate or possibly too poetic for general expression, but always in time they gave up their investigations. Ritchie, they discovered, had the emotional outlook of a child and the mind of a schoolboy. He was also not even particularly unhappy.

Now, when he had finished laughing, he rose and walked over to Gina.

"I shall go too, now, my dear," he said, smiling down at her with the mildest of blue eyes.

There was a minute pause, and he added charmingly:

"A delicious tea."

Gina's grey eyes narrowed as she smiled back at him.

"Sweet person, Ritchie," she said, and gave him her hand.

He took it for a moment, and then, after nodding to Curley, grinned broadly at Mike, whom he had always liked, and wandered off to find the door.

The three who were left smiled after he went out, but in a most kindly way. The warm silence remained unbroken for some time. Outside the first waves of the fog were creeping down from the park, but as yet its chill dirtiness had not penetrated into the gracious room.

Miss Curley sat in her corner, placid and apparently lost in thought. Those who knew her were used to Curley "staring through them" and her habit was a time-honoured joke in the office. She found it very useful. Her faded blue eyes were difficult to see behind the gold-rimmed spectacles, and it was, therefore, never easy to be sure whether they were focused upon one or not.

At the moment she was looking at Mike with steady inquisitiveness.

Michael Wedgwood was the son of the Old Man's youngest and favorite sister. His place in the firm had been assured to him since his childhood. He had been barely seven years old at the time of his uncle's death.

As she watched him Miss Curley reflected that his early training might easily have spoilt him altogether. A little boy brought up in cold blood to be a fitting member of any old-established publishing firm, let alone Barnabas, Limited, might have turned out to be a prig or a crank or worse. But there had been mitigating circumstances. The firm had suffered during the war and the Old Man's fortune had been very much divided, so that although the young Michael had been to the right schools he had never had quite enough money, and, in Miss Curley's opinion, there was a sobering quality in poverty greatly to be prized.

Mike had missed the war by a few months and had been actually in training at school when the Armistice was signed. Looking at him, sprawled out in the deep armchair opposite her, Curley wondered if he had not always just missed the big things. Until now she had seen him as an unscathed, untried sort of person. He was twenty-eight or nine, she supposed; kindly polite, good-looking, dependable and quiet; but, although she had understood his popularity, hitherto he had always seemed to her to be a slightly unsatisfactory being. It was as though all the vital part of him had been allowed to atrophy while his charm, his ease and his intelligence had occupied his full stage.

Curley's faded eyes did not blink. He was certainly good-looking. In his full manhood he had more of the Old Man's size and dignity than any of the cousins. The Barnabas features were there, too, the bright, sharp dark eyes, the strong characterful nose and the thin sensitive mouth. Curley's heart warmed towards him.

Now that the suspicions she had entertained for the past few weeks had virtually become a certainty, he had gained tremendously in interest for her, and, curiously, had also gone up considerably in her estimation.

She stole a glance at Gina, resting superb and quiet upon the high-backed couch.

"She doesn't know for certain yet." Curley's thoughts ran placidly on. "He's been careful not to say anything. He wouldn't, of course. People don't nowadays. The passions frighten them. They go on fighting them as though they were indecent. So they are, of course. So are lots of things. But the Old Man—" her lips curled in a faint reminiscing smile, "—he'd have got her. It wouldn't have been nice, his cousin in the firm, but he'd have got her. That was where he was different from these nephews."

Curley's old mouth pouted contemptuously as she considered them: John with his irascibility, his pomposity and his moments of sheer obstinacy; Paul lathering and shouting and making an exhibition of himself; and now the dark horse Mike, who had never really wanted anything before. Would any of them go out bald-headed for their desires, sweeping away obstacles and striding over impossible barriers to attainment, to get clean away with it in the end as the Old Man had done time and time again? Curley did not think so.

Mike was leaning back, his head partly in the shadow, so that only sometimes when the fire flickered was his face visible. Curley felt that he was very careful of his expression on these occasions.

Gina did not glance in his direction, but she was aware of him. Curley knew that by the studied calm, by the odd suggestion of tension which anybody but her, one of the most unemotional of women, must have found unbearable.

They were "in love," then. A ridiculous but illuminating phrase, Miss Curley reflected, suggesting "an uncomfortable state." It was a very awkward thing to have happened to either of those self-possessed, intelligent young people. Mike had been woken up under his skin, Miss Curley saw with satisfaction. The fever was upon him all right. It showed painfully through his ease and politeness, turning him from a slightly austere personality into something infinitely more appealing and helpless, and at the same time somehow shameful.

Of the girl Curley was not so sure. Her poise was extraordinary. The older woman speculated upon her possible attitude towards her husband. Of course she could hardly entertain much affection for him. There might possibly be somewhere in the world a woman thick-skinned enough to be able to ignore the series of small exposures which was Paul's life, but not Gina. His fake enthusiasms and windy lies, which were always being found out, his unconvincing braggartry—surely no physical passion could counteract the blast of these upon a sensitive intelligence.

Besides, what consideration did Paul give Gina? His mind was fully occupied in the hopeless and, in the circumstances, ridiculous task of putting himself over big. Where did she think he was now, for instance? Rushing off on some wild-goose chase, throwing his importance at the head of some dazzled scribbler, to return on the morrow drunk with enthusiasm for his own cleverness, only to be sobered and left sulky by the common sense of his elder cousin.

No. If Gina had ever loved him, a possibility which Curley was inclined to doubt, she could not possibly do so now.

Her reflections and speculations were cut short by an intrusion into the warm paper-strewn sanctuary. At a glance from Gina, Mike had leapt to answer the flat buzzing of the door-bell. There was the murmur of polite greetings in the hall and he returned with the newcomer.

Curley knew of Mr. Albert Campion by repute alone and was therefore quite unprepared and a little shocked when he came wandering in behind Mike. His slender, drooping figure, pale ingenuous face and sleek yellow hair were rendered all the more indefinite by the immense and unusually solid horn-rimmed spectacles he chose to affect.

"Party over?" he enquired regretfully, casting an eye over the dismantled tea-table and scattered chairs. "What a pity!"

He shook hands with Curley and Gina, and sat down, crossing his long thin legs.

"No tea? No party? It must be business then," he chattered on, smiling affably. "Cheap, clean and trustworthy, fifteen months in last place and a conviction at the end of it. Detective work of all kinds undertaken at short notice."

He paused abruptly. Curley's eyes were upon him in frozen disapproval.

Mr. Campion had the grace to look abashed. Gina came to his rescue. "You haven't met Mr. Campion before, have you, Curley? He gets some people down, but most of us grow used to him in time."

"It's an affliction," said the pale young man, with engaging embarrassment. "A form of nervousness. Think of it as a glass eye and it won't bother you any more."

Curley was only partly disarmed. The world in which she lived was besprinkled with consciously funny young men, most of them ill-mannered nincompoops. The difference between the newcomer and the average specimen dawned upon her slowly. In every case the flow of nonsense was in the nature of a protective covering, she knew, but here it was the reality which was different. Mr. Campion had more than poverty of intelligence to hide.

Meanwhile he was still talking.

"As an American, Gina, you have a thrill coming to you. We are on the eve of a real old London particular, with flares in the streets, busconductors on foot leading their drivers over the pavements into plateglass windows, and blind beggars guiding city magnates across the roads for a small fee. It's pretty bad in the Drury Lane vicinity now. I'm wallowing in old-world romance already."

Mike shrugged his shoulders and his dark eyes twinkled lazily.

"I hope you enjoy it," he said. "As a motorist, its romance leaves me cold. You'll hate it, Gina. It has the same effect upon the skin and clothes as a train journey from Paris to the south in midsummer."

"I see. Just another little British trick to entertain the foreigner."

The girl spoke absently, and for the first time Mr. Campion saw that the constraint in the atmosphere was not due to Miss Curley's presence alone.

"Well, ladies and gentlemen," he said cheerfully, "the Professor is here. The *ballon* she is about to mount. Bring out your misfortunes. Lost anything, Gina?"

There was a moment's awkward silence, and whereas Miss Curley's astute mind took in the whole situation, Mr. Campion, who was not in possession of the facts, perceived that he had made a gaffe. Mike glanced at Gina imploringly. Miss Curley leant forward.

"If you three want to talk business, my dear, I'll get my things."

Gina hesitated, and a faintly deeper colour spread over her face. It was the first trace of embarrassment to destroy her poise, and was all the more expressive because of its restraint.

"It's not exactly that, Curley," she said. "I don't know—you might be able to help us in a way—and yet——"

She broke off deliberately. Miss Curley leant back in her chair.

"I'll stay," she said firmly. "It's about Paul, isn't it? He'll turn up, my dear. He always does. All the cousins like to disappear now and again. It's quite a tradition in the family."

She had broken the ice completely, and there was a hint of relief in Mike's laugh.

"A sort of affectation," he murmured. "Good old Curley! You see through us all, don't you?"

Miss Curley eyed him. "I *see*," she said dryly.

"Wait a minute for Mastermind to catch up," said Mr. Campion protestingly. "What's happened to Paul?"

Gina turned slowly towards him, two bright spots of colour in her face.

"I suppose it's just foolishness," she said, "but I asked Mike to get you to come over for a sort of unofficial talk. Paul hasn't been around since last Thursday, and after all, he does live here—and—and——"

"Quite," said Campion, hurrying to the rescue. "I see your point perfectly. Whereas it's one thing to call in the police, it's quite another to pretend you haven't noticed your husband's absence for three days."

"Exactly." She looked at him gratefully and went on talking, the hint of pride in her soft lazy voice making it extraordinarily appealing. "I sup-

pose some wives would have gone haywire by this time, but with me—
I mean with us—it's different. We—well, we're post-war people, Albert.
Paul leads his own life, and so do I, in a way."

She paused wretchedly, only to hurry on again, forcing herself at her
fences.

"What I'm trying to say is, there's nothing really unusual in Paul going
off for a day or two like this without thinking to tell me, but I've never
known him to stay away quite so long without my hearing even indirectly
of him, and this morning I felt I ought to—well—just mention it to somebody. You do understand it, don't you?"

"Ye-es," said Mr. Campion a little dubiously.

The heavy white lids closed over the girl's eyes for a moment.

"It's not unheard of," she said, half defiantly. "Lots of people do the
same sort of thing in our crowd. He may be anywhere. He may turn up
tonight or tomorrow or next week, and I shall feel a fool for making
such a fuss."

"Let me get this straight." Mr. Campion's precise voice was as friendly
as any in the world. "I take it the dear fellow may easily have gone to
a cocktail do, drifted on to an all-night binge with some of the gang,
and finished up with a hang-over at a week-end house-party."

"Yes," said the girl eagerly, anxious, it seemed, to convince herself. "Or
he may have rushed over to Paris about this exhibition scheme he's so
keen on. But even so, I don't see why he should have taken so long about
it."

Mr. Campion pricked up his ears. "Is that the rare manuscript exhibition at Bumpus's in February?" he enquired.

Mike rose to give Gina a light. "Yes. Paul's putting his weight into
it. It's going to be a stupendous affair. Practically the whole of the Leigh
Collection will be on view."

"But not *The Gallivant*, I suppose?" murmured the visitor, venturing
Miss Curley's disapproving stare.

"No, I'm afraid not." Mike seemed genuinely regretful. "Paul put up
the suggestion, I believe, but John vetoed it promptly. The firm of Barnabas is hanging on to its past."

The Gallivant, that precious manuscript of Congreve's unpublished
play, set down by his own hand and never printed even in his unsqueam-
ish age, had come into the possession of the firm of Barnabas very early
in its dignified career. There had been something vaguely unsavoury in
the story of its acquisition, some unpleasant business of the gift of a few
pounds to a starving antiquary, but that was ancient history and half
forgotten.

The present grievance, shared by scholars and collectors alike, was the
fact that, through a certain Puritan streak in Jacoby Barnabas, the late
Old Man himself, the manuscript was never permitted to be copied or

even read. John respected his uncle's wishes, and it remained therefore one of the firm's assets only.

"Too bad," said Mr. Campion aloud, and forgot *The Gallivant* as he returned to the main subject. "No line on Paul anywhere at all, then?" he said slowly. "You don't know where he went on Thursday night, for instance?"

Gina shook her head. "No. As a matter of fact, I expected him home that evening. We—er—we had some things to discuss, and I arranged a quiet meal here for seven-thirty. When he didn't show up by nine o'clock I got peevish and went out."

"Yes, yes, of course." Campion was studying her face. "When you say you went out—you didn't go to look for him?"

"Oh, no, of course not." Her cheeks were flaming. "I phoned down to Mike and we went off to the Academy to see the revival of 'Caligari.'"

Something made Mr. Campion glance at his friend. He caught the man with the visor up and a warning light flashed through his brain.

Mr. Campion was old-fashioned enough to take the marriage contract seriously, but he was also sufficiently sophisticated to know that the nicest people fall in love indiscriminately and that while under the influence of that pre-eminently selfish lunacy they may make the most outrageous demands upon their friends with no other excuse than their painful need.

It suddenly occurred to him that what Gina probably needed most was a reliable and discreet enquiry agent capable of handling divorce, and was on the point of telling her so in the friendliest of fashions when he was saved from the blunder by a remark from Miss Curley.

"Where do you *think* he is, Gina?" she said baldly. "Running round the lovely Mrs. Bell?"

Once again Gina flushed, but she laughed as she spoke:

"No, Curley, I know he's not. As a matter of fact, I phoned this morning and asked her if he was down there. Oh, no, if it was only something like that it would be simply my own affair, wouldn't it? I mean it would be quite unpardonable of me to discuss it like this. No, I can't think where he is. That's why I'm telling someone. I mean, I'm all right. I can amuse myself. I can come down on Mike to take me around."

She smiled shyly at the other man.

"Of course," he said abruptly. "You know that. At any time."

"Oh, my hat!" reflected Mr. Campion, just as Miss Curley had done. "A genuine passion. She hasn't even been told."

His interest in the affair promptly revived.

"I say," he began diffidently. "I don't want to be inquisitive, but I must ask this. Any row between you and Paul?"

"No." Her slanting grey eyes met his squarely. "None at all, at the moment. That's another thing that made me wonder. I saw him for a moment in the office on Thursday afternoon. He'd been lunching with

Caldecott and he said then that he'd come here for dinner and we'd talk. No one seems to have seen him after four. He wasn't in his room when Miss Netley took some letters for him to sign just before five. I know that because she phoned me on Friday morning to ask if she should do them herself, as they ought to go off. John phoned to ask where he was, too. He was offended with Paul for being 'so damned offhand,' as he called it."

She paused, a little breathless, and sat up on the couch, the glowing end of a cigarette between her fingers as she glanced round for an ash-tray.

Mike rose and came towards her, his cupped hand held out.

"I'll take it—and chuck it in the fire," he said hastily.

She drew back in surprise. "Not like that. It'll burn you," she protested.

He did not speak, but nodded to her, his whole body expressing urgency and unconscious supplication. It was a ridiculous incident, so trivial yet curiously disquieting.

Bewildered and half amused, the girl dropped the burning fragment into the hand and Campion glanced away involuntarily so that he might not see the man's satisfaction at the pain as he carried the stub over to the fire.

The return of John Widdowson a moment later restored the trend of general thought. Gina's faithful charwoman, who had returned to do the tea things, had met him on the staircase and admitted him with her key. He nodded to Campion and glanced across at Curley.

"That book of clippings on *The Shadow Line* Fellowes sent us, Miss Curley; do you know where it is? It was a rather ornate little red thing, if I remember. What did we do with it? Send it back?"

Miss Curley considered. Somewhere neatly pigeonholed in her mind was the information. It was this gift for relatively unimportant detail which had made her so valuable in her youth, and now in her age her skill was a fetish.

"It's on a shelf with a lot of other miscellany on the right of the door-way in the strong room," she said at last, not without a certain pride.

Mike, who caught Mr. Campion's expression of polite astonishment, hastened to explain.

"The strong room is a bit of an anachronism these days," he said. "It's a sort of fortified basement in the cellar at Twenty-three and dates from the days when authors insisted on being paid cash down in gold. We haven't much use for it now, so it's used as a junk cupboard for odds and ends we don't want to lose—addresses and that sort of thing. It's a very fine affair. Tin-lined walls in the best Victorian style."

"All very interesting," said John dryly. "Would you like to run round there and get that folder?"

Mike hesitated. The older man's tone had been unnecessarily peremptory and he was in the mood to resent it.

"I'll get it for you, Mr. Widdowson. I know just where it is." Curley was already on her feet.

"Rubbish, Curley. I'll get it. The key's in your desk as usual, isn't it? All right. I shan't be a moment."

Mike strode out of the room and John sat down in the chair he had vacated.

"Fog's getting very thick," he remarked, leaning forward to jab unceremoniously at the fire.

At sixty-three, John, the eldest of the cousins, was as forceful a personality as he ever had been. Campion, leaning back in the shadows, had opportunity to consider him. A spoilt child of his profession, he decided. A little tyrant nurtured in his uncle's carefully prepared nursery. Still, he had met his battles and had fought and won them. Not a weak face, by any means.

Conversation became desultory. Curley never expanded in John's presence, and Gina was lost in her own unhappy thoughts. Mr. Campion did his best to keep the ball rolling, but without great success, since his peculiar line in small talk was hardly appreciated by the elder man. Long silences were bound to occur, and in the last of these they heard Mike's quick steps in the passage outside.

Just for a moment a wave of apprehension touched them all. It was swiftly gone, but the sight of the young man with the red and gilt folder in his hand was somehow reassuring.

Campion might have fancied that he was unduly jumpy had it not been for John, who, after peering at his cousin inquisitively, enquired abruptly:

"What's the matter? Seen a ghost?"

They all glanced at the newcomer. His dark face was a little paler than usual and he was certainly breathless. However, he seemed genuinely surprised.

"I'm all right. A bit out of training, that's all. Fog's getting very thick outside."

John grunted, and, taking his folder, trotted out again. Campion took up the main conversation where it had left off and spoke reassuring words.

After a while Miss Curley left, and presently Mr. Campion followed, leaving Gina and Mike by the fire. Campion had reflected upon the peculiarities of other people's lives and had dismissed Gina and her truant husband from his mind by the time he turned in just after midnight, so that it came with all the more of a shock to him when Miss Curley dragged him from his bed at ten o'clock the following morning with a startling story.

"Miss Marchant, one of the typists, found him, Mr. Campion." Her voice was unnaturally businesslike over the phone, and he had a vision of her, hard, cool and practical in the midst of chaos. "I sent her down to get an address file as soon as I got here, about half an hour ago. The door was locked. I gave her the key from my desk. She screamed from the basement and we all rushed down to see Mr. Paul lying there. Can you come over?"

Mr. Campion put a question and she answered it testily, as though irritated by his obtuseness.

"Yes, the strong room. Mike got the folder from it last night. Yes, the same room. Oh, and Mr. Campion—" she lowered her voice—"the doctor's here. He seems to think the poor man's been dead for some *days*."

Again Campion put a query, and this time Miss Curley's reply did not sound irritable. Her tone was awful, rather.

"Right in the middle of the room, sprawled out. No one could have opened that door without seeing him."

2 : *Funeral Arrangements Later*

There are moments which stand out in clear detail in the recollection of an hour of horror. They are seldom dramatic, and those who are haunted by them are sometimes puzzled to discover why just they and none other should have been singled out by the brain for this especial clarity.

Neither Mike Wedgwood nor Miss Curley ever forgot the instant when the doctor looked up from his knees and said half apologetically:

"I'm afraid we shall have to move him after all. I can't possibly see here."

It may have been that the bounds of their capacity for shock had been reached and that his words coincided with the moment immediately before the first degree of merciful callousness descended upon them and they were able to begin again from a new level. But at any rate, the scene was photographed indelibly upon their minds.

The extraordinarily untidy room stood out in every detail. They saw with new eyes its lining of dusty junk-packed shelves, only broken at the far end where an old-fashioned green and black safe replaced the cooking range which had once been there. They saw the heavy table which took up nearly the whole of the centre of the room, heaped high with books and files and vast untidy brown-paper parcels.

They were even aware of the space beneath it; that, too, fully occupied by flimsy wooden boxes whose paper contents would have overflowed had it not been for the books piled carelessly on top.

The fog, which enveloped the city and now crept into every corner, hung about the air like smoke, giving the single swinging bulb a dusty halo. The body lay upon its back, the head in the shadow of the table ledge and the sagging legs and torso sprawled out towards the doorway where they stood.

The doctor rose stiffly to his feet and faced them. He was a short man, grizzled and of a good age, but still spruce, and his little eyes were shrewd beneath his fierce brows. In contrast with his sombrely smart clothes his bare forearms, muscular and very hairy, looked slightly indecent.

"Where can we take him?" he enquired.

Miss Curley, who took it for granted that the question was addressed to her, considered rapidly. Space at Twenty-three was restricted. In the basement, besides the present room, there were only the packers' hall at the end of the passage, the stock room, or the little washroom next door, none of them suitable resting-places for a corpse. Upstairs the amenities were even less inviting, since the business of the day had begun and the staff was already hysterical.

She glanced at the table.

"If we move those things on to the floor and spread a sheet on the table you'll be right under the light, Doctor," she said. "I'll get a better bulb."

The little medical man looked at her curiously. He knew Paul had been a director, and although he did not expect office employees to have quite the same attitude towards a dead man as a family might have adopted, he was surprised to find an absence of the general tendency of laymen to get the body to the most comfortable place possible at the earliest moment. Aloud he said he thought Miss Curley's a most sensible suggestion.

Mike stepped into the room, avoiding the piteous thing upon the floor, and began to shift the dusty papers to the ground on the opposite side.

The place was dry from the furnace on the other side of the passage, with occasional icy draughts from the door into the yard. Mike worked like a man in a nightmare, his tall thin figure and deep-lined sensitive face looking curiously boyish and despairing.

The doctor bent down once again, and as he worked he grunted to himself at intervals and made little breathing sounds.

Miss Curley returned with a new electric light bulb and a pair of sheets borrowed from Mike's own flat next door. Her face was grim and she moved with a suppressed energy which made the doctor look at her sharply, but Curley was all right as long as she kept going.

It was she who superintended the changing of the bulb, a feat which Mike performed with unwonted clumsiness, and she who spread one sheet over the table and stood ready with the other, waiting for the doctor to move.

The two men glanced at each other. Mike was younger and considerably stronger, but he was very pale and there was sweat upon his forehead.

Doctor Roe spoke briskly. His calm was very comforting. Thirty-five years of general practice had built up an impersonal yet friendly shell which quite concealed the rather inquisitive, ordinary little man inside.

"I'll take the shoulders, Mr. Wedgwood," he said. "If you would grip the feet, now. That's right—just above the ankles. Are you ready? Now then . . ."

Mike looked down at the square-toed brown shoes. They were familiar. They were Paul's. This dreadful helpless thing lying on the dusty floor was Paul himself. Only the physical effort of lifting steadied him. Deliberately he forced his eyes out of focus so that he should not see his cousin's face. Miss Curley's expression was quite enough.

"That's right," said the doctor. "Ah!"

And afterwards, when he looked up and saw them:

"Perhaps you'd care to wait for me outside? This—ah—isn't a very pleasant business."

In the stone corridor outside the door Mike gripped the iron banisters of the staircase which ran up beside him and hung there for a moment, his crisp shorn head pressed against the stone.

"God, Curley, this is awful," he said at last. "Where the hell is John?"

"He's coming." Miss Curley's voice was sharp. "I sent round word to him as soon as I'd phoned the doctor. The woman said he'd been up half the night reading and wasn't dressed yet, but that he'd come over right away. It's a terrible thing. I haven't sent anyone to tell Gina yet."

"Gina? Of course—I say, Curley, I'll do that. Later—not now. She might come down and see him . . ."

He broke off.

Miss Curley's sympathy for him returned and the softer emotion crowning the fear nearly undid her. She took off her spectacles and dabbed at her eyes petulantly.

Mike was silent, his brows drawn down so that his eyes seemed deep sunken and darker even than usual.

At the top of the staircase on the floor above somebody paused and a greyer shadow thickened against the wall over their heads.

"Miss Curley! Oh, Miss Curley."

A girl's voice, tremulous with its owner's effort to appear unconcerned, floated down to them.

"Mr. Tooth is here."

"Put him in the waiting room, Miss James. Put every visitor in the waiting room."

Mike spoke before Miss Curley could open her mouth and footsteps above pattered away.

The doctor came out in what seemed an extraordinarily short space of time. They pounced on him, besieging him with questions, and as he washed his hands in the little toilet next to the strong room he talked to them over his shoulder.

"He's been dead about three days, I should say. Very difficult to be more accurate once the period of rigor mortis has passed. But I put three days as the minimum. How odd he should not have been found before."

For the first time Miss Curley noticed that his eyes were sharp and curious under his fiery brows, and unconsciously she spoke defensively.

"This room is very seldom used, Doctor. It's virtually a safe, you know. It's really extremely lucky that we found him this morning."

"But he must have been missed," the doctor persisted. "Surely his wife . . . ?"

"Mr. Brande was a man of very uncertain habits." Miss Curley had not meant to interrupt with such chilling asperity, and Mike attempted to come to the rescue with clumsy friendliness.

"We had begun to wonder where he was. We were only talking of it last night. No one thought of looking in there, naturally."

He stopped abruptly and as clearly as though he had proclaimed it aloud it became obvious that a startling recollection had occurred to him. He grew suddenly crimson and stared at Curley, who did not meet his eyes. The doctor regarded them both with interest.

"I see," he said hastily. "I see. And now, Mr. Wedgwood, is there any heating apparatus down here at all?"

Mike looked bewildered. "How do you mean? Do you want a fire? There's the main coke furnace under the staircase here if——"

"That's what I'm asking you," interrupted the doctor shortly. "Let's have a look at it."

Together they inspected the central-heating system and the stove built into the tiny cellar-like cupboard under the staircase.

The doctor asked a great many questions and measured the distance between the cellar and the strong-room door with ridiculously exaggerated strides.

To Curley, who was only bearing up under the shock with great difficulty, the performance seemed absurd.

"But how did it happen, Doctor?" she demanded impatiently. "How did he die? That flush on his face—it's very unusual, isn't it? How did it happen?"

"That, madam," said the little man, eyeing her with a pomposity which was oddly disquieting, "I am attempting to decide."

On the whole, it was very fortunate that John should have arrived at that particular moment. He came running down the stairs, his head held slightly on one side and his excellently cut clothes looking out of place in the draughty dinginess of the basement.

He brushed past Mike and Miss Curley and shook hands perfunctorily with the doctor.

"Where is he?" he demanded.

Although no one who actually saw him during those first five minutes could possibly have doubted that John was genuinely shaken by his cousin's death, a catalogue of his words and actions would have been misleading. He moved towards the door of the strong room with little, jerky, birdlike steps, paused for a moment on the threshold and peered in at the sheeted figure on the table.

He made no attempt to enter but stepped back sharply after a second's contemplation, beating his long ivory hands softly together, cymbal fashion.

"Terrible," he said shortly. "Terrible. We must get him out of here. We must get him home."

Mike recognized that tone of quiet authority. When John spoke like that his commands were automatically carried out. The younger man turned to him.

"Gina doesn't know yet," he said. "Let me warn her, at least. Give me five minutes."

"All right. But he can't stay here, poor fellow."

Both cousins had completely forgotten the doctor, and his diffident demur came as a surprise to them.

"Mr. Widdowson," he ventured, "I hardly know whether I can advise——"

"My dear sir—" John turned upon him with raised brows, "—he can't stay here in the office, in the strong room. Can you give me any valid reason why he should not be moved?"

The doctor hesitated. He had no story ready, no actual ground on which to stand. It was a situation in which the stronger personality was bound to triumph. Mike mounted the staircase.

"Give me five minutes to tell her," he said over his shoulder.

As for Miss Curley, she hurried up to her office and phoned Mr. Campion.

Gina was pottering in the big living room, clad in a severe man-tailored pyjama suit, when the woman admitted her visitor. She looked up from the hearth rug, where she was sorting her morning's correspondence, when he entered, and his vision of her, kneeling there in the warm navy blue suit, was the only lovely thing in all that day. He remembered afterwards that her red mules made little blobs of color on the white rug and her face turned to his was radiant with sudden pleasure.

"Mike, my pet! How nice to see you. Too early for some coffee? I'm just going to have some."

Conscious that the charwoman was hovering behind him, he hesitated.

All the old insufferable phrases crowded into his mind: "Gina, my dear, you must prepare yourself for a shock." Or, "I have bad news, I'm afraid." Or, "Gina, something terrible has happened."

Now that the moment had come they stuck in his throat and he was only conscious of her sitting there smiling at him, sane and lovely and adorable by a fire.

"He would like some, Mrs. Austin, please." Gina smiled at the woman and waved her hand to the sofa. "Sit down, animal, and don't stand there goggling at me. What's the matter? Can't we go to the Athertons this afternoon after all? Good heavens, it doesn't matter. Don't look like that."

Mike sat down heavily and raised his eyes to hers.

"Paul's dead," he said.

She had been in the act of placing a couple of envelopes in the flames when he spoke, and now her arrested movement, the shoulder half turned, the head bent, was more expressive than any sound she could have uttered. He dropped down on the rug beside her and put a hand on the small woollen back.

"Gina, I didn't mean to say it like that. Oh, my God, I am a fool!"

She turned to him at once. Her face was very pale, her eyes wide and dark.

"Tell me," she said quietly. "How did it happen? A car smash?"

"No." He paused. She was so close to him.

Presently he heard himself talking in a guarded unnatural way which he was unable to correct.

"He's been at Twenty-three the whole time. They've only just found him. They're going to bring him up here. You—you had to be told, you see."

"But of course I had to be told." Her deep soft voice had sharp edges. "Mike, what's happened? Was it suicide?"

"I—we—we don't know."

"But why should he? Why? Oh, Mike, why should he? We hadn't even quarrelled. He had no reason, surely. Surely, Mike?"

"Hold on, old dear." The man was gripping her shoulder tightly and she leant back into the crook of his arm.

Mrs. Austin set the coffee tray down on the table behind the sofa with a clatter and stood looking over it at them with the shrewd glance of a mendicant pigeon. Things *were* happening! She had been thinking they must get a move on for some time now, but if a man ignored his wife, well, he was asking for trouble; that was her opinion.

Gina became aware of her. She moved quietly to her feet.

"My husband is dead, Mrs. Austin," she said. "They don't know how it happened."

The full arc of Mrs. Austin's knitted bosom swelled. Her long face with

its festoon of chins grew blank and she emitted a long thin sound midway
between a scream and a whistle.

"No!" said Mrs. Austin. "Here," she added hastily, clattering with the
coffee-jugs, "you drink this, dear. You'll need it."

Gina sat in the big white chair, and sipped the coffee obediently, while
the other woman stood before her and watched her face. Mike glanced
at the woman wonderingly. Hitherto Mrs. Austin had been a mechanism
to open doors in his life. Now she had miraculously become a personality.
It was as though a shadow had taken substance.

"Will they be bringing him up here, dear?" she demanded, and behind
her ill-contrived sorrow Mike detected an awful secret glee.

Gina looked at Mike. He was still poised awkwardly, half kneeling on
the rug at her feet.

"They are coming now, aren't they?" she said.

He got up stiffly. "Yes—yes, they are. But look here, Gina, there's no
need for you to do anything, unless you want to, of course. I mean——"

He broke off helplessly, the situation beyond him.

"Oh," said Mrs. Austin, her little green-grey eyes fixed on him with
dreadful understanding, "I think I take your meaning, sir. Oh, well, there's
no need for the poor lady to see her husband for a bit. I'll do all the
necessary."

She crossed over to the girl and laid a kindly crimson hand on her
shoulder.

"Don't you worry, dear. Don't you worry at all."

Mike felt himself gaping at her with fascinated horror. There was a
ghastliness about this practical side of death which overtopped the sum
of frightfulness which had confronted him in that short morning. Mrs.
Austin was kind; sympathy and friendliness oozed from her every pore;
and yet she was enjoying the tragedy with all the shameful delight of
the under-entertained.

He glanced at Gina. She was thinking, her face white, her eyes dark
and blank.

He found himself feeling that she ought to cry and yet being relieved
that she did not. He knew it would never occur to her to adopt any
conventional attitude. The sudden loss of Paul could hardly be a great
emotional tragedy, but it was naturally a tremendous shock.

He was looking at her, trying to divine her thoughts, when Mrs. Austin
touched his sleeve.

"I'd like a few words with you outside, sir, please," she said, and before
the elaborate solemnity which scarcely veiled the exuberant curiosity
which consumed her he was helpless. He followed her meekly.

The fog was not yet at its worst, but the streets were as dark as at
midnight and the waves of bitter, soot-laden air softened and blurred the

edges of familiar objects until London was like an old brown lithograph chalked by a man with no eye for detail.

In the basement at Twenty-three John had taken charge of the proceedings, the doctor hovering ineffectually at his side. One of the smaller packing tables had been taken off its trestles and upon it the sheeted body of Paul Brande now lay. Under John's supervision the whole affair was being managed very decently.

Old Dobson, the chief packer, a bull-necked individual with arms like the forelegs of a cart horse and a red rim round his head where a cap had sat, took the head of the improvised stretcher, while the foot was supported by a Mr. Peter Rigget from the Accounts Department. Mr. Rigget had somehow appeared upon the staircase at the critical moment and, much to his delight, had been invited to assist. He was a squat, insignificant-looking young man, long in the body and short in the leg, with a solidarity which would become fleshy in a few years. It was his misfortune that he looked like the popular conception of the less attractive black-coated worker, even to the pink sensitive nose and the very shiny gold pince-nez. In a rather futile effort to combat this disadvantage he wore his very black hair *en brosse*, and, to his eternal credit, spent much of his spare time in the Regent Street Polytechnic Gymnasium hardening his muscles.

With a certain amount of assistance from the doctor, therefore, he was quite able to manage the task for which he had angled.

Mr. Rigget had been waiting to get into the heart of the excitement downstairs ever since his sensitive perceptions had got wind of it less than three minutes after the discovery of the body, for it was a tragic fact that, in spite of his struggles against his destiny, Mr. Rigget remained what he had been born and reared to be, an inquisitive, timid, dishonorable person with a passion for self-aggrandizement which was almost a mania.

"Not through the street." John made the statement sound like an edict. "We shall have to go the back way, through the garden and into the basement at Twenty-one. We can't have a crowd in front of the office. Are you ready?"

Not for the first time during the past ten minutes the doctor shot a curious glance at the elegant, elderly head of the firm. John Widdowson's complete preoccupation with his own particular aspect of the tragedy, and his utter disregard for any sort of pretence at conventional grief, was something unique in his experience.

He found it all the more puzzling because he did not know the man well and did not realize that it was the outcome of lifelong habit and was nothing to do with the unusual circumstances.

The procession moved off out into the yard through the narrow door between the strong room and the furnace cellar. Once in the fog the picture became macabre. The massive Dobson was blurred and transfigured into a shadow of heroic size, while Peter Rigget, bending forward under the weight, became foreshortened and spread out into something dwarfish and deformed.

The white burden between them widened and narrowed at every new angle which its path dictated, and the folds of the sheet hung limply in the cold still air.

They went down the stone way between the garage and the loading shed and turned sharply to the right, negotiating a little-used gate in the wall with difficulty.

Their progress through the other house was even more awkward, and both John and the doctor were forced to lend every assistance as they struggled and panted up the seven flights of stairs.

Mrs. Austin admitted them with red-eyed reverence as long as the door was open and whispering efficiency as soon as it was shut. She and the doctor understood each other instantly, and for the first time that morning the professional man received that mixture of awe and clumsy but well-meant assistance to which his long professional life had accustomed him.

"Mrs. Brande's quite laid out, poor thing," Mrs. Austin announced in a stage whisper, adding with ambiguous sentimentality, "Mr. Wedgwood's with her, comforting her as only he can. I've told him not to let her come out for a minute or two."

John looked at the woman as though he wondered what rather than who she was, and followed Dobson and Peter Rigget into the spare room, where nearly all the best linen had been set out by Mrs. Austin because a doctor was coming.

Dobson left at once, glad to go, but Peter Rigget lingered until bidden sharply by his employer to return to work.

Meanwhile, Mrs. Austin turned back the sheet.

John went out of the room. He felt he could not possibly be of any assistance, and he found the situation disagreeable.

Mike had only escaped from Mrs. Austin when the knock at the door heralded bigger game. He and Gina had barely spoken when John came in. He stood eyeing their questioning faces absently for a moment, his mind clearly upon other things, but as he sat down he addressed the girl.

"We brought him up, Gina, because he couldn't possibly stay down there."

"But of course not. Of *course* not," she said, her deep voice rising a little. "What's the matter with you all? Of course they must bring him to his home. I'll go to him."

Mike stood in her path and she looked up at him.

"You're not protecting me, you're frightening me," she said, and swung round to John. "Where did it happen, John? Where has he been all this time?"

"In the strong room." He still spoke impersonally, his mind preoccupied.

"In the strong room?" The girl repeated the words as though she doubted her senses. "But I thought that place was kept locked; locked from the outside and the key in Curley's desk."

John blinked at her. "It's all very terrible, I admit, my dear, but there are so many things to think of besides details."

Gina sat down suddenly. The change in her face was extraordinary. She looked haggard, blue-shadowed and years older.

"Mike," she said unsteadily, "you were down there last night."

"In the strong room? Were you really, Mr. Wedgwood? You must excuse me, but this is very curious indeed, isn't it?"

Little Doctor Roe stepped forward from the doorway, where he had been hesitating for the past few moments.

"Doctor, this is Mrs. Brande." John's voice was gently reproving.

The little man was pulled up short. He looked uncomfortable.

"Er—quite, quite; I see. Er—may I say how extremely sorry I am, madam? I am afraid you must have had a very great shock." Doctor Roe's best professional manner was to the fore as he pressed Gina's hand, but he returned to Mike immediately.

"You went down to the strong room last night?" he repeated.

"Yes, Doctor, I did." Mike's tone sounded over-friendly in his eagerness to explain. "Yes, I did. I went down for a folder for my cousin. I took the key out of the desk where it is always kept, unlocked the door, found the book, relocked the place and put the key back and hurried up here. I was only in there for a second but I—I didn't see anything."

There was a long pause. The doctor's eyes had become like John's, veiled and introspective.

"Well," he said after what seemed an interminable silence, "there will be certain formalities, you understand." He coughed.

"Formalities?" John looked up. "I don't quite understand. What was the cause of death, Doctor?"

The professional man hesitated. "I shouldn't like to commit myself just now," he murmured at last. "My opinion will be tested by postmortem before the inquest."

"Inquest?" John stiffened. "Really? Surely that's not necessary in a case like this?"

The authoritative tone somehow saved the question from sounding absurd.

The little doctor stood like a Trojan on the one piece of ground he knew to be firm.

"Mr. Widdowson," he said, "I did not attend your cousin before his death. I am not at all sure how he died and I am afraid I must refuse to grant a certificate."

"And what exactly does that mean?" John's tone was, if anything, slightly contemptuous.

The doctor looked profoundly uncomfortable.

"The case will automatically come under the cognizance of the Coroner as an uncertified death," he said slowly. "I—er—I am afraid I can do nothing more."

He still hovered, his eyes beneath their heavy brows interested and bright.

Gina pulled herself together with an effort.

"Doctor," she said, "I think I will go to my husband. Will you come with me, please?"

She moved quickly out of the room, the little man at her heels.

Mike strode restlessly up and down. The cousins were not communicative as a family and a crisis did not loosen their tongues. John remained silent for some considerable time. Finally he said:

"Inquest, eh? How extremely like Paul—flamboyant to the end."

Mike stared at him, but he went on in a perfectly normal tone:

"Ring down to Miss Curley, will you? Tell her to come up here herself and bring a notebook."

Mike hesitated, opened his mouth to speak, but thought better of it and went out obediently. He had just finished phoning in the little booth at the far end of the hall when the doctor and Gina came out of the spare room. He hung back to wait for her.

The little man was all kindliness.

"Leave it all to me, Mrs. Brande," he said, holding her hand. "I quite understand. The shock has been very great. Don't worry. Leave it all to me."

It passed through Mike's mind that Gina was like that. There was something essentially feminine about her, something that inspired a spirit of protection in the most unlikely breasts. However, there was nothing shrinking about her as she came hurrying down the corridor towards him.

"Oh, Mike, what *has* happened?" she demanded. "What are you and John doing? What are you hiding?"

"Hiding? My dear girl——" Mike was aghast. "You must forgive old John," he went on hastily. "He's much more knocked up than he shows, and after all, the firm does mean such a lot to him that he can't help thinking of it even at a time like this."

The girl placed her hand on his arm and looked up into his eyes.

"Mike," she said, "I do believe you actually mean all this rubbish. My dear, don't you see, the doctor won't give a certificate. He's not satisfied. How could he be in the circumstances? How could you be? How could

I be? I've asked him to report to the Coroner. He was obviously going to anyway. Oh, Mike, are you listening to me? Do you understand?"

"I only know that this ghastly thing has happened to you, of all people," he said. "Look here, Gina, don't get alarmed. We'll fix it somehow so that you don't have to go to the damned inquest."

The girl passed her hand over her forehead.

"Oh—oh, dear God!" she whispered, and crumpled at his feet.

Mike carried her into her bedroom.

It was over three quarters of an hour later when Mr. Rigget came creeping up the stairs. John held up his hand warningly as Mrs. Austin showed the excited young man into the room. It was one of John's peculiarities that he regarded himself as the undisputed owner of any room in the two buildings, and the fact that he was now using his bereaved cousin-in-law's studio as an office did not strike him as being in any way unfitting or extraordinary.

". . . suddenly at his place of business, Miss Curley," he was saying. "Funeral arrangements later. That's for the *Times, Morning Post* and *Telegraph*. The other paragraph Mr. Pelham can send out to the places he best thinks fit. Mr. Rigget, what do you want?"

The final phrase was uttered in such a complete change of tone that Miss Curley started violently. But Peter Rigget was not quelled. For one of the few times in his life he was the bearer of important news.

"Mr. Widdowson," he burst out, "there are two men at the office asking for you. I slipped out through the garden and came up the back way to warn you."

"To warn me?" John eyed the young man with a nice admixture of distaste and astonishment. "What are you talking about? What two men?"

"Well, sir," said Mr. Rigget flatly, cheated of his drama, "one of them's a Coroner's Officer and the other is a plain-clothes man. They only send the plain-clothes man, sir, when it's—serious."

3 : *Design for an Accident*

Mr. Campion sat in the waiting room at the Sign of the Golden Quiver and reflected philosophically that it is often the fate of experts to be called in and left in a corner. The young woman who had admitted him had been very firm: he was to wait.

As he sat in the shadow of the mahogany mantelpiece and sniffed the leather and tobacco-scented air he regarded the room with interest. There are publishers whose waiting rooms are like those on draughty provincial railway stations; others that resemble corners of better-class bookshops, with the wares tastefully displayed; and still others that stun by their sombre magnificence and give the odd impression that somebody very old and very rich is dying upstairs: but the waiting room at Twenty-three expressed the personality of Barnabas, Limited and was solid and comfortable and rather nice, like the dining room of a well-fed mid-Victorian household.

Mr. Campion caught himself glancing at the polished side tables and supposing that the silver had gone to be cleaned. Apart from a few early editions in a locked glass and wire-fronted cupboard there was not a book in the place.

A portrait of Jacoby Barnabas, the uncle of the present directors, hung over the mantelpiece in a grand baroque frame. Head and shoulders were life size, and it was evident from a certain overpainting in the work that the artist had striven with some difficulty for a likeness.

It showed a strong, heavily boned man of sixty odd with the beard and curling white hair of a Victorian philanthropist, but the light eyes set deeply in the fine square head were imperious and very cold and the small mouth was pursed and narrow amid the beautiful fleecy whiteness of the beard. A grim old boy, thought Mr. Campion, and turned his attention to the other visitor, who stood stiffly on the other side of a centre table which ought to have had a silver epergne upon it.

He was a fat young man with a red face, who looked less as though he had a secret sorrow than a grievance which was not going to be a secret very long. He regarded Mr. Campion with what appeared to be suppressed hatred, but as soon as the other ventured to remark inanely that it was a nice foggy day he burst out into the spasmodic but more than eager conversation of one who has been in solitary confinement.

Mr. Campion, who thought privately that all young persons who voluntarily shut themselves up half their lives alone, scribbling down lies in the pathetic hope of entertaining or instructing their fellows, must necessarily be the victims of some sort of phobia, was duly sympathetic. Moreover, his curiosity concerning the business downstairs was fast becoming unbearable and he was glad to have something to crowd it out of his mind.

The fat young man flung himself down in a chair.

"I'm waiting to see Mr. Widdowson," he said abruptly. "I usually see Brande, but today I've got to go to the Headmaster. They're all infernally casual, aren't they? I've been here half an hour."

In view of all the circumstances Mr. Campion did not know quite what to say, but his silence did not worry the other man, if indeed he noticed it at all.

"I expect Brande will be down in a moment," he went on explosively. "Do you know him? A nice chap. Very enthusiastic. Gets all het up about things. He's made a lot of difference to this place since he left the army.

He was in the States for a bit, you know, and then came back and started putting a bit of pep into this mausoleum."

He paused again but only for breath. Since neither of them even so much as knew the other's name Mr. Campion found him quite extraordinarily indiscreet, but he recognized the symptoms and understood that people who are forced to spend long periods alone can rarely chat noncommittally. The fat young man's tongue was running away with him again.

"Brande married an American, you know," he said accusingly. "Extraordinarily pretty girl, I believe. It seems a pity they don't . . ." He broke off hastily and rose to his feet again, glaring at Campion this time as if he had discovered him trying to surprise him into a confidence.

Mr. Campion looked comfortingly blank and as the other retired to a corner, crimson with rage and confusion, he rose himself and, wandering across to the heavily curtained windows, peered through them into the fog.

"I wonder where Brande is," said the plaintive voice behind him after a pause.

Mr. Campion stiffened and controlled the insane impulse to say, "There goes his body, anyway. Looks a fishy little procession, doesn't it?" and turned back into the room just as the door opened and a girl came in.

She was neither particularly good to look at nor possessed of an arresting personality, but she caught Mr. Campion's interest at once. She was small and very dark and affected the coiffure of a medieval page and a small straight blue serge dress with a white collar and cuffs. The effect aimed at was a twelve-year-old schoolgirl but the result was ruined by the maturity of her face, hands and neck. She smiled at the fat young man.

"Oh, Mr. Tooth," she said, "I'm so sorry you've been kept waiting. I'm afraid Mr. Widdowson won't be here today. He's been called away. Would you mind very much if we wrote you?"

Mr. Tooth grew red and then pale with indignation and Mr. Campion was inclined to sympathize with him.

"I'll go in and see Mr. Brande, then," said Mr. Tooth with dignity. "He's not engaged, is he?"

"Oh, no, he's not engaged, but I'm afraid you can't see him." There was a quality in the girl's voice which was hard to define. She was enjoying the situation, certainly, but she was not bursting to come out with the news. Rather, she was being unduly secretive about it. Mr. Campion was interested. Why should the staff of Barnabas, Limited have decided to try to keep Paul's death a secret? The death of a man is a hopeless thing to hide from his friends; after all, it is no little peccadillo or temporary embarrassment from which he may be expected to recover and afterwards prefer not to have discussed.

"Miss Netley, is there anything wrong?" Mr. Tooth had caught the savour of unrest in the air and Campion watched the girl. She did not look in the least confused.

"Well, he won't be here today," she said, not so much evasively as tantalizingly. "I'm so sorry."

A great desire to get to the heart of the trouble downstairs passed over Mr. Campion and unobtrusively he moved to the door. Mr. Tooth he dismissed from his mind. Their interests, he felt, did not meet. But there was something very curious about Miss Netley, something about her personality which was peculiar. He made a mental note of her name.

The wide entrance hall at Twenty-three was of a very simple plan and Mr. Campion had no trouble in locating the basement stairs. He sauntered through the gloomy shadows and stepped slowly down the first flight. He did not move furtively and at the first sound of his shoes upon the stone there was a warning cough from below and three men in packers' aprons slid out of a doorway below him and made for their own domain. The first two walked with their faces averted and the third glanced sharply but ineffectually at the young man's grey figure in the fog.

"Door not even locked, and plenty of visitors. The police will be pleased," murmured Mr. Campion as he wandered on towards the scene of the trouble which had been so neatly pointed out to him.

In the entrance to the strong room he paused. The retreating packers had not thought to switch off the light and the whole scene lay before him, inviting him to examine it. It was not difficult to see where the body had lain, especially as he had Miss Curley's telephoned description of its discovery firmly fixed in his mind.

The bare table puzzled him at first but it did not take a very acute mind to reconstruct roughly what had happened after the body had been found.

As Mr. Campion glanced at the heterogeneous collection of books and papers which Mike had heaped upon the floor his sympathy for any police detective who might come after him grew more intense. Since so much damage had already been done he had no hesitation in entering the room. One more set of footprints in the dust, he decided, could do little harm.

The construction of the place interested him immensely. It was clear that it had at one time been part of the kitchens of the house and its subsequent alterations had done something to enhance the dungeon-like qualities of the domestic offices of the eighteenth century.

The walls appeared to be lined first with some sort of metal and then with asbestos, while the window which had been immediately on the right of the doorway had been bricked up and covered by the shelves which ran all round the walls.

Mr. Campion sniffed the air. It was still stuffy, in spite of the open door, yet, as it seemed impossible that a room of its size could have been left entirely without ventilation, he took the opportunity of examining the outside wall.

Yet fog had penetrated even here and he could not understand it at first until his search was rewarded by the discovery of a tiny iron grating let into the wall directly beneath one of the lower shelves, where a brick had been displaced. The two centre bars of the grating had been broken, leaving a ragged hole some two inches in diameter.

At this hole Mr. Campion looked very thoughtfully. By squatting down on his heels he found that he could peer through the broken ventilator into some half-lit chamber beyond, which he erroneously decided was the loading shed.

He spent some time considering the shelf below the ventilator and restrained with difficulty his impulse to touch the papers thereon.

When at last he straightened his back and continued round the room his face was much graver than usual and narrow vertical lines had appeared between his eyebrows.

At the far end of the room, between the safe and the table, the chaos was indescribable, but, looking at it, Campion was inclined to think that it was the outcome of years of untidiness rather than the result of one frenzied five minutes indulged in by any hasty or excitable person.

It passed through his mind that the term "businesslike" rarely applied to business people. There are degrees of muddle to be found in the offices of old established firms which transcend anything ever achieved in a schoolboy's locker.

The strong room at Twenty-three seemed to have become simply one of those useful places where nothing is ever cleaned up, so that anything deposited therein may reasonably expect to remain in safety until it is again needed.

All the same, it occurred to him as he looked round that the amount of odds and ends which three generations of Barnabas directors had considered worth keeping was distressing when viewed in the bulk.

The safe, he decided, could well be the centrepiece in any museum which an enterprising burglars' guild might establish for the edification of junior members. It was massive enough in all conscience and looked as if it had been built to withstand shell-fire, but it opened with a key, a large key if the size of the highly decorated hole could be taken as a guide.

He was still looking at it when hasty footsteps pattered down the passage and the door leading out into the yard banged. Feeling a little guilty but not really deterred, Mr. Campion continued his tour.

Lying on a dusty parcel of manuscript on the shelf nearest the table he came upon an anachronism. It was a bowler hat, nearly new and only very slightly dusty. Turning it over gingerly he saw the initials "P.R.B." inside, and on the floor below was a neatly rolled umbrella.

Mr. Campion's frown deepened. The problem as he saw it had certainly a great technical interest, apart from its personal side. A man, dressed for the street, found dead in his own strong room, the door locked on the outside, four days after he had disappeared, presented a situation provoking thought.

Campion took another look at the ventilator and wished he might see the body.

A few minutes later he was examining the door of the room and had just decided that at no time had the lock been forced or picked when the pattering feet returned, this time from the courtyard. There was a rush of bitter air as the door swung open and next moment somebody paused and looked in at him.

Mr. Rigget and Mr. Campion exchanged glances.

For some seconds Mr. Rigget hesitated, torn between a desire to see what was going on upstairs and an inclination to investigate Mr. Campion's unexpected presence. He took stock of the stranger carefully, his eyes round and excited behind his glittering pince-nez.

He decided almost immediately that Mr. Campion was not a detective. Mr. Rigget's knowledge of detectives was small and his opinion bigoted. A thrilling alternative occurred to him and he came forward ingratiatingly.

"Could I help, I wonder?" he suggested, lending the offer a tinge of the underhand. "I shouldn't want my name mentioned at first, of course, but if there's anything you want to know . . . ?"

He broke off promisingly, adding a moment later as Campion's expression did not change:

"You're a journalist, of course?"

"There's no 'of course' about it," said Mr. Campion. "What's on the other side of this wall?"

"A—a garage," said Mr. Rigget, startled into speech.

Mr. Campion's eyebrows seemed in danger of disappearing.

"How many cars?"

"Only one. Mr. Wedgwood keeps his Fiat there. Why?"

Mr. Campion ignored the question. Instead he snapped out another. "Who are you?"

Neither his tone nor manner fitted in with Mr. Rigget's idea of the jolly, hard-boiled journalist he had seen so often on the films. He grew crimson.

"I have a position here," he said stiffly.

"Fine," said Mr. Campion heartily. "Toddle along and keep it up."

"You are a journalist, aren't you?" said Mr. Rigget, now considerably alarmed.

"Certainly not." Campion looked astonished by the suggestion.

"But you're not a detective. It wasn't you who came in with the Coroner's Officer just now."

"Ah! He's here at last, is he?" said the pale young man with interest. "Splendid! Good morning."

"Shall I tell him you're waiting?" Mr. Rigget's slender pink nose quivered as he caught a glimpse of this exciting chance to visit, if only for a moment, the heart of the enquiry.

"No," said Mr. Campion. "It wouldn't be true." And, brushing past his would-be informant, he moved quietly out of the room and mounted the stairs.

Mr. Rigget stood irresolute. Some instinct told him that it would not be wise to follow immediately. Moreover, the sense of mingled shame and apprehension, inevitable aftermath of a too hastily seized conclusion, was upon him. The scene of the trouble, on the other hand, was not a healthy spot in which to linger with the police in the house. In default of any other retreat Mr. Rigget shut himself in the washroom.

Mr. Campion hurried up the stairs. His face was unusually blank and there was a strained expression in his pale eyes. He had made a discovery, or at least he had unearthed a possibility which, if it should prove to be substantiated by other facts, was going to lead to serious trouble.

At the top of the stairs he hesitated. His next step presented difficulties. He was not at all sure of his own place in the proceedings. Miss Curley had invited him to the house presumably on her own initiative; therefore he was not working with the police but in the interests of his friends. In view of everything Mr. Campion was inclined to wonder what their interests would prove to be.

However, his curiosity overrode his caution and he considered the best means of getting the information he needed.

He was still hesitating in the fog-laden hall, wondering if he should take the bull by the horns and go up to Gina's flat, when he caught sight of a shadowy figure drifting down the stairs from the floor above. Ritchie, of course; Mr. Campion had forgotten him. He stepped forward, his hand outstretched.

"Mr. Barnabas," he began, "I don't know if you remember me——"

The tall, loosely built man paused abruptly and a pair of astonishingly mild blue eyes peered into Campion's own.

"Yes," he said. "I do. You're a friend of Mike's, aren't you? Albert Campion. You're the man we want. You've heard, of course?"

Campion nodded. The sense of shock and regret which he had missed in the office was here very apparent. Ritchie looked haggard and the bony hand he thrust into Campion's own shook.

"They've only just told me," he said. "One of the secretaries came up to my room. I was reading. I didn't dream . . . Mike went down there last night, you know."

He paused and passed his hand through his tufty grey hair.

"Twenty years ago . . ." he added unexpectedly. "But it was May then . . . none of this awful fog about."

Mr. Campion blinked. He remembered now the other's habit of flitting from subject to subject, linked only by some erratic thought process at which one could only guess. However, he had no time to study Ritchie Barnabas's eccentricities at the moment. There was something very important that he had to find out at once.

"Look here," he said impulsively, "I'm at a great disadvantage. I really haven't any business here at all, but I do want a few words with someone who has seen the body. Do you think—I mean, could you possibly . . . ?"

Ritchie hesitated. "I'll see what I can do," he said at last, adding abruptly, his eyes fixed anxiously upon Campion's like a dog who is attempting to talk: "The body . . . that was the terrible part of it then. . . . Nothing . . . not a sign. Poor young Paul!" And afterwards, in an entirely different tone: "A mild day it was, inclined to be misty. But no fog like this."

He turned away and had gone halfway up the stairs again when he paused and finally returned.

"Go upstairs to my room," he said. "It's right at the top of the house. Forgive me for not thinking of it before."

He went off again, only to turn at the landing to look back.

"I'll meet you there," he said. "Come up now."

Mr. Campion found his way to Ritchie's office with some difficulty. It lay at the very top of the house and was approached by a small staircase set behind the panelling of a larger room. Campion discovered it only by accident, having caught a glimpse of the swinging door as he put his head into the last room on what had at first appeared to be the top floor.

The office itself was a fitting place for its owner. It was very small and was built round an old-fashioned brick chimney, to which it seemed to cling for support. Apart from two dilapidated chairs huddled close to the minute fireplace, the whole place was a mass of manuscripts. They jostled and sat upon each other in tall unsteady piles rising up to meet the sloping ceiling.

A little window through which the fog now looked like a saffron blanket held up to the light filled one alcove, and, save for this and the glow from the fire, the place was in darkness.

Campion found the switch and a dusty reading lamp on the mantelpiece shot into prominence.

He sat down to wait. After the chill downstairs the room felt warm and musty, the air spiced with the smell of paper. It was a very personal place, he decided; like an old coat slipped off for a moment regretfully.

He had barely time to let its unexpected charm take hold of him when Ritchie returned. He came scrambling up the staircase like some overgrown spider, his long thin arms and legs barking themselves recklessly on the wooden walls.

"She's coming," he said. "Won't be a moment. Had to powder her face. Too bad . . . a child, Campion . . . only eighteen. Very pretty . . . typist or something. Good family . . . been crying . . . making statement."

He sat down.

Mr. Campion, who had deduced that he was not talking about Miss Curley, had an inspiration.

"You've got hold of the girl who found him?"

Ritchie nodded. "Terrible experience! Glad to get away from them all. Nice girl."

He brought a packet of cigarettes out of his pocket and lit one thoughtfully. He had replaced the package when, with a word of apology, he produced it again and forced a rather battered cigarette upon Campion.

"You knew Paul well?" he said. "Poor fellow! Poor fellow! You didn't? Oh, I see. . . . Well, it's a shock for everybody. It must be. . . . Dead three days, they say. Can't have been. Mike was there last night. Doctors don't know, do they?"

Mr. Campion was slowly getting used to this somewhat extraordinary method of conversation. He had experienced this jerky chatter before, but in Ritchie's case the man had a disconcerting way of fixing one with his gentle blue eyes with an earnestness which was somehow pathetic. It was evident that he wanted to be understood, but found speech very difficult.

In spite of his preoccupation with the pressing matter on hand, Campion noticed that the elder man used long sweeping gestures, completely meaningless in themselves, and he began to understand why the intolerant Jacoby Barnabas of the portrait in the waiting room had found this particular nephew so unsatisfactory.

Although he was still obviously very shaken, Ritchie seemed more at ease now that he was back in his own little room. He glanced about it, caught Mr. Campion's eye and smiled shyly.

"Been here twenty years, reading," he said.

Campion was taken off his guard.

"No remission for good conduct?" he said involuntarily.

Ritchie looked away, and for the first time the younger man was aware of something not quite frank about him.

"Get away sometimes," he said. "Week or two now and again. Why not . . . ? Must live."

His tone was so nearly angry that Campion almost apologized. He had the uncomfortable impression that the man was hiding something.

He put the idea from him as absurd, but the impression remained.

Ritchie was puffing furiously at his cigarette, his long thin fingers with their enormous knuckles gripping the little flattened tube clumsily.

"Strong personality," he said, his blue eyes once again fixed on Campion's face. "Moved very quickly . . . did foolish things. But to be found dead . . . terrible! Have you ever been in love?"

"Eh?" said Mr. Campion, completely taken aback.

"Don't understand it," said Ritchie with a wave of a long bony arm. "Never did. Paul didn't love Gina. Extraordinary. Mike's a good boy."

Campion was sorting out the possible relations between these disjointed ramblings when there was a movement on the stairs below and Ritchie got up.

"Miss Marchant," he said.

He disappeared for a moment, to return almost at once with a very pretty girl. She had been crying, and was still near tears. As he caught sight of her Mr. Campion was inclined to agree with Ritchie's sympathetic outburst. It certainly did seem a shame that this little yellow-haired girl with the big frightened eyes and demure, intelligent face should have been subjected to what must have been a very unpleasant experience.

Ritchie was already performing the introductions. He was less jerky and more at his ease when speaking to the girl, and there was a gentleness about him which was very attractive.

"Sit down," he said, taking her by the hand and leading her into the room. "This is Mr. Campion, a very clever man, not a policeman."

He peered down into her face and evidently thought he saw tears there, for he pressed a large white pocket-handkerchief into her hand without any explanation.

"Now," he said, squatting down between them on the dusty boards, "tell him."

Campion leant forward. "I'm awfully sorry to trouble you, Miss Marchant," he said. "It must be most unpleasant for you to go all through this again. But you would be doing me and Mr. Barnabas a very great service if you'd answer one or two questions. I won't keep you long."

The girl made a rather pathetic attempt at a smile.

"I don't mind," she said. "I'm glad to get away from them all. What do you want to know?"

Mr. Campion approached his point gingerly. It was not going to be easy.

"When you went down to the strong room this morning," he began, "did Miss Curley give you the key or did you take it out of her desk?"

"I—I took it. It was hanging on a little hook screwed into the underside of the flap at the back. It always hangs there."

"I see. And you just took it and went straight downstairs?"

"Yes. But I've told all this to the Coroner's Officer." Her voice was rising, and Mr. Campion stretched out a soothing hand.

"I know," he said. "And it's really very kind of you to tell it to me again. When you unlocked the door and went in, what did you do?"

The girl took a deep breath.

"I switched on the light," she said. "Then I'm afraid I screamed."

"Oh, I see. . . ." Mr. Campion was very grave. "You saw him at once?"

"Oh, yes. He was just inside the door. My foot nearly touched his foot. When I turned on the light I was looking straight down at him."

Ritchie nodded at her, and with a wave of a flail-like arm encouraged her to use the handkerchief he had just lent her. There was something so extremely comic in the gesture that just for an instant laughter crept out behind the tears in the round eyes.

Mr. Campion proceeded cautiously.

"Look here," he said very gently, "this is going to help a lot. Try not to think of the man you found as someone you've seen in the office, someone you've worked for; think of him just as a thing, a rather ugly sight you've been called upon to look at. What struck you most about him when you first saw him?"

Miss Marchant pulled herself together. Mr. Campion had been speaking to her as though she were a child, and she was a modern young woman of eighteen.

"His colour," she said.

Mr. Campion permitted himself a long intake of breath.

"He was pink," said the girl. "I didn't think he was dead, you see. I thought he'd fallen down in a fit—apoplexy or something. I went up to him and bent down, and then I saw he was dead. He was bright, bright pink, and his lips were swollen."

"And was he lying quite naturally?" said Mr. Campion, anxious to lead her away once the vital fact had been ascertained.

Miss Marchant hesitated. "I think so. He was on his back and stretched out, his hands at his sides. It wasn't—nice."

"Terrible!" said Ritchie earnestly. "Terrible! Poor girl! Poor Paul! All frightful . . ."

He hurled his cigarette stub into the fire and searched frantically for another, hoisting his gaunt body from side to side as he fought with his pockets.

Miss Marchant glanced at Mr. Campion.

"That's all," she said. "I ran out and told Miss Curley and the others after that."

"Naturally." Campion's tone was soothing and friendly. "Where was the hat?"

"The hat?" She looked at him dubiously for a moment, her brows wrinkled. "Oh, his bowler hat . . . of course. Why, it was there on the ground, just near him."

"Near his head or near his hand?" Mr. Campion persisted.

"Near his shoulder, I think . . . his left shoulder." She was screwing up her eyes in an effort of recollection.

"How was it lying?"

Miss Marchant considered. "Flat on its brim," she said at last. "I remember now. It was. I caught sight of the round black mound out of the corner of my eye and I wondered what it was at first. His umbrella was there too, lying beyond it, where it must have fallen when he fell."

She shuddered involuntarily as the picture returned to her, and looked younger than ever.

"On the left?" laboured Mr. Campion. "On *your* left?"

"No, *his* left. I told you. The side furthest from the table."

"I see," said Mr. Campion, and his face became blank. "I see."

Ritchie shepherded Miss Marchant to the floor below. When he came back his mild blue eyes rested upon Campion eagerly.

"Clearer?" he enquired, and added abruptly: "Sounds like gas, doesn't it?"

Mr. Campion regarded the other man thoughtfully. It had been slowly dawning upon him for some time now that Ritchie's disjointed phrases and meaningless gestures were disabilities behind which a mind resided. However, this last shrewdness was unexpected.

"Yes," he said slowly. "It does. Carbon monoxide, in fact. Of course one can't possibly tell for certain without taking a blood test but Miss Marchant's description does indicate it. Besides, it fits in damnably with one or two things I noticed downstairs."

Ritchie heaved a sigh of relief. "Garage next door to the strong room," he remarked. "Fumes must have percolated somehow. Accident. Poor Paul. . . ."

Mr. Campion said nothing.

Ritchie clambered into the chair Miss Marchant had vacated and sat poring over the fire, his immense bony hands held out to the tiny blaze.

"Carbon monoxide," he said. "How much of it will kill?"

Mr. Campion, who had been reflecting upon the problem for some time, gave a considered opinion.

"I'm not sure of the exact proportion," he said, "but it's something very small . . . just over four per cent in the atmosphere in some cases, I believe. The trouble with the stuff is that it's so insidious. You don't realize you're going under until you've gone, if you see what I mean. The exhaust of a car is pretty nearly the pure stuff."

Ritchie nodded sagaciously. "Dangerous," he said. "No ventilation down there with the door shut."

". . . And locked." The words were on the tip of Mr. Campion's tongue, but he did not utter them.

Ritchie continued. "Shouldn't have been there," he said. "Paul always poking about out of hours. Silly fellow . . . sorry he's dead."

The last remark was not put in as an afterthought. Every line of Ritchie's gaunt body indicated his regret, and his tone was as expressive as the most elaborate speech.

"I didn't know him well," said Campion. "I met him at most four or five times."

Ritchie shook his head. "Difficult chap," he remarked. "Great egoist. Too dominant. But good fellow. Impulsive. Not in love with Gina. Dreadful accident."

Mr. Campion's mind wandered to the little grating under the shelf in the strong room, and presently, when he and the other man went down the stairs together, it was still in his thoughts.

Ritchie was frankly overcome by the horror of the accident. The locked door and the time of death were both points that he had evidently shelved as minor details, while the significance of the position of the hat and umbrella had escaped him entirely.

As they crossed the hall, two policemen in plain clothes came up from the basement. Campion recognized one of them as Detective-Sergeant Pillow of the special branch. The man glanced up as he passed, and nodded, satisfaction in his little black eyes.

As Campion caught sight of the curious burden he carried, his heart missed a beat. Carefully wrapped round the middle with a dark handkerchief, its ends looped into drooping bows and its protected centre clasped in the Sergeant's stubby hand, was a length of rubber tubing such as is sometimes used for the improvisation of a shower-bath. Sergeant Pillow carried it as though it were his dearest possession.

4 : Relations

To Gordon Roe, Esq., Surgeon.

London.
To wit.
Sir,

By virtue of this my Order as one of His Majesty's Coroners for the County of London you are hereby required to be and appear before me and the jury on Tuesday the ninth day of February at eleven o'clock in the forenoon at the Court in the Parish of St. Joan's, Holborn, and then and there to give evidence on His Majesty's behalf touching the death of Paul Redfern Brande and to make or assist in making a post-mortem examination of the viscera of the Head, Chest and Abdomen of the body of the said Paul Redfern Brande without an analysis and report thereon at the said inquest. And herein fail not at your peril.

Dated the second day of February, 1931.

P. J. Salley,
Coroner.

Doctor Roe patted his pocket absently as he entered the hall of Gina's flat on the Friday following the discovery of Paul Brande's body and the Coroner's summons crackled responsively. The little doctor was following the anxious Mrs. Austin down the passage to the studio with a certain amount of curiosity.

"I really think you ought to have a look at her, Doctor." The charwoman spoke in a hushed voice and without looking round as she ploughed over the thick carpet in her soft shoes. "Not a mite of sleep she hasn't had. You can see it in her face. I said to her I said, 'You have the doctor, dear. After all, he can't make you worse nor what you are at present.' And she said to me, 'I think I will, Mrs. Austin.' 'Lie down,' I said, but she wouldn't, and there she is sitting in front of the fire like a lily."

Her speech lasted until they reached the door, but just before she entered she laid a plump, damp hand upon his own and looked up at him, a gleam of conspiratorial excitement in her eyes.

"Have they found out anything yet?"

Doctor Roe coughed. "I really don't know, Mrs. Austin," he said pleasantly. "I'm not a policeman, you know. Now where is our patient?"

Mrs. Austin raised her eyebrows, and, with many ostentatious precautions against noise, tiptoed heavily into the room.

"Here's the doctor, dear," she said in a sepulchral whisper which might well have given her employer a heart attack had their entry been really quiet.

Gina was sitting in one of the big white armchairs in a tailored black wrapper which contrasted with the pallor of her face and the brilliance of her eyes and hair. She made a pathetic attempt at a smile.

"I'm glad to see you, Doctor," she said. "Won't you sit down? That'll do, Mrs. Austin."

That good lady left the room, making it plain that she did so against her better judgment. Doctor Roe remained upon his feet. His professional personality inclined to heartiness and was seen at its best astride a hearth rug.

"Well, now, Mrs. Brande," he said, "what's the trouble? Not sleeping, eh? Well, of course, that's not to be wondered at, but you can help yourself much better than anyone else can, you know. You need courage, young lady, great courage. Any other symptoms? Eating well?"

Gina leant forward, her small white hands clasped together, her elbows resting on her knees.

"Doctor," she said, "what's happened about my husband?"

The little medical man stiffened, and something that was half alarm, half resentment, flickered in his eyes.

"I came here to discuss your health, Mrs. Brande," he said warningly.

"Oh, Doctor . . ."—the soft New England accent slurred the words— ". . . I don't mean to offend you. I don't understand professional etiquette and that sort of thing, but can't you see that the thing that's making me ill is not knowing what's going to happen—what is happening. What are the police doing? Why was the inquest on Tuesday adjourned for seven days? What do they expect to learn from the post-mortem?"

"My dear lady . . ." Doctor Roe's voice conveyed that his sense of decorum was outraged . . . "I'm a medical practitioner. I'm not a detective. You sent for me to ask advice about your health, and I'm prepared to give it to you. I can see you want sleep and I can prescribe something that will see to that. But I don't know anything about your other trouble, and if I did I couldn't discuss it. It would be most improper."

"But even if you're a doctor, you're human." The girl's voice was quivering. "Don't you see you're the only person who knows what the police are thinking? Just imagine my position. . . . My husband disappeared ten days ago. Four days later he was found dead. Without any warning, without any explanation, the police arrived. My husband's body was taken away. I was summoned to appear at an inquest the next day. It lasted five minutes at the outside. My cousin-in-law gave evidence of identification, and the Coroner adjourned for seven days. I've been subpœnaed for the second part of the inquest, and of course I shall go. Yet when I went out yesterday I was followed."

She paused, and the nervous tension behind her eyes was vivid and painful.

"If only they said *something!*" she said. "If only they told me! It's being kept in the dark that's getting on my nerves. Why are they watching me? Why should they think that I might run away? What's happening?"

Doctor Roe was not entirely impervious to the appeal of a very pretty woman, but there is perhaps no professional man who must protect himself more carefully than the physician.

"I'm very sorry for you," he said quite genuinely, "but I can't tell you anything about the police. They have their own methods and go about their affairs in their own mysterious way."

He frowned and looked slightly uncomfortable. Doubtless the recollection of his unpleasant morning's work with the police surgeon in the mortuary had returned to him. But he pocketed his sympathy. Some things were safe, others were not. He attempted to be consoling and at the same time noncommittal.

"I shouldn't worry," he said. "You have yourself to think of now, you know, and we mustn't have your health letting you down. Let me have your wrist, please."

He felt her pulse and compared it with his watch.

"A little excited," he announced, "but not seriously. I'll send you round something to make you sleep. You'll feel very much better in the morning. This period of suspense is very trying, I know, but you must try and pull yourself together. You've had a very great shock—a very great shock indeed—and your grief has naturally worn you down?"

The inquisitive soul which lurked behind the physician in Doctor Gordon Roe prompted the faint question contained in the last remark, and the girl responded to it without thinking.

"It's not grief," she said. "Not real grief. I'm sorry for Paul, but I was not in love with him."

Doctor Roe started. Even his most mischievous and unworthy hopes had not included a statement quite so damaging. He was both shocked and frightened by it.

"Come, come, you don't mean that, Mrs. Brande," he said peremptorily. "You're overwrought."

The girl looked at him in surprise for a moment and then her nerves seemed suddenly to fail her altogether.

"How horrible you all are!" she said explosively. "If I'd said that before my husband died you wouldn't have thought anything of it—no one would —and yet it's just as true now as it was then. Now I've only got to say that I didn't love my husband and you look at me as though you thought I'd murdered him."

Doctor Roe was panic-stricken.

"I—I must protest. Really!" he murmured into his collar, and made for the door, from which he summoned Mrs. Austin. "Get your mistress to bed," he ordered so sharply that she wondered whether he had divined that she had listened outside the door, and, having done what he considered was his duty, made his escape.

Meanwhile in a small flat over the police station in Bottle Street, Piccadilly, Mr. Campion was sitting at his desk attempting to write letters and at the same time to take a comparatively intelligent share in a conversation which he was holding with someone in the room next door.

"It's goin' to be a nasty case," a thick, inexpressibly melancholy voice announced bitterly. "Anyone can see that with 'alf an eye. You keep out of it. You don't want to get notorious. The way your name's been gettin' about lately you're a positive publicity 'ound."

"I resent that," said Mr. Campion, writing "hound" irrelevantly in the midst of a note to his bank manager and crossing it out again. "These people are my friends, you know."

"All the more reason you want to keep away," said the voice, adopting this time a flavour of worldly wisdom. "Friends'll ask you to do things what strangers would never dare. It's a sex crime, I suppose you know that?"

"What?" said Mr. Campion. He had removed his spectacles, which somewhat obscured his vision when writing, but now he replaced them and laid down his pen.

"Sex crime," said the voice from within. "You've bin pretty lucky so far keepin' out of that sort of degradation, but you won't look so pretty trailin' about with the mud of the cheap Press all over you. I couldn't associate meself with you after that, for one thing. You'll lose all your old friends."

"Lugg," said Mr. Campion sternly. "Come in here."

There was a rumble in the other room as though a minor earthquake had disturbed it, and, preceded by the sound of deep breathing, Magersfontein Lugg surged into the room.

His girth was increasing with the years and with it his melancholy. He had also achieved a certain sartorial elegance without losing his unconventionality in that direction. At the moment he was clad in what appeared to be the hind legs of a black elephant, a spotless but collarless boiled shirt and a black velvet jacket.

His employer surveyed him coldly. "The *vie de bohême*, I see," he observed. "How are the tiny hands?"

Mr. Lugg shook his head ponderously. "Turn it aside with a light word if you like," he said mournfully, "but here we are, all respectable, nice, good class and the first nasty eruption that breaks out you're in it up to the neck."

"Where did you get that coat?"

"'Ad it made for me," said Mr. Lugg, with intent to snub. "It's a gentleman's 'ouse coat and very smart. All the wear just now. I bought it because I see in the paper that a certain important relative of yours is not too well, and if anything 'appened to 'im and you were suddenly called to take your place in the world I should like to be prepared."

"Yes, well, of course, you're revolting," said Mr. Campion, getting up. "Ten years ago you climbed up the side of a three-story house with the agility of a monkey, let yourself through a skylight, opened a safe and got away as clean as a whistle and now look at you. You couldn't steal a bag of sweets from a two-year-old in a pram."

"I shouldn't want to, I hope," said Mr. Lugg, with dignity. "Besides," he added, lowering his puffy white lids over his little black eyes and achieving a superbly virtuous expression, "them things all belong to the past. It's the future we've got to think of, and that's why I do 'ope you'll steer clear of anything with a nasty flavour. It looked very bad in the evening newspapers and not at all the sort of thing you want to get our names mixed up with."

"You've gone soft, Lugg," said Campion, with regret. "I haven't given you enough work lately. I don't think there's much in this case for you, either."

"I'm glad to 'ear it." Mr. Lugg was positive. "When they was all talking about it at the club, discussin' the details, I said to myself, 'I do 'ope I keep out of this.' It isn't even as though we're on the side of the police."

Mr. Campion perched himself on the edge of the desk and wrapped the folds of his thin and rather dilapidated silk dressing-gown around his bony form.

"When you say 'the club,' do you mean that pub in Wardour Street?" he enquired.

A wooden expression crept into Mr. Lugg's face.

"No. I don't go there any more. I took exception to some of the members. Very low type of person, they were. If you want to know, I go to a very quiet, respectable little place in a mews up Mayfair way. There are several nice people there in me own line of business."

"Gentlemen's gentlemen, I suppose?" said Mr. Campion sarcastically.

"Exactly," agreed Mr. Lugg belligerently. "And why not? A nice superior class of person I meet and I hear all the gossip."

"I'm disgusted with you." Campion sounded genuine. "You make me sick. I've a good mind to sack you."

"You try," said Mr. Lugg, with a return of his old fire. "I'd like to know where you'd be—as helpless as a babe unborn. I've trained you not to be able to do without me. You drop the case and we won't say anything more about it. Nothin' could be fairer than that.

"After all," he went on persuasively as he noticed no sign of capitulation in Mr. Campion's expression, "once sex rears its ugly 'ead it's time to steer clear. You know that as well as I do."

Mr. Campion's mystified expression deepened.

"You're not trying to be funny?" he suggested.

"Do I ever try to be funny?" said Mr. Lugg, with justifiable reproach. "It's not a funny subjec'."

Campion stirred. "Where did you get this—this sex idea?" he said. "I thought the papers were very reticent. They must be, of course, the law of libel being what it is."

"Readin' between the lines," said Mr. Lugg darkly. "Libel or no libel, if you reads the newspapers properly it's always clear what's 'appened. It's not what they say: it's the way they say it."

Campion frowned. "There's a lot of truth in that, unfortunately," he observed. "After your little mug between the lines, what do you deduce?"

"The wife did it, of course. They published 'er photograph. Did you see it? Nice-lookin' little bit—just the type."

Mr. Campion shuddered. "Lugg, you've done it this time," he said. "Get out."

Before the vigour of the command Mr. Lugg was abashed.

"No offence, Cock," he said hastily. "I don't know anything about the inside story. I'm only tellin' you how it appears to the man in the street. That's what you want to know, isn't it?"

Campion was silent for a moment, a slightly less vacuous expression than usual upon his pale, inoffensive face.

"I know these people, Lugg," he said at last. "They're all right, I tell you. Charming, straightforward, decent people. Mrs. Brande is one of the most delightful women I've ever met, and yet you see, apart from the tragedy of losing her husband, her portrait appears in the newspapers and the opinion in the Mayfair pubs is that she did him in."

Mr. Lugg was rebuked, but it was not his temperament to admit the fact.

"The tragedy of losin' 'er 'usband?" he said contemptuously. "That's good, that is! Hadn't the fellow been missin' since the Thursday and was found dead in the office next door on the Monday? That's not my idea of a nice lovin' wife. Lets 'er old man be missin' three or four days and doesn't say a word."

"She sent for me," said Mr. Campion.

"Ho, she did, did she?" Lugg was interested. "That makes all the difference. Still, it didn't come out in the Press, did it? So how was I to know, or anybody else? Who do you think done it?"

Mr. Campion passed his hand over his fair hair and his eyes clouded.

"I don't know, Lugg," he said. "I don't know at all. I'm on the inside, you see, and yet you and your pals at the club have fixed the guilt already."

"Ah," said Mr. Lugg, "and I shouldn't be at all surprised if we wasn't right. Outsiders see most of the game, you know. You mark my words," he went on, gathering confidence, "before we know where we are up'll crop some nice young fellow she's 'ad her eye on. There'll be the motive and—there you are!"

Mr. Campion's reply was silenced by the trilling of the front-door bell. Lugg pressed his tongue against the back of his front teeth and emitted a clucking sound expressing both annoyance and resignation.

"What a time for anyone to come visitin'," he said.

Moving across the room, he opened the bottom drawer of a bureau and took therefrom, to Mr. Campion's horror, a remarkable contraption consisting of a stiff collar with a black bow tie attached. With perfect solemnity and a certain amount of pride, Mr. Lugg fastened this monstrosity round his neck by means of a button at the back, and moved ponderously out of the room, leaving his employer momentarily speechless.

Mike came into the room unannounced. The last two or three days had made a great difference in his appearance. His shorn black curls seemed to have receded a little and the skin over his forehead looked taut and lined. The old sleepy expression was still lurking in his eyes, but there was anxiety there also.

"I had to come round," he said abruptly. "I want to see you." He paused and glanced hesitantly at the sepulchral figure behind him, and Campion took the hint.

"That's all right, Lugg, please," he said.

The old ex-burglar raised his eyebrows. "I shall be in the kitchenette, sir, if you should require me," he said in so affected a voice that Campion gaped.

Mike was in no condition to notice extraneous details, however. As soon as he was alone he threw himself down in one of the deep chairs by the fire and sighed.

"This is damned awful, Campion," he said. "Losing old Paul's bad enough, but you can't imagine what it's been like this week. We haven't been able to call ourselves our own. Gina seems to be going to pieces altogether. Is there any way of finding out what the police have in their minds? I know you'll do your best for us. Have you found out anything?"

Mr. Campion, who was employed with a cocktail-shaker at the cabinet on the other side of the room, spoke over his shoulder.

"I went down to Scotland Yard," he said, "but Stanislaus Oates is on leave, and Tanner and Pillow, the men in charge of your business, were quite polite, but they weren't giving anything away. However, I shouldn't worry. Old Salley, the Coroner, is a good scout; a fierce old boy, rather abrupt, but hasn't held the office all this time without learning a thing or two. Have the police been round much since the postponement?"

"Round much . . . !" Mike groaned. "They're living in the office. We've all made statements till we're black in the face. Gina had a beastly experience, too. I persuaded her to go out a bit—sitting indoors brooding was doing her no good. She had a luncheon date with the Adelaide Chappel woman—the soprano. They went down to Boulestin's, and afterwards Madame Chappel had to go to Cook's, of all places. She always books through them, apparently, and she was off to Belgrade to sing in a concert there. Gina had nothing better to do, and went with her. She got the impression she was being followed, and actually saw a detective enquiring about her from a clerk. Since then there's been a man outside the flat. It's damnable, Campion, absolutely damnable! Why shouldn't she turn up at the inquest? Why shouldn't any of us? What have the police got up their sleeves?"

Mr. Campion handed his guest a cocktail before he spoke.

"What about all these statements you've been making?" he said. "I suppose they've been questioning you on your original essay dictated to the Coroner's Officer?"

"Have they not!" Mike spoke explosively. "I've gone over all that a dozen times, and so has Gina, to say nothing of poor old Curley and the poor little beast who found the body. They come to see us every day. This morning they were on a new track."

He drank the cocktail without tasting it and his eyes were fixed anxiously on Campion.

"They ask questions the whole time," he said, "but they never tell you anything. Today it was all the Thursday night stuff. Can you remember what you did last Thursday night—not yesterday, but the week before?"

Campion pricked up his ears. "Thursday night?" he said. "Did they ask everybody?"

"Oh, rather! I asked Pillow—a funny little chap, Campion, a sort of good-class head gardener, the last person on earth to be a detective—if they'd fixed the time of death, but he wouldn't say anything. Simply smiled surreptitiously."

Mr. Campion sat down on the edge of the opposite chair.

"Did he ask you about any special time on Thursday?"

"Yes. Between eight and nine o'clock. You've never heard such a tedious business. The whole office went through it. Poor Curley was nearly off her head. John couldn't remember where he was and she had to hunt up engagement books and phone through to inquisitive friends and business acquaintances. Finally it transpired that he was at the dinner given by the Quill Club to Lutzow, the psychologist. The secretary remembered him arriving at ten to eight and he didn't get back till eleven or twelve. Curley herself appears to have been in a Tube train on the Morden line. I was out until ten to nine. Gina was alone in the flat waiting for Paul. All simple ordinary activities, but difficult to remember when you're asked suddenly. Frankly, what's worrying me is that as far as I can see there's an ordinary explanation for the poor chap's death. The carbon monoxide must have soaked into the room and gassed him. The explanation of the locked door I suggested to Pillow was something like this: I think he went down there, let himself in, and left the key in the lock. The door swung to, and someone else, one of the employees, saw the key in the lock, turned it and took it upstairs and put it back in its place. Now they're probably too frightened to admit it."

Mr. Campion considered. "What did Sergeant Pillow say to that?"

Mike shrugged his shoulders. "Oh, you know what these policemen are! They're so darned clever. He said he'd look into it, and went on questioning me."

"How's your cousin taking it?" Mr. Campion put the question mildly.

"Who? John?" Mike permitted himself a faint smile. "He's quite fantastic. Simply doesn't realize that anything's up. Treats the police as though they were literary agents he'd never heard of, and spends his spare time thinking out little obscure paragraphs to send to the newspapers explaining why the funeral has been delayed. John's only thinking about Barnabas, Limited. He's believed so long that its reputation is sacred that he doesn't recognize a scandal when it comes along. He's had all the staff in crêpe bands, if you please, and has made arrangements for a very quiet and respectable funeral at Golders Green on the day after the inquest."

Campion replenished the empty glass.

"Mrs. Brande doesn't mind all these details taken off her hands, of course," he ventured.

"Gina? Oh, no." Mike spoke bitterly. "I think Gina always realized that Paul belonged to the firm much more than to her. He—well, he neglected her in an impossible fashion, you know."

He lowered his eyes as he spoke and busied himself lighting a cigarette.

Mr. Campion did not speak, and after a pause the other man went on.

"Paul wasn't a subtle soul at all," he said, "and he had the disconcerting habit of working himself into a fever to get hold of beautiful things and then forgetting all about them. It was the same with everything. He didn't appreciate the things he had."

Mr. Campion heaved a piece of coal into the centre of the blaze.

"As much as you might have done?" he suggested softly.

Rather to his surprise, Mike's dark eyes met his own squarely.

"That's the trouble," the younger man said quietly.

"How far has it gone?" enquired Mr. Campion.

"Not at all, thank God." Mike spoke fervently. "She's not particularly interested in me. I've just been about and we've naturally gone around together, but that's all. You don't understand Gina, Campion. No one does. I hope to heaven we can keep her out of this."

Mr. Campion was silent. For a moment he was aware of forces and counter-forces beneath the surface of the quiet lives surrounding Barnabas, Limited. There were revelations to come, he knew, some of them hideous, some of them piteous and others fantastic in their unexpectedness. He also knew that the man in front of him did not dream that once the searchlight of police and Press was turned upon them there could be nothing hidden, nothing protected, and that beneath the glare little intimate things would stand out in unnatural prominence.

Aloud he said: "You ought to have married years ago, Mike."

The other man stirred. "I'm damned glad I didn't. Things are complicated enough as they are. Forget it and shut up about it. I don't know why I come to you, blethering about my secret affairs when there's open trouble to discuss. Hullo, who's this?"

His last remark was occasioned by the sound of a woman's voice in the hall. They had not heard her ring, and when Lugg showed the black-clad figure into the room a moment later they were taken by surprise.

"Gina! What are you doing here?" Mike rose to his feet and went towards her. All trace of his nerviness of a moment before had vanished. He had himself well in hand, Mr. Campion noticed approvingly.

Gina stared at him without a word of greeting and turned abruptly to Campion.

"You didn't mind me coming, did you?" she said hastily. "I'm going mad sitting up alone in the flat, wondering what the police are thinking.

I even sent for the doctor, but he wouldn't tell me anything. Albert, what are they going to *do* on Tuesday?"

"Talk and talk and talk for hours, and write it all down by hand in the copybook," said Mike easily. "Look here, suppose you come and sit down in this expensive-looking chair and let Campion give you a White Lady."

She turned to him and her wide grey eyes searched his face anxiously. He met her scrutiny smiling.

"Things are going to be all right," he said. "There's nothing to worry about. You look very fine. Did you design all that white collaretting? What d'you call it—a jabot or a bertha?"

"Mike, I can't bear it," she said, turning away from him. "Albert, tell me, what's happened?"

She sat down in the chair as she spoke and her pale face was raised to Campion's appealingly.

"He doesn't know any more than we do, Gina, but he says the Coroner is a wise old boy who isn't likely to make mistakes."

Mike spoke soothingly and pulled another chair forward and sat down in it between them. The girl seized at the straw of comfort.

"Still, people do make mistakes, don't they?" she said slowly. "To the police things look different, worse than they are. I could see that when I was interviewed by Inspector Tanner last night. I told him something, and I could see as he wrote it down that he thought—well, that he thought about it in a different way from the one in which it happened."

"Tell us about it." Campion handed her a glass as he made the suggestion.

She hesitated, and some of the colour returned to her face.

"It doesn't seem so important now," she said. "I'm behaving very badly, I'm afraid."

"Let's have it."

"Well—" Gina cleared her throat, "—I didn't know you were going to be here, Mike. It's something you don't know about, and you'll probably be surprised or shocked, but there was my side to it, and it wasn't all my fault."

She hesitated again, and the two men watched her as she sat there, so small and fragile in her sophisticated clothes.

"The Inspector was asking me about Thursday night. I told him Paul and I were going to discuss something over a meal and that I waited in for Paul until nine o'clock, when I phoned Mike and asked him to take me out."

She paused and her eyes met Campion's gravely.

"The Inspector asked me what Paul and I were going to talk about, and I told him. When he heard, he seemed to think it important. It was only an impression I got, of course, and yet . . ."

"What were you going to discuss with your husband?"

Campion saw the danger signal before he heard her confirming words.

"A divorce. I'd been trying to get Paul to give me one for some time," she said.

"A divorce?" Mike's whisper seemed to fill the room.

She turned slowly round to him.

"Don't," she said. "Don't! No reproaches—not now. I'm just telling you what I told the Inspector."

A tremor passed over the younger man's face and it occurred to Campion that she did not realize her injustice.

"The Inspector was very interested," Gina went on. "He asked me if we'd spoken of it before, and I told him we had, lots of times, and that Paul wouldn't hear of it. But on the Wednesday I went to see a solicitor and that brought matters to a head. I knew where I stood. I knew I was tied to Paul if he—he—wouldn't desert or beat me, so I begged him to have an evening at home so that we could discuss it."

"You told the Inspector all this?" Mike's voice was very quiet.

"He got it out of me," she said helplessly. "Does it matter, Albert, does it matter? Will it make any difference?"

Mr. Campion rose to his feet. His face was very grave.

"I don't think so," he said at last, hoping his voice carried conviction. "You weren't quite alone in the flat when you were waiting for Paul, were you? I mean your woman was there to serve dinner?"

"Oh, yes, of course." Gina spoke carelessly. "Mrs. Austin was there until eight o'clock."

"Eight o'clock?" Mr. Campion's brows were rising.

She nodded. "I couldn't keep the woman all night," she said. "When Paul was a whole hour late for our conference and the dinner was spoiled, I told her I didn't care when he came in and I sent her off."

"Oh, dear!" said Mr. Campion, and, after a little pause, again, "Oh, dear!"

5 : *Inquisition*

It is perhaps not extraordinary that the mixture of anxiety, irritation and excitement typical of the backstage of amateur theatricals is nearly always reproduced at the moment when a family sets off for a public performance, be it wedding, funeral, or, as in this case, inquest.

John had arrived, already dressed for the ordeal, at Gina's flat no later than half past eight in the morning of Tuesday, the 17th. By a quarter to nine he had phoned Mike three times and had upbraided the startled Mrs. Austin because Curley had not yet appeared.

Gina very wisely kept to her own room and left him to rampage up and down the studio.

When Curley came, pink and breathless with the exertion of climbing the stairs, he pounced upon her with a grunt of relief.

"We've got to be there in less than an hour," he said. "We don't want to be late. Let me see, there's Scruby to come yet. Hang the fellow! I told him to be punctual. You told him, Miss Curley, over the telephone. We were all to meet here at nine o'clock. I thought I'd made that quite plain."

Miss Curley, who was making frantic and futile efforts to tuck her wispy grey curls under the tight headband of her fashionable but unbecoming tricorne, was apologetic.

"He has a long way to come, Mr. Widdowson. He lives out at Hampstead, you know. Don't you remember, I told you he said we weren't to wait for him, but he'd meet us at the court."

John sank down in a chair, placing his speckless bowler on a table within arm's reach.

"Well, I suppose as a lawyer he knows well enough it doesn't do to be late for court proceedings," he said. "But I should have liked him to have been here. Miss Curley, go and ring down to Mike. Tell him we're all waiting. No one seems to realize the publicity involved in an affair of this sort, and not at all the right sort of publicity for a firm of our standing. I was fond of Paul, as you know, Miss Curley, but this final piece of sensationalism makes it very difficult for one to respect his memory as one would have liked."

"Oh, well, he won't do it again," said Miss Curley absently, and then, realizing the impropriety and inanity of the remark grew crimson with confusion.

To her relief John did not appear to have heard. He was entirely absorbed with his own angle on the tragedy.

"It's holding up everything. There's three quarters of the Spring list to come out and the Autumn one not half made up," he observed. "Still, we must put all that behind us now. We've all got to be calm and courageous. We must see this thing through with dignity and then we must bury our grief and get on with the work."

He seemed to be much more at ease after he had delivered this little homily and Miss Curley suspected that he had been saving it for a larger audience which had not materialized. She glanced at him curiously. He was getting older than she had thought, she decided, and wondered why it was that the cares of a firm aged a man so much more unattractively than the cares of a family. There was a great deal that was positively inhuman about John.

"Mr. Wellington rang up yesterday," she said, drawing on her short black suède gloves bought for the occasion, "and he asked me in confidence whether I thought you'd mind if he made an attempt to get into the public part of the court today. He wanted to make it very clear that he was not going after copy, but simply as an old friend of yours and Mr. Paul's."

The mention of the distinguished author's name seemed to cheer John immensely.

"Oh, not at all, not at all. I hope you told him not at all," he said. "Like to feel we had friends there. It did go through my mind that we might ask one or two people, but it didn't seem our prerogative, so to speak."

Miss Curley looked at him sharply, but there was no shadow of a smile upon his deeply lined, yellow little face.

"I wore a band," he said. "I think we all ought to wear bands, don't you? Mourning's out of fashion I know, nowadays, but it looked well, I thought. I told Mike about it."

Miss Curley was growing calmer. There was something extraordinarily soothing about John's attitude towards the terrifying business. At night, when she went home and she had a little leisure to think of the facts, she found herself growing frightened of the disaster which had overtaken them, but back in John's presence the habit of a lifetime reasserted itself and she found herself adopting his attitude against her better judgment.

When the Dresden clock on Gina's mantelpiece chimed the quarter John could bear it no longer.

"We must go," he said. "It may take us several minutes to find a cab at this hour of the morning. We don't want to be late. Getting about in London is very difficult."

Miss Curley hesitated. "It couldn't possibly take us more than ten minutes on foot, Mr. Widdowson," she said. "The court's only just round the corner. And, anyway, there's a cab rank at the end of Bedford Row."

"All the same, I wish you'd ask Mrs. Brande to come in here at once." John was fidgeting. "As for Mike, I don't know what the boy's up to. With so many Press people about we can't afford to make a bad impression."

When Miss Curley was out of the room he rose to his feet and walked over to the long mirror on the far side of the room and stood there for a moment, surveying himself critically. No one who saw him could have dreamed for a moment that he regarded himself as anything but the Head of the Firm. His poise and stance proclaimed it. He was faultlessly dressed in a dark suit and overcoat, upon which the crêpe band was only just visible. His short grey hair was clipped to a point at which it would seem that its growth was discouraged and his perfect hat completed the picture.

He looked, as he hoped, a distinguished public man, shaken, but not bowed, by private grief.

He turned away from the mirror as Gina and Miss Curley entered. It did not occur to him for a moment to apologize for having commandeered her room for the family meeting place. Instead he regarded her critically and on the whole with approval.

Her black clothes suited her. They were smart yet very severe. The only touch of softness was the crisp white ruff at her throat, and to this he took exception.

"I don't know that I should wear that, Gina," he said. "It's very nice, my dear, very becoming, but I don't know whether it's quite the thing for an occasion of this sort. Let me see how you look with it off."

The girl stared at him. Her face was drawn and colourless and her eyes had receded until there were dark hollows where they should have been. She looked ill and on the verge of collapse.

She plucked at the ruff obediently, but the touch of its crispness against her fingers seemed to steady her. She stared at him coldly.

"Don't be absurd, John. I'm not going to appear on the stage. Leave me alone—for God's sake, leave me alone!"

The man was obstinate, but like others of his generation he had a horror of nerves in women.

"Just as you like, my dear," he said coldly. "Just as you like. But I do think you'd look better without it."

"What the hell does it matter what she wears?"

Mike spoke from the doorway, where he had just appeared.

John fixed his younger cousin with a disapproving stare.

"There's no need to lose your temper," he said stiffly. "I'm only trying to think what would be wisest and most dignified for us all to do. We share a common misfortune and we are going to share a common ordeal."

Mike swallowed his temper. "That's all right, John," he said. "But you might remember that Paul was Gina's husband."

"Paul was my cousin and my partner," said John, with dignity.

There was a pause and Miss Curley seized it.

"I think we should all go down now, Mr. Widdowson," she ventured. "It'll take us two or three minutes to get down to Bedford Row."

Mrs. Austin put her head round the door, and they stared at it not without justification, since it was adorned by all the rakish splendour of Mrs. Austin's "Best that had once belonged to a titled lady."

"I think I'll slip along now, M'm, if you don't mind," she said. "I don't want to be late."

Gina turned to her eagerly. "Mrs. Austin, I'll come with you. We'll go together."

She moved unsteadily across the room and the charwoman put an arm round her.

"That's right, duck," she said. "You come along with me. You've lost your 'usband and there's nobody else but me in *this* room that knows what that means."

And with this Parthian shot she swept the girl out into the passage.

"Gina's gone mad. . . . Stop her, Mike. Who is that woman? Where are they going?"

John was halfway out of the door before Mike detained him.

"They're going to the inquest," he said wearily. "We're all going to the inquest. Hundreds of people are going to be there—it's not just our show. And now for God's sake come along."

Miss Curley touched his arm. "I think Mrs. Brande should come with us," she said.

The boy looked at her curiously. "Oh, let her go," he said. "She's escaped from this family, Curley. Let her go with her friends."

In the end they all straggled down Bedford Row together, Gina and Mrs. Austin stumbling along in front and John, in high dudgeon, stalking between them and Mike and Curley, who brought up the rear. They arrived at the court with fifteen minutes to spare.

There were still remnants of the last week's fog hanging about the city and the court seemed to have trapped more than its fair share. To Gina at least the whole place seemed to be filled with a thick brown mist, through which the faces of people she knew and did not know loomed out towards her and peered at her questioningly, only to disappear again in the general maelstrom.

She avoided Mike and clung to Mrs. Austin, whose grim determination to assert herself and whose contempt for the police and all their works made her a very comforting pillar on which to lean.

Mike and Curley remained side by side. The old woman's shrewd eyes took in every detail. She saw the Press benches were crowded and had the presence of mind to nod to the immaculately dressed Mr. Wellington, who was doing his best to look sympathetic at a distance of twenty feet.

John had buttonholed old Scruby, the firm's solicitor, and was talking to him rather than listening to what he had to say, as was his custom.

Scruby was a little skeleton of a man with sparse white hair that had yellow lights in it. At the moment he was peering at his client with protuberant pale blue eyes. As his practice largely consisted of libel and copyright he felt somewhat out of his element in the present situation and was doing his best not to say so. Mike, catching sight of the two of them, experienced a sense of sudden irritation well-nigh unbearable.

Scruby evidently had an inkling of the seriousness of the situation, but it was quite beyond him to impress his fears upon John, whose principal concern seemed to be the probable newspaper reports.

A pale young man with horn-rimmed spectacles, accompanied by an enormous person in a long black overcoat, sidled into the back of the court. Mr. Lugg and Mr. Campion were not on speaking terms that morning. No open rupture had occurred, but each, it seemed, thought it better not to intrude himself upon the other's private thoughts.

The inquest began in an unorthodox way. Mr. Salley addressed the jury. His voice, like his appearance, which was small and fierce, was unexpected. It was deep and very quiet, with a quality of naturalness which took Gina by surprise. He was like the best type of country doctor, she decided; blunt and straightforward and obviously completely without fancies of any sort.

His first words to the jury provoked furious activity at the Press table. He leant over his desk and his sharp eyes ranged over the seven embarrassed-looking citizens.

"Before you hear the evidence in this case," he said, "perhaps it would be as well if I defined your duty to you. I do this because possibly some of you may be under a misapprehension concerning this important matter, due to recent misleading criticisms of Coroners and Coroners' juries which have appeared in the Press.

"In the laws of England your duties are specifically laid down. There can be no question about them. They are clear and rigid.

"First of all let me repeat the oath which you took before me on this day one week ago. I must ask you to listen carefully and judge for yourselves what is the meaning of these very plain words."

He paused and they blinked at him owlishly. Taking a card from his desk he peered at it through his spectacles.

"This is your oath," he said, "listen to it—understand it. 'I swear by Almighty God that I will diligently enquire and a true presentment make of all such matters and things as are here given me in charge on behalf of our Sovereign Lord the King touching the death of Paul Redfern Brande, now lying dead, and will, without fear or favour, affection or ill-will, a true verdict give according to the evidence and the best of my skill and knowledge.'

"There," he said, throwing down the card. "You have each of you repeated these words and I now ask you to consider to what you stand pledged. When the evidence has been set before you the law will demand of you that you answer several questions, and I think it would be as well if I told you now what those questions will be.

"Firstly, you will be required to state who the deceased was. Then how and where he died and afterwards how he came by his death."

He paused and regarded them steadily.

"This will constitute the first part of your verdict. But afterwards, and it is this point to which I want to call your attention because there has been much mischievous and misleading rubbish talked and written about it, you may possibly be called upon to answer another question. There is set down in Halsbury's *Laws of England*, a book whose authority cannot be questioned, the following incontrovertible decree. It is there stated that if the jury find that the deceased came by his death by murder or manslaughter those persons whom they find to have been guilty of such an offence, or of being accessories before the fact of murder, must be pointed out. It is the jury's responsibility, and they are in duty bound, if they know the persons guilty, to say their names."

Everybody in court save the seven people to whom these sober words were addressed seemed to be more than startled by them. The jury merely looked uncomfortable and cold. In the back of the court Mr. Lugg nudged Mr. Campion.

The Coroner had not quite finished.

"I wish to make it clear that this duty of yours does not apply in any particular or special way to the case you are about to hear today. It is your general duty. It is the duty of all Coroners' juries and I have called attention to it because I have found so much misapprehension on the subject, not only among the public, but even among members of the legal profession.

"Now we will hear the first witness."

6 : *By These Witnesses*

Gina shrank back in her seat and waited for a merciful unreality to settle over the proceedings. In the past embarrassing or even harassing situations had always had for her this mitigating quality. Today, however, it was absent.

Instead the reverse seemed to have taken place. Faces seemed clearer, their less pleasing qualities emphasized, while each spoken word appeared to be charged with underlying menace.

The Coroner and the jury took on a Hogarthian quality, and those witnesses whom she knew resembled brilliantly cruel caricatures of themselves.

She tried to disassociate herself from it all, and to look upon the enquiry as though it were a play, but it was not possible even when she forced her eyes out of focus and persuaded her ears to hear only meaningless unrelated sounds.

Presently she found herself listening intently to Miss Marchant giving evidence about the discovery of the body. The Coroner was taking her gently through her written statement, but his tone became peremptory at the point where the actual appearance of the corpse was mentioned, warning her that any display of nerves which she might have contemplated would not be received sympathetically.

The fair-haired girl stepped down, relieved and a little nettled, the colour in her demure face heightened and her blue eyes embarrassed. The jury looked studiously disinterested.

The two doctors followed, one after the other. Consequential little Doctor Roe bustled forward, giving everyone in the court the impression that he wished to appear in a great hurry. Gina stirred uneasily. Was this awful clarity to be the peculiarity of the whole enquiry? In other circumstances Doctor Roe's hurry might have passed as genuine, but here in court it seemed monstrously overdone, his self-importance and his vanity painfully obvious.

The repetition of his statement already made to the police went slowly on, the Coroner interpolating an occasional question and writing down the replies with unhurried calm.

Gina tried to fix her mind on the evidence, but the mannerisms of the man, his love of the Latin cherished by his profession, his unction and gratification at his own importance obtruded themselves and all but eclipsed his information.

The Coroner kept him only a very short time, and the police doctor, a wholly unexpected person called Ferdie, appeared upon the stand.

Doctor Ferdie was a Scot from Dundee, and thirty years of work in London had not robbed him of his accent. He was a vast, untidy old person draped in elephant-grey clothes which managed to convey that there was something extraordinary about their cut without being actually peculiar in any definable particular. His face was seamed and rucked like the bark of an oak and from out its mass of indentations two very bright and knowing blue eyes peered at the world.

He cocked an eye at the Coroner with the confiding air of a trusted expert confronting an old client and the whole court became alive.

Preliminaries, the names and addresses of witnesses who had attested to Doctor Ferdie that the body of Paul Redfern Brande was the body of Paul Redfern Brande and not any spare corpse which might have been lying around at the time; the little matter of the warrant for examination and the address of the mortuary were all disposed of with perfunctory speed, and the doctor passed on to the external appearances of the body indicative of the time of death.

"The body was that of a well-nourished pairson," he remarked, his bright inquisitive eyes fixed upon the Coroner. "Not sae lean an' not sae stout. Just ordinary, ye see. There was no death stiffening, or, as ma colleague Doctor Roe here would put it, rigor mortis. I examined the body carefully, and in ma opeenion death had taken place within three to five days."

He paused and added confidentially:

"There were certain signs, ye see."

The Coroner nodded comprehendingly and turned to his personal notes.

"The man was last seen alive on Thursday afternoon, January the twenty-eighth; that is to say, somewhere between ninety-four and ninety-five hours before you saw him," he began at last. "In your opinion would the condition of the body be consistent with the suggestion that his death took place within an hour or so of his disappearance?"

Doctor Ferdie considered, and Gina found her heart beating suffocatingly fast.

"Ah, it might," he said at last. "It might indeed. But I couldn't commit myself, ye see. There were definite signs of the beginning of decomposition and in ordinary condeetions these do not appear until after the third day. But I wouldn't go further than that."

"Quite." The Coroner seemed satisfied, and after he had written for some moments he looked up again. "In regard to these ordinary conditions, you have said that the deceased was a well-nourished person of normal weight."

"Ah, he was," Doctor Ferdie agreed. "A healthy normal pairson."

"I see. Did you examine the room where the body was found?"

"I did."

"Was there anything about it which might have hastened or retarded the natural decomposition of the body?"

"No. It was a cool dry room, very badly ventilated, but otherwise nothing extraordinary."

"I see." The Coroner glanced at the jury, who made a visible effort to appear more intelligent. "Would the coolness hurry the termination of the period of death stiffening?"

The doctor cocked an eye again and spoke to the jury rather than to the Coroner.

"No, ye see, it would rather tend to prolong it."

"Death might easily have taken place between eighty-eight and eighty-four hours before you saw him, then?"

"Ah, it might." The Scotsman hesitated. "I'd say it was very probable."

"Thank you, Doctor." The Coroner wrote again. "Now, as to the cause of death . . ."

Doctor Ferdie cleared his throat and launched into a careful and extremely delicate description of the colour of the face and chest, followed by a technical account of the autopsy which he and Doctor Roe had performed.

Gina's head began to swim. The brutality of the facts related in the soothing Scotch voice produced in her a sense of outrage.

She turned her head and caught a glimpse of Mrs. Austin. The woman was watching her with kindly but almost hungry eyes.

"Feel faint, duck?" she whispered hopefully.

Gina shook her head and passed her tongue over her dry lips. Mrs. Austin seemed disappointed.

Doctor Ferdie was still talking.

"It's lairgely a question of the colour of the bluid, ye see. I applied Haldane's test, and in my opeenion there was between forty and fifty per cent of carbon monoxide in the bluid. I took a test-tube containing a one per cent solution of the bluid to be examined. Then in a second tube I put a solution of normal bluid of like strength. Then I took a third tube an' . . ."

On and on it went, the details explained with endless patience to the seven self-conscious individuals whose acute embarrassment had given place to a sort of settled discomfort.

By the time Doctor Ferdie left the stand there could have been no reasonable doubt in anybody's mind that Paul Redfern Brande had died from carbon monoxide poisoning, and no very great question but that he had done so within eight hours of his last appearance in the office.

The doctor lolloped back to his seat and the Coroner's Officer, a plump uniformed person with a sternly avuncular manner, produced the next witness.

At the back of the court Mr. Campion sat up as Miss Netley walked hesitantly forward. Her schoolgirl affectation was enhanced today and she looked little more than fourteen in her severe blue jacket and sailor hat.

She gave her evidence in a very low voice, but her timidity did not quite ring true, and even Mr. Lugg's sympathetic expression faded into one of doubt as her plaintive answers reached him.

The Coroner was very gentle with her, and she smiled at him confidingly as he helped her through her very simple tale. It transpired that she had been Paul's secretary and that so far as anybody knew she had been the last person to see him alive.

"You say Mr. Brande went out of the office at about half past three of the afternoon of Thursday, the twenty-eighth of last month, and that was the last time you saw him alive? Is that so?"

"Yes, sir."

"And you say here"—the Coroner went on, tapping the statement upon his desk—"that when Mr. Brande went out he seemed to be excited. Suppose you tell the jury what you meant by that?"

Miss Netley blushed painfully.

"I don't know, sir," she stammered at last. "He just seemed to be excited."

Some of the Coroner's tenderness vanished.

"Was he pleased or worried? Alarmed? Anxious about something?"

"No, sir. He was just—excited."

Mr. Campion pricked up his ears. There it was again, that same indefinable thing he had noticed about the girl before. She wanted to be tantalizing and did not mind appearing a fool in order to achieve that end.

"How did you know he was excited?" the Coroner suggested.

Miss Netley considered.

"He moved as though he was," she said at last.

Mr. Lugg nudged his employer and made an expressive depreciatory gesture with his thumb, an indication which in the days of his vulgarity would have been accompanied by the succinct expression "Out her!"

The Coroner breathed deeply through his nose.

"You just knew by the way he moved that he was excited?"

"Yes, sir."

The Coroner returned to facts.

"How did you know it was half past three when Mr. Brande went out?"

"Because," said Miss Netley, "the afternoon post comes at five-and-twenty minutes past three."

"And the post had just come when Mr. Brande went out?"

"Yes, sir." Her expectancy was as evident as if she had expressed it in words.

The Coroner looked up.

"Did anything come by the post for Mr. Brande?"

"Yes, sir. One letter."

"Did you see it?"

"I saw it was addressed to him and I handed it to him," she said. "It was marked 'Personal.' "

The court began to sit up and even the police looked interested.

"After Mr. Brande had read the letter, did he decide to go out?"

"Yes, sir."

"Did he tell you where he was going?"

"No."

"Did he say when he was coming back?"

"No."

"Did he say anything at all?"

"No, sir."

The Coroner sighed.

"You are here to give us all the help you can, Miss Netley," he said sternly. "To return to this excitement you noticed in Mr. Brande; had it anything to do with the letter?"

The girl considered.

"It may have had," she said. "I noticed it after he had read the letter. He got up hurriedly, put on his hat and coat and went out."

"What did he do with the letter?"

"He put it in the fire, sir."

"And that's all you know about this business?"

"Yes, sir."

The Coroner glanced at the written page in front of him.

"All you can tell us, then, is that a letter came for your employer at five-and-twenty minutes past three on the twenty-eighth, that it was marked 'Personal,' and that after he had read it he thrust it in the fire, put on his hat and coat and went out and was never seen again alive as far as you know?"

"Yes, sir."

"You've taken a great deal of time to tell us that, Miss Netley. You're not hiding anything, are you?"

"Hiding anything, sir?" The big dark eyes grew round and shocked. The small mouth trembled. The years dropped away from the girl until she looked a child. "Of course not, sir."

"All right. You may sit down."

Miss Netley returned to her seat with all eyes upon her and Mr. Campion wondered. She was not quite the ordinary notoriety-seeker, and once again he made a mental note of her name.

The next witness was Detective-Inspector Tanner. He was tall, thick-set, and the possessor of a figure predestined to wear a uniform. His face was expressionless, but forbidding in structure, while his light blue eyes looked shrewd and obstinately honest. He gave his evidence in a flat care-ful voice, obviously different from the one in which he usually spoke. He made his statement with the awful conviction of the slightly inhuman, while the Coroner nodded to him from time to time and wrote it all down.

In the beginning it was the same story told from yet another angle. Gina glanced restlessly round the court and was startled to catch Mike's eyes resting upon her. He looked away abruptly, but she had seen and turned back to the witness, her body suddenly cold.

Mrs. Austin leant against her.

"Bear up, dear," she murmured.

The Inspector was making a great point of the fact that the body had been moved by the doctor after its discovery. Doctor Roe was recalled and stated amid much self-conscious protestation that the step had been necessary, or so he had been assured by Miss Curley and Mr. Michael Wedgwood.

Having successfully shifted the blame from his own shoulders to theirs, he bustled back to his seat and the Inspector was recalled.

As soon as he reappeared a tremor of interest passed through the whole court. The Press men scribbled vigorously and Mr. Lugg leaned forward to catch a glimpse of the Barnabas party seated in front of him.

"After I and my colleague, Sergeant Pillow, had taken statements from the witnesses present on the premises at Number Twenty-three, Horse-collar Yard, I made a detailed search of the said premises."

The flat voice droned out the words like a child reciting.

"In the room where the deceased was discovered I noticed a small ventilator beneath one of the shelves which surround the room. The ventilator is situated three feet from the ground and five and a half feet from the ceiling. This ventilator is not easily observed by anyone entering the room because it is hidden by the projection of the shelf beneath which it is situated. I and my colleague removed the ventilator from its position and took it to headquarters as evidence."

There was a sensation as the ragged piece of iron was produced and solemnly handed round to the jury.

"I observed," Inspector Tanner continued, "that two of the centre bars of the ventilator had been recently broken. The sharp metal edges were bright and there were signs indicative of force having been used upon them. I also noticed a quantity of soot of a certain nature sprayed over the papers and other débris on the lower shelf beneath the ventilator. My colleague and I then examined the lock of the door of the room and found that it had not been tampered with in any way. We then traced the outside wall of the building and discovered that the ventilator gave into a garage used by the directors of the firm. In the garage was a twenty-horse-power Fiat car, number PQ 348206, which we subsequently discovered belonged to Mr. Michael Wedgwood, junior partner in the firm of Barnabas, Limited and first cousin to the deceased.

"Continuing our search, we entered the building next door, known as Twenty-one, Horsecollar Yard, where the residences of Mr. Michael Wedgwood, Mr. John Barnabas and the deceased are situated. Among some miscellany in the passageway outside the heating plant of these premises we found a length of rubber pipe, eight feet three inches in length and one and a half inches in diameter. As far as we could ascertain it had once formed part of a shower-bath apparatus, but did not appear to have been used for this purpose for some considerable time. One end of the pipe had been hacked off recently and the other end, which was fitted with a nozzle designed to fit over a water tap, had been considerably stretched and mutilated.

"This pipe was black with soot on the inside and the nozzle end showed signs of burning."

He paused again and the length of tubing was passed round.

The inference was obvious and the Inspector proceeded to show how the cut end of the tube had passed through the ventilator and was able to point out the indention some six inches from the end where it had been held by the ends of the broken bars.

Gina closed her eyes. It seemed to her for a moment that everyone was staring not at the exhibit but at herself. She dared not look at Mike. At her side Mrs. Austin was breathing heavily, her eyes snapping with excitement.

The Coroner took the Inspector over his statement very carefully.

"In your opinion, Inspector, this pipe was passed through the venti-lator recently?" he suggested.

The Inspector stated that in his opinion there was no possible doubt whatever about the matter; he went on to say that the other end of the pipe had been tested in connection with the end of the exhaust pipe on the Fiat and finished up by producing that part of the car.

The jury stared at these three component parts and on their faces there appeared a gleam of something that could only be called satisfaction.

The Inspector stepped down and for a moment the court was full of whispers. Old Mr. Scruby was talking to John with an animation and authority quite foreign to his nature. Two or three reporters slipped out of their places and Mr. Lugg turned to Campion triumphantly.

"What did I tell you?" he murmured. "Here it comes."

Mr. Salley restored order and the next witness was thrust forward. He was a small square person with a large head, respectable clothes and in-nocent baby-blue eyes. It transpired that his name was Henry Cecil Pas-tern and that he had an expert knowledge of central-heating plants.

He made his statement with machine-gun rapidity.

"On the evening of the twenty-ninth of last month, at the invitation of Detective-Inspector Tanner, I made a detailed investigation of the boiler situated in the basement of the premises known as Twenty-three, Horsecollar Yard. It is a type of stove well known to me and when I examined it I found no defect of any kind whatsoever. Nor did I find evidences of any repairs having been made to it at any time. The stove is a comparatively new stove, not more than eighteen months installed. I do not see how any water gas or carbon monoxide gas could have es-caped from it into the basement at any time."

Careful and scrupulously fair questioning by the Coroner made it clear to the jury and the court that Mr. Pastern knew perfectly well what he was saying and that even if his words had a slightly official flavour they did in fact represent his true and honest opinion.

It was during the interval after this evidence that Gina caught sight of Ritchie leaning forward in his seat, a bewildered expression upon his face. The sight of him almost made her laugh. He was so hopelessly out of place. So were they all, John, Curley and certainly poor Mr. Scruby. She found herself wishing desperately that it would end. It was a nightmare which had gone on too long.

The midday adjournment came unexpectedly. Miss Curley came bus-tling over, consternation on her plain plump face and her tricorne thrust unbecomingly to the back of her head.

"I've got to go with Mr. John and Mr. Scruby. They want to talk," she said breathlessly. "Will you be all right, my dear?"

"No one shall touch an 'air of 'er 'ead while I'm beside 'er," said Mrs. Austin valiantly but unnecessarily.

Gina was amazed at herself. One part of her mind was half irritated, half amused by the banality of the woman. But there was another which was timidly grateful for her support.

As she came out of the court clinging to Mrs. Austin's arm she caught a glimpse of Ritchie mooching along, his hands in his pockets, his chin thrust out, and his lean, rangy figure looking unexpectedly distinguished. He did not see her but wandered over to Mr. Campion, who was standing in the lobby with a funereal individual whose face was only vaguely familiar to her.

The two women came out into bright sunlight completely unaware of the extraordinary picture they presented. Gina, with her hair sleeked beneath her Schiaparelli hat and her severe black suit clinging to her exquisitely fashionable figure, made a contrast with Mrs. Austin's exuberant Sunday Best which was positively arresting.

For a moment they stood hesitating, startled by the staring group on the pavement and the battery of cameras thrust mercilessly into their faces.

Glancing round her wildly, Gina suddenly saw Mike.

He was standing on the fringe of the crowd, his face turned towards her. As their eyes met he made an involuntary step forward, but immediately afterwards, as though a sudden recollection had occurred to him, he turned away and made off down the road at an exaggerated pace.

Somebody in the crowd laughed hysterically and Mrs. Austin gripped her firmly by the arm.

"If you ask my opinion," she said firmly, "what you want is a small port."

7 : *The Lying Straws*

The woman came forward to the stand self-consciously, constraining her natural gait into little mincing steps and holding her large hands, exaggerated by impossibly ornate gloves, in an affected position neither comfortable nor becoming.

John Widdowson turned to Mr. Scruby.

"Who's this?" he demanded with the startled expression of an author at rehearsal finding an unexpected character in his play. "I've never seen her before."

"Ssh," said Mr. Scruby apprehensively as the Coroner's glance shot towards them.

John gobbled in silence and the witness took her place.

She was a large woman, asthmatic and unhealthy-looking, with a white face, a pursed mouth, and gold pince-nez looped to her ear with a small chain. She wore a cheap black fur coat much too small for her and had filled up its deficiency in front with a heavily frilled blouse. She gave her evidence in tones of staggering refinement.

For a moment she was so absorbed by her unusual prominence and a delicacy either real or assumed that she did not hear the Coroner when he asked her name, but was at length prevailed upon to inform the court that she was Mrs. Rosemary Ethel Tripper, that she lived in the basement flat at Number Twenty-five, Horsecollar Yard, and that her occupation was assistant caretaker with her husband of the two blocks of offices, Numbers Twenty-five and Twenty-seven. She also took the oath.

Once again the sense of outrage crept over Gina. She realized that the police were under no compulsion to broadcast their affairs, but when those affairs were so very intimately her own it seemed unnecessarily cruel to have kept her so much in the dark.

At the Coroner's request Mrs. Tripper cast her mind back both to her statement and the evening of the twenty-eighth.

"I had been to the pictures with a lady friend," said Mrs. Tripper with the air of one recounting an interesting social experience. "I parted with her at the end of the street—at about five minutes to seven o'clock, I should say it was—and then I entered my flat and went straight into the kitchenette, where I made myself a cup of tea.

"Going into the bedroom to change my shoes, a habit I have had from a girl, I suddenly said to myself, 'Why, there's that car started up!'"

She paused triumphantly and the Coroner coughed.

"Perhaps you'll explain to us, Mrs. Tripper," he said, "what exactly you meant by that?"

Mrs. Tripper was taken off her balance.

"I was referring to the car in the garage at Number Twenty-three," she said sharply, her refined accent temporarily deserting her. "Although we can't hear the car in the daytime, of course, because of the traffic, any time after six o'clock the Crescent is so quiet you could hear a pin drop and of course you can hear the car then, because the walls are so thin— I often say it's a disgrace."

"The Crescent?" said the Coroner enquiringly.

The faint colour flowed into Mrs. Tripper's pale face.

"Well then, the Yard," she said defiantly. "Horsecollar Yard. It's really a crescent."

"I see," said the Coroner and bowed his head over his papers. "What time was it exactly, Mrs. Tripper, when you thought you heard the car start up?"

"I heard it start up at ten minutes past seven," said Mrs. Tripper. "I left my friend at five minutes to. Five minutes to walk up the street, five minutes to make myself a cup of tea, and five minutes to go into the bedroom."

"Five minutes to go into the bedroom?" enquired the Coroner in some astonishment.

Once again Mrs. Tripper was put off her stride.

"Well, let's say five past seven I heard the car," she temporized.

"Are you sure you heard the car start up soon after you came in?" said the Coroner with some asperity.

"Yes, I did. I heard it as plain as anything when I was in the bedroom after I'd had my cup of tea."

"I see. And how long did you stay in the house?"

"Till about half past seven," said Mrs. Tripper promptly. "And the car was running all the time. It was running when I went out. I noticed it because I said to myself, 'It's bad enough to hear that engine being turned on and off, without having it running in your ear the whole time,' and I meant to speak to the janitor at Twenty-three about it."

"You say about half past seven, Mrs. Tripper——" the Coroner was very gentle. "Could you be more exact?"

"Well, I *think* it was half past seven. Anyway I left the house and went down to wherever I was going, and when I got there it was ten minutes to eight—because I saw the clock."

"Where was this?"

Once again Mrs. Tripper flushed.

"It was a shop in Red Lion Street—a fried-fish shop, if you must know. It was very foggy and I hadn't been able to get about to do my ordinary shopping, and I knew my husband would like something hot for his supper and so I thought I might as well try some of their more expensive pieces. Some of these places are very high class, and the Red Lion shop is very nice indeed."

"Quite, quite," said the Coroner, rather taken aback by the vehemence of her confession. "You went straight to the fried-fish shop when you left your house and you arrived there at ten minutes to eight?"

"Yes, I did."

It was quite evident that Mrs. Tripper was torn between the desire to acquire kudos by admitting to a knowledge of interesting facts and irritation at having to disclose the more humble activities of her private life.

"And when I returned," she went on triumphantly, "the car was still running. I heard it turned off at ten minutes to nine or thereabouts."

The Coroner leant forward across the desk.

"I feel these times are important, Mrs. Tripper," he said. "I wonder would it be possible for you to cast your mind back and think of any concrete fact by which you can fix them? For instance, are you quite sure that it was not half past eight, or even a quarter past nine, when you heard the car turned off?"

Mrs. Tripper's narrow black eyes behind her gold pince-nez snapped.

"I've told you there was a clock," she said. "Haven't I? I stood talking in the shop a little while and suddenly I looked up and saw it was a quarter to nine. 'Oh, dear!' I said. 'My husband comes in for his supper at nine,'—he goes down to the club on Thursdays—'and I must get home,' I said. I remember saying it. I hurried off and I got home at ten minutes to, as far as I can judge."

The Coroner returned to his notes.

"I see that it took you twenty minutes to get from your home to the fried-fish shop, Mrs. Tripper, and only five minutes to get back . . ."

Mrs. Tripper's mouth set obstinately.

"That's all I can tell you," she said. "I hurried back and as far as I can judge it was ten minutes to, because my husband came in just as I'd got everything on the table, and he's always punctual. I came in at the door, I listened, and I heard the car still running. Then just as I was saying something to myself about it, off it went."

As she stepped down off the stand a sigh passed round the court and the jury whispered together.

Gina felt that she was crouching in her seat. She dared not think ahead. In her heart she felt there was nothing to be gained by thinking. There was a slow inexorable quality about this enquiry. Nothing could deter it. It was simple, brutal and unescapable.

She was still dithering when she heard her own name called, but for the first time, as she walked to the stand, she felt the longed-for sensation of remoteness. A wall of apathy seemed to have descended between her and the nightmare around her. Faces became vague and indistinct, voices heard from afar off.

She gave her name, her address and the fact that she was Paul's wife with a calm detachment which passed for extreme self-possession. Her voice was soft and carefully modulated and she held herself rigidly.

She repeated the oath calmly, unconsciously imitating the lack of expression of the Coroner's Officer.

The Coroner became a nonentity, a questioning machine, gentle and not at all unpleasant. He took her quietly through her statement. She remembered making it, remembered signing it, but only in an impersonal far-off way as though it had not been of very great interest.

"I last saw my husband at two o'clock on the afternoon that he disappeared. It was only for a few minutes. I went into his office and caught him, as he had returned early from lunch. We had a short conversation. Then I went back to my flat. I never saw him again alive."

She was completely unaware of the impression she was creating.

The average British crowd is quick to admire beauty, especially in distress, but there is a curious streak in the temperament which makes it distrust the quality of smartness, especially when it is allied, however remotely, to something questionable or suspicious.

The fact that she was a foreigner told in her favour naturally—foreigners may be forgiven for having chic—but her calm weighed heavily against her. Widows should weep and emotional display is not only expected but demanded of them.

The questioning continued.

"You say in your statement, Mrs. Brande, that you expected your husband to come home to dinner at half past seven and that you waited for him until nine, at which time you rang up your husband's cousin, Mr. Michael Wedgwood, who took you to see a film. Were you not worried when your husband did not appear for dinner?"

She repeated the word. "Worried? No. I don't think so. I was annoyed."

It occurred to her that she might explain that Paul was always late for appointments with her, that his neglect of her, his indifference to her feelings, had rendered her completely impervious to the sensation of alarm where he was concerned, but she did not want to explain. It seemed so unnecessary to go into details to all these stupid gaping people, who could never be expected to understand. She held her tongue.

The Coroner went on.

"You say that when you went to see your husband in his office that afternoon you had something very particular to ask him. What was it?"

"I wanted to impress upon him that he must dine with me that evening, because I wanted to talk to him."

It appeared to occur to the Coroner that she was making no effort to help herself and he bent forward.

"Mrs. Brande," he said, "how long have you been married?"

"Four years."

"Would you say your marriage has been a happy one?"

"No," she said, more vehemently than she intended. "No, I don't think it was."

There was excitement in the court and John would have risen had not Mr. Scruby held him down. The Coroner pursed up his lips.

"Perhaps you'd like to amplify that, Mrs. Brande," he said. "This is a court of enquiry, you know, and we want to arrive at the truth. Did you quarrel with your husband?"

"No," she said. "We were indifferent to one another."

As soon as she had spoken she was sorry. The publicity of the whole business struck her again, but not forcibly enough to make her angry. She was past anger.

The Coroner sighed and his manner became a little less friendly.

"Mrs. Brande," he said, "you made this statement voluntarily to the Inspector and the Coroner's Officer, I understand?"

"Of course," she said stiffly. "I had nothing to hide."

"She's a cool one." The court's comment was almost audible.

"Of course not," the Coroner agreed. "You say in your statement that

you were particularly anxious to confer with your husband on the evening
of the twenty-eighth because you wanted to persuade him to help you to
get a divorce?"

"Yes," she said.

"You do not wish to add anything to that statement now?"

"No, I don't think so."

The Coroner looked at her under his eyebrows. He had seen many
frightened women and to him her reaction was not incomprehensible, but
his duty was to enquire and she was not helpful.

"Why were you so anxious to talk to him about it at that particular
time, Mrs. Brande?"

"It is all in the statement," she said wearily. "I told Inspector Tanner
that I had visited a solicitor and found out exactly how I was placed. I
realized that I could not get a divorce from my husband unless he assisted me."

There was an audible murmur in the court and little Mr. Scruby
bounded to his feet. The Coroner acceded to his request that he might
be allowed to question the witness and Gina became aware of the little
man staring at her anxiously across the crowded room.

"Had you had any violent quarrels with your husband upon this subject,
Mrs. Brande?"

"No, of course not," she said in some surprise. "It was only that we saw
really very little of each other and I wanted Paul to consider my point
of view."

Mr. Scruby sat down, not at all sure that he had been of any real
assistance. The Coroner returned to the statement.

"You say you had ordered dinner in your flat for half past seven. Were
you alone?"

"No. I had my charwoman, Mrs. Austin, with me."

"I see. And you waited for your husband until nine o'clock?"

"Yes, until almost nine."

"Was your charwoman with you then?"

"No. I let her go about eight o'clock. I saw no point in keeping her after
that."

"You were pretty sure your husband would not come then?"

"I thought it extremely unlikely."

"Yet you waited for him yourself?"

"Yes. I hoped, you see."

The jury stirred. This was more like it.

"And at nine o'clock, or nearly nine o'clock—eight fifty-five, to be exact
—you rang up Mr. Michael Wedgwood in the flat below and suggested
that you go out together? The rest of the evening you spent in a picture
palace?"

"Yes. That is true."

There was a long pause while the Coroner wrote.

"Now," he said at last, "were you in the habit of ringing up Mr. Wedgwood and suggesting that he should take you out?"

She hesitated. Something odd about the question warned her to be careful, but there was no time for adroit manœuvring, even had she been capable of it.

"Yes," she said. "I was. We have been about a good deal together."

Mr. Campion felt the hair on his scalp rising and Mr. Lugg granted him a single reproachful glance.

"You were very great friends?"

"Yes. We are."

"Are you lovers, Mrs. Brande?"

She stared at him, hardly believing that she had heard the words. She was so completely taken aback that for a moment she was silent and during that instant of stupefaction her anger and indignation were transmuted into helplessness. The old apathy reclaimed her.

"No," she said evenly.

"You are not shocked by the suggestion?"

She opened her mouth to protest violently but thought better of it.

"It is too utterly ridiculous," she said and the proud quiet words were momentarily convincing.

A few unimportant questions followed and she was allowed to step down. She walked to her seat with the eyes of the whole court upon her, but it was not until she saw Mrs. Austin's sympathetic but horribly knowing face raised to hers that she realized quite what had happened.

Panic seized her. What had she said? What were they all driving at? The blood drained out of her face and Mrs. Austin caught her arm.

"Put your head between your knees," she whispered. "Shall I get you out?"

Gina had sufficient strength to shake her head and to turn her eyes resolutely towards the desk. She knew that John was staring at her angrily and in imagination she could see the startled little face of Mr. Scruby by his side.

Mike was the next witness.

The jury were wide awake now and their interest was not assumed. They had completely forgotten their own prominence and were absorbed by the story being unfolded so lucidly before them.

Gina did not take her eyes from Mike's face during the whole of his evidence. She felt she was seeing him for the first time. He was extraordinarily handsome, with the tall, lank Barnabas figure and the crisp curls shorn tightly to his head.

To those who knew him he betrayed his nervousness. He spoke with a drawl not natural with him and the ease of his stance was assumed.

His written statement was necessarily brief. He admitted helping the doctor to move the body on to the table and afterwards up to the flat, and gave a brief account of his cousin's position and activities in the firm.

The Coroner questioned him about the strong room. Evidence that had been given by other witnesses concerning its use was confirmed by him and he repeated that the car in the garage belonged to him.

"The yard gates are kept locked," he said, "but not the garage itself. I never considered there was any need for that."

The Coroner returned to the question of the strong room.

"I see in your statement, Mr. Wedgwood," he said, "that you admit to having visited the strong room on the night of the thirty-first, three days after your cousin's disappearance and on the evening before the discovery of his body."

The excitement at this point was intense and the Coroner had to enforce silence.

Mike's lank form seemed to be leaning back upon the air and his drawl became more pronounced.

"That is so," he said.

"Will you describe exactly what you did upon that occasion? It is all written down, I know, but I should like to hear it from you again."

Mike complied. He described how he had left the flat on Sunday night, had gone into the darkened office, taken the key from its usual place, opened the strong room and taken the folder which John had needed from its shelf, and had come away, locking the door behind him.

The Coroner seemed puzzled and he took the young man through the story again and again. Finally Mike's evidence was interrupted while Miss Curley and Miss Marchant were called to describe the exact place in which the body was found.

When the Coroner returned to Mike again his tone was peremptory.

"Can you offer any explanation why you did not see the body of your cousin on Sunday night?" he said.

"I'm sorry, I can't. It wasn't there. Or, if it was, I didn't see it."

Mike's exasperation was not unmixed with defiance. The Coroner dismissed the matter for the time being and went back to the Thursday night.

"Mr. Wedgwood," he said, "will you tell us what you did from three o'clock in the afternoon of Thursday the twenty-eighth until you answered the telephone at nine o'clock and went out to a picture palace with Mrs. Brande?"

Mike stiffened slightly and when he spoke his tone was defensive.

"I worked in my office all the afternoon," he said slowly. "My secretary was there the whole time. I left about half past five, intending to go to a cocktail party, and because it was slightly foggy and I was early I decided to walk. The house I intended to visit was in Manchester Square, but before I reached it I changed my mind and decided that I would go on walking."

He paused. The Coroner was looking at him and the seven pairs of eyes from the jury benches watched him narrowly.

"Yes?" said the Coroner.

"Well, I went on walking," said Mike lamely. "I had various things on my mind and I wanted to think them out. I went on walking until about half past eight. Then I got on a bus and came home."

The Coroner's pen traced idle designs on the blotting paper in front of him.

"Half past five till half past eight," he said. "That's three hours. It's a long time to walk on a foggy winter night, Mr. Wedgwood. Can you tell us where you went, exactly?"

"Yes. I went down to the far end of Westbourne Grove. I walked down Holborn, Oxford Street, Edgware Road, Praed Street, and Bishop's Road. Then I turned back and I went up one of those long terraces to the Park, I cut through from Lancaster Gate to Hyde Park Corner and came up Piccadilly. I went up Shaftesbury Avenue, Charing Cross Road and I took a bus at St. Giles's Circus. It's a long way and I was not walking fast."

"Did you stop anywhere? Speak to anyone?"

"No. I don't think so."

"Well, can you tell us, Mr. Wedgwood, why you went to Westbourne Grove? Had you any purpose in going there?"

A faint smile passed over the man's expressive face.

"Yes, I had, vaguely. I meant to visit a shop there. There's a little secondhand jeweller's and curio shop about halfway down the right-hand side. I don't know the name of it. When I got there it was shut. It was Thursday anyway—I'd forgotten that."

The Coroner was inclined to be impatient.

"You must see that this is a very unsatisfactory story," he said testily. "You say you walked nearly four miles to visit a shop and found it shut. Had you any particular purpose in going to that shop?"

"No, not really. I mean, nothing urgent." Mike seemed unduly embarrassed. "I thought I might find something of interest there, I have done so before."

"Some piece of jewellery?"

"Well, yes."

"I see." The Coroner paused significantly. "Well, then, when you found the shop was shut you walked back for no other reason than that you wished to walk?"

"That is so."

"And it was cold and slightly foggy—not a pleasant night for walking?"

"No, it wasn't. But I didn't really mind about that. I had things on my mind and wanted to work them out."

"Those things, I see, Mr. Wedgwood, were private affairs which have no bearing on this case?"

"They were business matters," said Mike briefly and unconvincingly.

"When you returned home to Horsecollar Yard what did you do?"

"I went down through my own flat, out of the back door, through the gate in the wall to the garage behind the office, and started my car."

The court gasped.

"Why did you do that?"

"The fog had cleared a little and I thought it would probably be quite bright in the country. I thought I would go out somewhere by myself for a run round."

"You were tired of walking?" observed the Coroner dryly.

"Yes, I was."

"According to your evidence, Mr. Wedgwood, you had nothing to eat all this time . . ."

"No. I wasn't hungry. I just wanted to be by myself."

"And so you started up the car?"

"Yes. I always do that. I let her run for a little while, five or ten minutes at the outside, before I take her out into the traffic in the cold weather. I find she runs much more easily."

"And then?"

"Then I remembered that the key of the yard gates was in my coat in the flat. I went up to get it. While I was there Mrs. Brande rang up and explained that Paul had not returned and I suggested that we should go out somewhere. As it was too late for a theatre we went to a film. Before I went up to fetch Mrs. Brande I returned to the garage and switched off my car engine. I estimate it had been running seven minutes."

"I see." The Coroner cleared his throat. "Now there are just one or two questions I want to ask you concerning this statement. When Mrs. Brande told you that her husband had not returned and that he was two hours late for an appointment, weren't you alarmed? Didn't you wonder what had happened to him?"

"No. Paul was like that. He was a most erratic person. Neither Gina—I mean Mrs. Brande—nor we at the office ever knew when he was going to turn up."

The Coroner wrote.

"But on the Sunday, Mr. Wedgwood, when you were having tea—with others—at Mrs. Brande's flat, didn't you wonder then what had happened to your cousin?"

"I did. I thought he had stayed away rather a long time, but I wasn't worried. As I say, my cousin was unreliable."

"Well, then, one other point. You say you were getting your car out, intending to crawl through the fog until you got to the open country, because you wanted to be by yourself. And yet as soon as Mrs. Brande

phoned you you suggested you should take her out to see a film? How
do you explain that?"

Mike shrugged. "I don't explain it," he said. "I'm just telling you what
happened."

"Mr. Wedgwood, is there a love affair between you and Mrs. Brande?"

"Certainly not."

"You have never at any time treated her in any way other than as your
cousin's wife?"

"Never."

"You realize you are on oath?"

"I do."

"Very well. Will you stand down, please."

Much to everybody's astonishment, including her own, the next witness
was Mrs. Austin.

She swept forward, a fine belligerent figure, skirts and streamers flying,
and after climbing into position turned and surveyed the court, Coroner
and police with self-possessed hostility.

She gave her name as Mrs. Dorothy Austin; her age (which was un-
asked) as forty-two; and an address in Somers Town.

"I've been visiting my lady, Mrs. Brande, for nearly four years now,"
she explained, "and if anybody knows her I do."

The Coroner looked up and smiled.

"We will stick to your statement as much as possible, Mrs. Austin,"
he murmured. "You say here that you were in the habit of arriving at
Mrs. Brande's flat at eight o'clock every morning, that you stayed until
twelve and returned again to cook and wash up after the evening meal
if necessary."

Mrs. Austin concurred.

"I don't see anything wrong in that," she said.

"No, no, of course not. Now, during your visits to the flat you have had
an opportunity of studying your employer and her husband. Would you
say their married life was a happy one?"

"No, I wouldn't," said Mrs. Austin vehemently. "If my husband had
treated me as Mr. Brande treated my lady I'd have left him long ago. It
was only her sweet nature that made her put up with him as long as she
did."

From the back of the court Gina looked at the woman imploringly,
but there was no way of stopping that well-meaning tongue or forcing
a little enlightenment into that shortsighted mind. Mrs. Austin imagined
herself a counsel for the defence and already saw her name large in the
newspaper as the champion of the downtrodden wife.

Pleasant, sturdy Sergeant Pillow looked down his nose. When he had
taken her statement it had seemed to him almost a pity that she should

have been so very much "in the mood," but after all the truth was the truth and the more easily it came out the better for everyone.

The Coroner had hardly any need to speak at all. Mrs. Austin not only remembered her statement but was quite willing to amplify it.

"They never came to blows—I will say that for them," she said, "but I often think it's a pity they didn't. The way he neglected her! Half the time he wasn't there at all and the other half he didn't notice she was there. No one could blame her if she went out a bit with Mr. Mike. A lady's got to have someone to take her about. She can't sit up like a sparrow on a housetop, not going anywhere. It's more than human nature can stand."

The Coroner interrupted the flow.

"Mrs. Austin," he said, "you say that you rarely stayed at the flat later than nine o'clock in the evening and never arrived there before eight o'clock in the morning. You are therefore not in a position to say whether, in the absence of Mr. Brande, Mr. Wedgwood ever stayed in the flat at night?"

"Well, of all the minds!" she began indignantly, but was silenced by the Coroner.

"You must answer me 'Yes' or 'No.' Did you ever know for a certainty that in the absence of Mr. Brande Mr. Wedgwood had stayed in the Brandes' flat overnight?"

"No," said Mrs. Austin, choked by the constraint put upon her. "But if he had I wouldn't have blamed him—or her, and that's the truth."

"That'll do," said the Coroner. "Now you were in the room, I understand, when Mr. Wedgwood came to tell Mrs. Brande that her husband was dead. I want you to describe that scene a little more fully than it is set down here. You admitted Mr. Wedgwood to the flat at about ten o'clock on Monday morning, the first of February. Do you remember that?"

"As clearly as the night my husband died," said Mrs. Austin a little unnecessarily.

"Very well. Now before Mr. Wedgwood arrived you saw your mistress?"

"Of course I did. I'd been running in and out of her room all the morning."

"At that time Mr. Brande had been missing for three days and four nights. Did Mrs. Brande seem worried?"

Mrs. Austin considered.

"Not exactly worried. I think she was relieved to be without him. One of us passed the remark that it was strange he hadn't come in."

"It did not occur to you that any harm might have befallen him?"

A ray of recollection flickered over Mrs. Austin's broad face.

"Now I come to think of it, I did say when I brought in her morning tea, 'I see the master's not back. I wonder if he's been runned over.'"

"Ah. And what did Mrs. Brande say to that?"

"Oh, she turned over on her side and said, 'No such luck,' or something like that."

Anyone of a more sensitive nature than the worthy Mrs. Austin must have noticed the tremendous sensation she was providing. The Coroner picked her up.

"When you say things like this, you must realize what they mean," he said severely. "Did Mrs. Brande use the actual words 'No such luck' in reply to your suggestion that her husband had been run over and killed?"

Mrs. Austin looked abashed.

"I think her actual words were, 'No, there's no escape that way.' I took it to mean 'No such luck.'"

"You're sure of these words, Mrs. Austin? Are you—yes or no?"

"Yes, I am. 'No, there's no escape that way'—that's what she said."

"And after that no mention of Mr. Brande was made?"

"No."

"You say you remember Mr. Wedgwood coming to the flat at ten o'clock that morning very distinctly. Will you describe it, please?"

"There was a ring at the bell," said Mrs. Austin dramatically. "I was just going to make some coffee, but I popped off my apron and opened the door. There stood Mr. Mike, white as a sheet, his hands twitching, his eyes starting out of his head. I knew at once something was up."

"Not unnaturally." The Coroner opened his mouth to say the words, but thought better of them. Instead he wrote down "Seemed greatly agitated" and put a further question.

"I see that you took Mr. Wedgwood into the room where your mistress was kneeling by the fire in pyjamas. Do you remember what she said?"

"Yes. She said, 'Mike, my pet, I'm glad to see you,' and asked him if he'd have some coffee. Her face lit up—she looked quite different."

"Then you went out of the room?"

"Yes, to make the coffee."

"And when you came back, what did you see then?"

"They were clinging together," said Mrs. Austin, with sentimental relish. "Clinging together on the hearth rug like a couple of children. Of course, when they heard me they sprung apart—as was only natural, me being an older person—and my lady said, 'My husband's dead, Mrs. Austin.' 'No!' I said. 'Yes,' she said. I give her some coffee quick. Then we all had some coffee and Mr. Wedgwood told us that they was bringing the body up. I made him come out and give me all the details so I should know what to get ready. As soon as he could he slipped back to her."

"Then you can't tell us any more about the conversation which took place between them after the death had been discovered," said the Coroner firmly. "Can you tell us what effect the news had upon your mistress? Did she seem surprised?"

"Surprised? She was horrified! I never saw such a change in anyone in all my life. One moment she was a bright laughing girl, not a care in the world except Mr. Brande's neglect and mental cruelty to her, and the next she was a drawn haggard woman, as you might say."

"Yes, but was she surprised?"

"She was thunderstruck, if you ask me," said Mrs. Austin.

Mr. Scruby, who jumped up some little time before and had only just succeeded in catching the Coroner's eye, begged to be allowed to put a question.

"When you say your mistress was in pyjamas, Mrs. Austin," he said, "do you mean her night clothes?"

The woman stared at him. "No, I don't," she said. "It's a new fashion. Little serge romper suits. Ladies wear them in the morning about the house. Very nice and respectable, they are, something after the style of a naval uniform."

"Thank you." Mr. Scruby sat down amid a titter of laughter and Mrs. Austin's appearance in the limelight came to an end.

She went back to her seat bursting with pride.

"I showed 'em," she said, sitting down beside Gina. "They didn't get much change out of me—nosy parkers!"

Gina said nothing.

The last witness was so well known to the whole of the Barnabas group that they stared at him in astonishment in this new setting. He was a little wizened person, very spruce and smart, but so nervous that he was almost incoherent. He gave his name as William Robert Dyke and explained that he was the janitor in charge of Twenty-one and Twenty-three, Horsecollar Yard, and had been in the employment of Messrs. Barnabas, Limited for twenty years.

He identified the piece of rubber tubing reluctantly as part of an old shower-bath attachment which he had saved some years before when it had been thrown out of Mike's flat during a spring-cleaning. Thinking that it might come in useful at some time or other, he had hung it over a large nail on the wall of the cupboard next to the furnace at Number Twenty-one, where a great deal of other odds and ends were stored. The cupboard had no door and its contents were easily visible to anyone and everyone who passed in and out of the building by the basement garden exit.

On the morning of Friday, the twenty-ninth, the day after the deceased had disappeared, he had noticed it lying upon the floor beside the other rubbish and had picked it up. He thought it looked a little dirty, but had not examined it carefully, simply replacing it upon its nail and forgetting it until the Coroner's Officer questioned him about it on the following Monday morning.

And there, with astonishing abruptness, the larger part of the enquiry came to an end.

Gina sat quite still. She did not want to look about her. Miss Curley tried to catch her eye, to give her a timidly reassuring nod, but the younger woman did not stir nor did she ever raise her eyes from her white-gloved hands folded tightly in her lap.

John and Mr. Scruby were conversing animatedly in whispers while Mr. Campion leant back in his seat, his arms folded and an even more vacuous expression than usual upon his face.

Outside the later editions of the evening papers were being unfolded at windy street corners by excited youths. Home news was scarce and the "Strong-Room Mystery Inquest" was a godsend.

Much had been made of the morning's disclosures and a photograph of Gina and Mrs. Austin leaving the court appeared on the front page of each paper.

Inside the courtroom the sense of drama was growing. It had been by no means a tedious inquisition and now there was breathlessness in the air as the Coroner began to sum up. From beginning to end he was scrupulously fair. His deep, matter-of-fact voice lent no hint of theatricality to his oration, but rather brought a salutary commonplaceness into the business, reminding his hearers that they were enquiring into the death of a man of no less or more importance than themselves.

He dissected the evidence of the various witnesses, but was careful to make no comment.

"Let me quote to you from a very old and respected book," he said at last, leaning across his desk and addressing the jury intimately. "I refer to Burke's *Justice*. There these words are set down for our instruction. I will read them to you.

" '*It is peculiarly the province of the jury to investigate and determine the facts of the case. They are neither to expect nor should they be bound by any specific or direct opinion of the Coroner upon the whole of the case, except so far as regards the verdict, which in point of law they ought to find as dependent and contingent upon their conclusions in point of fact. The verdict should be compounded of the facts as detailed to the jury by the witnesses and of the law as stated to them by the court.*'"

He looked up from his book.

"I have told you the law. You know what you must do and what questions you must answer. You may now consider your verdict."

The jury retired and were gone only fifteen minutes. When they returned the foreman was perspiring and the faces of the others were studiously blank. On ascertaining that they were agreed Mr. Salley put the first question, his pen poised.

"Who do you find the deceased was?"

The foreman, his voice squeaky and breathless with discomfort, spoke hurriedly.

"We find, sir, that he was Paul Redfern Brande, of Twenty-one, Horse-collar Yard, of this parish."

"How do you find that the deceased met his death?"

"Sir, we find that he met his death by poisoning from carbon monoxide gas."

"Where do you find that he died?"

"In the strong room in the basement at his place of business at Twenty-three, Horsecollar Yard, of this parish, on the twenty-eighth day of January in this year."

The Coroner wrote rapidly.

"Do you find how he came by his death?"

"Yes, sir. We find that he was murdered wilfully and with malice afore-thought."

There was a long pause and the court was unnaturally silent. The re-porters waited like greyhounds in the traps and Inspector Tanner sat up, his ears pricked.

The quiet voice of the Coroner continued.

"That is the first part of the verdict. We now come to the final ques-tion, about which you already know. You have declared that the deceased was murdered. If you know who is guilty of this terrible offence it is your duty to say his name. From the evidence which you have heard, do you find anyone so guilty? Remember, you must speak from the certainty in your hearts and not from any suspicion, but if you have that certainty it is your bounden duty to speak. Do you find anyone guilty of the murder of Paul Redfern Brande?"

"Yes, sir, we do." The foreman's voice squeaked ridiculously as his nerv-ousness robbed him of his breath.

"Then will you say his or her name?"

The foreman gulped.

"We find that Michael Wedgwood did wilfully murder his cousin Paul Redfern Brande."

Gina's head fell forward and she sank against the woman at her side.

John struggled to his feet, his dignity forgotten in his astounded horror.

The Coroner went on evenly.

"Do you find anyone guilty of being accessory before the fact of murder?"

"No, sir." The foreman mopped his dripping forehead. "We find no one guilty of being accessory before or after the fact."

8 : *Presumed Innocent*

Since the arrest which he had just made was not technically legal until the Coroner had finished with the jury's formalities and had signed the warrant, Inspector Tanner was content to wait patiently in a corner of the anteroom while John and Mr. Scruby monopolized his prisoner.

Mike stood looking at the two elderly men with unseeing eyes. He was pale and the lines on his face had deepened, leaving the skin taut and his skull oddly apparent, but his body had not lost its ease or his manner its natural lazy calm.

The sudden catastrophe seemed to have burnt up over him like the flare of a new gas mantle, leaving him visibly the same but stricken with a new vulnerability.

As though conscious of this he held himself mentally apart from the others, whose thoughts and words were still protected.

John was frankly hysterical. Little pinkish pouches had appeared in the loose flesh beneath his jaw and his eyes were flickering.

"We must keep our heads," he was saying, his long bony fingers gripping Mr. Scruby's arm with painful pressure. "We must keep our heads. It's a monstrous mistake—we know that. The Coroner has exceeded his powers and in due course he will be reprimanded and removed, but meanwhile the publicity involved is terrible. No compensation can make up for it."

"Mr. Widdowson, Mr. Widdowson." Mr. Scruby's timid voice was imploring. "This is not the time. We must talk later when we can see what is best to be done. Now we have only a few moments and I want to assure Mr. Wedgwood that we shall leave no stone unturned to defend him at his trial. You will receive a visit from someone at my office to discuss the defence," he hurried on, speaking directly to Mike. "Rest assured that we shall do everything in our power."

Mike was vaguely aware of an anxious, sympathetic face raised to his and he nodded to it gratefully.

John gaped at them both. The pouches in his neck quivered and his lips moved helplessly.

"But it was an accident. Obviously an accident. I *know* it was an accident."

"Doubtless," said Mr. Scruby dryly, and added with unexpected briskness: "It now remains for us to prove it. I do not know at this juncture, of course, what line the defence will take. That is for Counsel to decide."

John sat down suddenly on the bench which ran round the dirty pale green walls. He looked very old.

Mr. Scruby eyed him thoughtfully for a moment and returned to Mike.

"I need hardly advise you not to discuss your—ah—your situation with anyone at all until I or someone from my office can see you," he murmured. "Keep as cheerful as you can and——"

He broke off abruptly and swung round. The Inspector was interviewing someone at the door. After a considerable amount of whispering he stepped back to admit Mr. Campion, and behind him Gina and Miss Curley.

The Inspector was sympathetic.

"They'll clear off in a little while," he said confidentially to Campion. "You told your man to take the car round to the back of Chequers Street, did you? That's right. You'll be able to get the ladies away quite comfortably in a minute or two. It's these newspaper photographers, not the crowd, today. The crowd won't come until the trial."

His voice flattened and died as he became aware that they were all listening to him. He returned to his corner and presently, as Sergeant Pillow came to relieve him, went down to the courtroom for the warrant.

Mr. Scruby had stepped aside as the newcomers entered and now, his mild eyes unexpectedly shrewd, he watched the meeting between Gina and Mike. No woman, however lovely, is really improved in appearance by any of the tragic emotions, but to some a certain interestingness is lent by crisis. Now that the worst had come Gina had achieved a cold poise and an almost porcelain hardness in her face which gave her features a new decision. She looked at Mike and their eyes met steadily.

Mr. Campion and Miss Curley were firing remarks at John, practically speaking, at random, and Mr. Scruby was the only frank observer of the meeting.

For a moment Gina's lips moved, hovered over words, rejecting them unspoken. Finally she said the one thing which her brain had refused to consider ever since the discovery of the body. The words were jerked out of her, her voice unnatural.

"It's happened then," she said.

For an instant the man's self-possession wavered and the nakedness of his heart was exposed. The expression rushed back into his eyes and incredulity mingled with the other emotion there. He recovered immediately, however, and for the first time since the verdict a smile appeared upon his wide mouth.

"The vanity of the woman!" he said, and turned away.

The damage was done. The colour poured into the girl's face, her poise was destroyed and she stood awkwardly, suddenly looking very young and gawky.

There was a moment of acute discomfort and then the door opened once more, and Sergeant Pillow rose to admit a telegraph boy with an envelope for John.

The old man tore it open with hands that trembled uncontrollably and, because it was his habit to do so at the office, read the message aloud.

"Astounded have not been informed. Incalculable harm may result incomprehensible neglect. Do nothing till arrive. Barnabas."

John looked up, genuine astonishment in his eyes.

"God bless my soul! Cousin Alexander," he said. "I never thought—— No, no answer, boy. Miss Curley, give him sixpence."

Mr. Scruby came forward dubiously.

"Alexander Barnabas, the counsel?" he enquired, and there was no telling whether there was reverence or sheer apprehension in his tone.

John blinked at him. "Yes, my cousin. My uncle's only son. Took silk a good few years ago now. Great man in criminal cases, I believe. Great reputation——"

"Oh, yes," said Mr. Scruby gently, "I know him," and there was a little silence.

It was broken by the return of Inspector Tanner.

"You can get the ladies away comfortably now, sir," he said meaningly, and Mr. Campion, who saw that there was nothing to be gained by waiting, turned to Gina enquiringly.

She went with him willingly, almost eagerly, and Miss Curley followed after leaving a whispered message with the Sergeant for John, who had begun to talk to Mr. Scruby again, and a friendly handclasp with Mike.

In the doorway Gina hesitated without looking back, and the man under arrest, glancing up, caught a last glimpse of her small black figure, her head bent and the soft arc of her chestnut hair showing under her black hat.

At one of the back doors of the court Mr. Lugg sat proud and disapproving in the shining glory which was Mr. Campion's new Lagonda. He sprang out with an agility astonishing in one of his bulk and bundled the two women somewhat unceremoniously into the back.

"Now let's sheer off before we're seen," he said in a husky undertone to his employer.

Mr. Campion, who had the same idea but for less selfish reasons, slid in behind the wheel and the great car moved away.

When they were held up in a traffic jam in Holborn he glanced over his shoulder.

"I'm going to take you back to my flat for half an hour or so, Gina, if you don't mind," he said. "These Press photographers are tenacious beggars, and you don't want to run into a battery of them waiting on your door-step."

The girl did not answer, but Miss Curley's voice, brisk and practical, came from the darkness of the hood.

"I'm so glad you thought of it, Mr. Campion," she said. "It had been on my mind. Of course, I hadn't liked to suggest it." And in a lower voice they heard her add: "Keep your head well down, my dear. You'll feel better."

"I'm all right," said Gina, and her voice sounded unutterably weary.

The person who did not approve of the suggestion was Mr. Lugg. Mr. Campion caught a glimpse of his face reflected in the windscreen and smiled in spite of himself.

It was a dark, wet night and they were caught in the home-going rush, so that it took them some considerable time to reach Bottle Street.

There the lights were subdued and shed little puddles of radiance on the streaming pavements. Campion took Gina's arm and steered her towards the brightly lit entrance beside the police station. Miss Curley followed him and Lugg put the car away.

As Campion and the two women came up the staircase to the small hall on the second landing which contained Campion's front door, a woman rose from the chair which was the only furniture in the minute passageway and stepped forward.

Her appearance was vaguely familiar to Campion, and he had the impression that he had seen her somewhere recently. She was not a usual type and he was struck by something indefinable about her which he could only describe to himself as passive rather than active grief. She was middle-aged and, although smartly dressed, had none of Gina's essential style. It occurred to him that she belonged to the category known to his father's generation as "handsome women." She came forward timidly.

"I don't know if you're Mr. Campion," she said, "but if you are, could I speak to you for a minute?"

Her voice came as a surprise. Without being actually vulgar or uneducated, its refinement was not quite genuine.

Mr. Campion took out his key.

"Why, yes, of course. In just one moment," he said, and unlocked the door.

Miss Curley took Gina inside and as the light from the inner hall fell upon the girl's face Campion heard a smothered exclamation from his unknown visitor. He turned round to find her looking after Gina, an embarrassed and defeated expression in her eyes.

"That's Mrs. Brande, isn't it?" she said. "I didn't recognize her at first, in this light. I'm sorry I bothered you, Mr. Campion. Good evening."

She was halfway across the passage to the stairs before she had finished speaking, and Mr. Campion was puzzled.

"Won't you leave your name?" he said rather idiotically.

"No, no, it doesn't matter. I made a mistake. It doesn't matter in the least."

Her voice came back to him as she clattered down the staircase in her high-heeled black patent shoes. Looking over the banisters he saw her fox fur flopping up and down on her plumpish shoulders as she hurried.

Slightly bewildered, he went into the flat and put a question.

Gina looked up from the depths of his big armchair.

"Yes, I saw her," she said wearily, "but I didn't know her. I've never seen her before in my life. What did she want?"

"Goodness knows," said Mr. Campion.

9 : *The Daring Young Man*

On any other occasion and in any other circumstances the spectacle of Mr. Lugg in his latest rôle, serving afternoon tea to one of the principals in a *cause célèbre*, might easily have delighted Mr. Campion; but as it happened, such is the perversity of fortune, he found it irritating.

The change which had occurred to Gina in the anteroom of the court still persisted. The agitation and ill-suppressed terror of the last few days had now given place to a weary, broken weakness a thousand times more pathetic.

Miss Curley, on the other hand, had reacted by becoming an intensified edition of her normal self. Campion suspected her of being extra busy and efficient so that she might not have time to think. All the same, it was a difficult gathering and John's arrival was a relief.

He came in, scowled at Lugg, sat down in the chair which Campion had vacated on rising to welcome him, and announced querulously that he would like a cup of tea.

Lugg served him ungraciously, the expression in his little black eyes intimating clearly that he did not like his manners and was quite prepared to subject him to a course of instruction if the opportunity arose.

Having averted this danger by banishing Lugg, Campion glanced enquiringly at his new visitor.

Mr. Widdowson was fast recovering from his hysteria of earlier in the afternoon. The pink pouches had disappeared from his gills and his eyes were cold and steady.

"I've been talking to Scruby," he began peremptorily, his thin, academic voice raised a little above its normal tone, "and he agrees with me, of course, that the police are making a fantastic mistake. Apparently the Coroner is strictly within his rights, although Scruby feels he may come in for considerable censure. However, that's not the point. What we have to think about now is the best way of clearing up the ghastly business satisfactorily."

Mr. Campion eyed the man and wondered if it could be possible that even now he had not realized the full gravity of the position.

John leant back in his chair.

"I think Scruby feels that the police used the inquest to avoid shouldering full responsibility for the arrest," he announced. "He didn't say so in as many words, of course, but that's what I understood."

Gina had shrunk back into her chair and he appeared to notice her for the first time.

"We shall need you, Gina," he observed, pointing a long bony finger at her. "Scruby wanted me to impress it upon you that you're likely to be a very important witness."

She did not speak, and he evidently did not expect her to, for he returned to Campion.

"Scruby feels with me that an independent investigation on behalf of the family is absolutely necessary," he said slowly. "Time, you see, is going to be short."

Mr. Campion, who had drawn up a small, hard chair, now sat upon it and blinked at his client, his pale eyes vague behind his horn-rimmed spectacles.

"I'm sure Mr. Campion will do all he can to help Mike," put in Miss Curley so hastily that he smiled at her.

"Of course he will. Of course." John brushed aside the interruption irritably. "Now, Campion, we all know Paul's death was an accident. What I ask you to do is to prove it to the satisfaction of the most unintelligent member of the police and Press."

Mr. Campion rose. Wandering across the room, he took up a position of vantage, his hands in his pockets and his body supported by the edge of the desk.

"I say, I do hope you won't mind my saying it," he began gently, "but you're making a most unfortunate mistake, you know."

John stared at him. The quiet authority in the casual voice was unexpected.

Mr. Campion continued diffidently.

"I don't want to alarm you all, but frankly, you know, I've a tremendous respect for the police. They're about as good at their jobs as people ever get. Their occasional mistakes are the exceptions which prove the rule. They aren't trying anything out, or shelving any responsibility, or anything like that. I'm afraid it's much more devastating. You see, they feel they've got an open-and-shut case and so they're dealing with it in the quickest and most efficient manner possible. It's rather revolting when you see it from our present angle, I know, but there you are. . . ."

Mr. Widdowson appeared to be temporarily silenced, and it was Gina who spoke, her voice husky.

"Albert, you don't think Mike killed Paul, do you?"

"No, old dear," said Mr. Campion, "but somebody did. Don't let's lose sight of that."

There was a long pause. Miss Curley moistened her lips with the tip of her tongue, a regular movement more nervous than feverish.

"Moreover, someone murdered him very neatly indeed." Campion sounded apologetic when he spoke again. "And in spite of that the method has been detected already. That's another point I don't think we should miss. Our astute friends Tanner and Pillow aren't so very inefficient. They've dogged that much out all right, although they didn't get on the scene until the body had been moved and the most appalling mess made of the strong room. They're not fools and they're not dishonest. They don't want to arrest an innocent man, believe me. That's every police-man's nightmare. But on the other hand, they do want to do their job decently. Someone has murdered Paul and they're employed to catch him and stop him doing it to anybody else."

John sat up slowly and turned the full force of his famous disapproving eye upon Campion.

"You seem to be a very outspoken young man," he observed.

Mr. Campion appeared to be embarrassed.

"It's a very outspoken business," he said. "Do you still want me to have a look round?"

"Albert, you must." Gina had risen. The pallor of her face was ac-centuated and her mouth quivered uncontrollably. "I do see the danger. I've seen it all the time. It's been haunting me ever since that dreadful Monday morning. You must find out that Mike couldn't have locked the strong-room door and put the key away. You must find out why he didn't say he'd seen Paul when he went down there on Sunday—because he must have been there—and you must find out what he was really doing before I phoned him on Thursday night."

Her voice ceased abruptly and she stood holding out her hand to him, an involuntary gesture oddly appealing. He looked at her gravely.

"I'll do all I can," he promised.

John rose. "I know it was an accident," he said, and there was conviction in his tone. "If you want to oblige me, Campion, you'll prove it. Get to the bottom of the mystery and you'll find I'm right. Now, Gina, you're to come back with me. I want you in the house when Cousin Alexander arrives."

The girl rose obediently. A lifetime of authority had endowed John with a gift for it.

"An accident," he repeated firmly as he shook hands with Campion in the hall, adding naïvely: "Terrible publicity. Good night."

Gina clutched Campion's hand; her lips were trembling.

"Let me know what's happening, won't you—please," she whispered.

John was halfway to the staircase and she glanced over her shoulder at him, dropping her voice to a whisper.

"Albert, will they open his letters there?"

Campion met her eyes.

"I shouldn't write if I were you," he said earnestly.

"I see." Her voice died away and the dullness returned to her eyes. "Good-bye, and thank you."

Campion watched her until she disappeared and then went slowly back into the sitting room. He had forgotten Miss Curley, and now the sight of her sitting quietly in an armchair, her hat slipping back until it looked like a three-cornered halo and her near-sighted eyes thoughtful behind her pince-nez, startled him. He smiled at her guiltily.

"I thought I had better stay to tell you that I'll give you all the help I can," she said. "Mr. Widdowson is really terribly grateful to you for taking up the case, but of course he's worried just now. The shock has been tremendous, for one thing. But I thought I'd like to tell you that if you care to examine any room in the office or get access to any papers I'll see that you can do it without interference."

"I shall hold you to that," he said gratefully, and added impulsively: "I'm not really the sensitive soul you seem to think."

She sighed. "Well, as long as you're not . . ." she said. "Mr. Widdowson does give offence quite unconsciously at times. It's being in the office so long, I suppose."

And then, to his consternation, her voice broke and she began to cry.

"I'm all right—I'm all right," she said, waving him away with one hand and dabbing at her eyes with the other. "I don't know what made me so stupid. It's the suddenness of it all, I suppose, although I've woken up in terror of something very like it every night this week. Mr. Campion, why didn't they arrest her as an accomplice?"

Before this mixture of muddled thought and penetration Mr. Campion found himself a trifle bewildered, but he answered the direct question.

"Gina came out very well on the stand," he said cautiously. "Besides, there's no direct evidence of an affair—no letters or anything. The charwoman was pretty damaging, but it was fairly obvious she'd go to pieces in cross-examination."

"But there's no direct evidence against Mike," Miss Curley protested. "It's all circumstantial."

He nodded gloomily. "I know. But there's a devil of a lot of it. I rather fancy that Salley has been stewing up for a row with his critics for some time and is spoiling for a show-down. You see," he went on gently, "the police evidently believe not only that they're right, but that they're obviously right."

Miss Curley's moist eyes darkened reflectively.

"I've known Mike ever since he was a child," she said, "and I don't think——"

She paused and he regarded her quizzically.

"Are you sure?"

The old woman looked up at him.

"Men in love are not quite normal," she said. "I've seen it over and over again. But I don't—I can't think Mike would *kill* Paul. And, anyway," she added triumphantly, "if he had he wouldn't have done it like that."

Campion brightened. "That's what I'm banking on," he said.

Lugg put his head round the door.

"Bloke outside," he remarked, and then, catching sight of Miss Curley, started visibly. "I thought you had gorn, madam," he remarked when he had recovered his composure, and straightening up announced with remarkable change of personality: "A gentleman is waiting in the hall, sir. Would you see 'im?"

"Of course," said Campion, slightly ashamed of his old friend. "Do drop that accent, it's getting on my nerves."

A spiteful expression appeared in Mr. Lugg's small black eyes and he surpassed himself.

"Very blinking good, sir," he said, and stalked out.

Ritchie came in, stooping unconsciously to avoid the lintel.

"Gina gone?" he enquired. "Oh, hello, Miss Curley. Thought I'd come and see you, Campion. Been down to the place with some of Mike's things —pyjamas, toothbrush, comb, and so on. Still got to live, wash, eat, poor chap. It's a mistake, Campion."

He dropped into a chair as he spoke and his pale blue eyes regarded the younger man with that questioning, inarticulate expression which Campion had seen there before.

"Got to find out who did it," said Ritchie. "Must."

Miss Curley rose and held out her hand.

"Don't forget," she repeated, "if there's anything you want to see in the office, come to me."

Campion showed her out and on the steps she looked up at him.

"You're a good boy to help us," she said suddenly, and patted his arm.

Campion went back to Ritchie, who had drawn up to the fire and was gloating over it like some huge but benevolent spider trying to get warm.

"Cousin Alexander," he remarked, without turning round. "Eloquent —dramatic."

Campion took his mind off the immediate problem for a moment to consider Alexander Barnabas, K.C. The grand old man had been comparatively quiet for a month or so, he reflected. He could not remember seeing his name about since the Shadows trials in the summer. In view of the circumstances, he regretted that he had never seen the barrister in the flesh, although photographs of that magnificent head were familiar enough and the very mention of his name brought recollections of dramatic cross-examinations and sensational speeches.

Sir Alexander's history was stormy. Although he was Jacoby Barnabas's only son, he had avoided publishing and taken to the law, with his father's full consent and approval, and had made his name as a junior in the great days of Marshall Hall before the bar had followed stage into a quieter and less rhetorical style. After taking silk his practice had grown and he had been greatly sought after as a leader, until the unfortunate quarrel with the Judge in the Leahbourne case had done his reputation irreparable damage.

However, although it was still felt that his temper was not to be trusted, his triumphal return in the Dallas trial had restored him to popular, if not academic, favour, and he was now considered a fine showy counsel for the defence in sensational criminal trials and was often briefed by solicitors whose clients were backed by a newspaper.

Campion thought he understood Mr. Scruby's apprehension. A remark from Ritchie recalled his attention.

"Thought of something. Ought to mention it."

The man had turned in his chair and was looking up anxiously.

"Hose pipe—car exhaust—locked room—all that, not original," he blurted out at last. "Plagiarism. All in a book."

"In a book?" enquired Mr. Campion, a trifle mystified.

A vigorous nodding affirmed the question.

"Book called *Died on a Saturday*. Most of it in there. Read it myself. Recognized it in court."

"Who published it?"

Ritchie's face lengthened. "Us. Ten—twelve months ago. Not much of a sale."

Mr. Campion was looking at him anxiously.

"Who read this book besides you?—in the office, I mean?"

Ritchie's tremendous bony shoulders hunched in a shrug.

"Anyone. Handled by Mike's department."

"Are you saying that Mike brought out a book describing the method of murder which was used to kill Paul less than a year ago?" Campion demanded, aghast.

Ritchie's wretchedness increased.

"Fifteen months perhaps," he suggested.

Mr. Campion passed his hand over his sleek yellow hair and whistled.

Ritchie was silent for some moments, his awkward figure twisted over the arm of his chair.

"Somebody did it," he said at last. "Evidence showed that."

Campion looked down at him.

"What's your private opinion?" he enquired unexpectedly. "You were much closer to it all than I was. Who did it?"

Ritchie shook his ponderous head.

"Anyone," he murmured, and added with a sigh and a flail-like gesture: "No one."

Mr. Campion pursued his private thoughts.

"That Miss Netley, tell me about her."

Ritchie wrinkled his nose and achieved a masterpiece of pantomimic disapproval.

"Affected girl," he said. "Silly. Sly. Superior. Little snob. Stupid clothes."

"Anything else?"

The other man hesitated.

"Don't know much. Only seen her about. Fond of the ballet. Has a Post Office Savings Book. Arch," he added in triumph. "That's it—she's arch. Don't like her."

He rose to go shame-facedly, evidently feeling that he had not been very helpful in the cause, for he shook hands earnestly and, his blue eyes peering beseechingly into Campion's own, made a long and for him coherent speech.

"Do what you can, Campion, Mike's a good fellow—decent fellow. Never hurt a soul. Kind fellow—kind. Pleasant, friendly to me. Couldn't possibly get anything out of it. If we don't find out who killed affected ass Paul they'll hang Mike—kill him. Stop it, there's a dear chap."

After he had gone Mr. Campion sat at his desk and scribbled idly on the blotting-paper. He had no illusions concerning the task in front of him. Events had moved more swiftly than he had contemplated and the need for urgency was great.

Suddenly the thought which had been playing round the edges of his conscious mind so irritatingly for some time past came out into the open. He reached for the telephone directory and got on to Miss Curley just as she had entered her home in Hammersmith.

She heard his question with surprise.

"Mr. *Tom* Barnabas?" she echoed. "The one who—who disappeared?"

"That's the man." Campion's voice sounded eager. "What sort of person was he? What was he like?"

Miss Curley cast her mind back twenty years.

"A nice man," she said at last. "Good-looking, inclined to be reserved, but very odd. Why?"

"Odd?" Campion seized upon the word. "In what way?"

Miss Curley laughed, but when she spoke her words had a flavour of the macabre.

"He could walk upstairs on his hands," she said.

10 : *Twenty Years After*

It was wet and bitterly cold, with sludge on the pavement and dark grey blankets in the sky, when Mr. Campion walked thoughtfully down Nemetia Crescent, Streatham, and tried to imagine it as it had been on a May morning twenty years before.

To his relief, there was no sign of any recent building operations, and, although the neighbourhood had gone down a little, he suspected, there was no evidence of any structural alteration.

It was a melancholy little enclosure, a half hoop of flat-fronted houses looking out across a strip of wet tarmac at a bank of dilapidated shrubs.

He found the house out of which Tom Barnabas had walked on May the eighth, nineteen hundred and eleven, and stood in the rain looking at it. Dingy lace curtains covered the windows and a fly-blown black card in the transom over the unexpectedly nice door announced in silver letters that there were apartments within.

Mr. Campion passed on and turned the corner at the end of the Crescent. To his relief he saw that the deserted road in front of him tallied exactly with the description Miss Curley had given. A wall over six feet high and completely blank ran down the whole length of the road on the side nearest the Crescent, while on the other a row of little villas recessed from the road by overgrown gardens straggled down to the trams and the main street.

Campion paused and let his imagination dwell upon the facts of the story as he knew them.

It had been about nine o'clock in the morning. Mr. Barnabas had come striding from his house in the Crescent, had turned the corner, and was apparently marching on to the little tobacconist's at the end of the street, where it was his custom to stop and pick up a copy of the *Times* and the *Standard*, when unfortunately he stepped into the fourth dimension or was the victim of spontaneous combustion or some sort of accident to an atom.

The tobacconist's was still there. A row of newspaper boards decorated the far end of the wall, in spite of the rain. Mr. Campion wandered on, pausing now and again in spite of the weather and reflecting upon the few facts he had been able to glean that morning from the files of a newspaper.

For May 8th, 1911, the prophets had predicted fair to fine weather, warm temperature and slight mist. There had been an air smash in the Paris to Madrid race on the day before, when Monsieur Train had crashed at Issy, killing himself and seriously injuring Monsieur Monis, Premier of France, who had been present to see him start. The Court was just out of mourning for Edward VII, the Imperial Conference was opening the following day, and Freeman (J.) had been bowled by Hobbs for twenty-one in the presence of Their Royal Highnesses the Prince of Wales and Prince George.

The information was not very helpful. The world, in fact, seemed to have been going on in much the same way as ever. And since it is always easier to believe in a miracle which happened twenty years ago than in one of yesterday morning, Mr. Campion felt his suspicions aroused.

He looked at the wall. There was no way of telling what was on the other side. It might have hidden a pool, a back garden, or fairyland itself.

He walked on to the newspaper and tobacconist's shop. As he entered it his spirits rose. This stuffy little room with its doorway narrowed to the verge of the impassable by ancient paper-racks filled with brightly coloured periodicals, its acrid smell of newsprint, its two counters, one piled high with papers and the other decorated with every known brand of tobacco grouped round an immense pair of shining scales, could not have altered for forty or fifty, much less twenty, years.

He stood hesitating on the square foot or so of floor space for some moments before he realized that he was not alone in this sanctuary of smoke and light literature.

Over the paper department there was a species of canopy composed of yet more periodicals clipped into wire frames, and in the narrow opening between this and the counter he caught sight of two very bright eyes peering at him from out a pepper-and-salt wilderness of hair and whisker.

"Paper or a nice box of cigarettes, sir?" said a voice at once friendly and a trifle pert.

Mr. Campion bought both and had the satisfaction of seeing the remainder of the man as he came running out of his lurking place to attend to the tobacconist's side of his business.

He was very small, spry and compact, and his feet, which were tiny, were thrust into old sheep-skin slippers which flapped as he walked.

"Haven't seen you about here before, sir?" he enquired. "Moved into the district?"

"Not yet," said Mr. Campion cautiously.

"No offence meant and none taken, I hope," said the old man, running all the words together until they formed a single apologetic sound. "Only I saw you wandering up and down the road just now and it came into my head that you might be looking for lodgings. This part isn't what it used to be, but I could put you on to several nice respectable women who'd look after you very well. Perhaps you'd like a widow, now?" he finished, his little bright eyes watching Campion with the inquisitive yet impersonal interest of a sparrow.

"Not at present," said Mr. Campion, who had a literal mind. "As a matter of fact, I came down here on a sort of sentimental errand. A friend of mine disappeared, or is supposed to have disappeared, walking along this street."

Tremendous interest appeared at once on the small face.

"I believe you're referring to my phenomenon," he said. "I always call it mine, although it wasn't really. I just happened to be there. Now that *was* a funny thing, if you like."

"Do you remember it?"

"Remember it? Wasn't I in this very shop?" The little man seemed hurt. "Wasn't it me who gave interviews to all the newspapers?—or would have done, only they didn't believe me. It was hushed up really. Did you know that? In my opinion, sir," he went on, eyeing Mr. Campion with portentous solemnity, "that was the most important thing that ever happened to me in all my life. And, luck being what it is—" he spread out his hands and hunched his shoulders in a gesture of resignation, "—I turned me back on it."

"Infuriating," murmured Mr. Campion sympathetically.

"It was," said his informant and, returning to his position behind the paper counter, leant across it and took a deep breath. "I didn't always talk about this," he began. "My name's Higgleton, by the way."

"How d'you do?" said Campion pleasantly.

"Pleased to meet *you*, sir," complied Mr. Higgleton, with grace, and plunged into his story. "It was on a Monday—no, a Tuesday morning, I think it was. Or it may have been a Thursday—I can't really remember—but I can see it as plain as daylight. I didn't talk about it much at the time because—well, you know what people are. Once you start seeing things that other people know can't have happened, you're apt to get the reputation of being a little bit queer."

"Fanciful," suggested Mr. Campion.

"Exactly. But I remember that Wednesday morning as though it was yesterday. Only it was May then, not February like it is now. It was a beautiful clear morning, bright sunlight—we didn't have summertime then, so there was no hanky-panky—just a bright clear summer's day. This place is very pretty in the summer, though you might not think so. When there's leaves on those trees over there you can't see the houses. There were more trees in those days. It was when the children kept getting run over that they had one or two of 'em down. The children couldn't see the road from the gardens because of the trees and they used to run out and—there you are, as the saying is."

"I suppose that's why no one saw Mr. Barnabas from the houses?" said Mr. Campion.

"Barnabas!" said Mr. Higgleton, pouncing on the name. "That's it! That's it! Couldn't remember it for a moment, although it was on the tip of me tongue. That's why I was hedging about. Oh, I knew him as well as I know—you, I was going to say. Used to come in here every day for his papers. He was an ornament to the neighbourhood. I don't know what his business was; it was something in the City. But he used to turn out to it as though he was going to a——" Mr. Higgleton paused and searched in his mind for a simile.

"Ball?" suggested Mr. Campion idiotically.

His new friend glanced at him reproachfully.

"Well, not exactly a ball, but a wedding. City gentlemen used to dress more tastefully then than they do now. You probably wouldn't remember it very well, but they did. Silk hats and tail coats and fancy trousers were all the go, and a nice pair of yellow gloves to top everything off."

"And was Mr. Barnabas dressed like that when he disappeared?" said Mr. Campion.

"He was. A very well-dressed man indeed was Mr. Barnabas. I can see him now—in me mind's eye, of course—silk hat, nicely brushed, gold-topped cane and spats. A big handsome man he was, too, and very nicely spoken."

"How did it happen?" The question escaped Mr. Campion involuntarily.

"In the twinkling of a hand—like that!" said Mr. Higgleton, and snapped his fingers.

He had an odd trick of pausing after he had made an announcement and surveying his listener with a wide-eyed expression, as though inviting him to join in a wonder.

Mr. Campion, who had liked him from the start, began to feel a positive affection for him.

"I'll show you how it happened," said Mr. Higgleton, and, running out from behind the counter, he planted himself on the door-step. "Now here am I—see," he said over his shoulder, "standing on the corner of the street. It's nine o'clock in the morning, but I'm not so busy as all that, and I'm just standing here taking a deep breath of the ozone."

He gulped a lungful of rain-soaked, soot-laden air, and glanced at Campion for approval.

"Well, I see Mr. Barnabas turn the corner of the street down there."

He waved his hand in the direction of Nemetia Crescent.

"Now I *know* it is him—there's no doubt about that. (My eyes are better than what they are now, it being twenty years ago.) And I watch him coming up the street for a bit. There he is, striding along in the sunlight swinging his cane, looking as calm and happy as you please.

"Well, when he's about fifty yards away I say to meself, 'I'd better get his papers.' So I turn back into me shop like this," he trotted back to the counter and picked up a couple of newspapers which he thrust under Campion's nose. "There they are—see? Then I hurry back to the door and—" he stopped, and peered up and down the street, ventured out into the rain, and finally returned, bewilderment expressed in every line of his features, "—not a sign of him," he said. "Street empty all ways. You could knock me down with a wave of the hand, as the saying has it.

" 'Well,' I said, 'he's vanished!' And he had, too."

Again the look of wonder.

"Of course you'll say," he continued after a silence which Mr. Campion had not liked to break, "that he must have snapped into a trot and run past the shop. But he couldn't have done. I wasn't in here above five seconds. Besides, the constable who was standing on the corner saw him go. One minute he was there and one minute he wasn't. In the middle of the pavement about fifteen yards from this shop, just along by the wall there, he disappeared and was never seen by mortal eye again."

"Top hat, gold-headed cane and all?" said Mr. Campion.

"Yellow gloves *and* spats," said Mr. Higgleton. "Clean as kiss yer hand."

"I'd like to have met the policeman." Mr. Campion sounded wistful.

"So you should have. I'd have taken you round myself if he hadn't retired and gone to live in the country. Somewhere Norfolk way he is. But he drops in here now and again when he comes to town. He was here as little as two years ago. Next time I see him I'll tell him you're interested and perhaps he'll let you have his side of the story. His name's on the tip of me tongue, but I've forgotten it."

Mr. Higgleton thought for a while but to no purpose.

Mr. Campion expressed his thanks and made an attempt to leave, but he was not to get away so easily.

"I don't like to pretend I know what happened because I don't," said his new friend, skilfully edging between him and the exit. "But then funny things do happen. There was a man in that house over there—you can see it if you stand on the step—who ran off with every servant-girl his wife had in the course of twelve years. Every single one of them!"

This time the expression of wonder was a little overdone.

"She fetched him back one week and off he'd go with the new girl the next."

"What happened in the end?" said Mr. Campion, interested in spite of himself.

"Cut his throat on a golf-course in Scotland," said Mr. Higgleton. "And then there was the woman with the snakes."

"Really?" murmured Mr. Campion, moving adroitly to the right and gaining six inches in his progress to the door.

"She used to live in this house at the back of mine, on the other side," said Mr. Higgleton frantically. "Her garden used to run down behind mine and finish up alongside this wall. Of course, she left before the war, but at one time her place was *alive* with 'em. She used to breed 'em and train 'em. Some of them were very clever, I believe, but I never liked them."

He sighed. Mr. Campion was going to get away; he could see it.

"If ever that police sergeant should drop in, sir, perhaps you'd like me to give him your name?" he ventured, breathless with defeat.

"That's very kind of you." Campion drew a card from his wallet and Mr. Higgleton took it and placed it with great care behind a jar of tobacco on the shelf at the back of the shop. "Any time you want to know anything about this district," he said wistfully, "you'll come to me, won't you?"

Mr. Campion felt a cad.

"I certainly shall," he said. "Thank you very much."

"It's been a pleasure, sir," said Mr. Higgleton truthfully, and Campion went down to the High Street to find a cab, convinced in spite of his stern belief in the material that something very odd indeed had happened to Tom Barnabas twenty years before.

When he arrived back at Bottle Street he was still absorbed by the past and the urgent message from the present head of the firm of Barnabas and Company, Limited, demanding his immediate attendance at Twenty-three, Horsecollar Yard, brought him back to the problem of the moment with uncomfortable conviction that he had spent an unprofitable morning.

He arrived at the office at a little after two o'clock and was shown at once into John's big room on the ground floor, where a conference was in progress. Before he entered the room, while he was still in the hall, the sonorous voice from within warned him what to expect, and he did not come upon Cousin Alexander altogether unprepared.

The first thing he saw upon entering the room was the back of John's head and the arc of his forehead. He was leaning back in his chair, which had been turned away from the door, and appeared to be entranced or even stupefied by the spectacle confronting him.

On the hearth rug Sir Alexander Barnabas stood in one of his more famous attitudes, and Campion had the full benefit of his commanding presence. He was a big man, tall and heavy, with a magnificent physique and a great head surmounted by a mass of iron-grey curls parted sleekly down the middle and brushed up at the sides so that, whether by accident or design, one was almost deceived into thinking that his barrister's wig was a fixture.

His face was handsome in an orthodox way and its clean-shaven mobility had a trick of emphasizing the slightest inflection in its owner's voice with appropriate expression.

At the moment he was radiating authority. One long graceful hand was upraised to drive home some point while the other rested behind his broad, dark-coated back.

"There is no question of that," he was saying. "Ab-so-lute-ly no question." And Mr. Campion was quite convinced that, whatever the subject of conversation might be, there could indeed be absolutely no question about it.

At Campion's entrance John pulled himself out of the stupor into which he had fallen and performed the introduction.

Mr. Campion was aware of a personage condescending to do a great honour. Two immense fingers rested in his hand for a second, and then he was dismissed to the realm of unimportant things and Cousin Alexander's melodious voice took up the thread of his discourse once again.

"We must have an acquittal," he said. "Complete and unconditional acquittal with no stain left upon the boy's character. I shall work for that and I shall achieve it."

Mr. Campion sat down on the edge of a chair in the far corner of the room and listened politely. Miracles seemed to be the order of the day.

"But you must understand, John," the Counsel continued firmly. "The case against Mike is very strong. Circumstantial evidence can be very deadly indeed. At the moment Michael is in a position of the gravest danger."

Mr. Campion pulled himself together with a jerk. The effect of so powerful a personality at close range was disconcerting. When Sir Alexander spoke of gravity one automatically thought of international crises and in his mouth the word "danger" had the shrill insistence of a fire alarm.

John attempted to speak, but was answered before a word had left his mouth.

"I have seen the boy," said Cousin Alexander, "and I am convinced of his innocence. Innocence," he repeated and stared at Campion, who found himself feeling like a rabbit caught in the glare of a headlight. "Innocent." Sir Alexander again dropped his voice to a whisper. "I heard his statement. Only an innocent man would have dared to make such a damaging confession. Why did he admit he had no alibi? Because he was telling the truth. Because he was innocent."

His glance swept round the room.

"Can't you see what happened?" he went on passionately. "Are you blind? Or does the very nakedness of truth offend your modesty? Imagine it . . ."

His voice had become persuasive, his excitement passing as rapidly as it had arisen.

"Think of the story he told the police. Think of the damaging history of that fatal night, related as simply as a child might have told it, a child not only innocent, but so guileless as to believe that not for a moment would its innocence be called into question."

Mr. Campion settled back in his chair and reflected how much more bearable drama was when it had a little art to help it along. On the witness-stand Mike had presented a depressing tale, but in Sir Alexander's hands his story became an exhilarating experience if not in particularly good taste. Meanwhile the great man was off again filling the room with melodious but overpowering sound.

"The Coroner demanded to know where Mike was between the hours of five and nine in the evening, hours which have since proved to be critical in the history of this terrible case. What did the boy do? Did he invent a history of little alibis to be broken down one by one by a pitiless police enquiry? Or did he tell the truth? 'I walked,' he said. 'I walked alone through the London streets, amid thousands of my fellow men, not one of whom will come forward to bear me witness. I was unknown to them—a stranger. I was alone.'"

"Yes, but what was he doing?" said John irritably, the paralyzing quality of Cousin Alexander's peroration having apparently passed over his head. "What purpose could he possibly have had in wandering about like that?"

Just for a moment the great man seemed to have been taken off his balance. He was evidently not used to interruptions, for his eye wavered and when he spoke again there was a reproving quality in the beautiful voice which had very little to do with art.

"If you will have patience," he said, "I will tell you. Mike is a young man and he committed a crime which, although reprehensible, is one of those misfortunes which overtake young men in spite of themselves. He fell in love with another man's wife. But he did not tell her so. He stood by and saw her neglected and tyrannized over by a man who did not realize her worth. From beginning to end their association was innocent. It does not follow that because of this restraint his passion was any the less real. An evening came when he knew the woman he loved was going to have a long interview with the man to whom she was bound by every legal and moral tie which our civilization has devised. Imagine him——"

The sonorous voice took on a hushed quality that Mr. Campion, who felt he was listening to the truth in dramatized form, found a little shocking.

"Imagine him sitting at his desk early in the evening of that cold January day. He was due to attend some literary function where a great deal of rubbish, some of it witty, some of it not, would be bandied from mouth to mouth, while in the very house in which he lived, in the very room two floors above that in which he slept, the woman whose being was the very core of his existence was talking to the man against whom she was completely defenceless, the man to whom the law gave every conceivable right in her, the man from whom she could not escape and from whom he dared not protect her.

"Do you see him there?" he went on, fixing Campion with a steely blue eye strangely reminiscent of the portrait in the waiting room. And then, in an even quieter voice: "I do. He cannot work, he does not want to go to the witty gathering whose chatter cannot save him from himself, nor can he go to his own home because he knows that in the room upstairs *she* is talking to his rival, her husband.

"What more natural for him, then—" the voice became musical as its rich tones played over the euphonious words, "—than to feel he must get away? Even his car is denied him: the fog is too thick. So he walks. He takes refuge in the time-honoured escape which men of every age and every generation have used to soothe their troubled spirits.

"He walks through London, through the crowds, thinking of her, trying to reason with himself, no doubt: trying to wrest himself from the cloying embraces of the pitiless emotion which consumes him."

John attempted to rise to his feet at this juncture, but was subdued by the famous eye.

"The little shop in Bayswater," said Cousin Alexander. "A secondhand jewellery store. A little place of curios, sentimental trifles scarcely of any value. He went there to buy her something, so engrossed in his thoughts that he forgot the day, forgot that it was a Thursday afternoon, upon which the keeper of the shop took his holiday and closed the shutters over the little trinkets, bidding lovers and their ladies wait until the morrow."

He paused, evidently feeling that he was navigating a dangerous stretch, and his keen eyes appraised their discomfort.

"He turned back. He walked on through the wet, cold streets. He did not notice they were wet, he did not notice they were cold; he was thinking of her, he was thinking of the woman. When he reached his home he had still come no nearer his goal, he had still not thrashed out his problem. It remained as large, as terrifying, as piteous, as wearying as ever before. He still felt the need of escape."

The great voice quivered and boomed, and at such close quarters was well-nigh pulverizing.

"What did he do? He saw the night was clearer. He thought of his car. He thought of the cool roads, the open fields, little remote villages—freedom, solitude. He went round to the garage and because it was his habit, because he wanted complete obedience from his car, he switched on the engine, intending to let it run for a while so that the cylinders should be warm, the oil moving smoothly and evenly.

"And at that time he was completely unaware that his car had been, or was going to be, used by some enemy to destroy the very man to whom the woman he loved was tied. Unfortunately for him he did not take the car straight out of the garage. Instead he remembered the key of the yard gate and went to his lonely little flat to fetch it.

"Imagine the thoughts which must have come into his mind as he entered that room and realized that she was above him, closeted, so he thought, remember, with the husband who neglected and had no respect for her.

"Then, just as he was about to take the key, what happened? The telephone bell rang and he heard her voice. He went down, turned off the car, and these two young people went out together. Is that the sort of man who would have gone to see a moving picture if he knew that down in the strong room beneath the office, in the very house next to the one in which he was going to sleep that night, a man lay suffocated to death? Of course not! It is not feasible."

He allowed the last word to die away and then quite surprisingly dropped his artificial manner and became a different sort of person altogether.

"That's the truth, you know," he said. "That's what happened."

John pulled a crisp white handkerchief out of his pocket and wiped his forehead.

"I think you're right about Mike," he said. "You convinced me."

A smile, pleased and schoolboyish, appeared upon Cousin Alexander's handsome face.

"It's effective, isn't it?" he said, including Campion in the question. "Awfully effective, and true. But we can't possibly use it."

Mr. Campion said nothing. A purely academic consideration concerning the importance of technique in all phases of modern life had sprung unbidden to his mind.

"Not use it?" said John in exasperation.

"Oh, no, we couldn't use it." Sir Alexander was quite definite. "Not in this case, not in London. It's not suitable. We simply must not admit any love at all. In law love is suspicious. Bendex—he's going to be one junior and is devilling for me at the moment—points out that that is absolutely without question, and I see that he's right. I was only telling you privately why I know Mike's innocent. We'll think of something else. But that's the truth of that point, I'm sure of it. Who is that?"

The final remark was made with a trace of his old manner and both John and Mr. Campion turned towards the door, through which faint sounds, as of a slight scuffle, reached them.

"Come in," said John peremptorily and, the handle turning abruptly, the door burst open and Mr. Rigget was precipitated into the room.

It was evident at once that something more than the business of the Accounts Department had occasioned his sudden appearance. He was neat, as usual, but considerably more pink and clearly a little above himself. He was also breathless.

At the sight of the K.C. he wavered and for a moment it seemed as though his determination would desert him, but a glimpse of John's stony face seemed to pull him together.

"I thought it my duty to come to you at once, sir," he said in a squeaky rush, his eyes snapping behind his pince-nez and his phraseology oddly stilted. "I reached the decision to tell something of which I had become cognizant to the police only this morning and now that I have done so I thought it would be only fair to tell you as well."

He stood for a moment wavering. John was looking at him as though he were some particularly unpleasant species of life, repellent but not dangerous.

Cousin Alexander, on the other hand, was staring over his head, no doubt considering Truth from yet another angle. Mr. Campion alone remained politely interested.

From pink Mr. Rigget became crimson and a dappling of sweat appeared upon his forehead.

"I've just told Sergeant Pillow about the quarrel I heard," he said sulkily. "It was on the Wednesday morning before the Thursday on which Mr. Paul was killed. The door between Mr. Paul's rooms and the File Copy Office was ajar and I didn't like to shut it."

Cousin Alexander bent his gaze upon the wretched man for the first time.

"Eavesdropping?" he enquired blandly.

"I happened to hear certain words," said Mr. Rigget indignantly. "And," he added, a suggestion of a snarl appearing for a fleeting instant across his mouth with the surprisingly white teeth, "I thought it was my duty to repeat them to the police."

"Get out!" said John, suddenly losing his temper. "Get out! Get straight out of the Office."

"Wait a minute." Cousin Alexander's voice had become pleasant again. "Let's hear what this gentleman has to say. You've come here to help us, haven't you? That's extremely kind of you. My cousin appreciates it. What did you hear when the door was ajar? First of all, who was speaking? You were sure of the voices, were you?"

"Yes, I was," said Mr. Rigget, considerably taken aback by this mercurial change in the magnificent-looking old gentleman in front of him. "Besides, I'd seen Mr. Paul and Mr. Mike when I went through the room first."

"Mr. Paul and Mr. Michael . . ." said Cousin Alexander soothingly. "And what were the words you heard?"

"Well, they'd stopped talking when I went in first," said Mr. Rigget truculently, "and then I suppose they thought the door was shut so they went on with their quarrel."

"Or conversation," murmured Sir Alexander pleasantly. "And then what?"

Mr. Rigget swung round on John. There was intense satisfaction upon his ignoble face.

"Mr. Paul said, 'You mind your own damned business, Mike. She's mine and I'll manage my own life in my own way.'"

There was complete silence in the room after he had spoken and he had the satisfaction of knowing that he had achieved a sensation.

"And did you hear anything else?" Cousin Alexander's voice was cloying.

"Yes," said Mr. Rigget, blushing to the roots of his black hair. "He said, 'Make love to her if you want to—God knows I'm not stopping you.'"

"And then?"

"I didn't hear any more," said Mr. Rigget. "I came out then. But I could see what Mr. Mike was thinking."

"That's not evidence," said Cousin Alexander.

11 : *Fuse Cap*

After a tedious magisterial hearing Michael Wedgwood was committed for trial and on the afternoon before the day on which he was to appear at the Old Bailey Mr. Campion, with Ritchie at his side, steered the Lagonda through the traffic in New Oxford Street. It was one of those warm blowy days when every street corner is a flower garden presided over by a stalwart London nymph still clad in the wools and tippets of winter and the air is redolent with an exciting mixture of tar, exhaust and face powder.

However, neither of the men in the big car was in the mood to appreciate the eternal hopefulness of spring. Ritchie was talking, curbing his gestures with considerable difficulty because of the confined space.

"Want you to see her," he said. "Don't like her like this. It's getting her down, Campion. She's fond of him, you know. Loves him and probably feels responsible. Women always take responsibility. It's a form of vanity. Can't help it. Natural with them."

His anxiety seemed to have loosened his tongue and the fact that he now considered Campion an old friend made him more coherent.

"Bound to get him off, don't you think?" he added, cocking a wistful eye at the young man beside him. "Terrible experience anyway. All terrible," he went on, waving a tremendous arm between Mr. Campion's eyes and the windscreen. "All this. All these people. They're all in prison. All miserable. All slaves. All got to work when they don't want to, eat when they don't want to, sleep when they don't want to. Can't drink until someone says they may. Can't hide their faces, got to hide their bodies. No freedom anywhere. I hate it. Frightens me. Knew a man once who chucked it. I couldn't."

"It's a feeling one does get sometimes," Mr. Campion conceded.

"I always feel like it," said Ritchie and hesitated on the brink of some further confidence but thought better of it and was silent.

They found Gina sitting by the open window in the big studio and Campion, who had not seen her for some weeks, was shocked by the change in her. She was harder, more sophisticated, older. Nervous exhaustion had been replaced by general deterioration. She looked less chic, less graceful, less charming.

Her greeting was artificial and it was not until he had been sitting on the big white sofa for some minutes that she suddenly turned to him with something of her old genuineness.

"It was good of you to come," she said. "I'm not going to cry or do anything silly and I shall be perfectly composed in the witness-box. It's not hearing from him," she added, her defences suddenly collapsing. "No mental contact at all. He's just gone. He might be dead."

The natural embarrassment which the confidence might have engendered was swept away by the relief which Campion felt at seeing that her artificiality went no deeper. This was only a warning then of the damage which might be done to her and had not the awful finality of the accomplished fact.

"You—you haven't found out what really happened? I know you haven't. You'd have told me, of course. But haven't you got just an inkling— haven't you got a clue? When I asked John he said something about a new witness. Can't you tell me about that? Or is it all a secret, like everything else?"

The mixture of bitterness and pleading in her deep voice was disturbing. Mr. Campion wished in his heart that he had better news for her.

"The new witness may be useful," he said. "His name's Widgeon. I had an awful job getting hold of him. He didn't want to talk but when he realized how much depended on it he shelved his private considerations like a sportsman and came out with all he knew. He's employed by the Tolleshunt Press people. They've got a small office on the second floor of Number Twenty-one. Apparently he got tight at lunch on the Thursday and it took him all the afternoon to sober up, so that he came to himself about five with a splitting headache and all the afternoon's work on his hands. So he stayed behind and did it and was still hard at it between six and nine, when Mrs. Tripper was making herself cups of tea and coming home from pictures and trotting along to the fried-fish shop."

He paused and smiled at her encouragingly.

"His story is that he heard the car start up soon after six—he can't say how soon—and that the engine was running continuously until eight or thereabouts, and that he didn't hear it again until ten to nine, when it ran for only a short time."

"But that lets Mike out! That bears out Mike's story!"

For the first time during the interview a faint tinge of colour appeared in her pale cheeks and she seemed to take new life.

Campion looked uncomfortable.

"It bears out his story," he said, "but it doesn't let him out. He can't establish his alibi between six and the time you phoned him, remember."

"I see," she said. She sank back again, her slender body in the sleek, man-tailored gown lifeless and pathetic.

"It'll help," said Campion, anxious to be reassuring. "Apart from fixing in the jury's mind that the whole thing probably happened on the Thursday, it refutes the evidence of the Tripper woman, or muddles it at any rate."

"And you've discovered nothing else?"

"Nothing of value," he confessed. "There's been so little to go upon. Usually in these things you can get your teeth in somewhere and worry the whole thing out, but in this business there hasn't been a gripping place. I had great hopes of Miss Netley, but either she can't talk and simply tried to look as though she could out of vanity, or else there's no earthly reason why she should and she doesn't want to."

"Netley," said Ritchie and, getting to his feet, walked out of the room.

His exit was so abrupt that they both looked after him. Gina's eyes were wet when she returned to Campion.

"He's been so kind," she said. "I used to think he was inhuman, a sort of creature; not a lunatic, you know, but, well, just not quite a right thing; but since—since Paul died he's been the only person who's behaved normally, to me at any rate. He's genuinely sorry for me and terrified for Mike. The others, John and even dear old Curley and Mrs. Austin and the doctor and all the other normal people who I always thought were ordinary and real, and who I expected to have ordinary human reactions, have their own points of view so strongly that they have no room for mine or Mike's. D'you know, John's *only* thinking about the publicity and the firm, and Curley follows him. Mrs. Austin's thinking about her personal appearance. It's as though she was going on the stage . . ."

Mr. Campion looked sympathetic.

"They're in it, you see, old dear," he said. "It's touched their lives."

She nodded gloomily. "It's the first time I've ever seen anything terrible close to," she said. "I haven't shown up very well to myself."

There was a silence which Mr. Campion did not like to break and presently she spoke again.

"John brought that man he calls Cousin Alexander up here. I got hysterical and they sent a doctor to me. I didn't mean to but he just wasn't human as far as I was concerned. He was like an author planning a book or a play. They talked about hostile witnesses and witness for the defence not as though they were people but as though they were stray ideas, little pieces of construction."

"Sir Alexander is convinced that he'll get an acquittal," said Campion.

"I know." Her voice became strident. "Insufficient evidence! And what good'll that be? I talked all this out with Ritchie and he was as appalled as I was when he realized it. Don't you see an acquittal will only save Mike's life? The great damage is done."

She leant forward, her intelligent face turned to him and her eyes very steady.

"Don't you see," she said, speaking carefully, as though he were a child, "if they acquit him without finding the man who did the murder everyone will always believe that Mike did it, and if ever he is seen speaking to me that'll prove it from their point of view."

"I suppose what other people think matters?" said Mr. Campion weakly.

"Of course it matters," she said angrily. "It becomes the truth. What everybody thinks *is* the truth."

Mr. Campion was silent, knowing from experience that a discourse on ethics is rarely comforting to anyone in genuine distress.

"Somebody must have done it," she said. "Who was it? I've gone over it again and again so often that I sometimes think I shall go mad and imagine I did it myself. It was someone clever enough to think of arranging an accident, someone who had no idea how clever the police are. Albert, it wasn't Mike, was it?"

"No," said Mr. Campion quietly but with complete conviction. "It wasn't Mike."

She laughed unsteadily.

"When you're alone thinking, you believe anything."

Her voice died on the last word and she turned round. The door clattered open and Ritchie returned. Because of his excitement he was clumsier than ever and he lurched across the room dangerously.

"Any good?" he enquired, dropping something into Mr. Campion's lap.

Mr. Campion turned over the battered cardboard-backed book in some astonishment.

"Post Office Savings Bank?" he said. "Whose is it?"

"Girl Netley's." Ritchie seemed tremendously pleased with himself. "Might be interesting. Never know. Often thought it funny she brought it to the office. Keep bank books at home, not lying about."

"Where did you get it from?" Mr. Campion turned over the pages carefully.

"Out of her bag," said Ritchie without hesitation or attempt at mitigation. "Can't be conventional at a time like this."

Mr. Campion made no comment. Something in the book had attracted his attention and he sat for some considerable time turning over the pages and comparing entries.

"Thrifty kid," he said at last. "She saves ten bob a week regularly, every Saturday. There it is. It goes back nearly a year. Handed in at the same office just down the road here in Holborn. There were several sums paid in at Christmas—that's presents, I suppose—and she took out three pounds then too. I'm afraid it doesn't tell us much about her, unless—— Hello! What's this?"

Gina rose to look over his shoulder while Ritchie leant back in his chair, his long hands dropping over the arms and his eyes mild and inquisitive, like a dog who has brought a parcel and is content to see his master open it.

Mr. Campion ran a finger down a paying-in column and traced certain entries across the page to the circular stamp which showed at which office the deposits had been made.

"These can't all be birthdays," he said. "They're funny amounts, too; so irregular. A pound on October the twenty-second last year, paid in at St. James's of all places. Ten shillings in the middle of the first week in November at the same place. Then there's just the ordinary ten shillings until December the first, when she paid two pounds in at the St. Martin's Lane office. Then nothing odd until January, and then there's quite a lot. Three pounds on the tenth, another three pounds on the thirteenth, two pounds on the seventeenth, then three again on the twentieth and—I say— five pounds on the twenty-ninth. That was the day after Paul disappeared. I wonder . . ."

He turned over the pages and his frown deepened.

"And there's nothing since. That's odd in a way."

"Source of blackmail dead," suggested Ritchie crudely.

Mr. Campion did not scout the suggestion openly.

"It's not very much for blackmail," he murmured. "Eighteen pounds odd all told. It's the paying-in places that strike me as being odd. They're all over the shop. Only the first two alike. Of course, we're catching at straws now, you know. This doesn't prove anything. It may mean absolutely nothing. Still, it's worth looking up."

He closed the book and slipped it into his pocket.

"I think I'll go across and have a word with her."

"Say I took it if you have to," said Ritchie recklessly.

"God forbid." Mr. Campion spoke piously and left them.

In spite of the fact that he had become a familiar figure at Twenty-three during the last few months, custom insisted that he should be shown into the waiting room and there left to kick his heels until the person whom he sought should be discovered and delivered to him.

He was standing with his back to the door, surveying the portrait of Jacoby Barnabas afresh, when Miss Netley came in. She went to meet him, a smile upon her lips and the same smug secretiveness in her eyes which he had noticed at their first meeting.

"Here again, Mr. Campion?" she said pleasantly but with the faintest suggestion of amusement in her tone. "I thought perhaps you'd brought us a manuscript!"

Mr. Campion's smile was wholly charming.

"That's what I call intuition," he said. "Look at this."

He had the satisfaction of seeing her complaisance vanish as she caught sight of the little brown book in his hand. Her round eyes lost their ingenuous expression and her colour vanished.

"It's mine," she said. "Where did you get it? Thank you for returning it."

"Ah, but I'm not returning it," murmured Mr. Campion and she gaped at him.

"I've never heard such impudence in all my life," she burst out finally. "How dare you! Where *did* you get it anyway?"

"Took it," said Mr. Campion and put the book back in his pocket.

Miss Netley trembled. "It's outrageous!" she said unsteadily. "It's illegal, it's—it's stealing!"

"Of course it is," he agreed. "Let's go and tell Inspector Tanner all about it, shall we? He's a policeman."

She drew back from him, her lips sulky, her eyes narrowed and frightened.

"What do you want to know? I can't tell you anything."

Mr. Campion sighed with relief. They taught them to be quick-witted in offices, he reflected.

"I thought we might have a chat," he said.

"I've told the police everything—absolutely everything."

"About the murder? Yes, of course you have," he said, wondering how long they were going to be left alone in peace in the waiting room. "Let's talk about yourself."

Her suspicion increased.

"I don't understand."

Mr. Campion leant on the large table which filled the centre of the room. His expression was vague to the point of idiocy and his eyes looked guileless behind his spectacles.

"I hate to sound inquisitive and my question may sound a little in bad taste," he began, "but however much one's upset by a death one has to face facts, hasn't one? I do hope you won't think it impertinent of me to ask if your financial position has been very much upset by Mr. Paul Brande's death? It is frightfully inquisitive, I know, but I would be really obliged if you'd tell me."

She looked relieved and he saw at once that he was on a wrong tack.

"Well, I haven't lost my job, if that's what you mean," she said. "What other difference could it make?"

"None, of course. If you're staying on that's all right." Mr. Campion covered his tracks but her interest had been aroused.

"Just exactly what are you getting at?" she demanded.

He took the bank book out of his pocket, looked at it thoughtfully, and replaced it again.

"You told the police exactly what happened when Mr. Paul Brande got a letter by the afternoon post on the Thursday that he disappeared. You haven't remembered anything else since, have you?"

"I've told it all, every single word, over and over again."

There was an edge to her voice which warned him to be careful. He smiled at her brightly.

"You've got awfully strong nerves, haven't you?" he said. "Let's go into his old office and—just go through it. Please don't think I'm being a nuisance, but I would like to know just exactly what happened. It'll fix the picture in my mind, you see."

Miss Netley looked at him witheringly but the retort which rose to her lips did not come and without a word she led him up to the first floor and into the big comfortable room, a little too preciously furnished for an office, in which Paul had worked.

Mr. Campion sat down at the desk after placing his hat and stick carefully on a side table.

"Now," he said, "where were you when the letter came?"

Still sullen, and looking her contempt, Miss Netley seated herself at the typewriter in the corner.

"Now," said Mr. Campion, "I suppose the boy brought the letter in, gave it to you and you handed it to Mr. Brande?"

She bowed her head. It was evident that she did not trust herself to speak. Mr. Campion tore open an imaginary envelope, exhibiting much pantomimic skill.

"Now," he demanded briskly, "what do I do now?"

"Mr. Paul got up," said Miss Netley, indicating that she was not going to play, "scrunched up the paper and envelope and threw them into the fireplace."

"Like that?" said Mr. Campion, hurling an imaginary ball from him violently.

"No," she said unwillingly. "Just casually."

"And it burned?" he enquired, his eyes resting on her quizzically.

"It did."

"All of it? Every scrap of it?"

"Every tiny bit."

"You looked to see?"

She met his eyes defiantly. "After he had gone, yes, I did."

"We're getting on," said Mr. Campion cheerfully. "Now I get up, don't I? And I seem excited? What happens? Do I get red and seem a little flustered? Do I take up my hat and stick and make for the door without a word or a glance in your direction? Or do I say something?"

The girl hesitated. She seemed to be considering her course of action. "No," she said at last, grudgingly. "Mr. Paul asked me if a parcel had come."

"Oh, did he? What did he say? Can you remember his actual words?"

"He said"—she still spoke unwillingly—" 'Has that parcel come from Fortnum and Mason's yet?' "

"Fortnum and Mason's? And what did you say?"

"I said, 'No, Mr. Brande, I don't think it has.' And he said, 'Oh, well, it doesn't matter,' and went out without it. And now I hope you're satisfied."

"Well, it's a crumb," said Mr. Campion. "It's a crumb. Ten bob here, a pound there. Two pounds and five pounds—it all tells up, doesn't it?"

He stopped abruptly. If he had meant to terrify her he could not have been more successful. She was staring at him, her eyes wide and her lips open.

"What do you know?" she said huskily.

"Much more than you'd think." Mr. Campion spoke cryptically and he hoped convincingly. "Let's get back to Mr. Paul. You said the parcel hadn't come and then what happened?"

"I told you. He said it didn't matter. 'It does not matter,' he said. 'I will go without it.' Then he went out and shut the door and I never saw him again."

"Splendid!" said Mr. Campion. "You're not a good witness, you know, but it makes a lot of difference when you try. Now what happened to the parcel? Did it ever come?"

"Yes. It came about an hour after he left. I put it in that cupboard over there."

"Is it still there?"

"I don't know. I haven't looked."

"Then shall we look now?" he suggested.

She got up, sauntered across the room and jerked open the cupboard. "Yes," she said. "There it is."

"Bring it here," said Mr. Campion. "I wouldn't have you for a secretary as a gift."

Miss Netley reddened and opened her mouth to speak. A single unprintable epithet left her lips and then, as he looked completely shocked, she strode over to her typewriter and burst into tears.

Campion examined the parcel. There seemed to be nothing in any way extraordinary about it and he loosened the string. Inside was a square box, tastefully ornamented and containing two pounds of crystallized Cape gooseberries.

He sat looking at them in their green and pink sugar jackets, his head slightly on one side and his eyes puzzled.

"Who was the lady?" he enquired at last.

Miss Netley wiped her eyes.

"I don't know."

"Of course you do. Ten bob—two pounds——"

She laughed. "You're wrong. I knew you were wrong."

Her watery-eyed triumph was vindictive.

"Well, I know now," said Mr. Campion mercilessly. "Come on, I want the address."

"I don't know it."

He had the uncomfortable impression that she was telling the truth.

"Look here, young woman," he said severely, "an accident of nature has given you a certain amount of intelligence. Believe me when I tell you that now is the time to use it. Think! Pull your scattered little wits together. Get it into your head that now is the time to talk."

This sudden ferocity from the hitherto mild young man had the desired effect.

"There was a telephone number he used to ring up sometimes," she admitted. "He used to send me out of the room and then just as I was going I would hear him give the number."

"Well, then, out with it, for the love of Mike," said Mr. Campion, using the expression unconsciously.

"Maida Vale 58423. Now I can't tell you any more. I can't—can't! I don't know any more."

"Maida Vale 58423," said Mr. Campion, scribbling the number on the blotter in front of him. "All right. You clear off now and get your face washed."

"What about my book? You can't keep my book."

"I should trust me with it for a day or two," said Mr. Campion. "I might put something in it. You never know."

A stifled scream escaped the girl. He had a vision of her, white and trembling, and then the door banged behind her. Enlightenment dawned in Mr. Campion's pale eyes.

"So that's how he did it," he said and pulled the telephone towards him.

He heard the bell ringing in the far-off room for some time before a voice answered him.

"Yes? Maida Vale 58423. Who is it, please?"

Mr. Campion was puzzled. It was a woman's voice and it was familiar, but he could not place it. Completely in the dark, he proceeded cautiously.

"I say, I'm afraid you'll think it frightfully odd of me ringing up like this," he began. "I wonder if it would be too much to ask you if I could come along and see you? It really is important and I wouldn't take up more than ten minutes of your time."

"Do you know the address?" whispered the voice. "It's Thirty-two, Dorothy Studios, Denbigh Road, Kilburn. You open the garden gate and come down the steps."

"Splendid. I'll be right along," he said, completely startled. "My name's Campion, by the way."

"Yes, I know. I've been expecting you. My name's Teddie Dell."

Mr. Campion hung up the receiver slowly.

He was very conscious of the fact that he had never heard either the name or the address in his life before.

12 : *Somebody Died*

Mr. Campion saw the studio as soon as he pushed open the gate in the blank wall behind the huge margarine-coloured block of flats and came out on to the iron staircase high above the untidy strip of sunken garden.

It sat opposite him in the grass, trying to look like a country cottage and succeeding in suggesting a garden suburb. Its four tall windows faced south and the back of the flats and had diamond panes. The skylight had been leaded over.

There was a trimness about the whole building and a preponderance of bright colours which conveyed a personality childish or at least uneducated. The paint was green, the curtains blue, the window sills and step red-ochred, while a ridiculous little green dog kennel stood beside the door. It looked extraordinarily clean and new in the dinginess of Kilburn and no more in bad taste than a painted Noah's Ark, which it resembled.

It was six o'clock and not yet dusk, although the sun had gone in. The flats and studio appeared to be deserted and there was a quiet evening melancholy upon the scene.

Mr. Campion went slowly down the iron staircase and, picking his way over the grass, tapped with the brass knocker which bore a relief of Worcester Cathedral and had come from Birmingham via Bruges.

An excited yapping from within answered him, followed by a woman's voice admonishing the dog. Then the door opened.

"Come in," said Teddie Dell.

Enlightenment came to Mr. Campion as he recognized the woman who had been waiting for him outside the Bottle Street flat when he had come home from the inquest with Gina and Curley. She looked bigger and older in her indoor clothes. Her fairish hair was dressed close to her head and was cut in a thin unfashionably curled fringe, while her strong capable body was sturdy and unsuitably dressed in a very smooth blue skirt and a very frilly blouse.

There was a suggestion of strength about her face also, with its square jawbone and thick cream skin, its good teeth and wide-set blue-grey eyes.

"I'm glad you came," she said. "I've been wondering if I ought to ring you. Come in and sit down and have a cigarette."

The over-carefulness of her pronunciation struck him again, but her self-possession was unconscious and superb.

The dog was frantic with delight at his arrival and danced round him noisily in spite of his mistress's rebuke. He was a small smooth-haired yellow mongrel, spry and wiry on thin legs. Campion put out a hand and he offered a paw instantly. Campion took it and laughed.

"George, don't be a fool. Lie down! He's absurd, isn't he?"

The woman was laughing as she spoke and Campion glanced up to see that her eyes were swimming. She turned away to the mantelshelf and brought back cigarettes and matches, waiting on her visitor with the complete lack of self-consciousness of a nurse or a teashop waitress.

He found himself fumbling for a case to offer her at the moment when she held a lighted match to his cigarette.

The room in which they stood reflected the outside of the building. The floor was covered with imitation red and grey tiles and shone like a ship's deck. The dark oak furniture was ordinary and unpretentious. There was a divan under the windows and a comfortable chesterfield, flanked by two chintz-covered easy chairs by the fire.

Teddie Dell drew up the largest and most comfortable chair.

"Sit down," she said, indicating it, and he obeyed her.

Mr. Campion, the most unassuming of men, did not imagine for a moment that her solicitude for his comfort, her tacit acceptance of the fact that his ease was all-important, was due in any way to his personal charm. Teddie Dell, he realized, was behaving as she always had and always would behave, since she belonged to that most ill-used sisterhood, some of them wives, some of them mothers, and all of them lovers, who really believe that there is in the mere quality of manhood something magnificent and worthy to be served.

"You were pointed out to me at the inquest and I heard you were interested in the case," she said, seating herself opposite him and holding one hand up to the fire to shield her face from the blaze. "I didn't want to go to the police for obvious reasons. He wouldn't have liked it and she's only a kid, isn't she, and mixed up with nice people who don't understand this sort of thing. So I went round to your place. When I saw her come up with you I thought I'd better slip off. She's never heard of me, you see."

Mr. Campion nodded. He was wondering irrelevantly what Teddie Dell thought she meant by "nice people."

"It's been on my mind," she continued. "He came here when he left the office on the Thursday and the police don't know that. I wanted to ask someone about it and find out if it was any good me telling. He kept me a secret from his family for fourteen years and I didn't see any point in it all coming out now if it wouldn't help."

"Fourteen years?" said Mr. Campion involuntarily.

Her eyes rested upon him for a moment.

"We met in the war, in France," she said. "I've had this place since '23."

Her glance left his face and travelled round the yellow walls and there was an indefinable expression in her eyes.

"I never thought he'd marry," she went on abruptly. "But he was right: it didn't make any difference. That's why I was sorry for the kid. That's no marriage for a girl. I suppose she got hold of the young cousin and egged him on and teased him till he went out of his mind—although I don't know why they think he did it. My dear old boy had a lot of other enemies—ooh, he had a temper——!"

She broke off. Her eyes were a blank and her mouth very hard.

Mr. Campion looked at the dog, who lay upon the hearth rug, his nose between his paws and his ears cocked. Gradually he became aware of other things: a small silver golf trophy on the dresser and a pair of slippers, grey with age and long discarded, stuffed behind the coal-box, which was also a fireside seat.

"Was Mr. Brande here very long on the Thursday?"

He put the question diffidently but the woman gave him her whole attention at once.

"No, he couldn't stay. That often happened. He was such a busy man. I suppose they'll miss him at the office. He held the business together, didn't he?"

She spoke wistfully and for a moment Mr. Campion was able to take the impulsive, excitable, slightly ridiculous Paul at the dead man's own valuation. The woman was still speaking.

"We were going to have a bit of dinner and then he was going to read. We didn't go out much together since he got so well known. I didn't ask him to take me; I'm not a fool. But he came in just about four and said he couldn't stay, so I made him a cup of tea and he went. I wondered why he didn't ring up on the Sunday, but on the Monday I saw the papers."

Her voice wavered on the last word but she controlled it magnificently, out of deference, Mr. Campion felt, to the presence of a stranger.

"Do you know where he went when he left here?" he enquired.

"I know where he said he was going and there was no point in him lying. Besides, he never did to me. We knew each other too well. He said, 'I'm so sorry I can't stay, Ted. I've got to go down to fetch a key from Camden Town of all places, and then I've got to dash back and slip into the British Museum.' I asked him if there was any chance of him dropping in later but he said, 'No luck, I'm going to be busy tonight. I'll ring you Sunday.'"

Her voice ceased and she moved her position slightly so that her face was in the shadow. Mr. Campion felt he dared intrude no more.

"It's been very kind of you," he began awkwardly. "I'll let you know, of course, if I think you ought to come forward, but it's quite possible that it won't be at all necessary—if you don't want to."

She got up, raising herself wearily as if her bones were unusually heavy.

"Why should I?" she said. "It's not as if he were ill. He's dead."

The dog rose and yawned and stretched himself, only to lie down again, his nose between his forepaws. The room was growing dark and the firelight flickered over the bright floor and was reflected in some little bits of brass on the dresser. There was comfort in the place and an utterly unbearable sense of waiting. Mr. Campion hurried.

Teddie Dell escorted him to the door.

"I'll keep in touch with you," he promised and paused. Paul had not died penniless and Campion had a strong sense of justice. "Forgive me if I am saying the wrong thing," he ventured, "but are you all right for cash?"

She smiled and there were so many varying emotions in her expression that he only understood that she appreciated his thoughtfulness.

"Better let her have it," she said. "There isn't much. He spent like a lunatic. It would be charity too. I haven't any rights."

She was silent for a moment and he had a very vivid impression of her, square and sturdy in her little painted home, the dog peering round her skirts.

"We loved each other," she said and her voice was as proud and forlorn as high tragedy itself.

Mr. Campion came away.

13 : *A Craftsman of Camden Town*

"Would it be possible, Lugg," enquired Mr. Campion delicately, "for you to forget for a moment this respectability to which you are not accustomed and delve into the past?"

Mr. Lugg, who was taking off his collar because it was only his employer whom he had admitted, kept his back turned to the speaker and his attention fixed upon the drawer into which he was tucking this badge of refinement. The white roll of fat at the back of his neck looked smug and obstinate. Mr. Lugg had not heard.

"I suppose if I asked you to come off it," Mr. Campion began sarcastically.

Mr. Lugg swung round, his small black eyes unconvincingly innocent.

"I shouldn't understand what you meant," he said placidly, and returned to the drawer. "Some of the fellows down at the Mews wear butterfly collars and some wear straight," he observed over his shoulder. "I 'aven't made up me mind for good yet. Butterflies let yer neck through, but they're apt to look untidy."

Mr. Campion made no response to this implied question. Instead he put another.

"Lugg," he said, "if a man who had something to hide went to Camden Town to get a key, who would he go to?"

Surprise took Mr. Lugg unawares.

"Lumme," he said, "old Wardie Samson! He's not still at it, is 'e? Must be well over a 'undred. I remember 'im in my dad's day."

This family reminiscence was cut short by what was no doubt a recollection of the rigid society of the hostelry in the "Mews."

"A very low person," said the new Mr. Lugg. "Dishonest, reely."

"Do you know him?"

Lugg wriggled uncomfortably.

"I visited 'im as a lad with my father," he said at last, "but I shouldn't think 'e was the party to which you was referrin'."

"Well, take off that awful coat and get in the car, which is downstairs," said Mr. Campion. "We're going to see him."

"Not me." Mr. Lugg was defiant. "I'll give you 'is address if you like, but I'm not coming with you. It's more than me reputation's worth. You never know 'ow a thing like this might tell two or three years hence when your relation 'as gorn the way all good relations should go and you and me are established in our rightful place. What sort of a position should I be in if one of the 'ousemaids, or per'aps another gentleman who's come up in the world, should say, 'Surely I saw you in Camden Town, Mr. Lugg?' What sort of position should I be in then?"

"Even if I become a Duke," said Mr. Campion brutally, "the chances of you becoming a respectable person are remote—or at any rate, I shouldn't count on it. Come on. Hurry."

Before the authority in the tone Mr. Lugg's defiance turned to pathos.

"What's the good of me tryin' to better meself if you keep draggin' me down?" he said. "I've put the old life be'ind me. I've forgot it, see?"

"Well, this is where you do a spot of remembering," insisted Mr. Campion heartlessly. "And don't spoil everything by trying to impress your old pal with your new vulgarity, you fat oaf."

Mr. Lugg bridled. "That's a bit too thick, that is," he said. "You're destroying my ambition, that's about what you're doing. Mucking up me perishin' soul, see? All right, I'll come with you."

They drove for some time in silence, but as the wealthier parts of the city were left behind and they slid into the noisy poverty of the Hampstead Road some of Mr. Lugg's gloom deserted him.

"It's like old times, isn't it?" he observed.

Campion accepted the olive branch.

"We've got a delicate job ahead," he said. "I suppose your friend Wardie would give away a client if he was dead?"

"Wardie doesn't *give* anything." Lugg spoke reminiscently. "Doesn't know the meanin' of the word 'tick' either. Still, we can but try 'im. I 'aven't seen 'im for ten years, remember."

"When you were a lad," said Mr. Campion unkindly.

"When I was one of the lads," said Mr. Lugg, whose spirits were soaring. "'E was a clever old bloke, Wardie," he continued. "Give 'im an impression one day and in a little while 'e'd drop you a line and down you'd go to find a better key than the original. 'E did name plates, too—not for the same people. Only one thing aginst 'im, 'e was slow. Lumme, 'ow slow that man was! So busy making snide 'e never 'ad time for honest work. Used to make lovely 'alf-crowns. Made 'em out of the tops of soda-water siphons. That metal's just the right weight, y'know."

Mr. Campion showed polite interest. "Was he pinched?"

"Wardie? No. He was too careful. 'E never passed 'em. Wouldn't let any of 'is relations 'andle 'em either. Used to sell 'em—so much a gross—to one of these lads in the Ditch. 'E's a handy man, if you take me. I'm surprised at 'im still working, especially for outsiders. It's round 'ere, guv'nor. Better leave the car at a garridge. It's no good parkin' it. We don't want to turn up to Wardie's lookin' like bloomin' millionaires. Might give 'im ideas."

They left the car and continued on foot. For one who professed to have left this particular world behind him Mr. Lugg found his way among the maze of small streets with remarkable precision.

"'Ere we are," he said at last. "Now, look casual but not 'alf-witted. I don't want 'im to think I've turned up with a Killarney."

Mr. Campion, who in the course of a long association had come to realize that living up to Mr. Lugg was an impossibility, remained much as usual and they paused in the narrow, dusty little road littered with paper bags and kitchen refuse while Lugg went through an elaborate pantomime of noticing a small shop some few doors down on the opposite side.

"Why, there's Mr. Samson's joint!" he said, with theatrical astonishment. "I wonder if 'e's still alive? I'd better go and look 'im up. Just the same! The ole place 'asn't changed since I was a boy."

At first sight the Samson emporium was not impressive. It consisted of a very narrow door and a small window. Both were incredibly dirty and, while one revealed an even dingier interior, the other displayed a collection of old iron ranging from nails to the back of bedsteads, a notice which announced that shoe leather could be purchased within, and a quantity of cheap new razor blades. There was also, Mr. Campion noticed, a hank of bass, two large bales of twine and a skein of very thick elastic labelled "For Catapults." This last was crossed out very lightly and "Model Aëroplanes" substituted in wavering pencil.

With the nonchalance of a loiterer observing a policeman, Mr. Lugg lounged into the shop, beckoning Mr. Campion to follow him with a jerk of his shoulder.

It took them some moments to accustom their eyes to the darkness. The atmosphere, which was composed of a nice blend of rust, leather and Irish stew, took a bit of assimilating also, and Campion felt his feet sink into a sand of dust and iron filings.

There was a movement in the shop, followed by a snuffling, and presently a bright young man with a white face, dusty yellow hair and an enquiring manner sauntered towards them. Mr. Lugg showed surprise.

"Business changed 'ands?" he asked suspiciously. "I come reely to enquire after an old friend, Mr. Samson."

The young man eyed Mr. Lugg from the toes of his boots to the top of his hat.

"One of the old brigade, aren't yer?" he said cheekily, his narrow blue eyes astute and appraising.

Mr. Lugg was momentarily taken off his balance.

" 'Ere, what're you gettin' at?" he said, taking a menacing step forward. "When I want any lip from two penn'orth of string-bag I'll ask for it."

In spite of a certain flabbiness induced by high life, Mr. Lugg was still a formidable opponent, and he was not alone. The young man retreated.

"Gran'dad's in the back," he said. "If you'll tell me your name I'll go and see if he remembers you."

"Gran'dad?" said Mr. Lugg, a repulsively sentimental smile appearing on his great white face. "Don't tell me you're little Alfie? Not little Alfie what I danced up an' down on my knee?"

"Charlie," said the young man, without enthusiasm.

"Charlie! That was it. Rosie's boy—little Rosie. 'Ow's your mother, son?"

" 'Aven't seen 'er since she went off with a rozzer," said the young man, with that complete carelessness which is more chilling than any rebuke. "I'll go and tell Gran'dad. What's yer name?"

"Just tell 'im Maggers is 'ere," said Lugg, who was beginning to enjoy himself for the first time, Mr. Campion felt, for years.

"Shall I come with you?"

"No. You stay 'ere," said Charlie, with the first show of animation he had yet exhibited and disappeared into the darkness.

Mr. Lugg chuckled in a fatherly fashion.

"I remember 'im being born," he said, with inexplicable pride. " 'Ear what 'e called me?—'Old Brigade!' That's 'cos 'e knows I'm after a key. 'Is pals use oxy-acetylene. Nasty dangerous stuff. When that come on the market I knew my time was over."

" 'E'll see yer. Come on."

Charlie did not emerge from the shadows to make this announcement and they groped forward in the direction of his voice. After passing through a living room, into which the iron filings had percolated in the course of years, and which was apparently the fountainhead of the Irish stew, they came quite unexpectedly into the bright light of day. Their way led across a minute yard, dirty to a degree unknown by most users of the word, and into a small shed festooned with old bicycle tyres.

Seated at a bench was a large blank-faced old man, bald as an egg and clad in a very loose shirt and surprisingly tight trousers whose original colour could only be surmised. The round face was at once mild and cunning and possessed the serenity of a Buddha.

"Wardie!" said Mr. Lugg, enraptured, adding a little inopportunely: "I thought you was dead."

The old man smiled enigmatically as he held out a hand, and it occurred to Mr. Campion that he was deaf.

"Afternoon, gentlemen," he said, and his voice had a husky, secretive quality.

Lugg deserted Campion. He went round the back of the bench and seated himself beside the old man.

"I'm Maggers, Wardie," he said, thrusting a mighty arm round the other man's shoulders. "You remember me. I'm the fellow what was sweet on yer second daughter—the one what died. I'm coming back to yer, aren't I?"

"Lugg," said the old man suddenly. "Young Lugg."

They shook hands again solemnly and with great sentiment.

"Can you 'ear me?" said Mr. Lugg, rumbling into one of the great ears.

"Course," said the old man. "'Eard you all the time. Didn't know oo you were. Oo's yer friend?"

"Young fellow I go round with," said Mr. Lugg shamelessly. "You know me, Wardie: I wouldn't tell you wrong. Me and my pal we want a bit of 'elp from you."

He cocked an eye at his employer.

"You tell 'im, Bert."

Mr. Campion explained his business as well as he could.

"It's about a key," he said. "Lugg and I wondered if you could tell us anything about a key which a man picked up down here in Camden Town on Thursday, the twenty-eighth of January last. It's a long time ago, I know, but I thought you might remember. He was a well-dressed fellow, forty-fiveish, dark, and spoke well."

Wardie Samson shook his large round head.

"I don't know anything about keys," he said. "We don't sell 'em."

Lugg burst into a roar of unnatural laughter.

"You're takin' Bert for a 'tec!" he said. "That's a good one, that is! Old Bert a split! That'll be one to tell the boys!"

Wardie's inflamed and rheumy eyes shifted nervously.

"Can't tell yer about a key," he said. "Don't know."

Mr. Campion took a chance.

"It's private information I want," he said. "I'm willing to pay for it and I'll give you any assurance you like that you will never be questioned about it again. I am a detective, if you like, but I'm not a police detective. I'm not interested in your business, and all I want is a description, or, better still, a mould, of a key which the man I am interested in had made in this district. That's all I want. After I walk out of this shop you can swear blindly you've never seen me before. Lugg won't act as a witness."

The old man, who had been watching Campion carefully throughout this recital, seemed impressed.

"What date did you say, guv'nor? The twenty-eighth of January? Seems to me I read an interestin' bit in the paper about a gentleman who got his on that day. It wouldn't be him you was interested in, would it?"

"That's the ticket," said Mr. Lugg heartily. "Now you're bein' sensible. We're just blokes oo've come to an old pal for a bit of 'elp. As for that chap, 'e can't buy anything off you again, can 'e? 'E's in 'is box."

Mr. Samson seemed to have decided that his visitors were on the level, but he retained his caution of voice and expression, which seemed to be habitual.

"I sent 'im a letter telling 'im it was ready and 'e come down right away. Said 'e'd destroyed the letter for 'is own sake."

He cocked an eye at Campion, who nodded reassuringly.

"He had. We came to you by chance. Have you destroyed the impression?"

The old man nodded and seemed to debate within himself for a moment or so. Then, with a glance at Lugg that was almost affectionate, he opened a small drawer in the bench in front of him and, after rummaging in it for some time, produced a large, old-fashioned key. He threw it down in front of Campion.

"Always make two for luck," he said, and the faintest suggestion of a smile flickered for an instant round his mouth.

Another search in the drawer produced a dirty envelope. "Paul R. Brande," he spelt out awkwardly. "Twenty-three, Horsecollar Yard, Holborn, W.C.1."

Mr. Campion took the key and Lugg waved him out of the shed.

"Me and Wardie will fix this little matter up between us," he said magnificently.

Mr. Campion waited in the filth of the yard for some considerable time, and Lugg finally appeared.

"Three pound ten," he said. "I know it's a lot, but you 'ave to pay for these things."

Mr. Campion parted with the money and presently, with the key safely stowed in his pocket, he once more approached the garage where the car was parked. As they settled down and Campion turned the Lagonda out into Hampstead Road Lugg nudged him.

"'Ere's thirty-five shillings that belongs to you," he said. "I did a split

with Wardie. It's the worst of these dishonest people. They always expect
you to live down to 'em."

14 : *The Damned*

Even if Mr. Lugg was as hurt as he looked when his employer dropped
him at the corner of Regent Street, at least he refrained from referring to
himself as a "worn-out glove," an unsuitable simile of which he was very
fond, having, so he said, read it somewhere and thought it "the ticket."

Campion went on alone to Horsecollar Yard. He had no desire to discuss his afternoon's work with Gina, and was wondering how he could get
into Number Twenty-three without disturbing her, John, or an inquisitive
policeman when he observed a familiar figure striding out of the cul-de-sac.

Ritchie Barnabas possessed a striking appearance at all times, but, seen
at a reasonable distance in the lamp-lit dusk of a spring evening, he
presented a spectacle of fantasy. He lolloped along at a great pace, each
knee giving a little as it took his weight, and his great arms flapping about
him like the wings of an intoxicated crow.

He pulled up with a jerk which almost overbalanced him as the Lagonda
slid to a standstill at his side and thrust an anxious face into Campion's
own.

"The key of the office?" he repeated after the younger man had made
the request. "Certainly. Let you in myself. All the cousins and Miss Curley
have keys. John's out, anyway. Gone to see Alexander."

All the time he was speaking he watched Campion's face with the eager
but diffident curiosity of a child. The other man found himself apologizing.

"If I had anything definite I'd tell you," he said, "but at the moment
I've only got an idea, supported by two or three dubious facts."

Ritchie nodded humbly and his blue eyes blinked trustingly at his
friend. He opened the front door of Twenty-three and hesitated.

"Wait for you?" he enquired hopefully.

"I shouldn't." Unconsciously Mr. Campion spoke in that firm but regretful tone with which one tries to persuade a strange and friendly dog
not to accompany one home.

"All right," Ritchie agreed sadly. "Lock up behind you. Good night."
He strode off, to return at once.

"Only live in Red Lion Square, you know address," he murmured. "There
if wanted. Any hour."

He went off again, successfully this time, and Mr. Campion set about
his investigations, blessing the idiosyncrasy of the firm of Barnabas which
made them elect to have their offices cleaned out in the early morning
instead of at night.

It was practically dark indoors, and the big untidy rooms looked unfamiliar in the gloom; nor were they particularly silent. The ticking of clocks, the stir of papers in a draught and the vibrations of the nearby Underground railway combined to make the place sound alive.

Anxious not to advertise himself, Campion did not turn on the lights, but relied upon his torch. He went up to Miss Curley's room, a neatly kept glass-and-panelling cubicle built round one window in the typists' office. The strong-room key hung upon its hook on the inside of the old-fashioned desk. As soon as he handled it one of Mr. Campion's minor theories collapsed gently, to be replaced by a sense of misgiving and a wholly unwarrantable suspicion of the innate honesty of Wardie Samson.

He compared the two keys as they lay side by side on the desk in the gleam of his torch. Apart from the fact that they were both of the ordinary or old-fashioned type and were both over four inches long, it would have been difficult to find two such instruments more dissimilar. The key of the strong-room door was long and slender with three wards, but the key which Wardie Samson had made for luck was squat and heavy and had that curious unsatisfactory appearance which is peculiar to old-fashioned patent devices which have never been really successful.

Mr. Campion turned it over thoughtfully and an idea occurred to him. Placing both keys in his pocket, he went slowly downstairs. It was growing darker and the well of the front hall, which had no windows to admit the gleam from the street lamps, was completely black.

Because it is natural to keep quiet in the dark, Mr. Campion trod gently. At the top of the stone staircase leading down into the basement he paused to listen. His quick ears had detected something that was not one of the ordinary night noises and his interest quickened. It did not come again, however, and he went on.

On the landing, where the stair turned to face the basement wall, he paused abruptly, extinguishing his torch. Below him, at the end of the passage, a thin angle of light gleamed in the darkness. The strong-room door was ajar and there was a light within, a fact which might not have been so very astonishing even out of office hours had he not carried the only official key in his pocket.

Campion advanced cautiously, feeling his way down the shallow worn stone steps. His foot had just touched the concrete floor of the passage when the angle vanished as the light in the room went out.

He stood motionless, listening. The silence was uncanny and he hesitated to use the torch until he knew more of the situation. An unarmed man with a torch is an admirable target.

He was some half-dozen yards from the door and the basement was less disturbed by vibrations and draught-disturbed papers than the rest of the building, yet he could hear nothing. There was not a breath, not a rustle, not even the almost undetectable whisper of a well-oiled hinge. It was a paralyzed silence, not altogether natural.

Mr. Campion did not consider himself a nervous man, but neither was he sufficiently thick-skinned to let the piquancy of the situation pass by him. Someone, presumably with a guilty conscience and possibly with a gun, was aware of his presence and was waiting for him.

Campion stood quite still, holding his breath lest any sound should reveal his exact position.

The silence continued.

It came to an end at last, and in so unnerving a fashion that all his preparation was wasted. At the moment when he had decided that he must breathe deeply or burst, a yell so loud that its nature or even its origin was indeterminate sounded within a few feet of his ear and practically at the same time something apparently demoniacal struck him in the chest, knocking the torch out of his hand and most of the breath from his body.

There is to most of us a secret savage satisfaction in receiving a blow that one knows that one can repay with interest. As Campion staggered back against the wall beside the staircase his left came in contact with something that was hard enough to be a man's head. He heard a grunt and deep breathing and, as the knee came up to catch him in the stomach, he threw his arms round it, hurling his weight forward so that he went down on top of his unknown adversary.

During the next few seconds he had little time for speculation, but he became aware that he was fighting something human, since it was clothed, and of an iron hardness and ferocity which suggested a hank of steel rope temporarily possessed by a fiend.

Campion had some experience of catch-as-catch-can fighting. During his adventurous life he had enjoyed scraps in most stratas of society, so that he was aware that the Queensberry rules have many variations, but that evening in the pitch-dark basement he received an education.

The unseen creature bit, clawed, sobbed and pummelled, interspersing this unconventionality with occasional scientific blows. Campion was temporarily outclassed and was only relieved that his enemy had no weapon.

He was lying upon his face with a teetering, kicking thing trying to force him through the concrete floor when his groping hand caught an iron banister and he dragged himself up and let out with his right, the full weight of his body behind the blow.

It dawned upon him then, as he felt the wet chin go back under his fist, that he was fighting with a man in terror. The sobbing ceased and something thudded satisfactorily at his feet. Campion shook himself and waited, but there was no further sound from the floor. He moved unsteadily down the passage and, after a considerable delay, discovered the switch.

The first thing he saw as his surroundings leapt into view was a reflection of his own face in the mirror which hung just inside the open door of the little washroom. It was not a reassuring spectacle.

He did not stop to examine the damage, but swung round just in time to see a tousled object creeping furtively towards the stairs.

Mr. Campion leapt upon it, caught it by the remnants of what had once been a collar, and jerked back its head.

Shivering, whimpering, his face covered with blood and tears, cowered a star witness for the Crown, Mr. Peter Rigget.

Campion gaped at him and let him go. He dropped to the floor, crawled into a sitting position on the bottom step of the staircase, and wept. Never an irritable man, Mr. Campion felt himself excused in the exhibition of a little impatience. He pulled out his handkerchief and wiped some of the blood off his face.

"What in the name of all that's holy do you think you've been doing?" he enquired.

Mr. Rigget continued to blubber. Presently he stopped and his head fell forward on his chest. Campion bent over him, his eyebrows raised. But Mr. Rigget had not fainted. He was asleep.

Campion was not surprised. He had seen the same thing happen before when great physical exertion had been allied to the emotional upheaval. Since it is a natural phenomenon, only occurring to young people in exceptional health, Mr. Campion felt unreasonably angry with Mr. Rigget.

He left him where he was and retired to the washroom, where, with the door open, he could keep an eye upon the heavily breathing figure at the foot of the stairs.

A wrenched shoulder, a cut over the left eye, and four weals left by four fingernails travelling from his right temple to the top of his collar seemed to be his principal injuries. His clothes were in ribbons. There was a piece missing from the sleeve of his jacket which could only have been bitten away, and there was blood all over him.

He cleaned himself up as best he could and felt better after his head had been under the cold tap for a minute or two.

He let Mr. Rigget sleep for half an hour, and woke him by pouring a jug of cold water over his head. The puffed eyes opened sleepily and closed again.

Campion raised the stocky little body which was in such surprisingly good condition, and dragged it into the washroom, where he repeated his treatment until Mr. Rigget showed signs of returning life and intelligence.

"All right?" Campion enquired when once again the blue eyes looked out clearly from beneath their battered lids.

Mr. Rigget said nothing. He turned his back on Mr. Campion and began to wash his hands.

"I think we'd better have a chat, don't you, having been properly introduced?"

Still Mr. Rigget was silent. His hands seemed to require a lot of attention.

"What were you doing down here? You'll have to explain to somebody, you know. You'd better tell me."

Mr. Rigget was trembling violently, but no sound left his lips and he went on washing his hands.

Campion leant forward, turned off the tap and threw him a towel.

"Come on," he said, taking the other man by the arm. "We'll go into the strong room."

Mr. Rigget remained perfectly still. He was staring straight in front of him, his face pink where it was not discoloured and his eyes narrowed to pin-points.

Mr. Campion choked down his growing irritation.

"Since that face of yours is going to create a scandal in the witness-box, anyway, we may as well have the whole truth," he said. "And by the way, next time you go leaping on people in the dark don't lose your head, or you'll find yourself landed with a corpse which has been the victim of a murderous attack. Keeping yourself fit is all very well, but you don't want to turn yourself into a dangerous machine every time you get the wind up."

Mr. Rigget's trembling increased and suddenly, with an effect which was completely unnerving, he began to pray aloud. Mr. Campion took him by the shoulders and shook him.

"Pull yourself together!" he said firmly. "Don't try to mesmerize yourself. You need your brain at the moment. Use it."

Mr. Rigget relaxed cautiously.

"Where are you going to take me?" he demanded.

"Nowhere," said Campion. "We're going to stay here."

Mr. Rigget shuddered and glanced at the strong room.

"Not in there. I'll tell you. I'll tell you everything. I'm not really as bad as I look—at least I am, only I can't help it. Oh, God, I'm so tired!"

Mr. Campion sighed.

"My car's outside," he said. "I'll take you back to the flat."

Peter Rigget seemed agreeable to this suggestion, and they had started down the passage when he remembered the strong-room door and went back to it. To Mr. Campion's intense interest he thrust his hand into his tattered pocket, drew out a slender three-ward key identical with the one which Campion himself had borrowed from Miss Curley's desk, locked the door and returned.

"I'm tired," he said again.

He dropped to sleep in the back of the car, and Campion had to wake him again when they arrived at Bottle Street. Lugg, curious and openly appalled at his employer's condition, went down obligingly to put the car away and Campion and his captive were alone.

In the bright light of Mr. Campion's comfortable room Peter Rigget made a pathetic and embarrassing spectacle. His pince-nez were gone, and his normally thin sensitive nose was no longer thin, and his puffy red wrists stuck out some three inches from his torn shirt-cuffs.

Mr. Campion, who knew a great deal about exhaustion, gave him some food, which he ate eagerly, swallowing great hunks of bread and lump sugar as though he realized instinctively how great was his need of them.

Gradually his unnatural lassitude disappeared, leaving him weary, but otherwise normal. Mr. Campion sat opposite him.

"Still feel like talking?" he enquired pleasantly.

Mr. Rigget looked at the ground. He was young, Campion decided, younger than he had thought; twenty-five or six at the most.

"I'm not a nice chap," he said. "I can't help it. I fight against it, but my instincts are all wrong. I keep letting myself down."

A dreadful sincerity in the statement robbed it of its humour and made it merely embarrassing. Mr. Rigget appeared to be speaking the simple truth from the depths of a resigned rather than a contrite heart.

"I've been educated," he went on, "but it hasn't altered me. I'm a cad. I'm dirty."

"Let's get back to the strong room, shall we?" suggested Mr. Campion gently. "You've got a key, I see."

Mr. Rigget shuddered. "I had it made. It was so easy. They ought not to put temptation in your way like that. I know I'm rotten, but I was tempted. Fancy leaving the key there where anybody could get it! I took it home with me for a week-end in the summer and had another one made. Nobody noticed. Nobody asked any questions. Even the man at the shop believed me when I said it was the key of my own front door. I live with my people. They're very respectable. This is going to break them. They've educated me and made me a better class than they are, and now I've disgraced them."

He spoke sullenly and with a sort of masochistic satisfaction.

"Been using the key pretty regularly?" Mr. Campion enquired.

The young man stirred. "Fairly often. Whenever I could stay behind. There wasn't much in there. I didn't do anything. I didn't take anything. I only turned things over. They didn't keep anything valuable there. It's a sort of junk room."

"What was the idea?" Mr. Campion sounded merely curious, even friendly.

"I'm nasty," said Mr. Rigget, raising very blue eyes bright with tears to his inquisitor's face. "I just wanted to see if there was anything interesting there—something that might be useful. You don't understand me. I'm not ordinary. I'm not decent. I haven't got any instincts against prying into other people's affairs. Most firms are dirty, and I wanted to find out anything I could."

Mr. Campion had an inspiration.

"Like little evasions of income tax?" he suggested.

A secretive, rather repulsive smile appeared on Mr. Rigget's swollen lips.

"Yes," he said. "That's the sort of thing. Only I couldn't find any books or anything. They didn't keep 'em there. I suppose they're in the safe. Or more probably the important ones'd be at the bank," he added gloomily. "You're shocked, aren't you?" He looked at Campion resentfully. "You ought to be if you've got the right instincts. But I'm not. I used to try to be, but I'm not. I'm dirty and mean and low and underhand, and all the things they educate you not to be."

It was all very distressing. Mr. Rigget's excellent accent and obvious misery made him well-nigh unbearable.

"Did you ever get the safe open?" Mr. Campion found himself trying to put the question so casually that it would not sound offensive.

"Oh, no, I didn't touch the safe! That's criminal. I haven't done anything criminal."

Mr. Rigget uttered the word as though it were blasphemous.

"I've had the key in my hand, I admit that, but I've never used it." He writhed in his chair. "I've got a key of the safe, I may as well admit that, but I've never used it. I swear I've never used it! I daren't do anything criminal. I want to, but I'm afraid to. That's the sort of chap I am. I ought never to be in the sort of job I'm in. I'm only educated. I haven't got any instincts."

Mr. Campion realized that he was confronted by a serious modern sociological problem, but he decided that it was far too large to tackle, especially at the moment. He concentrated on the keys. Producing the instrument which Wardie Samson had made "for luck," he handed it to the man whom he was trying not to think of as his victim.

"That's it! Where did you get it? It was in my collar drawer, locked up at home. Mother didn't know it was there, nor did Father, nor did anyone. Oh, God, you've been to them! They know about me. I'll never dare to go home now. I never want to see them again." Peter Rigget trembled on the verge of hysterics.

"This is my key," said Mr. Campion firmly. "It's nothing to do with your key. Pull yourself together."

Mr. Rigget wiped the tears angrily from his eyes and squared his powerful shoulders.

"I give way," he said unexpectedly. "That's weak. That shows I'm all wrong. I've been hiding myself up ever since I was a kid, but it's coming out now. You can't alter your instincts. You are what you are born to be, whatever you learn. If I'd been brave I'd have told what I knew on the

Friday night, but I didn't want anybody to know I'd been down there. I was glad," he added, his voice rising. "I was *glad* it had happened, and I knew about it. I was *glad* there was going to be trouble. It made me feel excited and important."

It occurred to Mr. Campion that what Mr. Rigget really needed was some sort of reverse process of psychoanalysis. To know the truth about oneself, if it were both unpleasant and incurable, must be a variety of hell, he decided. He became quite sorry for him, but there was obviously much to be learnt.

"When you say the Friday night, was that the evening after Mr. Brande disappeared?"

Mr. Rigget nodded. "I got a fright when I saw him. Afterwards I was pleased. I knew he was there, you see. I knew he was there all the week-end."

Mr. Campion sat up, but Mr. Rigget was too engrossed in his own unfortunate reactions to life to notice any added interest in his hearer.

"I stayed behind on Friday. It's easier on Fridays. People go home earlier and don't notice you're hanging about. I shut myself in the washroom with the light out until they'd all gone—I did that tonight, and then I let myself out and unlocked the strong-room door with my own key and went in. I didn't see the body at first. It wasn't by the door where they found it. It was lying crumpled up in a corner beside the safe, hidden from the door by a lot of boxes and things under the table."

He hesitated.

"That's where I got my key of the safe," he explained at last. "It was in the lock and the safe door was open. I thought the key might be useful, so I shut the door and turned it. I was frightened, of course, but I was excited, too. I never liked Mr. Paul."

Mr. Campion sat enthralled. He did not like to break the thread of the story, but at the same time the man's attitude towards his important discovery was incomprehensible.

"You were terrified, I suppose?" he ventured.

"No," said Mr. Rigget. "I wasn't frightened because he was dead—I made sure he *was* dead. I'd have been more frightened if he'd been alive."

He caught Mr. Campion's expression and attempted to excuse himself.

"It wasn't anything to do with me, I hadn't killed him. I didn't think he had been killed then. I thought he'd just fallen down in a fit. I was frightened they'd catch me by the safe and think I'd opened it. I ought not to have taken the key of the safe. That's criminal, really. But I didn't use it. I never used it. I didn't bring it tonight because I thought I might use it and I wanted to put the temptation behind me. I took the other key, too," he went on, averting his eyes. "It was in the lock when I pushed mine in and it fell out on the floor on the inside. I picked it up and when I went out I put it back in Miss Curley's desk after I'd locked the door."

"Why on earth did you do that?" Campion demanded in astonishment.

Mr. Rigget was silent for some seconds and the sulkiness on his face increased in intensity.

"Well, I thought I ought to leave the door locked in case someone had tried it earlier in the day and had looked for the key and found it wasn't there. Then I thought they'd have to get him out some time, and I thought they'd probably smash the lock. Then my own key that I'd had made wouldn't fit any more. I'm mean!" he burst out passionately. "I do things like that. I'm always thinking of myself and how to save myself trouble—little petty things like that."

Mr. Campion's face was very severe.

"Look here," he demanded, "do you realize that Mike Wedgwood has been arrested and is going to be tried for his life largely on the evidence that Brande was found dead in a room locked on the outside? Now, according to your story, the dead man was in a room locked on the inside. You must see the difference."

Mr. Rigget shrugged his shoulders. "It wasn't anything to do with me, as far as I saw. I've told you, I'm selfish, I'm narrow, I'm mean."

Mr. Campion ignored the last part of his remark.

"You say when you found the body on the Friday night it was lying in a corner so that no one entering the door could see it immediately?"

"I didn't see it until I went over to the safe."

"But, good heavens!" exploded Mr. Campion. "Don't you see, you're corroborating Wedgwood's story? Didn't you follow the inquest?"

Mr. Rigget leant back in his chair. He looked exhausted.

"It wasn't any affair of mine," he said stubbornly.

"Had you got a grudge against Wedgwood?"

"No." Mr. Rigget's sullenness increased. "I didn't have much to do with him. *I tell you*," he said, his voice breaking, "you think I'm a beastly filthy little twip, don't you? Well, *I am!* That's what I keep telling you. I am and I can't help it. I know I'm being an unspeakable cad not to own up to what I did, to get him off. I know I am: that makes it worse."

"Why did you go back there tonight?"

Mr. Rigget's wretchedness would have been distressing on any less momentous occasion.

"I shall get the sack when the trial's over," he muttered. "You were there that day when I went to Mr. Widdowson and Sir Alexander and told them about the quarrel I'd overheard. They daren't sack me now, but as soon as the trial's over they will—unless I can get something on them first. That's why I was hunting for something that I could use."

"Yes, well," said Mr. Campion, with disgust, "I don't think much of an education which taught you that tampering with a safe was criminal but didn't mention blackmail."

"Oh, it wouldn't be blackmail," murmured Mr. Rigget. "It would only be something I could just mention. All this is going to come out now, isn't it?"

"Some of it'll have to."

"How d'you know I shan't kill myself?" Mr. Rigget spoke cunningly.

Mr. Campion looked at him. "You poor little beast, you might," he murmured. "That's why I'm going to take you over to Scruby immediately."

Mr. Rigget shrank back in his chair.

"I'm a witness for the Crown. You can't tamper with me. You can't persuade me to say anything I don't want to. I've been talking to you as I've never talked to anybody else, but I'm not going to do it in court."

Mr. Campion got up heavily.

"I shouldn't worry so much about coming clean," he said. "Ever heard of Nemesis? Come on."

15 : *Night Shift*

Those who live in that ghostly part of London which is the most crowded square mile by day and the most deserted by night insist that at three o'clock in the morning it is as peaceful as a country churchyard, and that there the black rats dance a leisurely saraband down the centres of the glossy streets.

Mr. Campion's hurrying footsteps made sharp echoes on the pavements as he strode through the unsavoury alley which is Red Lion Passage and came out into the shabby comfort of the square.

Most of the flat houses had been converted into offices long ago. Standing back from the road, they turned blank eyes to the street lamps and only a single brightly lit third-floor window twinkled at him mellowly through the budding plane trees in the dusty centre garden.

He made for it and was rewarded. Ritchie was evidently a man of his word and was sitting up. Having no desire to wake the whole house, Mr. Campion paused on the edge of the pavement and pitched a halfpenny expertly into the centre of the lighted pane.

Immediately a somewhat fantastic silhouette appeared at the sash, waved reassuringly and vanished.

Campion wandered up to the door, and it opened before him with so little delay that he experienced a slight shock of astonishment.

"Slide down the banisters?" he enquired facetiously.

Ritchie did not answer, and Campion, who could not see his face, received the disquieting impression that he was disconcerted. It was a ridiculous incident and passed at once. Ritchie's great hand caught his arm and forced him up the dark staircase of the house which had seen much better days.

"People asleep," his host confided in a whisper which was like a roar of the wind in a turret. "Only kind to be quiet."

It was a long way up, but the older man moved at a great rate and Mr. Campion came thankfully and a trifle breathlessly into the bed-sitting-room which was Ritchie's home.

It was a huge apartment with a very high ceiling, some two feet below which a shelf had been constructed round all four sides of the room. This ledge was the most striking feature of the place, and first caught a visitor's attention, since it evidently contained practically all Mr. Richard Barnabas's worldly possessions. Books, clothes and manuscripts were there stacked together neatly, albeit a trifle dustily, and were, of course, extraordinarily inaccessible.

What furniture the room contained was huddled together along the darkest wall, as though space were restricted. The wash-stand stood at the end of the iron bedstead, rubbing elbows uncomfortably with a minute dressing-table.

The rest of the room was virtually bare, the floor covered with several layers of dust under-felting. A small gas fire burned in the grate and a single folding armchair was drawn up before it.

"Sit down. Rather stand—sit all day."

A sweeping but completely meaningless gesture of one arm accompanied the hospitality, and Mr. Campion, who was beginning to understand his friend, obeyed meekly.

He was about to drop into the chair when he caught sight of something among the corduroy cushions and retrieved it in some astonishment. It was a spangled black tulle frill which immediately suggested to Mr. Campion a sentimental relic of a lady in tights dancing upon a *fin de siècle* stage.

If he showed surprise it was nothing to the effect the discovery had upon Ritchie. For a moment he stood gaping, utter consternation on his face, and then, whipping the furbelow out of Campion's hand, he thrust it for want of a better hiding place under the pillow on the iron bedstead.

"Never ask," he commanded, bright spots of colour appearing in his thin cheeks and his blue eyes unexpectedly belligerent. "Never ask."

Mr. Campion, who was tired and had by no means recovered from his encounter with the athletic Mr. Rigget, began to wonder if he himself were not a trifle light-headed. However, Ritchie was still regarding him truculently and he hastened to reassure him.

"Of course not," he said, with dignity.

There was a pause, during which Ritchie seated himself upon the floor, tucking his long awkward legs beneath him with extraordinary dexterity.

His excitement evaporated and his eyes became mild and friendly, albeit a trifle worried.

Mr. Campion blinked. The vision of a youthful Ritchie and a lady in spangled tights provided a bizarre note in the sober business of the evening and he reflected what an odd, attractive, simple soul his host was. Ritchie glanced at Campion.

"Been fighting?" he observed.

Campion gave him a rough outline of his evening's adventure.

"I roused poor old Scruby and left Rigget with him," he finished at last. "It means a flutter among the legal gents tomorrow, I'm afraid, but that can't very well be helped. The important thing is that the little rat's story contains two pieces of new evidence: one that Paul was murdered, the key being on the inside of the strong-room door, and the other that the body was moved after rigor mortis had passed and probably Mike went down to the strong room on Sunday night."

He paused and Ritchie regarded him owlishly from the ground. Campion continued.

"I rather thought that something like that last had happened when I first heard about the hat. A man doesn't set his hat upon the floor and then lie down carefully beside it to die. But there was no proof, you see. Everything had been so mucked about by the time the police arrived that they were hampered on all sides."

Ritchie nodded his comprehension.

"New evidence important?" he enquired. "Vital? Mean release?"

"Oh, no, I'm afraid not." Mr. Campion succumbed to the impulse to explain things gently to Ritchie. "It'll weaken the case, of course, but Mike must stand his trial. You see, to do everybody justice, Mike is the obvious person to have killed Paul. He had opportunity, he admits going to the garage and starting the car, the shower tube had belonged to him, he had bought and read a book describing the method of murder in detail, and in the police opinion he had a motive."

"Gina?"

Mr. Campion bowed his battered head.

"The degrees of familiarity between the sexes in ordinary social life differ from clique to clique and class to class more than anything else," he pointed out. "It's practically the only subject on which the authorities are consistently muddled. I'm afraid police circles are inclined to be prurient-minded and lawyers worse."

"Understandable," said Ritchie unexpectedly. "Always having unfortunate experiences."

Mr. Campion continued his dissertation.

"That's the positive legal case, roughly. But then there's all the negative evidence, which only counts in the back of people's minds. Someone killed Paul, someone killed him intentionally and ingeniously. That someone apparently killed him between six in the evening, when the office went home, and nine in the same evening, when Mike turned off his engine and both Mrs. Tripper and my new friend Widgeon noticed the noise had ceased. That someone had access to either Twenty-three or Twenty-one, because it was only through either of these houses that the car could be reached. That someone either knew that Paul would be in the strong room at that particular time or inveigled him into the place. That someone knew of the hose pipe and therefore also knew the back entrance at Twenty-one. The only people who could have known and done all these things are Mike, you, Gina, John, Curley and the janitor—or possibly Paul himself, although it seems an idiotic way to commit suicide. And, anyway, in that case who moved the body?"

"Might be others," said Ritchie dubiously. "If Rigget stayed behind why not others? Girl Netley. Rigget himself. Anyone in the office?"

"Well, let's hope so," said Mr. Campion cheerfully. "Otherwise Mike and Gina are very unfortunately placed. Everyone else has an alibi."

He leant back in his chair and removed his spectacles as Ritchie's eyes watched his face.

"Miss Curley left the office on the Thursday evening at half past five and went to Peter Robinson's to have her hair shampooed. She left there at six and hurried on to the cocktail party which Mike should have attended in Manchester Square. At seven-thirty she left and went on to dinner at Rule's with Miss Betcherley of Blenheim's literary agency, and at eight-fifty she caught a Tube train to Hammersmith."

He paused and smiled.

"Then there's you. You left the office early and came back here, where you collected your landlord——"

"Landlady's husband," corrected Ritchie in the interests of strict accuracy.

"—And went to the circus at Olympia," continued Mr. Campion imperturbably, "where you stayed until ten-thirty. John left his office at five and went to his club, where he was recognized and where he had a business interview. He returned to his flat and dressed for the evening with his usual deliberation and attention to detail. His housekeeper waited upon him the whole time. At seven-forty he went off in a taxi to the Dorchester for the Quill Club dinner, at which he spent the evening. The janitor left the office at six sharp and went off with some pals to the Holborn Empire. In fact, everyone behaved normally except Mike, who went walking, an exercise he hardly ever takes."

His voice died away and he regarded Ritchie steadily.

"Do you realize," he demanded suddenly, "that whoever killed Paul must have stood by and let that car pump gas into the strong room for at least an hour, probably an hour and a half? It wouldn't take long to put Paul under, of course, but the murderer must have gone on with the treatment for some considerable time to make sure of death. That's why these alibis are so very convincing."

Ritchie was silent. He sat upon his feet, rocking gently before the fire, his eyes hidden.

"No motives," he murmured almost, it seemed to Mr. Campion, regretfully. "No motives either."

"All the same," Campion put in hastily, "it's not a strong case against Mike, and all that row the Coroner came in for will prejudice both Judge and Jury in his favour. He's almost certain to get off."

Ritchie shook his head gloomily.

"Not good enough. Stigma all his life. In love—can't marry. Poor fellow!"

He was quiet for a full minute, his huge bony hands twitching in little indeterminate gestures. Suddenly he sat up and Campion was surprised by the purpose and vigour in his tone.

"Got to prove who did it. Only way. Where now?"

Mr. Campion glanced at his watch. It was a quarter past four.

"I came to get your key to Twenty-three again," he said. "I'm going to burgle the safe. Like to come?"

"Yes," he said simply, and Campion grinned at him, despite his weariness.

They accomplished their short eerie walk without mishap and let themselves in through the big Queen Anne door at Twenty-three during that darkest moment of the night when the street lamps suddenly go out half an hour before the dawn.

"Can see in the dark," Ritchie remarked unexpectedly as he piloted Campion across the pitch-black hall to the top of the basement stairs. "Not like day, of course, but fairly well. Ten steps down to the landing and then twelve."

They reached the strong-room door and Campion unlocked it with Mr. Rigget's cherished key. There was something ghostly about the chaotic little apartment, and Mr. Campion found his mind, which was not used to such fancies, dwelling upon the crumpled body which had lain for so many hours among the dusty boxes by the safe and on the murderer who must have returned and dragged the helpless thing out to the clear space by the door at a time when the ravages of death were beginning to show.

There was no sign of Mr. Rigget's activities. His little inquisitions had been performed with the greatest discretion. Campion turned his attention to the safe and was glad that Lugg was not with him to express an opinion on a firm which entrusted anything of value to such an antiquated contraption. Ritchie divined his thoughts.

"Cupboard really," he observed apologetically. "Safe cupboard. Valuables at the bank."

Mr. Campion inserted the squat key which Mr. Samson had made for luck and mastered within a minute or two the simple arrangement of turns and half turns which shot back extremely heavy bolts. The door, which must have weighed a quarter of a ton at the lowest estimation, swung back, and Mr. Campion and Ritchie peered into the steel recess within.

At first sight the contents were not enlightening. Two or three half-calf ledgers, two small notebooks containing addresses, and a file of letters were neatly arranged upon the lower shelf. And that was all, save for a package neatly wrapped in green baize and tied with pink tape.

Mr. Campion took it out carefully and unpacked it on the table which Mike had cleared to receive Paul's body. Inside the baize wrapping was a well-made blue leather case designed to look like a book and very beautifully gilded. Examination proved that it had no lock, but pulled out in two pieces like a card-case and contained a slender manuscript.

"*Gallivant*," Ritchie remarked, looking over Campion's shoulder. "Never examined it. Uncle Jacoby Barnabas very strict. Thought it indecent. Would have destroyed it but for the value. John carries on tradition. Probably dull."

Campion turned back the thin octavo sheets, which were unbound save for the faded ribbon tied about the centre of the bundle. The brown ink made a spidery but decipherable pattern on the soft rag paper. He read a line or two.

"*Gagewell*: 'O Sir, since Lady Frippet hath a bee in her bonnet, you must allow if the bee's not a queen the bonnet is at least à la mode.'"

"Clean bit," said Ritchie, with that complete simplicity which was the mainspring of his personality. "Nothing to help us there. Valuable, of course. Wrote it himself, in his own hand. Insured. Stands at twenty thousand pounds in the balance-sheet."

Mr. Campion raised his eyebrow.

"Along with the office freehold and the printing plant at Gravesend?" he suggested.

"That's right," the older man agreed. "Best place for it. Never liked the classics. Put it away."

Campion was some little time repacking the treasure, and Ritchie wandered over to the safe.

"Nothing else," he observed, without turning round. "What are we looking for?"

"Whatever it was that made Paul go to the trouble of getting a key to the safe made for him," Campion explained as he tied the pink tape round the green baize once more and stowed it away in the safe. "There's only one official key to this elegent invention, I suppose. Who keeps it?"

"Head of the firm," said Ritchie. "Another tradition. Explains why there's nothing much kept in it."

"I see. That means that John had the original key?"

Ritchie considered.

"Probably Curley," he said at last. "One or the other. Only a fetish."

Mr. Campion took off his spectacles and perched himself on the edge of the table.

"It seems very careless to keep *The Gallivant* there," he began. "I should have thought the insurance johnnies might have objected to a thing like that."

Ritchie's eyes clouded.

"Ought to go back to the bank," he agreed. "Fact is, this dreadful business—death, murder, trial, and so on—has probably put the whole thing out of their minds. Very likely haven't been down here since. Can't blame them."

"Oh, it's usually kept at the bank, is it?" said Campion, pricking up his ears. "When was it put in here? Do you know?"

Ritchie's discomfort increased.

"Before Christmas. Silly business. Curley annoyed. Couldn't really blame her."

Mr. Campion was patient. Ritchie's cryptogrammic replies were tantalizing, and he was thankful for everybody's sake that the well-meaning, inarticulate soul had not been subpœnaed for the morrow's trial.

After a certain amount of persuasion Ritchie amplified his story.

"Nothing in it," he said wretchedly. "Paul made an ass of himself over *The Gallivant*. Wanted to lend it to rare-manuscript exhibition. Up against tradition at once. Grand old firm's vulgar classic. Wouldn't do. Old-fashioned. Stupid. But John and Curley had last word. Paul not content—silly fellow. Tried to get it from bank manager. Being partner, succeeded. Curley saw messenger who brought it. Went to John. John furious, backed her up. *Gallivant* put in safe."

Mr. Campion was bewildered. It seemed incredible that such a little domestic quarrel in the firm could have any connection with the grave issues at stake. He was silent for some moments, considering. John, he knew, had a fanatical pride in the honour of the firm; Miss Curley might easily have hidden depths of prudery; and Paul certainly seemed to have made a nuisance of himself all round. But compared with the scandal which had burst about their ears the public burning of *The Gallivant* by the police—an eventuality, after all, unlikely, since authors dead over a hundred years are permitted great license on the principle, no doubt, that their work has had time to air—would have been negligible, unless——? An idea occurred to him and he looked up, a startled expression in his pale eyes.

"Look here, I'll have to wander off now, Ritchie," he said. "I've been rather late for the bus all along, but I believe I'm catching up with it now. I shan't be down at the Old Bailey at the beginning this morning, but I'll come along later. Keep an eye on Gina, but don't tell her anything."

"No," said Ritchie, with the obedience of a child, and Campion, looking at him affectionately, wondered how much of the mystery about him he saw and what, if anything, he thought of it.

It was half past six on a cold spring morning, with drizzle in the air, when they parted, and Mr. Campion went home to bathe and shave, since it was too early to begin his day's business. He also took the opportunity to submit himself to a patching process, of which Mr. Lugg was a past master. The spectacle of that mournful figure, clad solely in a pair of trousers, standing upon a bath mat at seven-thirty in the morning, a minute pair of surgical scissors in one enormous hand and an even smaller strip of sticking-plaster in the other, was one of those experiences that Mr. Campion frankly enjoyed.

He was sorry that they were not on conversational terms. Mr. Lugg was the victim of a two-way complex. His newer self revolted at the unpleasant publicity with which he saw his employer's name surrounded as the trial progressed, while his elder spirit was deeply hurt that Campion should have enjoyed a scrap in which he had not been permitted to take part.

"There you are," he said at last, stepping back from his handiwork. "Now I've wasted my time on you making you look like a gent again, go and smear yourself with society filth. Roll in it like a dawg—but don't ask me to clean yer. Mud sticks closer than them patches I've put on your dial."

"Mud of the soul?" enquired Mr. Campion affably.

"You know what I mean," said Lugg warningly. "And if we 'ad that charwoman I've ben thinking of I'd drive 'ome me contemp' in the way I was brought up to, even if I 'ave learnt spittin's not quite the thing."

Mr. Campion dressed in silence. At nine o'clock he was waiting outside the door of a little office on the third floor of a building in St. Martin's Lane.

Ex-Detective-Inspector Beth found him there when he came heavily up the stairs to open the little private enquiry office he had established on his retirement.

"Can't get my assistant to turn up before half past, Mr. Campion," he explained as he unlocked the door. "My word, if I had him in the Force for half an hour!"

He paused, enquiry on his round good-natured face.

"Surely *we* can't do anything for you, can we? Well, well, I thought they even took in your laundry work down at the Yard these days."

"Working a little light humour into the act, I see," said his visitor approvingly. " 'Divorce with a laugh' and 'Blackmail made fun'? It's not a bad idea. However, unfortunately, there's nothing very amusing about the small commission I am about to entrust to you at the moment. It is merely odd."

He took a limp brown bank book from his pocket and, opening it, entered into some careful instructions. The ex-inspector was puzzled.

"If it was a case of impersonation—someone taking it out—I could understand it," he said. "But who cares who pays money in?"

"I do," said Mr. Campion, who was very tired. "I'm a very proud young fellow, and I like to know where my money's coming from."

Beth turned the book over.

"Since when have you been called Dora Phyllis Netley?" he enquired suspiciously.

Campion leant forward confidentially.

"You must let a man have his secrets," he murmured. "Get on to it and let me have a report tonight."

"Tonight? What do you think we are?" protested his host.

"Private and enterprising. I read it on the door," said Mr. Campion, and hurried away.

It was just after ten when he reached the British Museum, and he paused for a moment at the foot of the great soot-stained granite flight of steps to feel in his breast pocket. His weariness was making him absent-minded, and just for a moment he could not remember if on changing his clothes he had slipped into his pocket a wallet containing a page of *The Gallivant* which he had stolen so shamelessly from beneath Ritchie's very nose. It was there, however, and he went on thankfully.

Time at the Museum is given the treatment it deserves from the custodians of the treasure of historic man, and Mr. Campion's godfather, Professor Bunney, did not arrive until late, so that the morning was considerably advanced when the tall pale young man in the horn-rimmed spectacles at last came out between the granite columns.

Mr. Campion walked slowly, accustoming himself to an idea. His godfather had been most helpful and he now knew without a possibility of doubt that the manuscript of *The Gallivant* in the blue leather box, which was insured for twenty thousand pounds and appeared in the balance-sheet of the famous firm of Barnabas, Limited as representing that sum, was certainly not, however genuine its contents might be, penned by the hand of Wm. Congreve, Dec. 1729, nor was the paper on which it was written manufactured one year earlier than 1863.

16 : *The Fourth Chair*

One of the unexpected things about the Central Criminal Court at the Old Bailey is that it is perfectly new. The carving above the Judge's chair, where the great sword hangs, is not an old carving, and the light oak of the contraption so like a Punch and Judy show, which is the witness-box, is not worn by the nervous hands of a thousand testators but retains some of the varnished brightness of the cabinet-maker's shop.

This newness might perhaps destroy some of the court's undeniable impressiveness were it not for one significant difference between this particular new room and others of the time.

Here ancient things have been replaced not by copies vulgarly disguised to appear old, nor yet by new things different in design and purpose from the old out of deference to the changing manners and customs which have altered the surface of life during the past five hundred years, but by new things replacing those worn out in a room where customs and manners do not change and where the business conducted is not concerned with the surface but with that deeply set, unchangeable streak embedded in the rock of civilization which is crime.

Miss Curley sat beside Gina in the block of seats at the back of the court which is reserved for witnesses and, looking about her, wondered if Mike had been properly fed in Pentonville.

The two women were wedged in a corner some three rows from the front. Gina, at Cousin Alexander's hinted instigation, had succeeded in making herself look almost dowdy. Certainly she appeared very young and very tragic, the high collar of her black coat shadowing her pale, distinctive face.

Immediately before them in the well of the court was the enormous dock, looking as large as and not at all unlike a very superior sheep pen in a country market.

Three chairs, the one in the middle a little in front of the others and directly facing the judicial desk, stood lonely and inadequate in the midst of the expanse.

Beyond was Counsels' table, already littered with papers and glasses of water, with the jury and witness-boxes and the Press table on its left and the solicitors' table and the bank of expert witnesses on its right.

Farther away still were the clerks' desks, directly beneath the dais and facing into the well.

Last of all was the Bench itself.

The seven chairs on the dais were equidistant and all very much alike, since the Lord Mayor and Aldermen of London are entitled to sit. They each had high leather backs emblazoned with the city arms and managed to look impressive even when unoccupied.

The fourth chair fascinated Miss Curley. It stood between the carved columns, the state sword, hilt downward, immediately above it, while before it, at the wide desk, a little clerk was arranging sheaves of paper.

The court was full of people. The witness benches were crammed and the public gallery over the solicitors' table seemed in danger of bursting and jettisoning its load into the dock. Press and solicitors' tables were full and junior counsel and the clerks were clustering round their own headquarters. Everyone was talking. Men in gowns hurried to and fro with papers, their shoes squeaking noisily on the wood. Now and again a late arrival was thrust into a seat in the witness benches by a fatherly official clad in what appeared to be some sort of police uniform augmented by a beadle's gown.

The jury, ten men and two women, looked on at the preparations like an absurdly small audience at an amateur theatrical show which had got completely out of hand and swamped the auditorium. They looked apprehensive and painfully uncomfortable and the foreman, an elderly man with pince-nez and a bald head, mopped his face repeatedly although the morning was inclined to be cold.

John sat at the solicitors' table oddly in the picture, his round head held slightly on one side and his long thin neck sticking stiffly out of his elegant grey collar.

Ritchie was behind Gina and his expression of frightened disgust as he noticed each new evidence of human bondage was pathetic or comic according to the onlooker's fancy. He showed no signs of fatigue, but his gentle eyes were anxious and his enormous bony hands fidgeted on his knees.

Among the legal broiling circulating round the court with a familiarity which proclaimed it their own fishpond there was a certain amount of pleasurable anticipation. A *cause célèbre* at the Old Bailey is bound to have its moments. The Lord Chief Justice, Lord Lumley, affectionately called "Lor Lumme" by his admirers in the best legal, police and criminal circles, still preserved sufficient humanity in his omnipotence to lose his temper on occasions and there was a persistent rumour, utterly unfounded, that he cherished a personal antipathy towards Sir Alexander Barnabas.

Then, in accordance with the custom at poisoning trials at the Old Bailey, the Attorney-General himself, Sir Montague Brooch, was appearing for the Crown and was leading Sir Andrew Phelps, with Jerome Fyshe and Eric Battersby as juniors.

There were rumours of last-minute trouble with important witnesses and altogether the prospects looked good.

Gina sat trembling.

"I'm going to see him—I'm going to see him—I'm going to see him—
I'm going to see him——"

The words made a singsong pattern completely without meaning in
her brain, neither conveying nor expressing any thought at all, but providing a deadening chatter which prevented her from thinking.

Miss Curley sat forward, straining her eyes to see Counsels' table. Something was happening and she could see flickers of amusement appearing
on dark faces beneath blue-white periwigs.

A clerk entered, laden with an assortment of paraphernalia which he
proceeded to arrange. First a dark cushion was placed carefully on a chair,
then a portfolio laid reverently on the table and round it a little ring
of oddments carefully set out. Miss Curley discerned a pile of exquisite
cambric handkerchiefs, a bottle of smelling salts, another of sal volatile,
a box of throat pastilles and a glass of water.

There was a long pause. The clerk stepped back and gazed expectantly
at the doorway behind him. His interest was not unnaturally echoed by
those about him and finally, when everyone in the court was aware that
somebody of importance was about to enter, a little door swung open,
there was a rustle of an old silk gown, a glimpse of a grey-blue wig, and
then, looking like a middle-aged Apollo in fancy dress, Cousin Alexander
swept up to the table and sat down.

Miss Curley waited for the Attorney-General and, disappointed, had
allowed her eyes to wander back to Cousin Alexander and away again
before she suddenly caught sight of him at the same table and wondered
if he had been there all the time.

The big hand of the court clock reached the half hour and there was
a sudden silence, followed by a mighty rustle as everybody rose. The door
on the right of the dais opened and an old gentleman in red appeared.

The squad of wigs bowed, looking slightly comic as black, brown and
even pink heads appeared for an instant beneath the queues as necks
were bent.

The Judge returned the bow as he settled himself, not in the fourth
chair beneath the sword but in the one beside it, and the untidy little
clerk rearranged his papers. The position brought him nearer the jury and
the witness-box and farther from Counsel, and the change was probably
pure pernicketiness and the desire to break the symmetry of the design.

The Lord Chief Justice, Lord Lumley, was a large old man with the
drooping jowls and bald bony eyesockets of a bloodhound. His upper lip
was shaven but he affected a square of close-clipped white hair about as
big as a piece of confetti in the centre of his lower one, which gave him
a slightly sporting appearance. He was over seventy and forced from time
to time to use eyeglasses, which he wore on a wide black ribbon.

As he sat in his high leather chair his scarlet robe fell sleekly with
deep wine-coloured shadows over his heavy form, and his square wig,

which was brown and inclined to look as though it were made of the
bristles usually fashioned into carpet brooms, overshadowed his face.

In his hand he held a formal bouquet, the nosegay dating from the
time when the air of the courtroom was not so hygienic as modern cleanliness has made it and a handful of flowers and herbs was at least some
barrier between a fastidious gentleman and the plague.

After a pause, he seemed to remember it suddenly, for he leant forward and placed it carefully in the tumbler of water on his desk, where
it stood for the remainder of the day looking like a motif from a Tudor
tapestry or a chapter end for *Alice in Wonderland*.

Meanwhile there was a whispering hush over the room, and presently,
from somewhere below the court, the sound of a door banging heralded
the arrival of the prisoner.

Gina was unfamiliar with the geography of the place and Mike's sudden
appearance from the well staircase in the bottom right-hand corner of the
dock almost unnerved her. He came up slowly between two warders,
whose care of him was that of hospital attendants. They were both square,
short-legged men, considerably his senior, and they patted him and murmured what must have been encouraging words as he towered above them
in the vast and shining sheep pen below the dome.

Miss Curley caught her breath. She had not seen him since his arrest
and was unprepared for the change in him. He did not look particularly
ill. His features were finer and his pallor made his eyes look darker, but
his crisp shorn head was grey and, as he stood facing the Judge with his
back directly to her, she saw the wide bones of his shoulders hunched
under his coat.

She stole a glance at Gina. The girl was crying, angry, indignant tears
hovering on the fringe of her lashes, and Miss Curley, who was liable
to unexpected flashes of feminine intuition, realized that, whatever her
other thoughts and emotions might be, Gina wept because his hair was
grey.

She looked away abruptly. An entirely new personality had taken charge
of the proceedings. The Clerk, who until now had been just another dark-
faced, grey-wigged person sitting at a desk directly beneath the Judge's
dais, had risen to his feet and revealed himself to be an unexpectedly
distinguished man with a deep, cultured voice and a casual manner
which robbed his words of their formality without over-emphasizing their
meaning.

"Michael Wedgwood, you are charged for that you, on the twenty-
eighth day of January, nineteen thirty-one, at London, murdered Paul
Redfern Brande. You are also charged on a Coroner's inquisition with murder. How say you, Michael Wedgwood? Are you guilty or not guilty?"

As the last word left his lips he sat down again with a great rustle of papers and there was a pause until one of the warders nudged his prisoner gently.

"Not guilty."

Mike's voice was unexpectedly loud and infused a note of tension into the friendly, businesslike atmosphere of the court. He remained upon his feet while the Clerk turned his attention to the business of swearing in the jury, and Lord Justice Lumley raised that part of his face where his left eyebrow should have been and remarked affably:

"You may sit down. The only time you have to stand in this court is when you are receiving sentence or when I address you."

He had a pleasant rumbling voice with a slight squeak in it at commas, which did nothing to detract from the magnificent oddity of his appearance or his unshakable dignity which clothed him as surely as his robe.

The jury being sworn, a proceeding conducted with the neatness and efficiency of a first-class acrobatic turn, the Clerk addressed them as they sat wriggling before him, twelve busy citizens with troubles enough of their own.

He sat down at last and bent over his desk and, while Miss Curley trembled, the Attorney-General rose to open the case for the prosecution.

Montague Brooch was a little crow of a man. His silk gown enveloped him and his wig gave his face an even sharper, beakier appearance than it possessed without it. In repose he was inclined to look insignificant, and few would remark him, if even for his ugliness, but the moment he opened his mouth he became a personality that was as unforgettable as it was utterly charming.

"May it please Your Lordship, Members of the Jury——"

The voice was virile yet confiding, attractive, deferential and pleasing in the extreme.

"—the charge against the prisoner, as you have heard, is murder. I must, I am afraid, open to you with a story of considerable detail, and, while it is not without its difficulties, it must, I think, show a very serious case indeed against the prisoner."

For the first time since the arrival of Cousin Alexander upon the scene Miss Curley felt genuinely afraid. Until now she had accepted John's valuation of the famous man without question and had allayed all her qualms for Mike's eventual safety by a recollection of that handsome, sanguine figure with the face of a hero and the confidence of a Harley Street specialist. But here was a real adversary. Cousin Alexander's charm was definable and all the more vulnerable because of it, but the personality of Montague Brooch was not capable of analysis and had a disconcerting habit of confusing itself with clear and reasoned argument, so that it was his thought and not the man one most remembered.

Miss Curley glanced at John now and saw him sitting forward in his chair, his head held on one side and his cold eyes fixed unwaveringly upon the little crow with the sweet voice who spoke so convincingly, and at the same time somehow so regretfully, of the crime. There was no way of telling his thought but Miss Curley fancied that he was disconcerted.

Behind her Ritchie was breathing heavily and down in the other witness benches she caught a glimpse of Mrs. Austin's broad back and untidy hair.

". . . *Now what happens on the Sunday night? On January the thirty-first you will hear that quite fortuitously, and when in the company of friends, the accused is asked to go down to the room where, it is the Crown's case, he knew the body lay. . . ."*

To Gina the Attorney-General was just a voice repeating facts she already knew and had heard proved over and over again until their significance was lost upon her.

To her the one reality was Mike himself, sitting directly in front of her. She could see his grey head and the short hairs at the nape of his neck and her throat contracted until the pain of it alone seemed sufficient to suffocate her.

There was not complete silence in the court while the speech went on. To Miss Curley's surprise there seemed to be no rule against whispering, and clerks, with great armfuls of papers and noisy shoes, tiptoed about.

Cousin Alexander, looking tremendously important and more handsome than any man over fifty has any right to be in his immaculate wig and bands, was rustling his papers, conferring with his juniors and polishing his glasses with a great flourish of the topmost handkerchief.

". . . *Let me take the next stage. Doctor Ferdie arrives. He agrees with Doctor Roe as to the cause of death and together these two men make a very careful autopsy. . . ."*

The delightful voice played over the unpleasant words, giving them just sufficient emphasis. Miss Curley found herself listening with detached interest. At the inquest the central figure had been the dead man but here Mike had taken his place and the story was told afresh from a new angle.

It occurred to Miss Curley, who had known Paul and had been amused by him, that he was easily the least important person in the whole story and that his personality alone did not emerge in the dreadful résumé of the manner of his dying. She could not see the public gallery and even if she had been able she would not have recognized Teddie Dell.

". . . *Inspector Tanner visited the strong room, where you have heard the body lay, and, after making a careful survey of the room and its environs, discovered a most ingenious device, of which he will tell you. . . ."*

Miss Curley, having located Doctors Ferdie and Roe in the benches behind the solicitors' table, was looking about for Inspector Tanner in the seats behind her when a large elderly man at her side turned round and, seeing her placid friendly face, whispered huskily:

"Makes you think, don't he? I remember him in a stuff gown."

Miss Curley gave the remark the conventional smile it needed and wondered who he was. There were a great many people in the benches whom she had never seen before and next time the stranger confided his admiration of Counsel to her with a muttered, "What a way with him!" she ventured to whisper back.

"Are you a witness?"

"No. Come in to watch."

He did not volunteer any information concerning the method by which he had obtained a seat and Miss Curley eyed his pleasant face, whose only striking feature was enormous eyebrows, covertly and reflected that it was difficult to generalize and that he was not at all the type she would have suspected of morbid curiosity.

Meanwhile, Sir Montague had spoken for the best part of an hour and his gentle voice was apologizing to Judge and Jury.

"... I have little more to say now. You will hear in detail every part of the tragic and abominable story I have outlined to you. But there are a few points which I should like to put into your minds at this stage. It is usual to look for a motive in any crime and, although in this case you will not find a motive which you, or I, I hope, would think adequate, I think you will see that it is more than possible that the accused had a motive sufficient for him. I must admit to you that the Crown has no direct evidence of immoral relations between the murdered man's wife and the accused. It may be that when you see Mrs. Brande you will decide that she is not the sort of woman whose principles are those which would permit her to stoop to that sort of irregularity, but you will hear on her own submission that she was a neglected wife, and the accused has admitted in his statement, which I have read to you, that he was in the habit of spending much of his time with her and that in fact at the very moment when, as I shall prove to you, her husband was lying dead in a basement room in the house next door, he took her to a cinema, bringing her back afterwards to the flat which she shared with her husband and returning immediately, I have no doubt, to his own home in the same building.

"You will also hear from Mrs. Austin, the honest woman who attended to Mrs. Brande's household work, of the scene which she witnessed when the accused came to break the news of Paul Brande's death to Mrs. Brande.

"Mrs. Austin came into the room to find them on the hearth rug, 'clinging together,' as she so graphically puts it. You may feel that this is not evidence of immoral relations and I would reiterate that the Crown does not allege immoral relations, but it does insist that there was deep friendship between the accused and Mrs. Brande, dating over a period of some years and increasing in intensity as Mrs. Brande's husband increased in his neglect.

"At what point, if any, a deep affection cherished by a young and virile man for a beautiful and virtuous woman some years his junior may grow into an overwhelming passion, in the grip of which his moral fibre is broken down utterly, it is for you to consider. The Crown is not dealing with conjecture. The Crown merely contends that a deep affection was entertained by the accused for Mrs. Brande.

"Mrs. Brande will tell you that she had visited a solicitor some days before her husband's death and had learned from him that there was no way open to her to obtain a divorce save through her husband's cruelty or through his co-operation. She will also tell you that the accused knew nothing of this, and indeed that he had no idea that any such project had entered her head. You must believe what you see to be the truth. If you believe that a deep friendship existed between these two you may think that it is improbable, even impossible, that any woman should keep such an important matter from such an intimate friend who saw her every day. If there was nothing but friendship between them, why should she hide it? If there was more, might it not have been even at the accused's suggestion that she approached the solicitor?

"However, you will hear that Mr. Brande would not consider a divorce and that it was to discuss this very matter, and to make his strong views known to his wife, that he had arranged to meet her on the very evening that he met his death, an appointment which he never kept. . . ."

Miss Curley stirred in her seat. Gina was rigid, her cheeks pallid and her lips compressed. A woman in the gallery craned her neck to catch a glimpse of her.

Gradually the speech came to an end. The Attorney-General's voice had never lost its gentle and impartial reasonableness and now it became even more soothing, even more deferential, than before.

"It has been necessary to address you at this length because you must know exactly what the facts are in this story, the burden of which the Crown will attempt to prove. If you feel, as I feel you must, that the evidence leads you to the conclusion beyond all reasonable doubt that this man, in order to marry his cousin's wife, did kill his cousin on the night of January the twenty-eighth in this year, you will have no hesitation in doing your duty.

"If, however, you find there is insufficient direct evidence to make you so sure, and that you have a reasonable doubt, then again you will have no hesitation in doing your duty.

"The case is a difficult one. All the Crown will do is to set out the facts on which you must rely. This is not a case in which you will be concerned with any possible verdicts such as manslaughter. A murder has been done and it is for you to decide if it was committed by the accused. If it was, if the Crown proves to you, as I believe it will, that this man did what he is charged with doing, then it is a crime utterly foul and

unpardonable. His cousin had done him no wrong. At worst he had neg-
lected his own wife. And yet, if you so find it, he sent him slowly and
insidiously to his death with a callousness which no rigour of the law can
equal.

"If you think it is fairly proved against this man that he so murdered
his cousin, then it will be your duty to send him to his account."

He paused, bowed to the Judge, and sat down.

And then, while the court was still tingling, a police photographer
bobbed up in the Punch and Judy witness-box, and began to testify as
to photographs taken in connection with the crime.

A surveyor had taken his place and was painfully describing the survey
of the ground floors and garden of Twenty-three and Twenty-one which
he had made, and had produced plans and had sworn to them, when
Miss Curley's neighbour turned to her.

"Shan't come back. Nothing more of interest today. Fireworks tomorrow," he confided in a warm whisper. "They'll adjourn in a minute."

"Adjourn?" murmured Miss Curley, who already saw Mike on the scaf-
fold. "What for?"

Her neighbour gaped at her as at a lunatic.

"Lunch, of course," he said.

17 : *Mr. Campion's Case for*
the Defence

Ritchie was standing in the huge multi-coloured marble hall at the Old
Bailey, which had the smell of a public library and was full of people
who talked together with that peculiar excited anxiety almost always reserved for other people's troubles, when Mr. Campion found him and
led him to one side.

He was obviously shaken by the experience of the morning and it was
some time before Campion, who was tired, could be sure that he was
getting his full attention.

"There won't be anything more of interest today," Campion repeated
slowly and with emphasis. "I want you to come away with me now and
give me a hand. It's important."

"Leave the court?" said Ritchie, his gentle eyes blinking at his friend.

"Yes, if you would." Mr. Campion was very patient. "I've seen Sir
Alexander and Miss Curley will look after Gina. Are you coming?"

The sweet air, or it may have been the sweet freedom, of Newgate

Street, revived Ritchie's powers of speech. He strode along to the car park talking with what was for him lucidity and volubility.

"Awful, Campion!" he shouted. "Ghastly! Jolly things like fancy dress, boxes for seats, coloured robes and policemen all made horrible and frightening. Like a serious harlequinade. Mike's grey. Hair's grey. Two men in delightful clothes arguing for his life. Like a game . . . rules . . . places to stand. Felt ill. Sick. Wanted to spew. Frightened, Campion."

The young man in the horn-rimmed spectacles was silent. The project he had in hand was a delicate one and he required co-operation. It seemed to him best in the circumstances to allow Ritchie's startled wits to re-assort themselves without assistance.

As they climbed into the car and waited to slip out into the slothful stream of traffic Ritchie sighed and shook himself.

"Like a dream," he said. "Absurd, like a dream. They'll hang him, Campion. That fellow with the voice is cleverer than Cousin Alexander. That's what counts."

By the time they reached Ludgate Hill he was better and his companion, recognizing in him a worried edition of his normal self, thought it safe to broach the subject in hand.

"You get on very well with Mrs. Peel, don't you?" he enquired.

"John's housekeeper? Known her for years. Nice old body. Why?"

"She doesn't like me," explained Campion regretfully. "She didn't like to trust me in the flat. Afraid I was going to pinch the ormolu clock with the china figures. That's why I had to come and get hold of you."

He paused and concentrated on his driving, wondering how far Ritchie's perception would lead him and with what results.

The elder man did not seem to perceive at all. He acquiesced quietly and they drove on in silence. It was warm and sunny when they arrived at the cul-de-sac and Twenty-one seemed to be deserted. Twenty-three was not closed but there was little sign of activity and the Morris sign of the Golden Quiver swung disconsolately in the light breeze.

"Mrs. Peel," remarked Mr. Campion as he sprang out of the car and came round to help Ritchie with the door, whose simple mechanism had defeated him, "thinks I am (A) a thief and (B) the police. You are coming with me to dispel both these delusions. Do you think you can do it?"

"Dear good intelligent woman," Ritchie observed, apparently in answer to the question. "Kind. Always liked her."

She stood in the dark entrance hall of John's flat when they presented themselves at the door a few minutes later and surveyed them with belligerent beady eyes, like some large elderly beetle surprised in its tree-trunk home.

She had a harsh unpleasing voice and when she said, "Back again?" Mr. Campion could not help feeling some of the shame which she intended to stir in him.

Ritchie stood looking at her helplessly for a moment and then, either by accident or design, achieved a master-stroke.

"No lunch, Peely . . . cocoa . . . bread and butter . . . anything," he murmured. "Campion and me, tired, hungry, want to sit down."

Mrs. Peel led the way into the dining room, grumbling as she went. Her brown serge dress hitched at the back, revealing untidy ankles, but her sparse hair was groomed and dressed to a neatness which suggested that each separate strand knew its duty in emergency and was determined to make up for its scarcity of companions.

As they sat waiting for food at the heavy mahogany table in the dark book-lined room with the thick curtains and half-drawn venetian blinds, Mr. Barnabas made a very curious remark.

"Pity about the food, Campion. Know how you feel. Old shibboleth, though. Couldn't be helped."

Mr. Campion's eyebrows rose and he shot his friend a single penetrating glance which completely destroyed for an instant the habitual vacuity of his expression, but Ritchie said no more and presently rose from his chair and opened a window, which Mrs. Peel promptly closed as soon as she returned with bread, butter, Gorgonzola and two cups of weak unpalatable cocoa.

"That two grown men with money in their pockets can't look after their creature comforts in a town of this size is extraordinary," she remarked angrily, but as she looked only at Ritchie as she spoke Mr. Campion realized with relief that he was accepted, if ignored.

He even ate the horrible meal, Mrs. Peel waiting upon him as if he had been a six-year-old, buttering his bread and cutting him small chunks of odoriferous cheese.

"Been to the trial," Ritchie mumbled into his cocoa cup.

Mrs. Peel made an indignant sound like a French railway engine.

"That murder! I never heard such utter nonsense in all my born days. It was an accident. Mr. John told me so himself."

"Were you here on the night it happened?" Mr. Campion ventured.

The woman turned round and looked at him.

"Well, of all the questions!" she exclaimed. "Of course I was. What are you trying to insinuate? That I was turning on the gas in the office? No. I was in this flat the whole time. At four o'clock I began to lay out Mr. John's clothes and when he came in at five-thirty I went to my room and sat with the door open, so that I could hear when he called me."

"And did he call you?"

Mr. Campion's face expressed polite interest.

"Of course he did," she said impatiently. "If Mr. John could dress by himself I should think he was ill. He called me to turn on the bath and when it was ready I told him so and went back to my room."

Campion was silent for some time and his eyes were thoughtful. He was forming the next question carefully when she answered it unbidden.

"The murder wasn't the only accident that happened that night," she observed in the tone of one mentioning a genuine trouble in the midst of a discussion on imaginary ills. "When I knocked on Mr. John's bedroom door to tell him the bath was ready he didn't hear me and all the time I thought he was having his bath he was in here. He sat down for a moment and must have dozed off. Anyway, he didn't hear me and at a quarter to seven I hear him come out of the bathroom in a fine rage. He had been to see if the bath was ready and had found it lukewarm. I had to hot it up for him. In the end he didn't go into that bath until seven o'clock and of course he wouldn't hurry himself—never would, not if the house was afire. And finally he went off to his dinner at a quarter to eight, dressed nicely but not shaved. He hadn't, I know, because I looked at his brush and it was dry. That shows you how accidents happen."

"Yes," agreed Mr. Campion with a solemnity quite out of keeping with the circumstances. "Yes, that's exactly what it does do."

"Well, then," said Mrs. Peel and began to clear away with a great clatter.

Mr. Campion rose to his feet.

"Where is the bathroom?" he enquired.

The woman stared at him, her brows raised into acute angles on her wrinkled forehead and a flush spreading upward over her face.

"I never did!" she said at last. "Really! Oh, all right . . . the second door across the passage. There is a clean towel there."

A few minutes later when Ritchie entered the old-fashioned bathroom with the big copper geyser and the enormous antiquated bath he found Mr. Campion leaning out of the window. The younger man drew in his head and straightened his back. Ritchie took his place.

A fire escape sprawled its ungainly way up the back of the elegant old house and one green-painted iron landing stage abutted on to the wall less than two feet below the sill over which he leant. He looked at it for a moment and then stepped back and he and Mr. Campion eyed each other. Ritchie was first to speak.

"Talk," he said urgently. "Downstairs."

Mrs. Peel made it clear that she was glad to see the end of them, if indeed, as she very much doubted, it was the end. She also mentioned that something for nothing was a very common quarry in her experience, but that since Mr. Ritchie was a relation she did not see that she was entitled to begrudge the cocoa. She also wished them a very good afternoon.

Ritchie led Campion downstairs to the ground floor and let himself into Mike's domain.

"Mike gave it to me," he explained, observing Campion's eyes on the latchkey. "Had to fetch him some clothes when they took him to that place. He won't mind us here. Good fellow, Mike. Grey hair, poor chap."

He waved his friend towards a dusty armchair in the sitting room which they both knew well and perched himself opposite on the edge of the table, where he sat with his long arms swinging and his shaggy head held up alertly.

"Know now?" he asked anxiously and for the last time the younger man surprised the dog-like, enquiring expression in his face. "Clear?"

"Yes, I think so," said Mr. Campion and sighed.

"*Gallivant* only a copy?"

Although he put the words as a question Ritchie seemed to have very little doubt as to the answer and Campion wondered afresh at his extraordinary mixture of shrewdness and simplicity. Aloud he said:

"They think the stuff itself may be genuine, but it's not the original manuscript. It's probably a copy made sometime in the last half of the last century."

"Uncle Jacoby," observed Ritchie blandly. "All prudish Victorians secretly dirty. Probably had it made for private reading. Like him, rather. Funny old man. What happened to Paul?"

Mr. Campion leaned back in his chair. He looked very tired but his eyes were bright and intelligent.

"Paul was too energetic," he said slowly, and added apologetically, "You'll have to forgive me if I take my time, but I've learnt the story the wrong way round."

"Tell it that way. Begin at the end."

"I don't know the end," said Mr. Campion. "That's the trouble."

Ritchie sat silent and expectant and presently Campion went on.

"Paul made himself a nuisance in the firm for four years, ever since he returned from America," he said. "In that time he seems to have got on the nerves of most people in publishing generally. Then he was bitten by the idea of exhibiting *The Gallivant* and, of course, there were excellent reasons why the manuscript should not be shown in a place where interfering people might ask awkward questions about the age of the paper and the quality of the ink, not to mention the authenticity of the handwriting. So he was stopped, but, being an enquiring and obstinate beggar, it dawned upon him that there was probably something fishy about the precious manuscript and he decided to examine it. He got the bank to give it up, but again he was stopped from looking at it and the manuscript was put in the safe. Whether that was done with malice aforethought I don't know, but I rather think so, for the safe key was left in his way long enough for him to take an impression of it and from that time on a pretty close watch was kept on Paul's activities and the watcher was paid small sums for her trouble."

He paused and Ritchie nodded comprehendingly.

"The day came," continued Mr. Campion, "when the watcher reported that a letter had arrived which had made Paul dash off in excitement.

It was a letter from Wardie Samson, for which he and his observers had waited. It was a signal for action.

"This is what happened to Paul. He came back to Twenty-three just after six o'clock, when he knew the place would be closed, let himself in and went up to Curley's desk, where he got the key of the strong room. He then went down to the basement. His new key fitted the safe, but the arrangement of turns and half turns got him bothered because he was nervous and in a high state of excitement. He had just got the safe door open when he was disturbed by footsteps in the yard outside. I imagine that a characteristic cough warned him, quite intentionally, that the newcomer was the one particular person he did not wish to find him there and I think he behaved quite normally and in the way the murderer foresaw he would behave, and not like that hysterical maniac Peter Rigget, who lost his head and went berserk."

Ritchie looked interested but so completely in the dark that Campion wondered if he could possibly be following this complicated reconstruction.

"Paul locked himself in and turned out the light," Campion continued. "He knew, or thought he knew, that he had the only key of the strong room, so that he was safe from the intruder, and as long as no chink of light showed anywhere there was no reason at all why anyone should suspect the place was occupied.

"In the dark he crept away from the door and waited for the other man to go. But the newcomer remained. He went into the garage and started the car and Paul, not sure if the back door was standing open, dared not slip out, even if he wanted to. Personally I think he decided to wait until the other man had gone. Probably he imagined that Mike was with him. Anyway, whatever he thought, it did not occur to him that carbon monoxide fumes were pouring into the unventilated room through the rubber pipe pushed through the grating in the opposite wall.

"He noticed the smell of exhaust gas, of course, but since he could hear the car and probably guessed there was an air brick leading into the garage somewhere he thought nothing of it.

"Within five minutes he was drowsy and sat down, I think by the safe. Five minutes later he was unconscious, and after the best part of an hour, when the murderer returned and switched off the engine, he was dead."

"Murderer returned?"

Mr. Campion looked up.

"Yes," he said. "In the interim he went back to his home by the way he had come, found his bath was cold, blew up his housekeeper, had the bath heated again and bathed. When he had finished he put on his underclothes and trousers, probably, under a dressing-gown, and went out once more through the bathroom window, down the fire escape, through the door in the garden wall, switched off the car, threw the rubber tubing in at the basement door as he returned, then finished his dressing and went out to dinner, unfortunately not having had time to shave.

"I'm open to bet that he wore gloves not because of fingerprints, but so that he should not dirty or burn his hands."

There was a long silence. Ritchie was rocking himself slowly backwards and forwards.

"Not dozing in dining room, watching street for Paul to go into Twenty-three," he said at last. "Wouldn't have been seen on fire escape from street at other end of yard. Foggy all that week. Risky, Campion."

"Risky!" Mr. Campion caught his breath. "It was so risky that no one who did not imagine himself a species of god about the place would have thought of it, much less attempted it. Mike might have come home earlier, although, of course, he was supposed to be at the cocktail party. But anyone might have gone into the garage to see why the car was running. Hang it! Even a policeman might have enquired. . . . Besides, Paul might not have stayed there. He might have come out at the very beginning and asked him what the hell he thought he was up to."

"Wouldn't have mattered," Ritchie observed. "He'd have won. He'd have told Paul to mind his own business and go away. Paul would have gone. Strong personality . . . strict, you know . . . authoritative."

Mr. Campion remained thoughtful.

"On Sunday he must have been getting restive when he sent Mike down to the strong room," he said quietly. "He sent him to get a folder, expecting him to find the door locked and the key missing and so start the excitement which would lead to the finding of the body. It would have been a weak move if Mike had found Paul. As it turned out, of course, it complicated the issue tremendously. Mike didn't see the corpse and came back as though nothing had happened. That must have jolted our man considerably. So afterwards, probably late at night, he went down there himself, dragged the body into a prominent position, and, after placing the hat by its side, left it for Miss Marchant to find in the morning. He couldn't very well leave the door locked on the inside, so he put the key back in Miss Curley's desk.

"It's a mad sort of crime, so mad that it came off. It was the man's mental make-up which made it possible. All murderers are a little crazy. The people who get away with incredible things are those who never look round the subject, but just go straight ahead and make for their objective with blinkers on. It's like the drunk who walks across the parapet. He only knows he wants to get to a window next door, sees a straight path and takes it, oblivious of the ten-story drop on either side of him."

"John . . ." said Ritchie. "Obvious really."

"Obvious?" enquired Mr. Campion, his professional pride stirring in its latent bed.

"From the beginning," said Ritchie placidly. "John said he knew it was an accident. John's not a fool. Got a logical mind. Reasonable, except where personal infallibility is concerned. If he knew it was an accident he must have arranged it himself: everyone else thought it was a murder. Queer chap . . . law of his own. Terrible for Mike."

"Not too good for Paul," murmured Mr. Campion dryly. "But that's not the question at the moment. The trouble is I can't prove this story. It depends too much on your friend Mrs. Peel, and even if she could be persuaded to tell the same yarn in the witness-box what should we have then? A case against John just about as strong as the one they've already got against Mike. The police wouldn't consider it. Why should they?"

Ritchie sat silent for a long time. Finally he looked at the younger man, his mild blue eyes dark and pained.

"Terrible for Mike," he repeated. "Caught, imprisoned, killed."

"No," said Campion hastily. "He'll be acquitted. I'm sure of it. If I wasn't I'd be at the Yard now doing anything I could, making a fool of myself probably. I'm banking on an acquittal. Anyway, there'll be the appeal. That's not the point. Unfortunately in an imperfect world acquittal does not mean that a man is proved innocent to the satisfaction of the people with whom he has got to live."

"What shall we do?"

Ritchie invited a command and Mr. Campion made up his mind. He rose and walked over to Mike's desk.

"I think we'll leave a note," he said.

Taking an envelope from a pigeon-hole, he addressed it to John, adding briefly: "With Mr. Campion's compliments."

Inside he placed the folded page from the copy of *The Gallivant* and the key of the safe which he had received from Mr. Rigget. Together he and Ritchie carried the missive upstairs and left it with Mrs. Peel.

18 : *In Reply to Your Letter*

Their visit to John's flat and subsequent conversation had taken much longer than either Ritchie or Mr. Campion had dreamed, and when they met Gina and Miss Curley on the door-step of Twenty-one they were astounded to learn that the court had adjourned for the day.

Miss Curley was grimly capable, keeping her head with a conscious effort. Gina was silent and, had it not been for a glazed expression in her eyes, might have appeared sullen. Her chestnut hair warmed the whiteness of her skin and her mouth was resolute.

"She must eat," said Miss Curley in an undertone to Ritchie. "You come up with me and talk to her until I find something."

Gina looked at Campion.

"They're making a strong case," she whispered. "Even John's beginning to see it now. He stayed behind to speak to Cousin Alexander. It all fits in so horribly the way they put it."

"Wait till you hear the defence," said Campion, with forced cheerfulness. "The prosecution is always convincing till you hear the defence. Don't worry."

She looked at him as though he had said something absurd, smiled mechanically and passed on up the stairs, Miss Curley following her. Ritchie turned to Campion.

"Better go," he said. "Poor girl!"

There was a pause in which he seemed to be struggling for words. Campion thought he had never seen such intensity of feeling in a face before.

"To escape," said Ritchie suddenly. "Escape, Campion. Escape all . . . this."

A great wave of a flail-like arm included, as far as his hearer could judge, the civilized world and all that lay within it.

Mr. Campion made no direct reply. Apart from the fact that no one could ever be quite sure what Ritchie was talking about, there seemed to be no comment upon such passionate feeling which would not be an impertinence.

"Good-bye," he said. "See you to-morrow."

"To-morrow," said Ritchie, and in his mouth the word had the bitterness of eternity.

Mr. Campion went home. Age, he reflected, was beginning to tell on him, and, since he was a person not given to self-consideration, it came to him with all the force of a major discovery that nearly thirty-five and nearly twenty-five are two very different kettles of fish where nervous stamina and the ability to do without sleep are concerned.

He was so depressed by the thought that he decided to go to bed immediately upon arriving at Bottle Street, and would have done so had it not been for the visitor who awaited him.

Ex-Inspector Beth rose from his chair in the sitting room and grinned as his host came in.

"Didn't expect to see me here, did you?" he said. "And with the goods."

"No," said Campion truthfully. "I did not."

"He's bin 'ere for an hour talking about 'imself, until you'd think 'e was still a flattie," observed Mr. Lugg, who had wandered in from the next room, collarless and in his house coat.

"Oh, I have, have I? Well, no one would think you were still a cat burglar," countered the ex-inspector spitefully.

"No, I've bettered meself," said Lugg, with ineffable complacency. "I'm a house gentleman now."

"What's the report?" cut in Mr. Campion, who was not in the mood for cross-talk. "Anything definite?"

The visitor became businesslike immediately.

"Pretty good, Mr. Campion, pretty good. As far as I can ascertain, nearly all the amounts paid into the bank book since December last, and not handed in at the Holborn post office, were paid in by an elderly gentleman. Is that what you expected?"

"Only 'nearly all'?" enquired Campion, with interest.

"All those I could ascertain," said the Inspector firmly and with reproach. "There are five instances in which the assistant remembered, because he or she thought it queer; two doubtfuls; and one plain rude and unhelpful."

"Any description of the man?"

"Fair." The ex-inspector consulted his notes. "Tall, thin, sixty-ish, well-dressed, yellow face—that's some person's word alone—quiet, stranger to each office. Any good?"

"Good enough," said Mr. Campion. "Good enough for my own information. No good as evidence."

"I don't see why not." The inspector was hurt. "Some of them remember him clearly. The idea of him doing it tickled 'em. You know what these youngsters are nowadays."

"Oh, it's not your end. That's fine." Campion spoke soothingly. "It's the information received. That's the part of the story I couldn't pin down."

Ex-Inspector Beth's large face assumed a puzzled expression. He had never been a man who liked to see good work wasted, and he now mentioned the fact in passing.

"For information received, was it?" he continued. "That makes it darker still to me. I can't see at all what you're driving at, Mr. Campion. The amounts were so small. If there was any hanky-panky you'd imagine they'd have been paid in cash."

Campion sat down. He felt the ex-inspector was entitled to an explanation, but had never felt less like making one in his life.

"Beth," he demanded, "have you ever met a woman who conveyed interesting information without actually saying it?"

"Hinting?" enquired the inspector dubiously.

"No, not exactly." Campion hesitated, looking for the word. "A woman who gossiped to the point," he said at last. "She knows, and you know, that she's telling you something, and yet for reasons of discipline or dignity or discretion neither of you ever admits to the other that you are interested or she is informing. See what I mean?"

"Exactly."

Beth nodded sagaciously and Mr. Campion, finding it easier than he had expected, went on.

"Now suppose you want to reward such a woman. You want to encourage her and yet you don't want to commit yourself by giving her money in her hand. You can't trust her not to come out into the open with a direct question if you leave a pound note on her typewriter."

"Yes?"

"Well, suppose she sees your difficulty and one day you find her Post Office Savings Bank Book lying in your room. It may have been a mistake; it may not. What is to prevent you paying a pound or two in at an unfamiliar post office? If she likes to query it you know nothing about it. If she accepts the cash and it encourages her, well, you're on the same footing as you were before. You've never come off your pedestal. You've never descended to a familiar word. You've done it and yet you haven't done it."

"And if an old ex-policeman goes round asking questions?" murmured the practical Inspector Beth.

"Ah," agreed Mr. Campion, "but I don't think you're the sort of man who would imagine that possible. You're a conceited beggar. You think your dignity gives you a special pass to ignore enquiring policemen and all their works. It's your own personal dignity in relation to the woman who is your employee which counts with you. That's the sort of man you are."

"Oh, am I?" said the ex-inspector. "Well, in that case, Mr. Campion, you can take it from me that I might do abso-bally-lutely anything. What a tale! If you'll pardon a professional question, how did you get on to it?"

"She's that sort of woman," said Mr. Campion, and Beth was satisfied.

It was half an hour later before Campion got rid of him. Lugg was in lordly mood and in the vein for a bout with an old sparring partner, while the ex-inspector evidently had time to waste. Eventually, however, he departed and Campion was thinking affectionately of his bed when the telephone summoned him to his feet again.

"Hello, is that you, Campion?" The dry precise voice sent a thrill through him. "John Widdowson here. I got your note."

"Oh, yes?" Campion heard his own voice studiously noncommittal.

"You made a most natural mistake." The tone was conciliatory, but by no means ingratiating. "You've discovered the manuscript in the safe is a copy, of course. I don't think anyone knew that except myself. I congratulate you. It was made for my uncle many years ago and for reasons of extra-special safety I put it in the place of the real play, so that if there should be any attempt at theft I should be doubly protected. You follow me?"

"Perfectly." Campion's inflection was unmistakable.

"Good. Well, what I want to say is this. I feel that since you have made the discovery and it has evidently led you to a mistaken conclusion, I naturally very much want you to see the real manuscript, so that any—

ah—unfortunate surmises you may have made can be contradicted. That's quite reasonable, isn't it?"

Mr. Campion's tired brain considered the concrete evidence he had gathered against the man at the other end of the wire and found it nil. He had no doubt that John Widdowson could have murdered his cousin, and in his heart he believed he had done so, but he realized that if the real *Gallivant* was still in the firm's possession the motive he had so carefully reconstructed was gone, and if there was no motive the strongest part of the case fell to the ground.

John was still speaking.

"I want you to see that manuscript and I want you to see it at once, so that you can concentrate on finding the truth. Mike's life is in danger. We've got to move quickly before these imbeciles decide to hang him. I'm in conference with Sir Alexander now. He's hopeful, I may tell you, but he realizes that it's going to be a hard fight. We're grateful for Rigget, Campion, but it's not enough."

There were urgency and anxiety in the voice not unmixed with a hint of reproof, and Mr. Campion found himself shaken by that rarest of the emotions, honest astonishment.

John went on.

"I'm a little irritated, naturally. Although I do see exactly how the misapprehension arose. You are a friend of poor Mike's, but you don't know me. We will say no more about that. I admit that were I unable to produce the genuine manuscript my own position might very well be open to question. I see that now, although it certainly gave me a shock when you pointed it out. I want you to see the real manuscript, Campion."

"I should like to." Campion sounded annoyed, in spite of himself.

"You must. You must see it at once. I want all your energies concentrated on Mike's trouble. Will you give me your promise that you'll settle this point tonight?"

Mr. Campion's weariness had given place to bewildered resignation.

"Yes, of course. I want to see it."

"You'll be able to recognize it, you think?"

"I think so."

"Splendid. It's not in a very inaccessible spot, thank God, but one of the safest I know, one where I keep things when I want them protected from the inquisitiveness of my own family. Do you know our Paul Jones premises?"

"No," said Campion, who felt like a child waiting to see what would happen next.

"They're in the phone book, of course." John was clearly trying to keep civil in the face of crass idiocy, and finding it difficult. "Eighty-seven, Parrot Street, Pimlico. It's a large building. Take a cab. Any driver will know it. I can't come with you myself, unfortunately, because I shall be closeted with Sir Alexander into the small hours. But I want you to go at once. You can't do anything useful while you're still on a wild-goose chase. You see that?"

Mr. Campion found himself thinking, quite unpardonably, that he had never been treated as a blundering employee before and that the experience was refreshing, stimulating and probably good for the soul. Aloud he said:

"All right. I'll go."

"You'd be behaving like a young ass if you didn't," said the voice, with some asperity. "I'll telephone to the caretaker to admit you on your card. He won't know where the manuscript is, of course. You'll have to find that yourself from what I tell you now. It's very simple. The last room on the fourth floor, that is to say, at the top of the building, is the directors' office. The room number is forty-five. If you forget it the caretaker will show you. In the room is a carved desk—oak or ebony, I forget which—and in the left-hand top drawer you will find the key of the cupboard. Open it, and the manuscript is in a newspaper parcel on the second shelf with two or three others. My uncle always kept it like that. His contention was that no one would look for it there or recognize it if they found it, and when he gave over he passed the tip on to me. Lock up after you, of course."

"Yes," said Mr. Campion meekly.

"I shall expect you to phone me later in the evening to tell me you're satisfied, and, perhaps—" the cold authoritative voice betrayed a hint of condescending amusement, "—to apologize. I'll phone the caretaker immediately. Oh, wait a moment; Sir Alexander may want to speak to you."

There was a considerable pause while, presumably, Cousin Alexander was fetched from another room, and then the magnificent voice rumbled over the wire.

"That you, Campion? I'm sorry, but I must have John here for some time yet. Terribly sorry, my dear fellow, but anxious times, you know—anxious times. Good night."

Before Mr. Campion could reply he had gone and John had taken his place again.

"Go along and satisfy your mind, my boy," he said. "You'll know where you are then. As soon as you clear the line I'll ring Jenkinson. He'll be waiting for you. Good-bye."

Mr. Campion hung up the receiver and walked slowly back across the room. Standing by the window, looking down into the lamplit street, he tried to sort out thought from instinct and wished he were not so incredibly tired. That afternoon he had been sure of John's guilt. Even now, when he considered his painfully forged chain of half-facts, he could not believe that it was composed entirely of unrelated coincidences; and yet, if John were innocent, could he possibly have made any more reasonable move than the present one? On the other hand, if he were guilty, what could he hope to gain by the production of yet another faked manuscript, or even no manuscript at all?

There was one other alternative, and Campion considered it in cold blood. In the course of an adventurous career he had received many invitations which had subsequently proved to be not at all as innocent as they at first appeared, and the common or garden trap was not by any means unknown to him. And yet, in cold blood, the absurdity of such a suggestion in the present case was inclined to overwhelm every other aspect.

While he was still wavering there returned to his mind a maxim often expounded by old Sergeant McBain, late of H Division: "If you think it's a frame, go and see. Frames is evidence."

Mr. Campion put on his coat and had reached the front door when another thought occurred to him, and rather shamefacedly he returned to his desk and, taking a little Webley from its drawer, slid it into his pocket.

Leaning back in a taxi cab nearly fifteen minutes later he surveyed Parrot Street, Pimlico, with interest. It was a long dingy road lined with solid slabs of Georgian housing, intersected by occasional side streets or great yawning gaps where demolition and rebuilding were in progress. Office staffs had long ago displaced the comfortable families for whom the houses were built, and at eight o'clock in the evening Parrot Street was a gloomy and deserted thoroughfare.

Number Eighty-seven was a dishevelled building. Its windows were dirty and uncurtained and here and there patches of plaster had chipped away, showing the brick beneath. One of its immediate neighbours had been taken down and huge wooden joists supporting the structure along one side did not add to its distinction. Altogether it was not a likely sister for the elegant Twenty-three, Horsecollar Yard.

The explanation, of course, was the old one. Like hairdressing and hotel-keeping, publishing is forced to be class-conscious, and just as front-rank restaurateurs are sometimes known to have smaller, cheaper establishments tucked away in the back streets, where, under less dignified names, money is made and odds and ends used up without waste, so sometimes distinguished publishing houses have humbler sisters where less rare but equally filling mental dishes are prepared and distributed.

Messrs. Paul Jones, Ltd. published children's picture-books, light love stories of the cheaper sort, translations, and a vast quantity of reprints, and were kept alive by the possession of some twenty or thirty copyrights of the great Fairgreen Fields' earlier works, which they republished at three and six, half a crown, one and three, one shilling, ninepence, sixpence, and fourpence simultaneously and over a period of years, without ever, apparently, overlapping or saturating any of that fine "blood" writer's many markets.

The firm was owned by Messrs. Barnabas, without being in any way affiliated to them socially, and was run by a separate staff.

The taximan pulled up outside the dilapidated doorway and Mr. Campion got out. The dirty transom showed a faint light in the entrance hall, and as soon as he knocked the door was opened by a woman as untidy and disheartened as the house itself.

"Me husband's hurt his foot," she said before he had time to open his mouth, "and I said for him not to move himself now he was got comfortable. I knew you wouldn't mind."

She looked up at him with a confiding leer which showed gappy teeth in pale gums.

A wail from the lighted doorway at the far end of the passage indicated that she was not in attendance upon her husband alone.

"I'm coming!" she shouted in a voice surprisingly raucous after her husky conversation tone. "See to 'im, Dad, do!"

Mr. Campion gave her his card, and she took it under the bulb to read.

"That's right," she said, with idiotic but ingratiating surprise. "Campion. That was the name Mr. Widdowson said. Shall I keep this, sir? D'you know where to go? It's Room Forty-five, right at the top of the 'ouse."

She glanced abjectly at the dusty wooden staircase and back again.

"I can turn on the 'all lights from 'ere," she added, and rubbed her hands on the back of her skirt.

Mr. Campion looked down at her.

"How long ago did your husband hurt his foot?" he enquired unexpectedly.

"Week last Monday. One of the van boys let a box down on 'im—clumsy young monkey! Mr. Widdowson said surely it was well by now. I didn't 'alf tell 'im off over the phone. 'Well,' I said, ''e's not an idol, Mr. Widdowson.'"

She spoke without heat or humour, and her tired face turned towards the stairs again. In the back room the baby roared.

"I'll come up with you if you like," she said.

Suddenly Campion laughed.

"Don't bother. Is the door locked?"

"Oh, no, sir. We're always here, you see. There's only this entrance and the one at the back which we use. Nobody could get in. You'll go up, then?"

"I will. I'll see you when I come down."

"Thank you, sir." He saw her quick hopeful smile and she wiped her hands again. "I'll just turn on the lights."

The beautiful staircase, which had been a Georgian housewife's pride and responsibility and was now a danger trap to van boys and caretakers, was flooded with dusty light as Campion set foot upon it.

The premises at Eighty-seven were even less attractive inside than out. The two lower floors were used as a warehouse and stretched out behind over what once had been a garden in vast ramifications of the book-producer's trade. The very air was thick with dust and the sweet, acrid smell of ink.

Campion went up slowly, his hand on the Webley. In spite of his conviction that the idea of attack was absurd, he took no risks. His senses were alert and he walked with quiet springy steps.

He was not disturbed. The rows of greasy doors on each landing were silent and no creaking board, either behind or above him, answered the tread of his own feet.

It was a long way up. He climbed steadily on, pausing only once to look down the well to the hall, small and far away below.

The fourth floor was a little cleaner than the rest of the house. One or two of the doors had been freshly painted, throwing the shabbiness of the walls into painful prominence, and there was a strip of floor-covering of sorts down the centre of the passage.

Outside room number forty-five he paused and stood for a moment, listening. The silence was everywhere. Very gently he tried the handle. It turned easily and the door swung open, revealing an apartment only faintly lit by the light from the street lamps below.

With his left hand, his gun in his right, he shone his torch round the room. It was unoccupied and appeared to be in normal order.

A glance at the light fixtures assured him that there was nothing untoward in that direction, and he turned over the switch.

It was a big room, comfortably furnished with that particular brand of red Turkey carpet which is to the City office what the bowler hat is to the City clerk, a bookcase, a few chairs and the desk of which John had spoken. The walls were covered with show-cards, book jackets and galleys of advertisements.

Mr. Campion looked for the cupboard door and saw two, one beside the desk, the other behind it. They were both used as notice boards, the wooden panelling being particularly suitable for the reception of drawing-pins. The miscellany hanging there told him little more than the date, several publication fixtures for books of which he had never heard, and the details of the train service to Chelmsford.

He did not hurry. In the back of his mind something was warning him of impending danger. Looking about him, the instinct seemed ridiculous, and he remembered that he was tired and probably jumpy.

He went over to the desk unwillingly and pulled open the first drawer on the left-hand side. It contained at first sight nothing more remarkable than a tin of biscuits and a pair of gloves, but after removing these cautiously he saw a key with a piece of string through the ring lying half under the paper with which the drawer was lined.

He took it out and looked at it suspiciously, but it was quite ordinary and of no particular interest in itself.

Feeling foolish but still puzzled, he carried it over to the door behind the desk.

It fitted the lock, but he did not get the door open until he realized with a wave of self-dislike that it opened outwards and was not even locked. He thrust it open and stepped back, taking out his torch once more.

The cupboard proved to be a cloak-room containing an incredibly dirty wash-basin and a row of clothes-hooks, upon one of which a dilapidated umbrella hung dejectedly.

He came out and went over to the other door. Once again he fitted the key in the lock, the old sense of danger assailed him, and he swung round to face the landing, but all was silent and dirty and ordinary as before.

Then, from far below, he heard a little angry sound, thin, high and furious. Mrs. Jenkinson's baby was protesting violently at some parental indignity. It was too much. Mr. Campion cursed himself for his hysteria, his cowardice and his approaching age. He turned the bolt over and pulled the handle.

The jamb did not move and he remembered it probably opened outwards. He tried it gently, but it was stuck and he drew himself back to throw his shoulder against it.

That miraculous sense which is either second sight or the lightning calculation of the subconscious mind, which nothing escapes, arrested him, and, changing his mind on the instant, he pulled his gun and kicked the door open, police fashion.

For a moment it still stuck and then shattered open sickeningly and he stood overbalancing, shuddering horror fighting with the realization of a certainty.

There was nothing there at all; only the wide sky threadbare with stars and fringed with a million chimney-pots, and, far, far below him in the cool darkness, the jagged stone foundations of the house that had been next door.

19 : *Under the Sword*

Miss Curley cleared her throat, pushed her hat a little further on to the back of her head, and wondered rather helplessly if the truth could be any more apparent after five days' talk, when it seemed to be so hopelessly hidden after one and a half.

At her side Gina sat immobile. All through the day she had preserved the same aloof expression. Her eyes were no longer dazed, but had assumed instead a settled coldness. Miss Curley was anxious about her.

In the luncheon recess she had taken the girl to a city restaurant and had made her eat, but she had done so without interest and had not talked.

Even John's absence, the non-appearance of Ritchie, and the unaccountable desertion of Mr. Campion had passed her by as unworthy of comment and only once, when Mike had been brought back into the dock, had she shown by a single quickening glance the least sign of interest in the proceedings.

Miss Curley's other neighbour, on the contrary, was evidently not only following, but enjoying, the case. He had reappeared at the morning session as eager as a child at a play, and Miss Curley, a patient, tolerant woman, had gradually become used to his muttered commentary.

The afternoon was very warm for the time of the year, and the sun shone on the dome, making the court comfortable and bright. Lord Lumley leant back in his high leather chair, his scarlet robe catching the sunlight and the colour flickering on the lenses of his eyeglasses. Before him the eternal bustle of the court continued.

Cousin Alexander sat in his place, his silk gown shining and his eyes eloquent, ready at any moment to leap up and pounce upon a witness.

The first three sessions of the enquiry had established much of the Crown case and the Attorney-General had reason to be pleased with the way events were shaping. The jury now fully understood the mechanics of the crime. They had examined the hose pipe, seen the photographs of the strong room and garage, and had heard the medical evidence.

They had also heard Mrs. Austin do her well-meaning damnedest, and Mrs. Tripper had repeated her story of the running car engine.

At the moment the red-headed and vivacious Roberta Jeeves, author of *Died on a Saturday*, was giving her evidence, struggling between the desire to escape all responsibility and a certain shy pride in having invented a murder which would work.

She had, she said, no idea whether Mr. Michael Wedgwood had read her book or not. It did happen sometimes that a publisher did not read every book he sponsored.

Was that not usually only in the case of well-established authors? Fyshe put the question innocently.

Miss Jeeves reluctantly supposed it would be, and Counsel begged leave to enquire if Miss Jeeves considered that she had been a well-established author at the time of the publication of *Died on a Saturday*.

Miss Jeeves confessed with not unnatural irritation that she had no idea.

Fyshe asked humbly if it were true that in view of the complicated mechanics of the device described and the faithfulness with which they had been executed in real life Miss Jeeves had felt it her duty to call the attention of the police to her book.

Miss Jeeves, holding strong views on the subject of coincidence, was fairly embarked upon a dissertation upon them when she was gently and courteously stopped by the Judge.

Cousin Alexander did not cross-examine.

Miss Curley stirred and smiled nervously in reply to her unknown neighbour's wink and nod of appreciation. She looked round the court again. Until now she had believed that court proceedings were tedious beyond all bearing and that the greatest ordeal participators had to face was one by ennui, but so far the effect of cumulative drama had never faltered and always just in front of her there had been that strong wide back of the young man she knew, who might be going to die.

Others might find the technicalities of doctors and central-heating experts dull, but to Miss Curley every word was of vital importance, every point reached her, and every time the jury whispered together her heart contracted painfully.

Miss Jeeves having returned to her seat, there was a rustle at Counsels' table. Fyshe sat down and the Attorney-General rose to examine as Peter Rigget stepped into the box.

His slightly dilapidated appearance was not enhanced by the green reading light which, shining down upon his papers, was reflected up into his face. He looked puffy because of Mr. Campion, unhealthy because of the light, and thoroughly vindictive, which was his own affair.

Miss Curley, who knew nothing about his secret self-deploration, had no sympathy for him at all.

"Strong case," whispered the man at her side. "Now they're coming to it . . ."

Miss Curley wondered if it was her imagination or that a new excitement was, in fact, growing in the big bright room. The Lord Chief Justice looked as placid as before, but there was certainly a rustle among the clerks and the jury leant forward to see the witness better.

It was evident at once that Mr. Rigget was aware of his importance. He even permitted himself a sickly nervous smile, which was rendered frankly horrific by the green light reflected in his glasses.

Cousin Alexander noticed the little man's self-satisfaction with grim approval.

Miss Curley glanced at Gina. The girl was very still, her eyes fixed upon the silent figure in the dock. It occurred to the older woman that she was praying.

The Attorney-General began gently in his softest, most ingratiating tone, and Mr. Rigget made his opening statement happily.

"I am an accountant employed by Messrs. Barnabas. I have known the accused and the deceased for about two years, ever since I came to work in the office. On January the twenty-seventh I went into the deceased's room at the office and on into the book-file room, which leads off it. When I entered the room the two men were talking. They ceased when they saw me, but when I went into the little office they continued their conversation."

"Was the door open or shut?"

"Open."

"Could you hear what was said?"

"Clearly."

"Can you repeat what you overheard, word for word?"

"I can."

"Is it not extraordinary that you should remember a chance conversation so clearly?"

"No, because it was an extraordinary conversation."

"Will you repeat it?"

Mr. Rigget considered and began in a slightly affected voice.

"Mr. Paul, the deceased, said: 'You mind your own damned business, Mike. She's mine. I'll manage my own life in my own way.' And then after a pause he said: 'Make love to her if you want to. God knows I'm not stopping you.'"

"Did you hear any more?"

"No. I came out then and they stopped talking."

"Did you see both men?"

"Of course."

"How close to them were you?"

"I passed quite close to Mr.—to the accused, within two feet."

"Did you notice anything about him?"

"He was very white. His hands were clenched. He looked as if he could —he looked very angry."

"Had you ever seen him like that before?"

"I had never seen him like that before."

Miss Curley's neighbour nudged her.

"They'll get him," he whispered jubilantly, and then, as she turned to him, coughed apologetically into his handkerchief and reddened round the ears.

Cousin Alexander rose majestically and scattered a sheaf of papers to the floor with the sleeve of his gown. While Mr. Rigget's attention was still distracted by the incident he put his first question.

"Some time before you entered the employment of Messrs. Barnabas,

Limited, you were employed by Messrs. Fitch and Sons, paper merchants, were you not?"

Mr. Rigget started violently.

"Yes."

"Is it true that after you left them you gave evidence for the prosecution in an action brought against that firm by the Inland Revenue Department and were rewarded by that Department for information received?"

The Attorney-General sprang up and protested violently, and for the first time real heat was infused into the chill argument which had taken place between the two Counsels. Lord Lumley blinked at Cousin Alexander.

"I confess I don't see the purpose of such a question, Sir Alexander," he rumbled mildly.

Cousin Alexander bowed.

"I will not press it, My Lord," he said virtuously, and Mr. Rigget was sufficiently ill-advised to smile.

"Are you an accountant?"

"I am."

"Have you very little to do with the book publishing side of Messrs. Barnabas' business?"

"I suppose I have." Mr. Rigget spoke grudgingly.

"Is it true you do not know even the titles of all the books they publish?"

"No, not all," said Mr. Rigget nervously.

"Is it true that you did not know, for instance, that in January Messrs. Barnabas acquired the rights of an autobiography entitled *My Own Life*, by Lady Emily Trumpington?"

"No—o."

"Did you or did you not?"

Cousin Alexander's chill eyes suddenly reminded Mr. Rigget of the portrait in the waiting room.

"I may have heard of it."

"Did it occur to you then or does it occur to you now that what you really overheard the deceased say on the occasion when you were 'overhearing' in the next office was: 'You mind your own damned business, Mike. She's mine. I'll manage *My Own Life* in my own way,' meaning, of course, the author, Lady Trumpington, is my client and I will manage her book—that is to say, I will publish her book—in my own way."

"No," said Mr. Rigget, turning a dull brown in the green light. "No. I thought he was talking about his wife."

"You thought . . . I" began Cousin Alexander, apparently temporarily overwhelmed by the iniquity of fools, but recovering himself with pretty dignity. "What made you think that he was talking about his wife?"

"Well," said Mr. Rigget uncomfortably, "there had been a bit of talk in the office about Mrs. Brande and the accused carrying on, and I naturally thought——"

His voice trailed away.

"A bit of talk." Cousin Alexander's tone rose melodiously. "A bit of talk in the office. Tittle-tattle among the employees. A's wife has been seen with B, and so when A and B talk heatedly it must be about Mrs. A. Is that how you reasoned, Mr. Rigget?"

"I—I may have done."

Lord Lumley leant forward.

"When you heard the words 'my own life,' did they sound like the title of a book? Were they said with equal emphasis on each word, or on one or two words only?"

The quiet affable question brought the whole tricksy business back to earth again, out of the realms of cleverness into the quiet line of enquiry the results of which should determine if Mike was to hang by the neck until he was dead.

Mr. Rigget dithered while the court held its breath.

"I can't remember," he said at last, and the ready tears which were such a constant source of embarrassment to him crept into his eyes.

Cousin Alexander let the admission sink in before he tackled the next stage of his enquiry.

"You have told us that you cannot remember the inflection on the words 'my own life,'" he said quietly. "Are you sure that you remember the words 'make love to her if you want to, God knows I'm not stopping you'? You are sure you heard them?"

"I am sure."

"Did the accused say anything at all while you were in the inner office?"

"Nothing."

"Are you saying that you heard him say nothing?"

"I heard nothing."

"Might he have whispered?"

"No. I should have heard him if he had."

"Were you listening carefully?"

"I was."

"Were you remembering everything you heard?"

"Everything."

"And yet you are not sure if the deceased was talking about his own life or the title of a book."

"That's your suggestion," sneered Mr. Rigget.

"Yes, it is," said Cousin Alexander, with lightning heat. "And it is also my suggestion that in order to convince yourself that you had heard Mr. Brande talking about his wife, you imagined the second part of the statement."

"No."

Cousin Alexander took a deep breath.

"Consider those two remarks, first side by side and then concurrently. Do you think they could have been made by the same man, the same man in the same mood and on the same point? Are they not directly contradictory? 'I'll manage my own married life in my own way; make love to my wife if you want to.' Taken together, do they not sound absurd?"

"I heard it," said Mr. Rigget obstinately.

"I suggest," said Cousin Alexander, "that you thought you heard it."

"No, I heard it."

"Is it possible, Mr. Rigget, that you may have been mistaken in what you heard?"

There was a blessed quality of moral absolution in the word "mistaken," and Mr. Rigget fell for it.

"Perhaps," he said, and Cousin Alexander sighed.

"Do you like the accused?—or rather, is it true that you bear no grudge against him?"

"I hardly know him."

"Yet you knew the intimate affairs of his life. You knew he had been 'carrying on' with Mrs. Brande."

"I had heard it."

"Do you think now that you may have been mistaken?"

"I had heard it."

"May it have been untrue?"

"It may."

Cousin Alexander began to enjoy himself. His elation, which had been slowly growing ever since Mr. Rigget had entered the box, was shared by all those whose personal feelings were not harrowed by the case. Throughout the last part of the cross-examination people had been coming into the room. Barristers from other courts slipped in unobtrusively and the undercurrent of whispers which broke out in every pause became a natural part of the proceedings.

Miss Curley was stirred by the excitement of it all, in spite of herself. She could not help reacting to the general animation which had arisen so suddenly. It frightened her. She felt that it was at moments like these when mistakes were made, but she could feel the exhilaration and her neighbour was quite frankly beside himself with delight.

There was so much movement going on all round the room that she did not notice that the Attorney-General had left the court. It was Gina who called her attention to the fact.

"Where's Sir Montague Brooch gone?" she whispered. "A note was brought in to him and he hurried out. Did you see? Where's Albert Campion? They'll need him, won't they? Something's happening."

Miss Curley realized with a shock of self-reproach that the different atmosphere in the court had not registered upon the girl. Gina was concerned only with the truth and the man in the dock. Cousin Alexander's dexterities had passed her by.

"I don't notice anything," she whispered back, and before she had time to consider the suggestion Cousin Alexander began again.

"We will leave for a moment the question of what you do and do not remember, Mr. Rigget," he said graciously, "what you are sure you heard and what you cannot remember if you heard, and go on to something which happened so short a while ago that I am sure you will have no difficulty in calling it to mind. I put it to you that you visited the strong room where the deceased was found after office hours on the ninth of this month on the eve of this trial. Did you or did you not?"

Mr. Rigget's glance turned nervously towards the prosecution and he saw for the first time that Sir Montague Brooch was not present. Sir Alexander was still waiting.

"Did you or did you not?"

"I may have done."

"Come, come, Mr. Rigget, that's no answer to a perfectly straight-forward question. It is now Thursday. Did you on Tuesday night go down to the strong room of the office where you are employed after office hours?"

Again Mr. Rigget looked round helplessly, and this time even Miss Curley was aware that something untoward was afoot. Cousin Alexander's junior tugged his gown and slipped a note into his hand, and at the same time the Clerk, who had been in conference for some minutes with Fyshe, rose and whispered to the Judge.

Mr. Rigget, finding himself temporarily forgotten, said "Yes" sulkily, and the whole court waited.

"'Ullo? 'Ullo?" murmured Miss Curley's unknown neighbour expressively, and at the same time Gina caught the older woman's hand.

"I told you something had happened. What is it? More evidence against Mike? I can't bear it, Curley, I can't bear it!"

"Hush, dear, hush," said Miss Curley, patting the hand she held and moistening her lips with the tip of her tongue.

Cousin Alexander bustled out of court and his junior rose to take his place. The Clerk still stood whispering and Lord Lumley, looking more like a very old and very wise bloodhound than ever, sat forward, his head on one side. Now and again he nodded gravely and sometimes put a muttered question, which was answered by more whispered volubility from the Clerk.

The junior for the defence repeated Cousin Alexander's last question and received the same sulky reply from Mr. Rigget, but its importance was lost. The jury were whispering heatedly, and only the little group in the dock sat stolidly silent, waiting.

"While you were there, what did you do?"

"I looked for things."

"Were you on the firm's business?"

"Yes."

"Did anyone from the office know you were there?"

"They may have done."

Mr. Rigget's eyes were snapping. He saw his opportunity and was taking it. The junior had no terrors for him, and he saw his chance to deny the truth of the statement he had made in Mr. Scruby's office. He supposed he could get that respected firm of solicitors and the odious Mr. Campion into the devil of a row if he played his cards carefully.

Looking up, he saw Mike's eyes resting upon him, and he turned away hastily from that pale unhappy face.

"Will you tell the court what was the nature of the business on which you were engaged in the strong room at that unlikely hour?"

The fact that the court was certainly not listening to anything Mr. Rigget might have to tell unnerved the young barrister and the question lacked authority.

"I was looking up some royalty accounts for our department," said Mr. Rigget mendaciously, and remembered suddenly that perjury is a crime.

"Had you any authority to do that?"

"No, but I like to do my job thoroughly."

The whispered conversation at the bench had ceased, and now Sir Andrew Phelps was talking to the Clerk.

The cross-examination went on its desultory way.

"While you were there were you disturbed?"

"Yes, I was. I was set upon and nearly killed."

"Did you not attack the man who discovered you there?"

"No, he attacked me."

"You must be more explicit. Did your assailant come straight into the room and hit you?"

The quiet voice from the bench at his side startled Mr. Rigget out of his wits. Under cover of the mysterious upheaval which seemed to have distracted the entire court, he had been happily chirruping on. Now it was as though God had stretched out a great finger and pinned an impudent sparrow to the gate. He gasped.

"No. I went out to see who it was, and he hit me then."

Counsel continued.

"Did you turn on the light?"

"No, I ran out into the passage in the dark."

Mr. Rigget's face grew rigid after he had spoken. His eyes blinked piteously and he trembled, waiting for the next question.

It was a very long time in coming, and at last he looked up in sheer desperation, only to see the Attorney-General and Cousin Alexander back at the table again. Both men seemed slightly excited. There was a flush on Sir Montague Brooch's thin dark cheekbones and Cousin Alexander was forcing a smile, which was clearly not genuine. There was a pause. The Attorney-General looked at the Judge, and when His Lordship nodded to him imperceptibly he rose.

"My Lord—" the beautiful voice was a little thin, "—in view of certain circumstances which have arisen, and of which I understand Your Lordship is already aware, it is the intention of the prosecution to call no further evidence."

Before the words were finally out of his mouth, Cousin Alexander was on his feet beside him. Even in that moment of bewilderment it flashed through Miss Curley's mind that his agility was extraordinary for his age and weight. An usher signalled Mr. Rigget out of the box, and was too startled to notice whether he obeyed.

"My Lord," said Cousin Alexander, "in view of my learned friend's decision, it is my duty to demand a verdict from the jury."

Mr. Rigget was still in the box, forgotten and too terrified to move.

The Lord Chief Justice cleared his throat and tapped gently with his eyeglasses upon the vivid sleeve of his robe.

"Yes, Sir Alexander," he said in a quiet unemotional voice which temporarily robbed, for Miss Curley at least, his words of their momentous meaning. "I think that is a very proper request."

He turned to the jury, where they sat gaping at him like a double row of somebody's stupid relations, and addressed them simply.

"Members of the Jury, as you have just heard, certain circumstances have arisen which have caused the prosecution to decide to call no further evidence in this case. That means the Crown does not press the charge against the accused. Therefore it is my duty to direct you to find the prisoner not guilty and to acquit him of the charges which have been brought against him. Do you understand?"

There was a mutter in the jury-box, too confused and hasty to be dignified by the word "consultation," and the foreman stumbled to his feet with a nervous nod.

"We have—I mean we do, My Lord. Not guilty, My Lord."

As the jury writhed and murmured, overcome with delight and relief, the Judge addressed the prisoner. Mike rose stiffly to his feet. He looked young, broken, and inexpressibly alone in the great bare dock. The Judge's voice was very kind.

"Michael Wedgwood, you have been found not guilty of the charges brought against you. You may go."

The young man stood quite still. The whispering around him turned into a roar, and Cousin Alexander hurried over to him.

"'S'truth," said the man next to Miss Curley, as they rose while the Judge made his stately exit, his flowers in his hand, "what's happened now?"

Gina clutched Curley's arm.

"I want to get out!" she said wildly. "I want to get out!"

Miss Curley put her arm round Gina's shoulders and they were swept by an excited throng to the doorway. Mike was surrounded, she saw, and it occurred to her that it would be better if the two young people did not leave the court together.

What's happened? Why? What's happened? The question overtopped all the other crowding thoughts racing through her bewildered mind. Mike free—no need for Gina to give evidence—what's happened?—where are they all?—what's happened?

Over her shoulder she had her last glimpse of the court, the empty bench, the sword, the coats-of-arms, the excited throng, wigs, bands and silk gowns shining in the sunlight under the dome, and the witness-box with Mr. Rigget still inside it, peeping out like a bewildered green parrot in a cage.

What's happened?

They came out into Newgate Street, running almost, with the weight of the crowd behind them. The sun shone in their eyes and the hubbub of the traffic surged about them.

What's happened? With the return from the slightly *Alice in Wonderland* atmosphere of the court to the sturdy matter-of-factness of a London afternoon the question became urgent.

"What's happened?" The words themselves were on her lips when Gina stopped abruptly on the pavement. "Look!" she said huskily.

An old man in a ragged raincoat, who wore three out-of-date hospital flags in his cap, was leaning against a brilliant pillar-box, an apron of newspaper bills slung round his waist.

WEDGWOOD TRIAL
MAN DEAD

Miss Curley's eyes let her down. She took the paper the old man proffered her and fumbled with it blindly.

"What's happened?"

Gina's voice sounded very harsh and far away.

Miss Curley was aware of a red, unshaven Cockney face and two very bright sparrow eyes looking at her with kindly curiosity.

"There it is, lady, right on the first page. It happened this morning, but trust the perlice to keep it dark until they knoo what was what. 'John Widdowson, cousin of the man on trial, found dead.' Look, Ma, *there*."

Miss Curley did not speak. She was staring through the paper and her shoulders shook a little.

"Found dead in 'is bath, killed the same way as the other bloke was, with carbon monoxide gas. 'Ousekeeper found 'im."

The paper-seller supplied the details out of pure kindness of heart.

"Suicide," said Gina, and drew a long breath.

"Very likely," agreed the old man, politely noncommittal. "But it looks to me as if the perlice thought it was murder. What price the case for the prosecution now? Get you a taxi, lady?"

20 : *The Fourth Dimension*

It was nearly dark in the hallway at Twenty-one when Mike came home. He was alone. Because of John's death there was a man on the outside door and reporters, friends and sightseers were temporarily kept at bay.

He came slowly down the passage, feeling for his second key. His lean figure did not droop, but some of the dignity of his ordeal still clung to him, and he looked unapproachable, like a man in great grief.

As he paused to open the door a shadow detached itself from the darkness of the first half-landing and came slowly down to meet him. It was Gina.

She looked smaller and thinner than he remembered her, and her old quiet self-assurance had gone, leaving her pretty and young but not a commanding personality.

"Hallo, Mike," she said.

He paused and looked at her awkwardly, wishing she had not come.

"Hallo, Gina."

There was a painful silence and she stood on the bottom step, hesitating.

"I'm glad you're free."

"Thank you."

There was another gap, and he felt weary and very glad he could not see her face.

"It's terrible about John." Her voice had a quiver in it, and, because he could not bear any more emotion and because he felt sick and so flat that the Day of Judgment might have come and he been overlooked, he snubbed her.

"Quite terrible," he said over his shoulder, and he bent to unlock the door.

He did not step inside instantly, but turned back apologetically. She was in the passage and the light from the door caught her face.

"I'm tired, old girl," he said awkwardly. "Hopelessly tired." He went in and shut the door. The girl went quietly upstairs.

On the threshold of his sitting room Mike stopped abruptly. Mr. Campion was sitting there alone.

"Have a drink?" he suggested, raising a glass.

Without a word the newcomer helped himself from a decanter and siphon on the elbow-table and accepted a cigarette. He did not speak until he was seated and had half finished his glass. Then he looked at his friend and a hint of the old lazy humour returned to his eyes.

"What a mess," he said.

Mr. Campion stretched himself.

"The best possible thing in a way," he murmured depreciatingly.

"We couldn't have brought him to trial, poor chap, even if we'd felt like it."

"Alexander's been telling me." Mike shook his grey-black head. "I was in a bedroom at his club, hiding from newspapermen, while he was talking to you. Poor old chap! He seems quite cut up. I think he'd been looking forward to his speech in my defence. I was sorry I missed you, but I've heard all about *The Gallivant* and the fire escape and——"

"—the ever-open door," murmured Mr. Campion. "But I forgot, you don't know about that. John was a difficult chap. This was the best way."

"It was suicide, wasn't it?" Mike put the question anxiously. "Cousin Alexander struck me as being a trifle reticent on that point. What happened exactly? How did he die?"

Mr. Campion sipped his whisky.

"At nine o'clock this morning," he said, "John turned on the bath in his flat, locking the door probably out of force of habit, although he was alone in the apartment. Mrs. Peel had been called out, so he had to light the geyser himself. The window wouldn't open—stuck or something—and he was shut in with that awful old brass death-trap, one of the first geysers ever produced, I should think. Water takes off the stink of carbon monoxide, you know, and very little of the beastly stuff can do you in. Anyway, when Mrs. Peel returned at about eleven o'clock she found the door still locked and, getting no reply to her knock, she got the janitor up and they forced the door open. John was in the bath, his head under the water. He had passed out with the gas and slipped under. Actually he was drowned."

Mike sat up and passed his hand wearily over his forehead.

"It sounds like an accident to me," he said. "How did I—I mean, how did it affect me?"

Mr. Campion blinked at him.

"Mrs. Peel had the presence of mind not to raise a general alarm. She phoned Tanner and he came hareing round to find that the vent-pipe on the geyser had been bunged up with a towel. You can reach it quite easily from the fire escape. From one or two other things Tanner began to suspect he'd made a mistake. Very soon he was quite sure he had. I had a little yarn to tell him which had a bearing on the case, and finally he did the necessary. The police don't want to convict the innocent, you know! That's the one thing they say their prayers about."

"What an extraordinary way to commit suicide," said Mike. "I suppose John thought it was self-explanatory, since he left no note."

Mr. Campion nodded absently. There were one or two points which he had no intention of mentioning at the moment. One of them was that the bathroom window had been wedged from the outside and another that the telegram which had summoned Mrs. Peel to her married daughter's untelephoneable house in East Putney had not been sent by the lady whose name appeared as its signature.

Mike leaned back and closed his eyes.

"It's true, Campion," he said. "The awful thing is that it's not a nightmare. It's happened."

"Let's clear off," said Campion unexpectedly. "Let's go abroad. Miss Curley is cut up now, but she'll get over it and running the office will—er—take her mind off things. Besides, you've got some good men. A personal telephone call to each author will keep the business sweeter than anything; that's one thing, authors do understand the desire for solitude."

A flicker of interest appeared in Mike's eyes.

"It wouldn't be bad."

"I'll hold you to it," said Campion. "Going to stay here alone now?"

"No. Jimmy Bengers was in court. He came up to me after the trial and suggested he should come round this evening. Know him?"

"The golfer?"

"That's him. He'll be here any minute now. Good chap, Jimmy. Understands how to shut up. I've known him all my life. Ritchie will roll in too, I expect. I suppose someone's told the poor old beggar about everything?"

"I suppose so," said Mr. Campion vaguely. "I say, I think I'll go now. I've got one or two things to look into. I'll phone you in the morning."

He left Mike in the armchair and had the satisfaction of passing Mr. James Bengers in the outside hall. That large young man had a straw-covered bottle in one hand, a hamper in the other and a hastily caught-up toothbrush peeping shyly from his breast pocket.

Mr. Campion nodded to the man on duty and pushed his way through the crowd on the pavement. Afterwards he went down to Scotland Yard and stayed there for some time, talking to Superintendent Stanislaus Oates, an old friend who had much that was interesting to tell him.

It was just after ten when he returned at last to Bottle Street, and was met by Lugg in the hall of the flat. Lugg was wearing his collar, a certain portent of strange company, and Campion's heart sank. Lugg was indignant.

"Bloomin' ex-rozzer," he murmured in an all-too-audible undertone. "Old Beth's bad enough for one week and all right in 'is way, but this chap's never bin more than a *sergeant*. Can't get rid of 'im. You 'ave a try."

Had Miss Curley been with Mr. Campion as he entered the sitting room she would have recognized the visitor immediately. Mr. Campion saw a large, oldish ex-policeman, with a round red face and very bushy eyebrows, who rose as he appeared and grinned at him in a fashion both shy and friendly.

"Mr. Campion, I presume?" he said. "I'm Mr. Livingstone, late of the Met-ro-politan Police. You'll have to excuse me calling on you so late in the evening, but I'm off on the six-forty back to Norwich to-morrow."

The mention of the Norfolk town brought a great light to Mr. Campion, and to Lugg's disgust he shook the newcomer's hand warmly.

"This is an Act of God," he said. "You're the man I want to see. Higgleton sent you, I suppose?"

"Yes." Mr. Livingstone sat down again and accepted the drink Campion offered him. "Old Charlie Higgleton and me are what you'd call friends, although we don't see much of each other now I've retired. On the quiet, I came up for the trial," he added confidentially. "I like to keep in touch with old times, as it were, and when I see a certain firm was implicated, in which I was interested because of a funny thing which happened in the past, I said to my wife, 'I'll have to go and see that.' And so I came."

"Did you get in?"

Mr. Livingstone drooped a heavy eyelid.

"There's ways and means," he said darkly, "naming no names, of course. But we—er—we——" He hesitated.

"Old blues?" suggested Mr. Campion affably.

Mr. Livingstone beamed.

"Exactly. We police, we stick together and remember old pals. The end come as a real shock to me this afternoon. I thought the youngster was for it."

He looked at Campion enquiringly, but his host did not rise to the implied question, and after a pause he continued.

"Well, when I went back to Charlie's, where I'm staying, and was talking about it and about old times, he remembered you and found your card. I recollected seeing your name in connection with the case, so I hopped on a bus and here I am."

Mr. Campion purred over him.

"You're providential," he said. "Tell me, did Mr. Higgleton tell you about our conversation in the spring?"

Mr. Livingstone looked pointedly at Lugg, and when that excellent person had been persuaded to leave them he smiled self-consciously at Campion.

"It's not a tale to put about," he murmured apologetically, "but since you was interested I thought I'd like you to hear my side of it. We're referrin' to a certain party who disappeared about twenty years ago, aren't we?"

"That's right," said Campion. "Tom Barnabas was walking down the road from Nemetia Crescent, Streatham, when he vanished."

"And was never seen of more," added Ex-Sergeant Livingstone in a voice so sepulchral that Campion jumped. "Well, since you're interested I may tell you it's true. It was a sunny May morning with a touch of mist in the air and that shimmery look on the pavements and the trees. Mr. Barnabas was walking along the road on the side nearest the wall. Charlie Higgleton saw 'im and went in to get his paper for 'im, and I was standing on the corner on the opposite side of the road. I saw 'im coming and I recognized 'im. I didn't watch 'im closely, of course—why should I? I didn't know 'e was going to walk into the fourth dimension."

"Of course not," agreed Mr. Campion reasonably.

"It's a high wall," said his visitor. "You've seen it, so you know. As high as the top of 'is silk hat. I mention it because him being against it, as it were, he stood out very clear, if you take me."

Mr. Campion nodded comprehendingly and Livingstone went on earnestly.

"When he was about a hundred yards away from me on the opposite side of the road, and there wasn't another soul in sight, I looked away from him and glanced into Charlie's shop. But I could still see Mr. Barnabas, although it was only out of the tail of me eye and I wasn't really lookin' at him. You follow me?"

"Perfectly."

"Well, 'e vanished," said Mr. Livingstone, staring at Campion with boot-button eyes.

Mr. Campion was suitably impressed.

"Look here," he said, "let's get this right. When you looked once he was there, and when you looked a second time he wasn't."

"No, that was the funny thing," said Mr. Livingstone. "I saw 'im out of the corner of me eye the whole time. I saw 'im go."

"Did you, by Jove? Which way?"

"He went . . . up," said Mr. Livingstone.

There was a slightly uncanny silence and Mr. Campion rose.

"Higher than the wall?" he enquired at last.

"I think he did. I remember him melting into the foliage above the wall and then 'e was gone. It happened like *that*."

He struck one palm noiselessly against the other, an oddly expressive gesture.

"Of course I didn't report it quite like that at the station," Mr. Campion's visitor continued in a different tone. "We wasn't used to miracles twenty years ago, and if I'd gone to the Inspector and said I'd seen a big heavy bloke in a top hat, tail coat, white spats and gold-headed cane disappear into thin air in front of me very eyes I'd have been sent to the doctor and never heard the end of it all me born days. So I took the wise course, and you'll see in my reports that I saw 'im coming along and I looked away, and after that I didn't notice 'im any more. I thought he must have gone into the shop. It was Charlie Higgleton who stuck to the miracle story, although it was me who saw it. That was a funny road altogether. On the other side of the wall was a garden full of snakes. A woman used to breed 'em. London's a rum place. I miss it sometimes up there in Norwich. London's got the fascination of a girl you never quite get to know."

He made the final remark regretfully and without affectation.

Mr. Campion was silent for some time. Finally he looked up.

"Do you like miracles?" he enquired.

"Like 'em?"

"Do you mind them explained?"

"Oh, I see what you mean." Mr. Livingstone had the honesty to hesitate, and his host liked him for it. "Yes," he said at last. "Yes, I'd like to know what really happened. He wasn't never seen again, you know."

Mr. Campion went to the cupboard in the bureau and, after rummaging for some time in its depths with his back towards his visitor, he suddenly swung round, his left arm outstretched.

"Look," he commanded.

Mr. Livingstone's eyes bulged and he sprang to his feet with an exclamation. A particularly murderous-looking knife was sticking through Campion's forearm with about three inches of crimson blade projecting from the side opposite the hilt.

Mr. Campion was apologetic.

"Sorry to startle you," he said. "I thought you'd probably seen these things. They sell 'em at the toyshops. It's a sort of bracelet, see?"

He took the contraption off his arm and revealed its secret, which was no more mysterious than a half circle of steel wire connecting the hilt with a three-inch length of painted blade.

Ex-Sergeant Livingstone took a child-like delight in the trick.

"You startled me!" he said, chuckling. "I thought, 'Lummel 'E's barmy,' before I see you laugh."

"Yes, well, there you are. There's the explanation of your miracle." Mr. Campion sounded a little regretful.

His visitor was still puzzled.

"Do you mean it was a trick wall, sir?" he ventured dubiously. "I dare say you know best, sir, but I knew that road pretty well and I'd have known at once if there was anything funny about the wall."

"Oh, no, not a trick wall," said Mr. Campion. "A trick man."

"A trick man, sir?"

"Yes, look here. Suppose if instead of a stolid city gentleman advancing on middle age you'd seen a great strong fellow in shorts and a singlet striding down the road towards you; and if you had read a poster which told you that Mr. Tom Barnabas, the vaulting champion of the world, was going to perform; and if, while you were looking at him, he suddenly swung up an enormous right arm, and caught the top of the wall, which was six foot ten high, and pulled himself over it as swiftly and neatly as a dog swallows a chunk of fish, would you still have thought it a miracle? No. You'd have thought what a first-class performance it was."

Mr. Livingstone took some moments to digest this revelation.

"Was Mr. Barnabas a champion vaulter, sir?" he said. "I never heard that."

"No," said Campion. "He wasn't. That's why it was such a good trick. I don't even know if there were such things; but he could walk upstairs on his hands and I imagine that he had one or two other accomplishments of a like nature. He also had a sense of theatre and I suspect a touch of humour."

"But the snakes . . ." protested Mr. Livingstone, impressed in spite of himself. "The garden on the other side of that wall was full of snakes."

Mr. Campion eyed the ex-sergeant.

"I think he was probably very fond of snakes," he said. "And I think he knew those particular creatures very well."

"Well!" said Mr. Livingstone, and was silent.

He sat quiet for some little time and finally glanced up wistfully.

"You've got it," he said. "I remember now after all these years I caught a glimpse of him turnin' in the air and I thought he was going up in a sort of spiral. But when I got me head round he was gone. Still," he added, taking leave of his miracle with reluctance, "what about his belongings, if he disappeared on purpose? He left everything, you know. Money in the bank as well."

"I think," said Mr. Campion, with deliberation, "that he only took one piece of luggage into the fourth dimension, and he sent that in advance."

It was clear that he did not mean to dilate further upon the subject, and Mr. Livingstone did not press him. The explanation of his miracle had saddened him and he was subdued.

Gradually, however, his thoughts drifted from the past to the present and he sat up.

"I'll be going," he said. "It's late. Thank you very much for your information, sir. It's explained a lot to me. I'm glad you told me, I am really. I wonder if you could tell me one other thing? In the present case the Crown stopped that trial because the police believed there'd been another murder done in exactly the same way as the first, and probably by the same man. Now are they going to hunt out the murderer, or are they going to let the papers think it was a case of suicide done in remorse and leave things alone?"

Campion looked at him, heavy-eyed.

"My dear chap, I don't know," he said, and his voice was sharp with anxiety. "I only wish I did."

After his visitor had gone he flung himself down in his chair and stared morosely at the carpet, a strange heaviness in his heart. For what he had not told Mike, and what the police were so far attempting to hide from the Press, was the indisputable fact that at eight o'clock that morning Mr. Ritchie Barnabas had paid his bill at his lodgings, divided his personal effects impartially between his landlady and his landlady's husband, and had gone out ostensibly to take his annual holiday and had vanished as utterly and unobtrusively as his brother had done twenty years before.

21 : *The Spangled Frill*

It was September, and the hot airs of the long summer were beginning to be dispersed by the light breezes which precede the mistral, when Mr. Campion and Mike stood upon the long concrete platform of the railway station at Avignon and waited for the Paris train.

It was just dusk and inside the walls of the city the plane trees were making high tents against the sky, while down in the *place* the rival cafés jostled each other off the cobbles, the different colours of their painted chairs alone proclaiming their irregular boundaries.

Both men looked well and exceedingly pleased with themselves. Mike especially was frankly jubilant, as every now and again he glanced at his wrist-watch.

"I still think we ought to have gone on to Paris," he said. "I can't see why you're so insistent about staying here. Of course, I am very grateful to you. I shouldn't have sent that wire by myself. I hope it'll be all right though: this isn't exactly a pleasure city."

"It's a lovely town," said Mr. Campion, with dignity. "The French Colchester. When you compare the two you see the essential differences between the French and English temperaments. We've had a nice vulgar holiday all over the show, and this is journey's end, and very nice, too."

Mike grunted, and after a pause glanced at his friend sharply.

"I don't want to butt in," he said diffidently, "but have you had any idea in your mind while we've been gadding about?"

"Idea?" echoed Mr. Campion, a trifle hurt.

"Well, purpose. All this trip, ever since May, you've been jittering around the Continent like an agitated tourist. We've avoided the cities, but I should think we've visited every second-size town in Italy, Dalmatia and France, stayed about ten minutes and rushed off again. Now at last you've settled down in Avignon of all places. Found anything?"

Mr. Campion was silent. He did not appear to have heard. Mike hesitated.

"Don't think I'm not grateful," he went on seriously. "I am. I've got everything in perspective now and my own troubles don't quite fill up the landscape any more. I had a line from Curley. Everything seems to have blown over. It seems extraordinary when you think back, but people soon forget. The latest rumpus in our world is the autobiography row. The author's hiding in a nursing home terrified of all the angry females who haven't been put in the book."

He laughed shortly, and Campion, eyeing him, decided that his cure was practically complete.

"Train's due," he said.

"Is it?" Mike swung round and gazed up the track and Mr. Campion felt himself forgotten.

The engine came roaring in, and instantly the dozens of recumbent blue figures who had hitherto lain moribund sprang to vociferous life and, amid all the excitement of the arrival of the winners in a motor rally, the daily mid-evening train drew in.

The door of the Pullman burst open and Campion heard Mike's "Gina" above the parrot-house hubbub all round him.

She stepped out, radiant and coolly excited, and Campion, who had a proper respect for any woman who could end a twelve-hour summer journey in a Paris-Sud train looking as though she had stepped out of a bandbox rather than an ash-pit, admired her elegance.

She did not see him at first. Mike absorbed her complete attention.

"I got your wire," she was saying as Campion drifted up to them.

Mike held her at arms' length, his eyes eloquent, although his words were hardly inspired.

"And you came?"

"I came," she said quietly, and he caught his breath as she linked her arm through his.

Mr. Campion shook hands hastily and said he was going to the circus. They watched him stride off, a long, thin, inoffensive figure, personable, but by no means arresting.

"We owe him a lot, that one," the girl remarked quietly.

"Too much," said Mike fervently. "I daren't think of it. Look here, sweetheart, you've got to hurry. The chef of the hotel is waiting for you. He tells me he is a man of perception. I'm afraid he may come and cry over us."

She laughed and they stepped out of the station together and climbed into the crazy old *voiture* which was to carry them into the walled city.

Mr. Campion crossed the bridge over the wide, lazy Rhone, reflecting idiotically that the new bridge was better than the old Pont d'Avignon of the nursery rhyme because there was enough of it to reach to the other side.

It was a magnificent dusky evening, the air soft and tainted by the wine-presses and jubilant with the excitement of autumn, which is so much more comfortable than the excitement of spring.

In the fields on the other bank of the river, on the road to Villeneuve, the *cirque* was already established. It was not a grand affair, designed to attract the *tourisme*, but a little noisy jollification for the natives now that the visitors had gone and left a few spare centimes behind them.

There was one big tent, five or six side-shows mainly of the freak variety, and a cluster of painted living wagons. Electric light bulbs strung on yards of dangerous cable sprawled everywhere and the Provençal *en toute famille* laughed and joked about the frankly comic sides of ordinary life which seem to be so very offensive if one is not amused.

The show in the big tent would not begin for half an hour, and Campion, having seen the spider lady and the tallest Ethiopian in the world, found himself outside the largest of the living wagons. This was a slightly baroque affair, decorated with the Queen of Sheba on one side and a view of Naples on the other, and glittered with brass rails and several varieties of scroll-work. A man sat upon the steps reading a newspaper by the light of a festoon of coloured bulbs draped over the wagon.

He was a large man, still tough at sixty and very fine to look at, in spite of a pink shirt, stiff collar, tight black trousers and Texan sombrero. There were two diamond rings on his fingers and his shoes were English hand-sewn.

He looked up at Campion, who saw his face and rejoiced.

"M'sieu'?" he enquired.

Campion presented him with his card. The stranger took it between an enormous finger and thumb and sat looking at it thoughtfully for some time. Campion bent forward.

"I came to tell you," he said quietly in French, "that John Widdowson killed his cousin Paul Brande, and afterwards, when he was discovered, was found dead in his bath. The general opinion in England now is that he committed suicide."

"And the police? What do they think?"

"The police," explained Mr. Campion, "preserve an open mind. There is one whom they would interview if they found him, but I do not think they are looking for him. As long as he does not reappear . . ." He shrugged his shoulders expressively.

The man rose to his feet and held out his hand.

"How d'you do?" he said in English. "Let me introduce you to Madame."

He went slowly up the steps and bent his head to enter the caravan.

He was extremely tall, a giant of a man, with the long supple muscles of an acrobat. Campion caught a few of the murmured words within.

"*Un ami vrai . . . absolument. C'est lui . . . le jeune gen lui-même. Ne vous enquietez pas.*"

There was a rustle and Madame appeared. She was large, dark and gracious, wearing a trifle too much jewellery for camping, perhaps, but she gave Mr. Campion her hand and flashed her black eyes at him and he liked her, snakes, diamonds and all.

They entertained him on the steps. It was a warm night, and it occurred to Campion that she might just possibly keep her more favourite pets in the caravan.

"How did you find us, my friend?"

It was Madame who enquired, and Mr. Campion, feeling he could do no less, explained.

"I went through the old mailing lists, and when I found that M. Robert, proprietor of Robert's *Cirque*, one time c/o the World's Fair, received copies of Spring and Autumn catalogues in company with several thousand householders, I thought he might be worth looking up. It has taken me three months."

The man who called himself Pierre Robert smiled, and reminded Campion of his brother.

"Rubbish!" he said. "It has taken you twenty years. Remember," he continued, speaking English carefully as though he were not used to the tongue, "you are a friend of his. We feel you are his friend."

"But of course," agreed Madame, "the young man is a friend. I knew it as soon as I saw him. You see," she added, beaming upon Campion, "for so many years now he has spent his holidays with us. Now it is all holiday."

"He is free—that's the main thing," her husband remarked. "Been imprisoned, as I was, all his life. Now the fellow's free—free as air."

Mr. Campion hesitated. There was something he very much wanted to ask, and was wondering how to put it.

"It seems—er—unexpected," he ventured at last. "I mean, after *publishing* . . ."

His host turned to his wife.

"The portrait," he commanded, and while she scrambled into the wagon he launched into a brief and formal history.

"My father was an impulsive man, but very much under his brother Jacoby's influence. He fell in love with a beautiful woman, carried her off and married her. She gave up everything for him, but Jacoby still considered it a mésalliance, and after her two sons were born she died of a broken heart. They kept her mewed up in the country, where she was looked down upon and misunderstood."

His visitor had just time to nod his comprehension when Madame returned with a faded cabinet photograph, which she placed reverently in his hands.

Mr. Campion's startled eyes rested upon one of the most supremely comic figures of his life. A corseted lady in tights and a bustle had been caught in the act of gripping a broken column as though for support. He had a fleeting impression of gentle eyes, a coronet of flowers and a fine piece of gilt script announcing "*La Palone, the Queen of the Wires.*"

His host took the photograph away.

"My mother," he said, with a dignity which was as unassailable as Lord Lumley's own. "That's the explanation. My grandfather was a tumbler."

It was altogether a most delightful gathering. Madame brought glasses and a bottle of Royal Provence, that wine of Paradise which the tourist ices and derides because it does not taste like champagne. They drank it in the dusk and Mr. Campion no longer felt anxious.

As he rose to leave he turned to his new friends.

"Mr. Barnabas," he enquired unexpectedly, "what did you do with *The Gallivant?*"

"Sold it to a collector," said Tom Barnabas promptly. "Fellow was a crook. Believe he cheated me. Anyway, I got enough to buy the show, which was all that mattered."

A grin passed over his face and Campion saw him as he must have been in the days when Miss Curley had admired him.

"I didn't steal it, you know," he continued. "I wanted to sell out my share in the business when Uncle Jacoby died, but old John wouldn't hear of it. So to save trouble I took the firm's most mobile asset and went off, leaving John with my share in exchange. It was quite fair."

"Taking his fortune, he leapt into space?" murmured Mr. Campion under his breath.

Tom Barnabas sighed.

"What a leap that was!" he said. "I couldn't do it now."

Madame laid a plump hand on his shoulder.

"Do you want to?" she demanded. "Of course not."

Tom Barnabas looked at Campion and laughed.

" 'Voir, M'sieu'. Au 'voir."

Mr. Campion wandered off into the fair. The big tent was crowded. An appreciative audience was applauding a lady who was hanging by her teeth from a trapeze, while her son and daughter swung lightheartedly from her ankles.

The turn finished with much bowing and kissing of hands and, while a resplendent attendant wound up the trapeze, a wild exuberant cry sounded from the artists' entrance and a flying figure came whooping into the ring.

He was attired as only French clowns are dressed, in a monstrous carica-ture of everyday clothes. An enormous black sleeping-suit, on which a

white shirt and waistcoat front had been crudely painted, enveloped his
gaunt form. Grease-paint half an inch thick obliterated his features and
gave him a wide, pathetic smile.

A little white head covering, which Campion saw with a shock was a
regulation barrister's wig, decorated his skull and round his neck was a
tulle frill spangled with gold.

From the moment he appeared he was a success. His flail-like gestures
were here understood. Here his mute appeal was answered, his wide smile
echoed. The children shouted his name: "Moulin-Mou! Moulin-Mou!
Moulin-Mou!"

He bowed to them gravely and lolloped to the side of the ring purposefully. There he took a basin from an unexpected cupboard in the
skirting. He broke eggs in it and added sawdust from the track. His face,
now miraculously anxious in spite of his painted smile, appealed to them
to sympathize with him in his insuperable difficulties.

To his foredoomed concoction he added all sorts of unlikely ingredients,
his dubiety growing and his eyes wild and apprehensive. He stirred, he
looked, he smelled. He offered the basin to a little white dog, who lay
down and covered its nose with its fore-feet. He wept. He went on stirring.

Then just at the moment when defeat and disgrace seemed inevitable
he started. He smiled. He beamed at the breathless company and finally,
amid howls of delight, produced triumphantly half a dozen very stale buns
and threw five of them to the delirious audience. The sixth he held in his
hand for an instant, looking about him with bright child-like eagerness.

Campion was aware of two very gentle blue eyes, infinitely appealing,
infinitely friendly, and so far away that they peered at him from another
world.

The sixth bun dropped into his lap.

He rose to his feet and waved and some of his neighbours rose with
him. Moulin-Mou threw up his arms and bellowed. Campion saw him,
rigid for an instant, his great flail-like arms outstretched, his face hidden
forever behind the most impenetrable disguise in the world.

The next moment he had gone and a young lady on a horse had taken
his place.

Mr. Campion went back over the Pont Neuf, the bun in his hand. He
was still carrying it when Mike and Gina met him on the steps of the
hotel.

"Horrible," said Mike, staring at the unattractive object with suspicion.
"Who gave you that?"

Mr. Campion looked at them solemnly.

"The King's Executioner," he said so gravely that they did not question
him.

DANCERS
IN
MOURNING

This Book Is for Nerney

Chapter 1

When Mr. William Faraday sat down to write his memoirs after fifty-eight years of blameless inactivity he found the work of inscribing the history of his life almost as tedious as living it had been, and so, possessing a natural invention coupled with a gift for locating the easier path, he began to prevaricate a little upon the second page, working up to downright lying on the sixth and subsequent folios.

The book appeared at eighteen and sixpence, with frontispiece, in 1934, and would have passed into the limbo of the remainder lists with thousands of its prototypes had not the quality of one of the wilder anecdotes in the chapters dealing with an India the author had never seen earned it a place in the news columns of a Sunday paper.

This paragraph called the memoirs to the attention of a critic who had not permitted his eminence to impair his appreciation of the absurd, and in the review which he afterwards wrote he pointed out that the work was pure fiction, not to say fantasy, and was incidentally one of the funniest books of the decade.

The public agreed with the critic and at the age of sixty-one William Faraday, author of *Memoirs of an Old Buffer* (republished at seven and six, seventy-fourth thousand), found himself a literary figure.

He almost succeeded in looking the part as he sat in his box at the Argosy Theatre, his small bright eyes fixed upon the stage where the three hundredth performance of *The Buffer*, the musical show which had been built on some of the bones of his book, was taking place.

Having seen the show some thirty or forty times, he naturally tended towards the critical, but he enjoyed it nevertheless.

The rest of the audience was not so surfeited. It exulted, hugged itself and, in the cheaper parts of the house, became a little hysterical.

Even the consciously intelligent element was happy, enjoying a rare burst of spiritual freedom. A Jimmy Sutane-Slippers Bellew show was a recognized intellectual leveller and provided one of those blessed Alsatias wherein the eyes of the moron and the highbrow meet and wink. There were Sutane fans in stalls and gallery; childlike spirits, hid in most unexpected bosoms, followed his angular ecstatic figure in its graceful yet faintly grotesque interpretation of Mercer's music with all the heart-rending pleasure of imprisoned birds observing flight.

It was an occasion, a night to be remembered and recalled with embellishments. A party spirit enveloped the old Argosy and even the florid goddesses above the candelabra in the auditorium seemed to infuse a new enthusiasm into their painted sports.

The various managerial staffs, gay if exhausted, wrestled twice as vigorously as was strictly necessary with the telegrams, the insufferable idiots expecting seats before Christmas, the flowers in ice from Australia, and the expensive and importunate Atlantic phone calls.

The programme girls in their fresh uniforms glanced at the stage with new interest even when Sutane was not upon it, while the orchestra, basking in an unfamiliar sense of security, became almost elated in spite of the new number in the second act.

That disturbing emotional experience, the first night, was a thing of the past. That had been a nightmare with a happy awakening. This, the three-hundredth performance, had the pleasant quality of reality about it. The "House Full" boards appeared to be a permanency outside the doorways in Shaftesbury Avenue and the library order was no longer a matter for prayer.

Mr. Faraday leant forward. His small bear's body in its black-and-white elegance swayed to the fox-trot rhythm of the *première* hit of the show. The amusing backcloth of grotesque faces which Pavalini had designed hung across the back of the stage and habitués in the audience nudged their companions, whispering to them to notice the villainous caricature of the Doremus woman on the croupier's extreme right.

As the light increased the chorus boys appeared in their twenty, fifty and a hundred franc plaque costumes. They came trotting on, more and more and more of them, drilled to automaton perfection, bobbing and clattering in carefully contrived disorder until the suggestion of a shower of counters on a boule table was complete.

The giant roulette wheel in the middle of the stage began to glow, the music softened, and the applause drowned the cue, as it always did, when the audience saw the familiar figure in the suit of white tails leaning on the silver turntable. Then came the cue again and the small, charming voice, which knew all there was to know about putting a song over and little enough about singing, pattered neatly through the first chorus.

> "What's the odds I'm on your number?
> It's a thousand—a million to one.
> It's a cert. It's a twist.
> It's a chance you have missed—
> A thousand—a million to one."

The face was a blur to eighty per cent of those in the theatre, a little white speck in a paper storm of subdued colours, but everybody knew the high forehead, the round mournful eyes, the long duck's-bill nose and the mouth which widened so amusingly into a sophisticated smile.

As the chorus was taken up by the others the wheel began to turn and the tap dance, which had made stage gossip and was likely to make stage history, began for the three-hundredth time. The small white figure with the amazing feet ricochetted and pirouetted round the wooden slats, tapping out its own music with a quality in which mere accuracy merged into the miraculous. Faster, faster and faster! A thousand—a million to one . . . a thousand—a million to one. . . .

The crisis came in a breathless moment. The audience swayed, satiated and exquisitely at peace. The wheel began to slow down, the beat of the pattering feet became sparse, and the tune slurred agonisingly an octave lower. The chorus took up the song again, the lights turned the wheel into a vast zero, and applause, like the sound of wind passing through a cornfield magnified to terrifying proportions, swept down upon the white figure grinning in its midst.

William Faraday turned to the man who sat beside him.

"It's a damned shame, Campion," he murmured, the words rumbling between his lips. "Something's got to be done, my boy. See that with half an eye. Means so much, you know."

Mr. Campion nodded. The roar from the great pleased animal whose vastness filled the theatre, and of which he was so alarmingly a part, made conversation impossible. He sat leaning back in the shadows, the light from the stage catching his horn-rimmed spectacles and the unexpectedly strong line of his chin.

He was not a handsome man. There was a certain vacuity in his expression which counteracted the pleasant angles of his face and lent his whole appearance an indefinable quality, so that those who knew him were apt to find him hard to recollect and impossible to describe.

At the moment Mr. Faraday, who knew him well and had excellent personal reasons for believing in his resource, wondered if he had heard and, if so, had understood him.

"More trouble here, shouldn't wonder," he muttered a few minutes later as the curtain rose on the old-time music-hall scene and the music for the extra number inserted into the show in honour of the occasion began its lazy, insinuating measure. "Don't understand why they want more dancing. Theatrical people beyond me—always were. Never liked this gel in the old days. Too damned highbrow by half. Must be an oldish woman by this time."

He turned in his chair, the shortness of his neck making a rather complete movement necessary.

"Lookin', Campion?"

"Naturally." Mr. Campion seemed startled.

His host grunted. "Here she comes. Could tell you something about her."

The art of Chloe Pye belonged to an earlier age than the inspired patterings of Jimmy Sutane, and Mr. Campion himself wondered why, on her return from a long colonial tour, she should have elected, much less been invited, to attempt a comeback in the midst of such strong competition. He had been a schoolboy when he had first seen her taking up a quarter of the bill at one of the better music halls, her rather mediocre talent helped out by a personality so feminine that her gentle seductiveness reached out well over the footlights. Her act had always been the same, a series of little dances each telling a story, each delivered in varying period costume, parts of which were discarded as the performance continued. The mild indelicacies involved were invariably excused by the dictates of the tale. Thus a vision of Chloe in Stuart underwear was archly exhibited under the title "Nell Gwyn Prepares for Court," and Victorian petticoats and the pantalettes in entirety were displayed with equal timid vulgarity in "Morning, 1832."

Her success in the days after the war when modern underclothes had reached an uninteresting minimum was considerable and her turn had borrowed an added glamour by the gossip which surrounded her private life.

In those days promiscuity had still the remnants of novelty and her affairs were eagerly discussed, but today, when the weary business of polyandry was arriving at the end of its melancholy cul-de-sac, her reputation, when it was remembered at all, detracted from rather than enhanced her appeal.

So, too, the return of underclothes in shopwindows and on the familiar bodies of wives and sisters destroyed the attraction of the original idea, and tonight there was no murmur of tolerant protest as petticoat after petticoat dropped to the ground.

"Highbrow?" murmured Mr. Campion, harking back to his host's earlier criticism.

"Historical," explained Mr. Faraday briefly. "Don't see why he put her in. Nothin' to do with the book. They tell me she used to draw. Won't sell a seat now."

Looking at her, Campion was inclined to agree with him. The audience, thoroughly warmed and friendly, was kind, but it was obvious that its mood was anticipatory and it only awaited the return of Sutane and Slippers in their "Round the World in a Four-in-Hand" number, to the tune which Mercer had written one afternoon while Jimmy talked to him and which was now all over two continents.

"Don't like the woman," Mr. Faraday murmured. "Might have thought she was at the bottom of it if she hadn't only just come back to England. Look at her—fifty if a day."

With his eyes on the dark vivacious figure on the stage Campion reflected that he was wrong. Chloe Pye was forty-two and in excellent physical trim. It was her mind, not her body, that was so hopelessly *vieux jeu*.

His companion touched his arm.

"Come behind," he whispered gustily. "Can't stand this. Shouldn't say so, of course. Want your help, my boy. Relyin' on you. Come along."

The Argosy was an old theatre and, true to its type, its backstage accommodation had never received any serious thought. Campion edged through a door which inconvenienced him in height almost as much as it incommoded Mr. Faraday in width, risked his neck by climbing down an iron staircase with a wobble, and came out into a corridor which looked and smelled like one of the less frequently used passages in a riverside tube station.

Mr. Faraday glanced over his shoulder, his eyes brightening.

"Used to come here to see Connie. Before your time," he murmured. "Pretty little woman. Must be old now." He sighed and added with a shy confiding which was almost the whole of his charm, "Still gives me a thrill, you know, this sort of thing. *Vie de bohème*, lights, far-off music, smell of the grease paint, women and so on."

Fortunately Mr. Campion, who was somewhat at a loss, was spared the necessity of comment. One of the doors a little higher up the corridor burst open and a golden-haired young man in exquisite evening clothes appeared wheeling a silver-plated racing bicycle. He was very angry and the expression upon his face, which was a little too beautiful to be altogether pleasant, was sulky and absurd.

"It's all very well for you to behave revoltingly, Richards, but I can bring my bicycle where I like," he said over his shoulder. "You know it as well as anybody."

"I'm sorry, Mr. Konrad." A harassed uniformed man with weary eyes and an untidy moustache came out of the door. "Mr. Webb told me himself to see nothing of the sort come into the theatre. There's not enough room for the artists, let alone you bringing in bicycles."

"But Miss Bellew brings in her great Dane." The young man gripped his machine with something approaching ferocity, but the doorkeeper spoke with the obstinacy of old authority.

"Miss Bellew is a principal," he said heavily.

The boy with the bicycle stiffened as the colour rose slowly over his face into the roots of his curling golden hair. For an embarrassing moment it seemed as if he were about to cry.

"This bicycle was presented to me by my admirers," he said. "Why should I let pure jealousy on the part of some people"—he shot a waspish glance back through the doorway, presumably at some third person within —"prevent me from showing it to anyone I like? You're making a fool of yourself. I shall certainly speak to Jimmy himself about it. Why don't you keep your eye on the important things that keep happening?"

There was defiance in the last words, as though the speaker deliberately touched on a tabooed subject. A spot of colour appeared in the door-keeper's grey cheeks and he glanced behind him. Seeing Campion, he started forward angrily, only to fall back reassured at the sight of Mr. Faraday, to whom he nodded. Shaken but still obdurate, he returned to the job in hand.

"Now, Mr. Konrad," he began, laying a heavy hand on the glittering machine, "we'll have this outside, if you please."

The boy with the golden hair relinquished it to him with a contemptuous shrug of his graceful shoulders.

"Oh, it's Uncle William," he said. "Do look here and see what the Speedo Club has insisted on sending me. Isn't it too absurd?"

Mr. Faraday coughed noisily. "Magnificent," he said fiercely and, gripping Campion's arm, he propelled him firmly down the corridor. "I hate those fellers," he muttered in an all too audible undertone. "Called me Uncle William—did you hear him?—impudent little tick! Don't mind it from my friends—rather like it. Used to it. Notice you've dropped it. Don't hesitate, my dear feller. But a worm like that . . . turns my stomach over, don't mind tellin' you. Golden curls! . . . Come on, we'll slip into the wings. Know my way about by this time. Want you to see Slippers. Nice girl. No damned nonsense about her. No sex appeal off, though," he added regretfully and coughed again, as if he feared he had betrayed himself.

The "Round the World in a Four-in-Hand" number was at its height as they approached. Over Mr. Faraday's shoulder Campion caught a glimpse of the two figures, so familiar to the fashionable audiences of both continents. Slippers Bellew was a pale gold flame flickering over a twilit stage, while beside her moved Sutane, faithful as a shadow, and contriving by his very sympathy of movement to convey the mute adoration which the song demanded of him and which was so great a part of his appeal.

The roar of the audience at the end was tremendous. The harsh sound swept in on them like a great hot breath, and they stepped back through the crowd of girls and small-part folk coming down for the "Little White Petticoats" finale.

The excitement which is never wholly absent from the theatre, even on the three-hundredth night, forced itself upon Campion and he, too, was aware of the power of the Sutane personality which dominated the house, both before and behind the curtain. He tried to analyse it as he followed Uncle William to the dressing room. There was grace and skill personified in the man, but that alone was not sufficient to make so deep an appeal. It was the sophisticated, amused but utterly discontented intelligence which constituted the real attraction, he decided, an ease and dignity which was yet emotionally unsatisfied—the old pull of the hero in love, in fact.

His companion was still talking.

"Wait for him in here," he remarked, tapping at a door with a One on it. "Wants to see you. Promised I'd bring you along."

They were admitted to a large room, overlit to the point of discomfort, by a stolid young man in a white coat and spectacles with very thick pebbles.

"Come in, sir. Glad to see you," he said, conducting the elder man to an armchair beside the dressing table.

Uncle William grunted gratefully and sat down.

"This is Henry, Campion," he said with a wave of a pudgy hand. "Good feller, Henry."

The young man beamed and set a chair for the other guest. He managed to convey at once that he was not at all sure if he was behaving like a first-class manservant but thought that there was a very good chance that he was.

"A nice drop of whisky, sir?" he ventured hopefully.

Uncle William looked interested. "Good idea," he said consideringly and Henry coloured as if he had received a compliment.

While the decanter was forthcoming Campion had leisure to observe the room, which displayed three different influences in sharp contrast. There was the florid taste of the original furnisher, which ran to Turkey carpet and a day bed with gilded legs; the somewhat militaristic neatness and a feeling for gadgets as expressed by the bar concealed in an old gramophone cabinet, which was obviously Henry's contribution; and something else, not so easy to define. Apart from a mass of papers, photographs and telegrams mostly, there were several odd indications of Jimmy Sutane's personal interests. Two or three cheap mechanical toys lay upon the dressing table beside a box of liquorice all-sorts and a bunch of white flowers, while on a shelf in the corner sat a very nice white Hotei and a tear-off calendar, complete with an astrological forecast for each day of the year.

Uncle William sat back in his chair, the bright lights glinting on the double row of near-white curls at the nape of his plump pink neck. He looked worldly and benign, and somehow bogus, with his watery blue eyes serious and his expression unwontedly important.

"Well," he demanded, "anythin' new?"

Henry paused in the act of laying out a suit but did not turn round.

"It just seems funny to me, sir," he said sulkily. "Miss Finbrough may take it seriously but I don't."

"Miss Finbrough, eh?" Uncle William cleared his throat. "Things have to be pretty bad for her to get the wind-up, I should think."

"You'd say so, sir." Henry was deliberately noncommittal and still did not turn round.

The elder man was silent for a moment or so.

"May be nothin' in it," he said at last.

Henry swung round, his face red and unhappy.

"Theatrical people aren't like ordinary people, sir," he burst out, blushing with shame at his own disloyalty. "I'm new to it and I notice it. They're *theatrical*. Things mean more to them than they would to you or me—little things do. There's not a nicer gentleman than Mr. Sutane anywhere; no one's denying that. But he's been in the theatre all his life and he hasn't been about like an ordinary person. Suppose little things do happen now and again? Aren't they always happening? Being in the theatre is like living in a little tiny village where everybody's looking at everyone else and wondering what they're going to be up to next. It's small, that's what it is. And Miss Finbrough . . ." He broke off abruptly. Someone turned the door handle with a rattle and Jimmy Sutane came in.

He stood for a moment smiling at them and Campion was aware of that odd quality of overemphasis which there is about all very strong personalities seen close to for the first time. Confronted suddenly, at a distance of a couple of yards, Sutane presented a larger-than-life edition of his stage self. The lines of his famous smile were etched more deeply into his face than seemed possible in one so thin, and the heavy-lidded eyes beneath the great dome of a forehead were desperately weary rather than merely tired.

"Hallo, Uncle," he said. "This Mr. Campion? Awfully good of you to come along. God, I'm exhausted! Henry, give me a drink. 'Fraid it's got to be milk, damn it."

The pleasant boyish voice was unexpectedly resonant, and as he closed the door and came into the room the place seemed to have become smaller and the walls more solid.

While Henry brought a glass of milk from the bar cupboard and assisted him out of his clothes and into a dressing gown there was a constant stream of interruptions. Excitable dinner-jacketed figures put their heads in, apologised and disappeared. More notes and telegrams arrived and the phone bell clamoured incessantly.

Campion sat back in his chair in the corner and watched. After the urbanity of his greeting Sutane seemed to have forgotten his guests. There was a nervous tension, a suppressed excitability, about him which had not been noticeable on the stage. He looked harassed and the nervous force which exuded from him like vibrations from a dynamo was not directed at any one thing but escaped abortively, creating an atmosphere which was uneasy and disquieting.

A minor climax came when he turned on an unsuspecting newcomer who was pushing the door timidly open and sent him scuttling off with a passionate protest.

"For God's sake, Eddie!—give me ten minutes . . ."

The explosion embarrassed him and he grimaced at Campion, his temporary audience.

"I'm going to pieces," he said. "Henry, get on the other side of that door and put your back against it. Tell them I'm saying my prayers. Unhook the phone before you go."

As the door closed behind the obedient dresser he turned to Campion.

"Come down tomorrow, can you? I've got conferences and things about this *Swing Over* show for the Orient, but Sunday is more of a breather than any other day. I don't know what you'll think of it all. Something's going on; I know that. This fat ass here says I've got persecution mania . . . my hat, I wish I had!"

He laughed and, although the familiar gaiety was there, the man watching him saw suddenly that it was a trick of line and feature rather than an expression of genuine feeling. It was typical of him, Campion reflected. His very skin and bone was make-up. The man himself was within, intelligent still but different.

"It began with the 'House Full' boards," Sutane said slowly. "Someone stuck 'Last Week' slips across them. That was irritating but it didn't mean anything. Then, as far as I remember, there was an outburst of the bird in the gallery one night. It was a claque and the rest of the house was annoyed. That didn't matter in itself but little paragraphs about it got into the Press. I put Sock Petrie onto it at once and he traced one or two of them to phone calls put through the same night."

He paused.

"It's nothing much to talk about, I know, but it's been so continuous. We've had to put fresh glass over my photograph outside almost every other day. Someone smashes it regularly. Never a trace of him. There have been dozens of other trivial little things too; nothing in themselves, you know, but alarming when they mount up."

His dark eyes grew sombre.

"It's now that it's spread out to our place at home that it's getting me down. Finding strangers in the garden with silly excuses and that sort of thing."

He broke off lamely and turned to the elder man.

"That woman Chloe Pye is going down there tonight," he said. "She says my wife asked her and she's going. I told her I'd rather she didn't, but she laughed at me. Can't chuck her out, can I?"

Uncle William made a depreciatory sound and Mr. Campion retained his habitual expression of polite interest. Sutane paused and reddened suddenly under his grease paint.

"I'm damned if it's all coincidence!" he burst out. "You come down tomorrow, Mr. Campion, and see how it strikes you. It's getting on all our nerves, these little petty digs at me. There was a rumour all over the place last week that I'd torn a muscle in my arm. Nine different people rang me up in one morning to sympathise."

His voice had an edge to it, and his long fingers drummed on the glass top of the dressing table.

"It doesn't matter so far," he said, "but where's it going to end? A reputation like mine, which depends on good will, can get pretty seriously damaged by a campaign like this. Yes?"

The final word was addressed to the doorway, where an apologetic Henry stood hesitating.

"It's Mr. Blest," he ventured. "I thought . . ."

"Blest! Come in." Sutane seemed relieved. "You know Mr. Faraday. Mr. Campion . . ."

Ex-Inspector Blest grinned and nodded to the tall figure in the corner. "Evenin'," he said. "Didn't expect to see you here, Mr. Campion. It's as serious as that, is it? Well, Mr. Sutane, it's all quiet tonight. Nothing to report at all. There's not a word uttered out of place in the whole theatre. Ever since you engaged me to keep an eye on things I've been keeping my ears open, and you can take it from me, sir, there's nothing but friendliness towards you everywhere."

"Is that so?" With a movement so sudden and angry that the detective stepped back involuntarily, Sutane took up a face towel from the table and wiped his cheek. "What about that?"

The four men in the room looked at him curiously. From a point just below the left eye and following the line of the nose to the upper lip was a deep ragged scratch. Sutane ran his finger down it.

"D'you know what that is, Blest? That's the oldest, dirtiest little theatre trick in the bag. A pin in the grease-paint stick. God knows how long it's been there. One day I was certain to work down to it. It happened to be tonight."

Blest was astonished in spite of himself. His round heavy face was crimson and he looked at Henry suspiciously.

"D'you know anything about this?" he demanded. "Who could have had access to your master's paint?"

"Oh, don't be a fool." Sutane's tone was weary. "The show has run for three hundred performances. My dressing room isn't always locked. Hundreds of people have been in and out of here in the last eight months. It's a long pin, you see, and it has been stuck up through the bottom of the stick. The head was buried in the silver-paper holder."

He began to pile cream on his face to get the rest of the paint off.

"Then there's the bouquet," he went on lazily, half enjoying the sensation he was creating. "There it is. A messenger boy handed it in at the stage door just before the show began."

"Flowers?" The ex-inspector was inclined to be amused. "I can't say I see anything funny about that, sir."

He took up the little white bunch gingerly and eyed it.

"Not very grand, perhaps. Star of Bethlehem, aren't they? Country flowers. You've got a lot of humble admirers, you know."

Sutane did not speak and, finding himself ignored, the ex-policeman raised the flowers to his nose and sniffed them idly. His sudden change of expression was ludicrous, and he dropped the bouquet with an exclamation.

"Garlic!" he ejaculated, his small eyes round with astonishment. "Garlic! Hey, what d'you know about that! A messenger brought it, did he? Well, I think I can check up there. Excuse me."

He retrieved the flowers and plunged out of the room with them. Sutane caught Campion's eye in the mirror and turned round to face him.

"It's all trivial," he said apologetically. "Little tuppenny-ha'penny squirts of malice. They're negligible on their own, but after a month or so they get one down."

He broke off and smiled. When he spoke again it was to reveal the essential charm of the man, a charm which was to puzzle and finally defeat an Albert Campion who was then barely in existence.

"It's worse for me," he said. "I've been such a blasted popular sort of fellow for so long." His grin grew lopsided and his eyes were sad and childlike and intelligent.

Chapter 2

Afterwards, when the tide of circumstance had reached its flood and there was no telling what were the secrets beneath its turbulent waters, Mr. Campion tried to remember every moment of that long and catastrophic day. Details which had seemed unimportant at the time flitted about in his mind with exasperating vagueness and he strove to catch at them in vain.

Yet the whole story was there, so clear to read if only he had been looking for it.

On the momentous Sunday Mr. Campion went to White Walls in the morning. On that day Chloe Pye plumbed the final depth of inconsideration, entirely outclassing all her previous efforts. This, in itself, was a remarkable feat since her total disregard for those who entertained her was a byword among the host of near friends who composed her circle.

Uncle William Faraday sat beside Mr. Campion in the Lagonda and pointed out the way with most of the pride of ownership. It was July and the roads were hot and scented, cow parsley making a bridal avenue of every lane. Uncle William sniffed appreciatively.

"Twenty miles from London. Nothing in a car. But feel you're in the heart of the country. He runs a flat, of course, but gets down here most evenings. Don't blame Sutane. Sensible feller, at heart."

He glanced at his companion to make sure he was attending.

"Dear old place," he went on, receiving a nod of encouragement. "You'll like it. Used to belong to his wife's uncle. Girl wanted to keep it when it came to her and Sutane suddenly thought, 'Why not?' That music writer, Squire Mercer, who did the stuff for my show, has a little house on the estate. Had it for years. Matter of fact, it was at his place that Sutane met Linda, his wife. She was stayin' with her uncle up at White Walls and Jimmy came down to see Mercer. They fell in love and there you are. Funny how things work out."

He was silent for some little time, his old eyes speculative and his lips moving a little as though he rehearsed still further details of Sutane's private life. Mr. Campion remained thoughtful.

"This persecution business has got on his nerves, has it? Or is he always as excitable as he was last night?"

"Always a bit mad." The old man pulled the large tweed cap he affected for motoring more firmly over his ears. "Noticed that as soon as I saw him. Don't think he's very much worse than usual. Of course you can understand it when you see the life the feller leads. Most unnatural . . . overworked, thinks too much, no peace at all, always in the thick of things, always in a hurry . . ."

He hesitated as though debating on a confidence not quite in good taste.

"It's a rum ménage for a decent house," he remarked at last. "Don't know what the old servants make of it. My own first experience of Bohemia, don't you know. Not at all what I thought."

He sounded a little regretful and Campion glanced at him.

"Disappointing?" he enquired.

"No, my boy, no, not exactly." Uncle William was ashamed of himself. "Freedom, you know, great freedom, but only in the things that don't matter, if you see what I mean. Very rational, really. Like you to meet 'em all. Turn down here. This is the beginnin' of the estate. It's a modern house on an old site. This is the park."

Mr. Campion turned the nose of the car down a flint lane leading off the secondary road. High banks, topped by a chase of limes and laurels so dear to the privacy-loving hearts of an earlier generation, rose on either side. His passenger regarded these screens with satisfaction.

"I like all this," he said. "Since it's a right of way, very sensible. Notice this?"

He waved a plump hand towards a high rustic bridge overgrown with ramblers which spanned the road ahead of them.

"Pretty, isn't it? Useful too. Saves havin' steps down to the road. The house, the lawns and the lake are over here to the right and there's an acre or two of park on the other side. Must cost him a pretty penny to keep up."

They passed under the bridge and came on to the drive proper, wide and circular, leading up to the house. Campion, who had entertained misgivings at the term "modern," was reassured.

Standing on high ground, its wide windows open to catch a maximum of sun, was one of those rare triumphs of the sounder architects of the earlier part of the century. There was nothing of the villa in its white walls and red-tiled roof. It possessed a fine generosity of line and proportion and succeeded in looking somehow like a great white yacht in full sail.

"French-looking," commented Uncle William complacently. "Take the car through into the yard. Like you to see the stables."

They passed under the archway of the stable buildings on the left of the house and came into a brick yard where several cars were already parked. Apart from Sutane's own black Bentley there were two small sports cars and one remarkable contraption of considerable age on which a young man in overalls and a cloth cap was at work. He grinned at Uncle William.

"It's back again, sir," he said. "Universal joint gone this time." He nodded to Campion with impartial friendliness, indicated a parking spot, and returned to his work.

"See what I mean?" said Mr. Faraday in one of his disastrous asides. "No formality in the whole place. That's Petrie's car he's at work on. Feller they call 'Sock.' Can't quite understand him. Like your opinion."

As they emerged from the archway Mr. Campion became aware of a certain hesitation in his companion's manner and, looking up, he saw the cause coming down the drive towards them. It was Chloe Pye.

She was dressed in a small white swim suit, high-heeled shoes and a child's sunbonnet, and managed to look every one of her forty-odd years. Off the stage she, too, presented some of that self-exaggeration which had been so noticeable in Sutane. Her body was hard and muscular and one saw that her face was old rather because of the stuff it was made of than because of any defect of line or contour. She was swinging a long bright scarf and carried a book and a deck chair.

At the sight of the visitors she threw the scarf round her shoulders and stood hesitating, arch and helpless.

"How providential!" she called to Uncle William as soon as he was within earshot. "Come and help me, darling."

Mr. Faraday bustled forward, self-conscious and incompetent. He raised his cap to her carefully before taking the chair.

"And who's this?" Chloe Pye managed to pat Uncle William's arm, hand him the chair and indicate that she was waiting for his companion to be introduced all in one movement.

Campion came up and was conscious of pale green eyes, a trifle too prominent, which looked up into his face and found him disappointing.

"They're all in the house," she said. "Shop, shop, nothing but shop the whole time. Shall I have the chair under the trees, Mr. Faraday? Or do you think it would be better by the flower bed?—that one over there with the silly little red thingummies in it."

It took some little time to get her settled and themselves out of the reach of her tenacious conversational openings, but they broke away eventually and once again headed for the front door.

"You won't believe a word they tell you, will you?" she shouted as they reached the path. "They're all quite mad, my dears. They're just seeing insults on all sides . . . Tell somebody to bring me some ice water."

The front door stood open and from it came the sound of a piano. The unsuspecting Mr. Campion had just set foot on the lowest step when there was a roar above him and a gigantic Dane, who had been sleeping on the mat just inside the hall, leapt down, his neck bristling and his eyes uncompromisingly red.

"Hoover!" protested Mr. Faraday. "Down, sir! Down! Somebody call the dog!"

The thunderous barking shook the house and a woman in a white linen coat appeared in the doorway.

"Lie down, you little beast," she said, hurrying down the steps and cuffing the animal with a broad red hand. "Oh, it's you, Mr. Faraday? He ought to know you. Get back, Hoover. Go in and watch your mistress."

The authority in her voice was tremendous, and Campion was not surprised to see the brute cower obediently and slink into the house, his tail drooping.

The newcomer came down another step towards them and suddenly became a much shorter, stockier person than he had supposed. She was forty-five or so, with red untidy hair, a boiled pink face and light eyelashes. Campion thought he had never seen anyone more self-possessed.

"He's working in the hall," she said, lowering her voice and giving the personal pronoun a peculiar importance. "Would you mind going round through the sitting-room windows? He's been at it since eight o'clock this morning and hasn't had his massage yet. I'm waiting to get hold of him."

"Of course not. We'll go round at once, Miss Finbrough." Uncle William was deferential. "This is Mr. Campion, by the way."

"Mr. Campion? Oh, I'm glad you've come." Her blue eyes grew interested. "He's depending on you. It's a thoroughgoing shame. Poor man, he's got enough worry in the ordinary way with this new show he's producing without having all this trouble. You run along. He'll see you soon."

She dismissed them with a finality that would have daunted a newspaperman. It had done so, of course, on many occasions.

"An extraordinary woman," confided Uncle William as they went round the side of the house. "Devoted to Sutane. Looks after him like a nurse. Come to think of it, that's just about what she is. Went in the other day and she'd got him on a mattress, stark as a plucked chicken, pummellin' the life out of him. Henry, the feller we saw last night at the theatre, is terrified of her. Believe they all are. Wonder if we'll get in here."

He paused outside a pair of very high french windows which gave out onto the terrace on which they stood. Here, too, there was music, but softer, the beat less insistent than the other which still sounded faintly from the hall. It ceased abruptly as a man at the piano caught sight of the visitors, and a voice so slovenly that the words were scarcely articulated welcomed them in.

Campion followed Mr. Faraday into a large light room whose original style of decoration had followed a definite modern scheme embracing pearl-grey panelling and deep, comfortable black chairs, but which now resembled nothing so much as a playroom devoted to some alarmingly sophisticated child.

Temporary tables ranged round the room supported piles of manuscript, sheaves of untidy papers, model sets, and whole hosts of glossy photographs.

In the center of the polished floor was a baby grand and behind it, nodding at them, sat the man who had spoken. He was an odd-looking person; yet another "personality," thought Mr. Campion wryly. He was extraordinarily dark and untidy, with a blue chin and wide bony shoulders. The jut of the great beak of a nose began much higher up than usual so that his eyes were divided by a definite ridge and his mild, lazy expression sat oddly on a face which should have been much more vivid.

He began to play again immediately, a mournful little cadence without beginning or end, played over and over with only the most subtle of variations.

The other two people in the room rose as the newcomers appeared. A large rawboned person who could only be described as disreputable disengaged himself from the chair in which he had been sprawling amid a heap of newspapers and came forward, a pewter tankard in his hand. He shook himself a little and his creased woollen clothes slipped back into some semblance of conventionality. He was very tall, and his cheekbones were red and prominent in his square young face.

"Hallo, Uncle," he said. "This is Mr. Campion, is it? Sorry James is so very much engaged, but it can't be helped. Sit down, won't you? I'll get you some beer in a minute. Oh, you won't? All right, later on then. Do you know everyone?"

He had a pleasant but powerful voice and a natural ease of manner very comforting to a stranger. His black hair was strained off his forehead and appeared to be plastered with Vaseline, while his small deep-set eyes were sharp and friendly.

Uncle William plumped himself in a chair and looked at Campion.

"This is Sock Petrie," he said in much the same tone as he might have pronounced "Exhibit A." "Oh, and this is Eve. Sorry . . . I didn't see you, my dear."

He struggled to get up out of the low chair and was defeated.

A girl came forward to shake hands. She was obviously Sutane's sister. Campion had never seen a resemblance more clearly marked. He guessed that she was seventeen or eighteen. She had her brother's arched brows and deep-set, unhappy eyes, as well as a great deal of his natural grace, but her mouth was sulky and there was an odd sense of resentment and frustration about her. She retired to a corner immediately after the introduction and sat very still, her thin body hunched inside her plain cotton dress.

Sock glanced round.

"Let me present Squire Mercer," he said. "Mercer, for God's sake shut up a minute and say how-d'you-do."

The man at the piano smiled and nodded at Campion, but his fingers did not cease their endless strumming. He looked pleasant, even charming, when he smiled, and his eyes, which were not dark, as they should have been, but a light clear grey, grew momentarily interested.

"He's just a poor bloody genius," said Petrie, flopping down among the newspapers again. He splashed his beer over himself as he swung one huge leg over the arm and exhibited a runkled sock with an inch or so of bare leg above it. The visitors got the impression that Mercer's lack of hospitality embarrassed him.

Campion found a chair and sat down. Petrie grinned at him.

"Furious activity mingled with periods of damn-all, that's what this life is," he remarked. "What d'you make of this last business? Had time to consider it at all?"

There was a weary sigh from the corner.

"Must we go all over it again, Sock?" Eve Sutane protested. "Silly little odds and ends of rubbish that don't mean anything. They're all so petty."

Petrie raised his eyebrows.

"That how you see it, poppet?" he said. "It's getting James down, I can tell you that, and it's bad for his reputation. I haven't handled his publicity for five years without being able to say that definitely. It's happening from the inside, you know, Campion. That's the annoying part. . . . Mercer, must you keep up that same silly little tune?"

The song writer smiled contentedly.

"It's a funeral march for a dead dancer," he said. "'Mutes in Dance Time.' I like it."

"Very likely. But you're giving me the pip."

"Then go away." There was unexpected fury in the tone and it startled everybody.

Petrie reddened and shrugged his shoulders.

"Go ahead."

"I shall."

Mercer continued his strumming. He was quiet and happy again, lost, it seemed, in his own private and particular world.

Petrie returned to Campion.

"There's a par in the *Cornet*," he said, "and another in *Sunday Morning*. Look at them."

He took out a wallet which would have disgraced a lie-about and extracted two ragged scraps of newspaper. Campion read them.

GARLIC FOR THE STAR

was the *Cornet's* heading.

There are many feuds in stageland. Once a star, of whatever magnitude, becomes really unpopular there is never a shortage of people anxious and able to let him know it. Among the tributes handed over the footlights at a certain West End theatre last night was a little bunch of white flowers. The star took them and pressed them to his nose. Only a long training in the art of self-control prevented him from flinging the bouquet from him then and there, for the white flowers were wild garlic. Somebody disliked him and chose this graceful way of saying so.

Sunday Morning treated the matter in its own way.

DANCING WITH TEARS IN HIS EYES?

Who was the joker who sent Jimmy Sutane a bunch of garlic on the three-hundredth night of The Buffer? It could not have been a comment on his work. Jimmy's flying feet don't need encouragement of this sort. Maybe he made someone cry and they wanted to return the compliment.

"I can't get a line on these until the Press boys get back to work." Sock retrieved the paragraphs. "But you see what it means. Someone turned that information in early. It was the end of the show when James told that ass Blest about the flowers—far too late to make these rags. That leaves Henry, who I'd pin my shirt to, Richards the doorkeeper, who is beyond suspicion, and, of course, the chap who sent 'em." He paused. "The information reached these blokes by phone. Any other paper would have rung up for confirmation, but these two print anything. The *Cornet* left out the name and *Sunday Morning* got round the libel with a compliment—

not that they care for libel. If they don't get five actions a week they think the rag's getting dull."

He grimaced and replenished his tankard from a bottle behind the chair.

"It may be all poppycock but it's damned unfortunate," he said. "If it came from outside it might be one of the poor lunatics who badger stage folk until some merciful bobby locks 'em up, but when it's from inside, like this, there's genuine malice in it and it's not so funny."

Mr. Campion was inclined to agree with him and his interest in the affair revived. Sock Petrie breathed an atmosphere of worldly common sense.

"Is Sutane likely to have any enemies?" he enquired.

Mercer cut in from the piano.

"Jimmy? Oh, no, everyone likes Jimmy. Why shouldn't they? I mean, I do myself, and I shouldn't if he wasn't a good chap."

The words were articulated so carelessly that the sense was only just clear. Campion glanced at him curiously, looking for some hint of sarcasm in the remark. He met the light grey eyes directly and was astonished. Mercer, he saw suddenly, was that rarity in a modern world, a simple literalist. His face was bland and innocent; he meant exactly what he said.

Sock smiled into his tankard and afterwards caught Campion's eye.

"There's a lot in that, Mercer," he said, and there was more affection than patronage in his tone.

The man at the piano went on playing. He looked calm and happy.

A shadow fell across the threshold and Uncle William sat up abruptly.

"Ice water," he ejaculated guiltily and Petrie groaned.

Chloe Pye came into the room, conscious of her figure and ostentatiously annoyed. She ignored both Campion and Uncle William, who had struggled out of his chair at great personal inconvenience to meet her, and spoke plaintively to Eve.

"Would it be too much trouble for me to have some ice water? I've been sweltering in the garden for hours."

"Of course not. I'll send for some, Chloe." The girl pressed a bell push in the panelling. "By the way, this is Mr. Campion. You know Uncle William, don't you?"

Miss Pye regarded the strangers with open hostility. Her lips were petulant and, Campion was amazed to see, there were actual tears in her eyes.

"We met in the drive," she said and, turning her back on them, leant on the piano to talk to Mercer.

It was an odd little display and Campion, whose experience did not include many women of forty who dressed and behaved like sulky six-year-olds, was a little shocked. He felt elderly and out of his depth.

An unexpectedly correct manservant appeared in answer to the bell and was dispatched for the water. When it came Miss Pye took it modestly.

"I hate to be so much trouble," she said, making big eyes over the rim of the glass, "but poor Chloe was t'irsty. Move up, Squire darling. She wants to sit on the music bench too. What are you going to play for me?"

Campion, who had expected a minor explosion, was relieved to see Mercer make room for her. He was not pleased but did not seem to be disposed to make a fuss. The woman put her glass down and thrust an arm round his shoulders.

"Play some of the old songs," she said. "The ones that made you famous, sweetheart. Play 'Third in a Crowd.' It makes me cry whenever I hear it, even now. Play 'Third in a Crowd.'"

Mercer appraised her with his frank eyes.

"But I don't want to make you cry," he said and played again his little half-finished melody, which was beginning to irk even the iron nerves of Mr. Campion.

"Don't you, darling? You are sweet. Play 'Waiting' then. 'Waiting' reminds me of happy days in the sun at Cassis. Or 'Nothing Matters Now.' 'Nothing Matters Now' was pure genius, pure, unadulterated genius."

Mercer, who seemed to accept the tribute without surprise or embarrassment, played through the chorus of the song, which had captured the great hairy ears of the unfastidiously musical a few years before. He guyed it gently but without bitterness and when he had finished nodded thoughtfully.

"One of the better of my Wurlitzer numbers. Pure Vox Humana," he observed.

"You're not to make fun of it," protested Chloe. "It's got the sexual urge, or whatever they call it. It grips one in the tummy . . ."

"Whether it makes one sick or not," put in Petrie. "How right you are, Miss Pye."

"Oh, Sock, is that you, darling? I saw a heap of smelly old clothes in the chair. Don't interrupt me. We're getting off quietly. Play something else, Squire."

Eve rose to her feet.

"Lunch in half an hour if it's not postponed," she said. "I'm going to wash."

She slouched off and Chloe looked after her.

"Like Jimmy, but no lift—no lift at all," she said. "An odd little face, too. Squire, I'll play you one of your own songs that you've forgotten. Get your hands out of the way."

She wriggled closer to him and began to play a melody which was only faintly familiar. It had been popular in the early post-war days, Mr. Campion fancied, somewhere about the time of "Whispering" and "K-K-K-Katie." The name came back to him suddenly—"Water-Lily Girl."

"Corny old stuff," said Mercer. He seemed a little irritated.

"No, you're to listen." Chloe was insistent. Over the piano's broad back they could see her looking up into his face while she played the song execrably, separating the chords and lingering sickeningly on each sentimental harmony.

She went right through the tune, playing the verse as well as the chorus. Mercer seemed to have resigned himself, but when she had finished he edged her gently off the seat and went back to his little half-born melody.

Miss Pye walked over to Sock and perched herself on the arm of his chair. She was still angry with Campion and Uncle William, it seemed, for she ignored them pointedly. Sock pulled her down onto his knee.

"What a nasty little girl," he said, managing to convey that he was a man of experience, that she was a nuisance, and that while he knew perfectly well that she could give him at least ten years she was a pretty little female thing and he forgave her. "So precipitate," he continued. "You met us all for the first time last night and now here you are crawling all over us in a bathing suit."

Miss Pye got out of his arms and settled herself on the edge of the chair again.

"You're rude," she said. "Jimmy and I are old friends, anyway, and I met you once at the theatre."

"That's no excuse." Sock was only partially playful so that the scene was not without its embarrassment. "That is Mr. Mercer, the composer, you've been talking to over there. He's a bachelor and a misogynist. He saw you for the first time late last night. If you work too fast you'll give him blood pressure."

Chloe laughed. She was childishly excited.

"Squire, shall I?"

"What? Sorry, I wasn't listening."

"Shall I give you blood pressure?"

Mercer blushed. His dark face looked odd suffused with sudden colour.

"I don't think so," he said carelessly and began to play loudly, making an interesting addition to the tune at last. This development seemed to absorb him and came as a blessed relief to everyone else in the room.

Miss Pye became dignified with a lightning change of mood which comforted Uncle William, who had been watching her with growing dismay. She left Sock and walked across to the window with conscious grace.

"Jimmy has quite a charming estate, hasn't he?" she remarked. "I do think surroundings have a definite effect upon one. He's losing all his old *joie de vivre*. Here comes Mrs. Sutane. Poor woman, she's not used to you all yet, even now, is she? How long have they been married? Seven years? I like her. Such an unassuming soul."

Footsteps sounded on the path, and Mr. Campion rose to his feet to meet his hostess and the only woman of whom Chloe Pye had ever publicly approved. He never forgot the moment. Long afterwards, he remembered the texture of the arm of the chair as he put his hand upon it to pull himself up, the formation of the fat cumulus clouds in the half oval of the window, and a purely imaginary, probably incorrect, vision of himself, long and awkward, stepping forward with a foolish smile on his face.

At that point his memories of the day and the chaotic weeks which followed it became unreliable, because he never permitted himself to think about them, but he remembered the instant when Mrs. Sutane came into the living room at White Walls because it was then that he gave up his customary position as an observer in the field and stepped over the low wall of the impersonal into the maelstrom itself and was caught up and exalted and hurt by it.

Linda Sutane came in slowly and as though she was a little shy. She was a small gold girl trimmed with brown, not very beautiful and not a vivid personality, but young and gentle and, above all, genuine. With her coming the world slipped back into its normal focus, at least for Mr. Campion, who was becoming a little dizzy from close contact with so many violent individualists.

She welcomed him formally in a comforting voice, and apologised because lunch was going to be late.

"They're still so busy," she said. "We daren't disturb them. Besides, no one can get into the dining room. There's a piano across the door."

Sock Petrie sighed.

"I am afraid we all disorganise your house, Mrs. Sutane," he said.

He spoke with genuine regret and it was the first intimation Mr. Campion had of the curious relationship between Linda Sutane and the brilliant company which surrounded her husband. It was a perfectly amicable arrangement based on deep respect on both sides, but kept apart by something as vital and unsurmountable as a difference in species.

"Oh, but I like it," she said, and might have added that she was profoundly used to it.

She sat down near Campion and bent forward to speak to him.

"You've come to see about all the trouble?" she said. "It's very kind of you. I hope you won't decide that we're all neurotic, but little things do get round one's feet so. If they were only big obvious catastrophes one could get hold of them. Sock showed you the paragraphs? Don't mention them to Jimmy. It makes him so angry and we can't do anything until the newspaper people get back to their offices."

Chloe cut into the conversation.

"Don't say you're going to start in on it all over again," she said plaintively. "Ever since I've come to this damned house I've heard nothing but 'persecution,' 'practical jokes,' 'someone's making fun of Jimmy.' Don't you let it get you down, my dear. Actors are like that. They always think someone's after their blood."

Mr. Campion looked up into her face, which was so distressingly raddled on that strong, trim body, and controlled a sudden vicious desire to slap it. The impulse startled him considerably. Linda Sutane smiled.

"I think you're probably right," she said. "Mr. Campion, come and see my flower garden."

She led him out onto the terrace and into a formal old English garden, walled with square-cut yews and ablaze with violas and sweet-scented peonies.

"I ought not to have forgotten she was there," she said as they walked over the turf together. "Naturally she doesn't find it interesting, but someone must tell you all about it or you'll be wasting your time. This is a very difficult house to get anything done in in the ordinary way, but just now, while they're all at work on this *Swing Over* show, it's worse than usual. You see, *The Buffer* has been such a great success that Jimmy and Slippers are anxious not to leave it. They were under contract to do *Swing Over*, though, and finally they came to an agreement with the Meyers brothers whereby Jimmy produces it and goes in on the business side and in return they let him out personally. Unfortunately negotiations took such a long time that they're late with production. They've got the principals here now, rehearsing. That's why Jimmy couldn't see you at once. They had to work in the hall because of the stairs. Ours are particularly good for some reason or another. Jimmy had them copied for *Cotton Fields* last year. I think you ought to know all this," she added breathlessly, "otherwise it's very confusing and you might think us all mad."

He nodded gravely and wondered how old she was and what her life had been before she married.

"It makes it clearer," he agreed. "What do you think about the business —the trouble, I mean? It hasn't actually touched you personally, has it?"

She seemed a little surprised.

"Well, I've *been* here," she said dryly. "We may have imagined most of it. We may have thought all the odds and ends of things were related when they weren't. But a great many irritating things have happened. There are people in the garden at night, too."

Campion glanced at her sharply. She had spoken casually and there was no suggestion of hysteria in her manner. She met his eyes and laughed suddenly.

"It's ridiculous, isn't it?" she said. "I know. I've been wondering if I live too much alone or if the hypersensitiveness of the stage is catching. But I assure you there are people in this garden after dark. Plants are trampled in the morning and there are footmarks under the lower windows. The servants get unsettled and I've heard whispers and giggles in the shrubs myself. You see, in the old days when my uncle was alive— I used to come and stay with him sometimes—the village policeman would have been warned and he would have watched the place, but we can't do that sort of thing now. When a man's name is part of his assets he can't afford to do the simplest thing without taking the risk that it will be seized on, twisted and made into an amusing story, so we just have to sit still and hope it all isn't true. That's not fun, with Jimmy in his present nervy state. He's beginning to feel it's a sort of doom hanging over him."

She spoke wistfully and Campion looked away from her.

"It's all rather indefinite, isn't it?" he said severely. "Mercer tells me Sutane has no enemies."

She considered. "I think that's true, but Mercer wouldn't know if he had. Mercer's a genius."

"Are geniuses unobservant?"

"No, but they're spoilt. Mercer has never had to think about anything except his work, and now I don't think he's capable of trying to. You don't know everybody yet. When you do you'll find you know them all much better than they know you."

"How do you mean?" Mr. Campion was startled.

"Well, they're all performers, aren't they? All mild exhibitionists. They're so busy putting themselves over that they haven't time to think about anyone else. It's not that they don't like other people; they just never have a moment to consider them."

She paused and looked at him dubiously.

"I don't know if you're quite the man to help us," she said unexpectedly.

"Why?" Mr. Campion did his best not to sound irritated.

"You're intelligent rather than experienced."

"What exactly do you mean by that?" Campion was surprised to find himself so annoyed.

Linda looked uncomfortable.

"I don't mean to be rude," she said. "But there are roughly two sorts of informed people, aren't there? People who start off right by observing the pitfalls and the mistakes and going round them, and the people who fall into them and get out and know they're there because of that. They both come to the same conclusions but they don't have quite the same point of view. You've watched all kinds of things but you haven't done them, and that's why you'll find this crowd so unsympathetic."

Mr. Campion regarded the small person at his side with astonishment. She returned his glance timidly.

"It's all very upsetting," she said. "It makes one rude and unnecessarily forthright. It frightens me though, you see. Do help us out if you can and forgive me."

Her voice was quiet and had the peculiar quality of capitulation. Mr. Campion nearly kissed her.

He came so near it that his common sense and natural diffidence combined, as it were, to jerk him back with an almost physical force only just in time. He stared at her, frankly appalled by the insane impulse. He saw her dispassionately for a moment, a little yellow-and-brown girl with a wide mouth and gold flecks in her eyes. All the same, it occurred to him forcefully that it would be wise if he went back to London and forgot the Sutanes, and so he would have done, of course, had it not been for the murder.

Chapter 3

Chloe Pye tied a long red silk skirt and a kerchief over her bathing dress in honour of lunch, which was served with obstinate ceremony on the part of the servants at a quarter to four.

The two visiting stars had departed with apologies, already two hours late for other appointments, and Ned Dieudonne, Sutane's invaluable accompanist, had been given a drink and a sandwich and bundled off to return the borrowed score to Prettyman, in Hampstead, who was doing the orchestrations.

The rest of the party ate hungrily. Apart from those he had already met, Campion noticed only two newcomers at the table: the young man with the golden curls whom he had last seen fighting with the doorkeeper over a silver-plated bicycle, and the incomparable Slippers Bellew.

Slippers was a nice girl. As soon as he saw her Campion understood Uncle William's regret. In her short white practice dress, her warm-yellow hair knotted high on the top of her head, she was about as alluring as any nice healthy child of twelve. She, Sutane and the golden-haired boy, who turned out to be Benny Konrad, Sutane's understudy and the young man in the "Little White Petticoats" number in *The Buffer*, ate rather different food from the rest of the gathering and drank a great deal of milk.

Sock Petrie did most of the talking, skilfully keeping Chloe Pye occupied so that her attention was diverted from Mercer, whom she was inclined to tease.

Campion sat next to Sutane, who talked to him eagerly, his thin mobile face reflecting every change of mood and lending every phrase an emphasis quite out of keeping with its importance.

"We'll snatch half an hour after this," he said. "I've got Dick coming down at half past four with a fellow I've got to meet. The chap wants to put some money into *Swing Over*, so we mustn't discourage him, bless his heart. Has Linda told you about the trouble down here?"

He used his hands as he talked and Campion was reminded again of the dynamo simile. The nervous force the man exuded was overpowering.

"I heard about the people in the garden at night, but that might be just inquisitive villagers, don't you think? You're an exciting household, you know, to a quiet country community."

"It might be so." Sutane glanced out of the window, his eyes, which seemed to be nearly all pupil, dark and resentful. "We're too near London," he declared suddenly. "It's convenient, but there's a suburban note about the place. No one seems to realise we have work to do."

He paused.

"I hate that," he said vehemently. "You'd think they'd use their heads."

Mr. Campion was silent. He thought he understood this part of the situation. He knew something of country life and the social obligations which certain houses seem to carry as though they had a personality quite apart from their owners. He imagined a bored community, in which every member had at least a nodding acquaintance with every other, thrown into a state of chattering excitement by the knowledge that a national hero was coming to join it, only to be disappointed and irritated to find that the celebrity retained his inaccessibility and merely deprived them of one of their woefully few houses of call.

He glanced down the table to where Linda sat, flanked by Uncle William and Mercer. She looked up and caught his eye and smiled. Campion turned back to his host.

"I thought I'd go . . ." he began, but Sutane interrupted him.

"You stay here a day or so. I shall feel happier if you do. What I want to know is this: how much of it is my nerves and how much real mischief? . . . Good God, what's that?"

The final words escaped him with a violence which silenced all other conversation.

Campion, who was sitting with his back to the window, glanced over his shoulder and saw the phenomenon. Coming slowly down the drive, with a dignity befitting its age, was a large Daimler, *circa* 1912. It was driven by an elderly chauffeur in green and carried a very youthful footman in similar uniform. Behind it came a Buick, also chauffeur-driven, and behind that again a taxicab. In the far distance yet another car was discernible.

Sutane glanced at his wife questioningly. She shook her head. She looked positively frightened, Campion thought.

Meanwhile, the Daimler was depositing its passengers: a resplendent old lady and a willowy girl.

The peal of the front-door bell echoed through the house and the Dane, who had been asleep under the table, got up and began to bay. Slippers quietened him after some little time, and an ominous silence fell over the room, while from outside in the hall the murmur of voices and the patter of feet upon the polished floor came in to them.

Presently, just as other cars appeared in the drive outside, another sound, an undignified lumbering noise, was added to the chatter. Slippers giggled.

"That's the piano," she said. "We moved it across the drawing-room door. There wasn't time to get it back. Jimmy, you told Hughes not to bother."

Sutane pushed back his chair. He was suddenly and theatrically furious.

"Who the devil are all these damned people?" he demanded. "What the hell are they doing calling in here? God! There's millions of them!"

Benny Konrad laughed nervously.

"Doesn't anybody know them? How marvellous! Let's all go out and fraternise."

"Shut up!" Sock Petrie was frowning, his deep-set eyes fixed anxiously on Sutane.

The star was trembling and his long fingers gripped the back of his chair.

The door behind him opened softly and the elderly manservant who had conducted the meal came in. He was red and flustered.

"A great many people have called, sir," he began in an undertone. "I've put them in the drawing room, and one of the maids is opening the double doors into the living room. Would you wish me to serve tea?"

"I don't know." Sutane glanced at his wife helplessly.

Linda rose. "It's cups, I suppose. Cups and cake, and milk of course. How many people have come?"

"About thirty at the moment, madam, but . . ." The old man glanced down the drive expressively. Another car pulled up and a group of ex-cited young people got out.

"Oh, well, do what you can." Linda sounded resigned. "There's a case of sherry in the pantry; that may help. Hughes, is there anybody you know?"

"Oh, yes, madam. There's old Mrs. Corsair from the Towers, Lady Gerry from Melton, Mr. and Mrs. Beak, Miss Earle—they all called on you, madam." He managed to convey a gentle reproach. "I'll go and attend to them. Will you come?"

The girl glanced down at her brown cotton dress.

"Yes," she said at last. "Very well."

She hurried out after the butler, looking, Mr. Campion thought, like a very small ship going into battle.

Chloe rose. "We ought all to go and help her," she said, not without a certain relish. "Who are all these people, Jimmy? Your local audience?"

Sutane ignored her. "The cheek of it!" he exploded. "To come to one's house in hordes when one's got work to do!"

Mr. Campion coughed. "They've been asked, you know," he said gently. "People don't turn up by the hundred at four o'clock precisely without an invitation."

"God bless my soul!" said Uncle William.

Benny Konrad squeaked. "It's a dirty practical joke," he ejaculated. "I say, someone's got their knife into you, Sutane. What are you going to do?"

"Disappear," said Jimmy promptly. "It's hard on Linda, but I've got a business conference in twenty minutes."

"I say, old boy, I shouldn't do that." Sock's voice was quiet but very firm. "Bad publicity, you know. It's a swine's trick but you'll have to make the best of it. Both you and Slippers *must* appear. Go out and say pretty things. Explain you've been practising and that's why you're in these clothes. It's absolutely the only thing to do. We'll all back you up."

Sutane stood irresolute.

"It's a damned imposition."

"I know it is, but what can you do?" Sock was appealing. "Once someone realises that the whole thing is a hoax the story will get out and it'll make good reading. Do go along, there's a good chap."

Slippers, who had a kindly feeling for Sock, linked her arm through Jimmy's.

"Come on, loov," she said. "We'll make our entrance."

"Will they applaud?" murmured Benny and giggled.

Sock kicked him gently and he grew red and, ridiculously, raised a hand to hit back.

Mercer came over to Campion and Uncle William.

"I suppose they've got all three pianos?" he said. "Do you know?"

They looked at him in surprise and he frowned.

"They're bound to use all the rooms. I'll go home. It's only across the park."

He opened a window and swung himself out into the drive, much to the astonishment of some new arrivals who all but ran him down. He stepped aside and scowled at them ferociously and the last Campion saw of him was his short top-heavy figure striding off across the park.

Chloe Pye peered at herself in a compact mirror.

"Will I do?" she said to Uncle William, and, on receiving his startled nod, plunged out into the hall.

The party, as a party, was the fiasco its perpetrator had evidently planned. Any house is uncomfortable when strained to the uttermost limits of its capacity, and thirteen bottles of amontillado and forty cups of tea, including six kitchen mugs, will not, in these degenerate days, satisfy the five thousand. The furniture was in the way and the empty beer bottles, the relics of Sock's morning refreshment, did not grace the living-room piano where a thoughtful guest who had stepped amongst them placed them for safety.

All these were minor disasters, however, compared with the real misfortune of the afternoon. As he was jostled to and fro among the crowd

Mr. Campion made an interesting discovery. The company was mixed by a hand that pure ignorance could scarcely have directed. The snobbish distinctions which are the whole structure of any country society in England had been deliberately flouted. Campion was inclined to suspect a telephone directory as the source of the selection. The upper stratum had come because it had called and been called upon in return and was therefore technically acquainted with the Sutanes; the others were simply those who had been gratified to receive an invitation from a celebrity. Since the one fraternity waited on the other, for the most part, in the way of trade and were therefore well acquainted, it was a particularly unfortunate mixture.

Altogether it was a disastrous gathering.

A man called Baynes, who appeared to be a councillor from some borough unstated, since the two excited young women who accompanied him persistently addressed him by that title, was inclined to be noisily friendly, but the remainder of the gathering was stiff and mulishly uncomfortable.

Chloe's bathing dress was not a success, in spite of her crimson skirt, and her brush with the old lady who had been the first to arrive provided an unhappy five minutes for all within earshot.

Sutane did his best, but his entrance with Slippers instead of his wife, which was the purest accident, was not forgiven him.

Campion saw him standing at one corner of the room, slender and excitable, talking gracefully to people he did not know, with Sock at his elbow lending moral if not sartorial support.

Linda was even less fortunate. A great many of the visitors were her own country kind and they believed that she had deliberately embarrassed them. Campion saw unwonted colour in the small face with the wide mouth and the eyes with gold flecks in them, and was profoundly sorry for her.

Uncle William strode about manfully and made conversation of a somewhat sporadic and explosive kind, addressing his remarks to anyone who did not actually scowl at him, and Eve did her sulky best.

It was a harrowing experience for all concerned. The cars began to leave. The called-upon departed in a measured rout; the others followed, taking their cue from their leaders.

Finally only the councillor remained and even his friendliness vanished when Sutane, his brittle nerves breaking beneath the strain of an hour's acute embarrassment, told him brusquely not to call him "old pal."

As the last car vanished down the drive with its cargo of nettled guests Linda sat down abruptly in an armchair and blew her nose. Sutane stared at her.

"We'll sell the damned place," he said.

She shook her head. "They'll get over it in time."

"So I should hope." Sutane was contemptuous. "Good heavens, they must have seen we were taken by surprise. Surely they don't imagine any-one in his right mind would ask two hundred people to tea one Sunday afternoon and provide them with forty cups between them?"

Linda looked up.

"They think *we* might," she said. "They've always suspected we were a little queer and now I'm afraid they're convinced of it. The trouble is they think we're rude as well. They've gone home thinking it was just slackness."

Sutane remained looking down at her, his face growing dark. In com-mon with many members of his profession, he had a strong streak of the snob in him, and her suggestion was both distasteful and convincing. He turned to Campion.

"Now am I imagining things?" he demanded, his voice rising. "It's got to stop, I tell you! It's driving me off my head. It's got to stop."

"Jimmy old man, I told you four-thirty."

An injured voice from the doorway interrupted the outburst and Cam-pion, glancing up, saw a little man with a tragic, ugly face hesitating on the threshold. Everything about him was tiny but very masculine. His hands were coarse but minute and his chin was as blue as Mercer's own.

He came quickly across the room and spoke in a low and confidential tone, which Campion afterwards discovered was habitual with him.

"I didn't know you were having a tea fight. We arrived in the middle of it and I took Bowser straight up to the den. He's a busy man, Jimmy. Come along."

Sutane sighed with exaggerated weariness and grimaced at Campion with a flicker of his old charm.

"I'm coming," he said and they went out together.

"That's Poyser, Jimmy's manager," murmured Sock, lounging across the room to Campion. "This is a bit of bad luck, isn't it? He was nervy enough already. It's got to be stopped somehow."

Campion nodded. He was standing by the chair in which Linda sat and his long angular form shadowed her. He looked down and spoke apologetically.

"I seem to have been here a long time and done nothing of the faintest use to anybody," he said. "D'you know anyone who came this afternoon well enough to take into your confidence? If we had one of the invitation cards which were presumably sent round we might be able to locate the printer, or at least find out when they were sent and where from."

"No, there was no one," she said stiffly. "I recognised two or three peo-ple who called on us when we first came, but the rest were complete strangers."

Sock grinned. "They knew each other all right, didn't they?" he said. "There were some pretty sizzling remarks floating around."

"I heard them." The girl looked up at them and they were embarrassed to see tears in her eyes. "I'll go and talk to the kitchen," she murmured. "I'm afraid there may be a minor crisis down there."

As the door closed behind her Sock thrust his hands in his pockets and smiled wryly.

"Poor old girl, she's rattled," he said. "But we can't do anything. That idea of yours would be perfectly sound in the ordinary way, but you see the difficulty in the present case. These good people, whoever they are, can chatter among themselves about the funny actors, but they can only say the place was in a bit of a mess and there wasn't enough food to go round. But once the hoax story gets out it makes a little news par, doesn't it? See what I mean?"

"It seems a bit hard on Mrs. Sutane."

The other man looked at Campion curiously.

"Quite a lot of things are hard on Mrs. Sutane," he observed. "You'll notice that if you stick around."

A cold meal was served at half past eight, at which no mention of the incident of the afternoon was made, out of deference to a solid, frightened-looking person called Bowser who sat between Sutane and his manager and kept his eye on his plate.

Mercer, who had appeared again as soon as the coast was clear, made several attempts to bring up the matter, in which he was assisted by Chloe, who was in mischievous mood, but they were both restrained by the able Mr. Petrie.

Dick Poyser carried Sutane and his guest off again after the meal. Like most people directly concerned with the management of money, he had a curious preoccupied mannerlessness, as though he and his mission in life were somehow sacrosanct and privileged. He did not speak to anyone outside his two charges and ignored his hostess completely, yet there was no deliberate rudeness in the man.

After the meal Campion cornered Uncle William.

"Leave, my dear fellow?" The old man was aghast. "Of course you haven't made any progress yet. Haven't had a moment. No, no, wait a little while. Must see Sutane before you go, anyway."

He stumped off, anxious to avoid further conversation.

Campion sat down in a corner of the living room. There was a restlessness in the big house which had nothing to do with noise. Outside, the garden was warm and scented, a light wind playing in the lime trees.

On the lawn below the terrace he could see Chloe walking between Petrie and Benny Konrad, and her high thin laugh came up to him every now and again.

The others had disappeared.

He sat there quietly for a long time until the yellow light died on the treetops and the colder shadows of the approaching night swept over the garden.

Once he heard voices in the hall and the closing of doors, but then all was quiet again. He lit a cigarette and smoked it thoughtfully, his long thin hands loosely clasped across his knees. He was angry and dissatisfied with himself.

The hand on his sleeve and the voice so passionate in its enquiry startled him considerably.

"What's your name?"

It was a child in a big old-fashioned overall. She was not pretty but her plump face was eager and flushed with excitement, and she had round eyes with startlingly familiar gold flecks in them.

Mr. Campion, who was a little afraid of children, regarded her with something akin to superstition.

"What's your name? Tell me your name!"

Her demand was vehement and she clambered over the chair towards him.

"Albert," he said helplessly. "Who are you?"

"Albert," she repeated with satisfaction. Having attained her objective she was now inclined to shyness as violent as her first overture had been. She wriggled away from him and stood hesitating. "Albert's a dog's name," she said.

"Who are you?" he repeated and wondered at his dislike of her.

She stared at him as if she guessed his antagonism.

"I'm Sarah Sutane. I live here. I'm not allowed to talk to you or anybody, but I want to. I want to. I want to."

She flung herself sobbing into his arms and rubbed a wet unhappy face against his tie. He sat her up on his knee, doing his best to look as if he were not pushing her away from him, and felt for a handkerchief, which seemed the moment's most pressing need.

"How old are you?"

"Six."

"Sarah." Miss Finbrough and a woman in nurse's uniform appeared at the french windows. "I'm sorry, Mr. Campion. She ought to be in bed. Come along, child, do. She ran away just before bedtime. Where have you been hiding? In the garden?"

Sarah shrieked and clung to her link with the outside world, who rose, embarrassed and dishevelled. In the end the nurse took her and carried her off, kicking. Her angry screams echoed faintly and more faintly as a succeeding procession of doors closed after her. Miss Finbrough raised her eyebrows.

"She's a nervy child," she said. "Still, what can you expect? She wants other children to play with. She's lonely, but you can't have the place overrun with kids. It's not like an ordinary house. D'you know I haven't been able to get hold of Mr. Sutane all day?"

"Doesn't Sarah see anyone?"

"Oh, well, she sees her mother and her nurse, and me. Her mother spoils her, but she agrees with Mr. Sutane that she can't run loose among the guests. She'd get spoilt and precocious and pick up I don't know what words. Mr. Sutane has a horror of her becoming what they call a stage child. I keep telling them she ought to go to boarding school."

"At six?"

"That's what her mother says." Miss Finbrough showed her impatience. "Still, if a child's got an overworked genius for a father it's got to take the consequences."

Mr. Campion felt his usual urbanity deserting him.

"You're a little hard, aren't you?"

"Hard? Have you seen him dance?" The plain woman's face was flushed and her eyes were bright. "You can't expect *him* to upset his health, filling the place with children." She checked herself. "Mrs. Sutane's out in the garden looking for the child," she said. "It would run away just when we were so upset already. I wonder if you'd mind telling her?"

Campion went out into the dusk. On the lower lawn he encountered Chloe and Sock Petrie, who was carrying a portable gramophone and a case of records. The woman was excited, he noticed. The twilight softened her face and her eyes were brilliant.

"I'm going to dance by the lake," she said. "This warm, passionate, *exulting* night!"

She threw out her arms to the opal sky.

Petrie scowled. "I'll put on a couple of records for you and then I've got to have a look at my bus," he said ungallantly. "She's got to get me to town tonight, poor old trumpet."

Chloe laughed at him.

"So you think," she murmured.

"So I damn well know, my dear," he retorted. "Hullo, what's Donald Duck want?"

Benny Konrad sprinted across the lawn towards them rather too consciously like a young faun.

"I say, Sock, Sutane's gone," he began with a hint of relish. "Yes, he took a fancy to one of the guests who came today and he's gone tearing off in the Bentley to see him. After his invitation card, I expect."

Sock put down the gramophone and swore.

"He would," he said finally. "Oh, my God, he would. Here, Benny, take these blasted things and go and put on records for Chloe. I'm going round to the garage to see if Joe knows where the lunatic's gone."

"I think you're insufferable," said Miss Pye to his retreating figure and spoilt the dignity of her reproach immediately afterwards by shouting: "Come back when you've finished!"

Sock did not reply and Benny picked up the gramophone.

"I'll dance too," he said. "I say, what was the matter with Eve?"

Chloe turned on him with unexpected interest.

"When?"

"Just now. After food. She was crying divinely, all alone under a little rosebush. When she saw me she ran away."

"Where to?"

"I don't know. Up to her room, I suppose."

He giggled and for an instant Chloe Pye stood irresolute. Then she shrugged her shoulders.

"Be careful with the records," she said.

Albert Campion went on his way to find Linda. She was in the park. He came on her as she stood shouting for Sarah in a small, appealing voice.

"Please, darling, come out! Sarah pet, come out. Please come out for Mummy."

He dropped into step beside her.

"Sarah's in bed," he said.

She turned to him with relief and he was gratified to see welcome in her eyes. They strolled back through the garden to the house and sat on the terrace talking until it grew dusk, when they returned to the morning room, too engrossed in each other to notice the continued absence of the others.

Campion was not conscious of the time. His carefully trained powers of observation were temporarily in abeyance. He had ceased to be an on-looker and was taking part. He was extraordinarily happy. His good conceit of himself grew. He felt capable and intelligent and he talked with all the old animation of his early youth. All trace of vacuity vanished from his face and his eyes became alive and amused.

Linda was sparkling at him.

As they talked of the disastrous party of the afternoon the affair began to present its purely humorous side and a frankly hilarious note crept into their consideration of the entire problem.

They were each aware of a new sense of freedom and discovered together, as they paid each other the irresistible compliment of complete comprehension, the most delightful and the most dangerous quality of mutual stimulation.

The rest of the household and their weary, worried and excitable personalities were forgotten. It was a long and supremely satisfying evening.

The inevitable ending of such a spring dance came when neither of them expected it. He looked across at her and grinned.

"This is very good," he said.

She laughed and sighed and stretched herself like a small yellow cat. "I'm very happy."

"I believe you are," he murmured and got up lazily with every intention of kissing her. It was a completely casual, unpremeditated movement, arising naturally out of the unself-conscious exuberance of his mood, and he was halfway across the rug towards her when the world returned to him with a rush and he became acutely aware of himself and who and what and where he was.

For the second time that day he was seized by a sudden terror that he had gone completely out of his mind.

He shot the girl a startled glance. She was looking at him gravely. The gaiety had died out of her face and a faint bewilderment had taken its place. It occurred to him that she had shared his experience. She rose and shivered a little.

"I'll go down and see if I can cajole some coffee out of the baleful company in the kitchen," she said lightly. "They're very much on their dignity after the fiasco this afternoon. I've done all I can. They've had their wireless on all night, which is against the rules on Sunday when Jimmy's at home—you can hear it, can't you? They've got a passion for military bands and they've been bribed with port and sweet words. Yet Hughes gave me notice this evening. He's outraged, poor dear. I'm doing my best to woo him back. I can't lose him. He was with my uncle."

She went out quickly, closing the door softly behind her.

Left to himself, Campion stubbed out his cigarette and passed his hand through his sleek fair hair. Resentment not untinged with amusement at the utter unreasonableness of his own hitherto decently controlled emotions consumed him.

"It doesn't happen," he said aloud and looked round guiltily, terrified lest he had been overheard.

The cry across the park came so faintly at first that only a part of his mind was aware of it, but as it was repeated, growing steadily in volume and insistence, it burst into his thoughts with the force of an explosion.

"Come, damn you! Somebody come! Come at once! Where is everyone? Somebody come!"

At the moment that Linda stepped back into the room the thudding feet came pounding onto the terrace and Sutane, his face livid, appeared at the open windows. Even then his sense of the theatre did not quite desert him. He paused and stared at them.

"I've killed her," he shouted. "Oh, my God, Linda, I've killed her! I've killed Chloe Pye."

Chapter 4

There are moments of acute sensation before the mind gets to work again when shock is no more than a feeling of physical chill, and at these times the details of one's surroundings are apt to take on a peculiar vividness.

Linda became aware of the untidiness of the brightly lit room, of Chloe's red handkerchief folded neatly on the piano with her book upon it, and of Campion's long, dark, suddenly important back as he stood arrested, half turned towards her husband.

Then there were footsteps in the hall behind her and Sutane's manager, Dick Poyser, his sad eyes inquisitive, came in.

"I heard a noise," he said. "What's the matter, Jimmy?"

Sutane stepped into the room. He was a little unsteady on his feet.

"I've killed Chloe . . . she chucked herself under the car."

"For God's sake, shut up!" Poyser looked round him involuntarily and his thought was as evident as if he had spoken it. "Where is she?" he went on, adding instantly: "Anyone see you?"

"No. I was alone." Sutane shook his head as he spoke, his naïveté almost childlike beside the other man's authority. "She's down in the lane on the grass. I put her there. I didn't like to leave her in the road. The car's there, too, because of the lights. I couldn't leave her in the dark. I cut across the park."

"Sure she's dead?" Poyser was staring at him in horrified fascination.

"Oh, yes." The light pleasant voice was dull. "The wheels went clean over her. It's a heavy car. What the hell shall we do?"

There were other movements in the house now and Mercer's voice, lazy and inarticulate as usual, sounded from the little music room across the hall. Uncle William's characteristic rumble answered him. Poyser turned sharply to Campion.

"Are you something to do with the police?"

"No." Campion glanced down at him curiously.

"Thank God for that!" His relief was heartfelt. "We'll go down. Where did it happen, Jimmy? Give him a drink, Linda. Pull yourself together, old boy. Steady now, steady."

"I should phone for a doctor and the police at once." Mr. Campion's quiet impersonal voice cut into the conversation.

"Why the police?" Poyser pounced on the word suspiciously.

"Because there's been an accident. It's the rule of the road, to start with."

"Oh, I see . . ." The little man looked up, a faint smile which was both knowing and appreciative twisting his mouth. "Yes, of course. I forgot that. Linda, that's a job for you. Give us three minutes to get down there and then phone. First a doctor, then the police. Just be perfectly natural. There's been an accident and someone's hurt. Got that? Good. Now we'll go. Jimmy, you'll have to come, old chap."

Just before he went out after the others Campion glanced back at the girl. She was still standing halfway across the room. Her hand covered her mouth and her eyes were round and frightened. He realised suddenly that throughout the whole scene she had said nothing at all.

As soon as the three hurrying men stepped out into the darkness they saw the pale haze of headlights above the trees in the lane. Sutane was talking. He was excited, but his extreme nerviness of earlier in the day had gone. Campion received the impression that he was watching his words as carefully as he could.

"I told her not to come here at all," he said as they strode over the grass. "I told her frankly I didn't want her here. But she insisted, you know she did. This must have been in her mind all the time. What an incredible trick! On *my* place! Under *my* car!"

"Be quiet." Campion caught the gleam of Poyser's little black eyes as they flickered towards him. "Be quiet, old boy. We'll see what happened when we get there."

They hurried on in silence for a little while. Sutane was breathing heavily.

"I was blinding, you know," he said suddenly. "Didn't see her until I was over her."

Poyser took his arm. "Forget it," he said softly. "We'll get it straight in a minute or so. How do we get through this hedge?"

"There's a gap somewhere. I climbed the bank and forced my way through. It's only laurels."

They came slithering down the high bank to the road, bringing great clods of sandy yellow earth with them. The car stood in the middle of the lane, her engine still running, while behind, ghastly in the faint red glare of the taillight, was something white and quiet on the grass verge. Poyser tiptoed forward, oblivious of the absurdity of his caution. He bent down and struck a match. He stood holding it in the still, warm air until it burned his fingers.

"Lumme," he said softly at last, and the old-fashioned expletive was more forceful than any other he could have used.

As Campion and Sutane came up he swung away from the body and took the actor's sleeve.

"Where was she when you hit her?"

Campion left them. He had a pencil torch in his pocket and now knelt down beside the dead woman with it. Chloe Pye was still in her white swimming suit. She lay on her back on the verge, her head dangling over the grass-grown ditch and her thin body limp and shapeless. The near-side wheels of the car had passed over her chest, crushing her rib cage.

There was dirt and considerable laceration of the skin, but very little blood. Her hand was cool when he touched it, but not clammy.

Mr. Campion sat back on his heels. In the darkness his face was blank. Poyser's voice recalled him.

"Have you got a flash lamp there? Bring it here a moment."

Campion rose and went over. The skid marks were easily discernible on the flint road. By the light of the little torch they found the spot where Sutane had jammed on his brakes, and a little farther on the dreadful smother of stones and dust with the pitifully small stain in it where the woman had fallen. Sutane's teeth were chattering.

"She just dropped in front of me," he said. "I didn't see her till she flashed past the windscreen. She chucked herself under the car. I didn't know what had happened until I came back to see what I'd hit."

"It was an accident." Poyser's voice was pleading. "A pure accident, old boy. Where was she standing?"

"Don't be a fool. She did it deliberately." Sutane's voice was exasperated. "That's where she came from." He snatched the torch and sent its beam flickering upward.

Poyser swore because the unexpected sight startled him.

"The bridge . . ." he said, staring up at the rose-hung arch. "Good God, didn't you see her fall?"

"No, I keep telling you." Sutane sounded sulky. "I was blinding. Naturally I was looking at the road, not up in the air somewhere."

"All the same, I should have thought the headlights would have caught her," the other man insisted, still staring up at the leafy span above him.

In the faint light from the torch Campion saw his small face alive with worry and invention.

"That's it," he said abruptly. "That's what happened. I see it now. That's what happened, Jimmy. She saw you coming and waved to you to stop. Probably she leant right over, imagining she was a fairy or a bumblebee or something—it's the sort of crazy idea she might have—and somehow or other she overbalanced and fell under your wheels before you could stop. That's what happened. It'd make it much more simple if you'd seen her do it. You must have seen her up there."

"But I didn't, I tell you." Sutane was obstinate. "I was blinding with my eyes on the road and my mind on those damned invitations. Suddenly something plumped down just in front of me and I slammed on the brakes. There was a sort of jolt and I pulled up when I could and backed the bus down the road. Then I got out and went round to the back of the car and there she was."

"Jimmy"—Poyser's voice was wheedling—"it *must* have been an accident. Think of it, my dear chap, think of the situation. It *must* have been an accident. Chloe wouldn't kill herself. Why should she? She was making a comeback in your show. She was a visitor in your house. She wouldn't deliberately chuck herself under your car. That's the kind of story newspapermen dream about when they're half tight. She was trying to attract your attention and fell over. That's the obvious truth as I see it, and believe me it's bad enough."

Sutane was silent. The vibrations of Poyser's arguments still hung about in the darkness. He shuddered.

"It may have been so," he said with an unsuccessful attempt at conviction. "But I didn't see her, Dick. On my oath, I did not see her."

"All right. But it was an accident. Do understand that."

"Yes. Yes, I do."

Mr. Campion asked if he might have his torch back, explaining that he wished to examine the bridge.

"Good idea." There was an element of conspiracy in the way Poyser thrust the pencil into his hand, and it occurred to Campion that the tactics of businessmen were elephantine capers. He hoped devoutly that the affair would remain a country one and that the astute Mr. Poyser would never be confronted by a metropolitan detective.

He scrambled up the bank again and, forcing his way through the shrubs, found the path without much difficulty. The bridge itself was a much more solid structure than it had appeared from the road. The parapets, although constructed of "rustic" work, were astonishingly steady and were further reinforced by a tangle of American Pillar and wild white convolvulus. The bright red roses looked unreal and somehow Victorian in the artificial light of the torch as Campion examined the hedge of flowers carefully, his discomfort increasing. The creosoted boards beneath his feet told him nothing. The dry summer had left them smooth and barely even dusty.

He worked over the ground with hurried inquisitiveness and at every step his uneasiness grew. Yet it was not his discoveries which so disturbed him. Poyser's voice, carefully lowered to an inarticulate murmur, floated up to him with the scent of the flowers in the warm, soft air. Now and again Sutane answered, his voice clear and irritable.

"It would be like her," Campion heard him admit.

And again, after a prolonged muttering from Poyser:

"Yes, she liked secrets."

At this point another beam of light swung down the lane and came racing towards them. Campion hurried off the bridge and plunged back through the laurels. In view of everything, he was anxious to be present when the police arrived.

He came out through the bushes and slid into the road just as a car came to a standstill within a few feet of him so abruptly that the engine stopped. He saw it was a large Fiat, a few years old, a portly vehicle. The near-side window came down with a rattle and an old voice, slow with the affectations of the educated seventies, the father, as it were, of Uncle William's voice, said sternly:

"My name's Bouverie. Somebody telephoned to my house to tell me that someone was hurt."

"Doctor Bouverie?"

"Yes." The curtness of the monosyllable suggested that the speaker was irritated at finding himself unknown. "Get that car out of the way. You've taken the patient up to the house, I suppose."

"No. No, we haven't. She's here." It was Sutane who interrupted. He had hurried forward and now adopted unconsciously the tone of nervous authority which he kept for such of those strangers whom he did not instantly set out to charm.

"Are you Mr. Sutane?"

The voice in the car had authority also, and of the magisterial variety.

"I think I met you at your house this afternoon. Were you driving the car?"

Sutane was momentarily taken off his balance.

"Yes," he said. "Er, yes, I was."

"Ah!"

The door opened.

"Well, I'll take a look at your victim, don't you know."

Campion never forgot his first glimpse of the figure who climbed slowly out of the darkness of the car into the tiny circle of light from the torch. His first impression was of enormous girth in a white lounge suit. Then he saw an old pugnacious face with drooping chaps and a wise eye peering out from under the peak of a large tweed cap. Its whole expression was arrogant, honest, and startlingly reminiscent of a bulldog, with perhaps a dash of bloodhound. He was clean-shaven except for a minute white tuft on his upper lip, but his plump, short-fingered surgeon's hands had hair on the backs of them.

A Georgian tough, thought Campion, startled, and never had occasion to alter his opinion.

He had not seen the doctor at the disastrous party of the afternoon and rightly supposed that he had been one of the many who had come late only to leave almost immediately afterwards.

Sutane remembered him, so much was obvious. His face wore that indignant, contemptuous expression which is always more than half embarrassment.

Poyser, who saw trouble brewing, came forward ingratiatingly.

"It was a pure accident," he volunteered, attempting to be matter-of-fact and succeeding in sounding casual.

"Oh!" The newcomer raised his head and stared at him. "Were you in the car?"

"No, I wasn't. Mr. Sutane was alone. Mr. Campion and I have just come down from the house. We——"

"Quite. Where is the patient? It's a woman, you say? Where is she?"

Dr. Bouverie had brushed past the discomfited Poyser and addressed Sutane. His whole manner was truculent and highhanded to an extent which would have been ridiculous or merely rude had it not so obviously sprung from a lifetime of authority. As it was, he was frankly awe-inspiring, and Mr. Campion, who knew the signs, felt his heart sink.

The doctor produced an eighteen-inch torch from his enormous coat pocket and gave it to Sutane to hold.

"In the back of the car, I suppose," he said, advancing upon the Bentley.

"No, she's here." Sutane swung the beam of light onto the verge with a suddenness unconsciously dramatic, and the newcomer, who was growing more like the spirit of rural justice incarnate at every step, paused in his tracks like a startled grizzly. He made a little teetering sound with his tongue, expressing astonishment and, it would seem, disgust.

"Come closer, will you?" he said. "I want the light actually on her. That's a little better. If you can't keep it steady one of the others must hold it."

Poyser took the torch and the old doctor knelt down on the grass, having first assured himself that it was not damp. His whole poise suggested extreme distaste and disapproval, but his square hands were exquisitely gentle.

After a while he got up, disdaining Sutane's assistance.

"She's dead," he said. "You knew that, of course? What was she doing running about naked?"

He pronounced it "nekkit" and the affectation gave the word an odd shamefulness.

"She used to do that," said Sutane wearily. "She's worn a bathing dress all day. What on earth does it matter?"

The old eyes under the peaked cap stared at him as at a curiosity and Poyser interrupted again. He insisted on giving his version of the affair, investing it, in his extreme anxiety to be both lucid and convincing, with a glibness which sounded positively inhuman.

The monstrous old man listened to him until the end, his head slightly on one side. It was a hopeless encounter, Mr. Campion reflected; like a clever fish trying to talk to an equally clever dog, an experiment predestined to end in mutual distrust.

Dr. Bouverie directed his torch at the bridge.

"But if she fell off there by accident, don't you know, she must have climbed out over those roses—an extraordinary thing to do so lightly clad. Ah, here comes the man we want. Is that you, Doe?"

"Yes, sir. Good evening, sir." A police constable, young and remarkably handsome in the uniform which seems to vary between the impressive and the comic, solely according to its wearer's face, swung himself off his bicycle and laid the machine carefully against the bank. The doctor advanced upon him.

"There's been a shocking accident," he said, sounding like an army colonel addressing a favoured subordinate. "The woman either fell or threw herself off the bridge here under Mr. Sutane's car. This is Mr. Sutane. The woman is dead. I shall want the body taken down to Birley and I'll ring up the coroner first thing tomorrow morning and probably do a post-mortem a little later."

"Yes, sir."

The doctor had not finished.

"Meanwhile," he said, "I should like to take a look at that bridge. How d'you get up to it, Mr. Sutane?"

"I climbed up the bank, but there's a gate a little farther along." Sutane's utter weariness was pathetic.

"Then I'll use it. Perhaps you'd be good enough to direct me." The old doctor was brusque and bursting with energy. "Doe, throw a rug over that poor woman and then come along."

Mr. Campion did not join the party. As was his custom when his immediate presence was not necessary, he succeeded in effacing himself. As soon as the policeman's steady steps disappeared down the lane he wandered over to the Fiat and looked inside. The back of the car contained a bag, a folded rug and a wedge-shaped wooden box fitted with small flower containers in little sockets arranged in neat equidistant rows. The rest of the interior told him nothing and with infinite caution he raised the bonnet.

Sutane was the first to return. Campion was standing aimlessly by the Bentley when he came up. Overhead on the bridge there was the murmur of voices. Sutane was trembling with fury.

"Surely that fellow's exceeding his job?" he began in a whisper. "The bobby treats him as though he was God Almighty. What's it matter to him if she committed suicide or not? Blithering old ass!—he's about ninety."

"Then he probably *is* omnipotent in this district." Campion lowered his voice discreetly. "A personality like that would make an impression anywhere, given time. Look out; he's probably on the Bench."

Sutane wiped his forehead. In the glare of the headlights he looked like one of his own photographs outside the theatre, a fantastic figure caught for an instant in a nightmare world of towering shadows.

"This is the last straw," he said. "It's got to be an accident, Campion. I see that now. Poyser's right. For all our sakes it's got to be an accident. Good God! What did she want to do it for?—and why here?"

"What's happened?" Sock came slithering down the bank behind them, a tousled scarecrow in the uncertain light. "Linda told me something frightful—I couldn't believe it. Jimmy, my dear old chap, what's up?"

They told him and he stood looking down at the rug-covered mound, his shoulders hunched and his hands in his pockets.

"Oh, Lord," he said, something like tears in his voice. "Oh, Lord."

Campion touched him on the shoulder and, leading him a little to one side, made a request.

"The old boy's going to be nasty, I'm afraid," he finished. "He came to the party this afternoon and didn't understand it. I'd go myself, of course, but I want to be here when he comes back."

"My dear chap, anything I can do." Sock's voice was still tremulous. Like many intensely virile men, he was bowled over by emotion of any sort. "I'll be back in a moment. Delighted to be able to do anything I can. I'll tell the others to stay up there, shall I? After all, they can't do much."

He went off, clambering up the bank again, and footsteps down the lane announced the return of the others. Dr. Bouverie was still in charge.

"Unless she was actually standing on the parapet, a thing no woman in her senses would do, surely, I don't see how she managed to fall." The old voice, which was yet so powerful, made the statement for his companions' information. He implied no doubt whatever: he simply did not see how she managed to fall.

"Oh, but she might easily have done that, Doctor. I knew her. She did that sort of thing." Poyser's soothing tone was wearing thin.

"Was she unbalanced? Her costume, or lack of it, does suggest that."

"Oh, no, nothing like that. She was impulsive—temperamental. She might easily have climbed up there to wave to Sutane."

"Indeed." Dr. Bouverie was not impressed. He turned to the constable. "Well, I've finished, Doe. You know what to do. Treat it just like an ordinary accident. You can get some sort of conveyance probably. I shall be at Birley about ten tomorrow morning. Probably Doctor Dean will be with me. Good night, gentlemen."

He climbed into the car and pressed the starter. The Fiat did not respond.

The next fifteen minutes was devoted to the car by the whole company. Any man in an obstinately stationary car seems to be a responsibility to all about him, but Dr. Bouverie in that predicament was a sacred charge. Aware, no doubt, that a god in a machine that won't go may easily degenerate into an angry mortal, he kept his dignity and controlled his temper, but contrived, nevertheless, to appear somehow terrible in the more ancient sense of the word. The tragedy of Chloe Pye's death faded into obscurity for a moment or so.

Sock Petrie's arrival in Campion's Lagonda was nicely timed. As Poyser shifted the Bentley to let the grey car pass, Campion made his graceful suggestion.

"Let me run you home, sir," he murmured. "There's a good man up at the house who will put this right and bring your car along."

Dr. Bouverie wavered. His keen eyes regarded Campion inquisitively and, seeing nothing to dislike in him, he accepted with unexpected charm.

"Extremely civil of you," he said. "It's my own fault. I ought to have got my man up, but he's done a hundred and twenty miles with me to-day, so I thought I'd let the feller sleep, don't you know."

As they set off down the lane at a sedate pace Campion prepared himself for a delicate campaign.

"Excellent roads," he began cautiously. "This is my first visit to this part of the world. I noticed them at once."

"Think so?" A trace of satisfaction in the old voice warmed his heart. "They ought to be. We had the devil of a job getting the authorities to realise that a side road is as important to the residents of a district as the main ways that cater for all these damned trippers who do their best to ruin the country. Still, we hammered it into their heads at last. You're a stranger, you say? Were you at that gathering this afternoon?"

"Yes." Mr. Campion sounded regretful. "A most unfortunate business. The mistake of a secretary. Dates mixed, you know."

"Really? Oh, I see. Thought it curious myself. These Londoners don't understand our country ways. Forgive me, I didn't catch your name?"

Mr. Campion gave it and added that he was a Norfolk man. To his relief they discovered a mutual acquaintance and, as the old gentleman softened considerably, he took heart.

"A frightful accident," he ventured. "Miss Pye seemed in such good spirits all day."

"Ah, indeed. We turn to the left here if you don't mind. How pleasant the clover smells in the dark. Notice it?"

Campion took the hint and played his best card.

"Isn't this a great district for roses?" he enquired, remembering the wedge-shaped box in the Fiat.

His passenger brightened noticeably.

"Finest in the world. I take a little interest in roses myself." He paused and added with an unexpected chuckle: "Twelve tickets out of fourteen at Hernchester yesterday. Five firsts for roses, and a cup. Not bad for an old 'un, eh?"

"I say, that's extraordinarily good." Mr. Campion was genuinely impressed. "Do you believe in bone manure?"

"Not on my soil. I've got a streak of the genuine clay."

They discussed roses and their culture for several miles. Even Campion, who was used to strong contrasts, was aware of a certain nightmare quality in the drive. Dr. Bouverie talked of his hobby with knowledge and the passionate interest of a young man in his twenties. The brittle world of White Walls and the stage seemed a long way away.

By the time they pulled up in a darkened village the doctor was engrossed in his subject.

"I'll show you those Lady Forteviots. If you've missed 'em you've missed a treat," he said. "Here we are."

Campion discovered that the dark wall which he had taken to be the side of a rural factory was the front of a bleak Georgian house. A Victorian porch, fastened with solid wooden doors, stuck out into the road at an angle which no modern council would dream of sanctioning.

The doctor rang the bell and bellowed "Dorothy!" at the top of his surprising voice. At the sound a lamp appeared in a window on the first floor and Campion followed its passage through what seemed to be endless galleries, the faint beams flickering through window after window until they disappeared in the darkness directly above their heads. A moment later the doors began to rattle and after a considerable delay wherein bolt after bolt was drawn they clattered open and an elderly woman appeared holding a paraffin lamp above her head. It was a Dickensian greeting. She did not smile or speak but stood back respectfully to allow them to pass. The doctor strode into the darkness beyond the circle of light and Campion followed, very conscious that it was after midnight.

The old man clapped his hands, a sultanic gesture curiously in keeping with his personality.

"Whisky and water in the dining room, and go down to the cottage and tell George I want him."

"He'll be in bed, sir."

"Of course he will, if he's a sensible feller. Tell him to put on a coat and a pair of trousers and meet me in the conservatory. I want to show this gentleman some roses."

"Yes, sir." She set down the lamp and went off into the darkness.

Campion demurred feebly.

"Oh, no trouble at all." The old man sounded like a stage schoolboy out of a Victorian revival. Campion thought he had never seen anyone so gloriously happy. "We're up at all hours of the day and night here. A doctor's life, you know."

He took up the lamp and Campion discovered that the thing he had been half leaning against under the impression that it was the banister head was a full-sized stuffed wolf. He glanced round him and got a fleeting impression of narrow walls covered with cases of stuffed birds.

"Do any shooting?" said his host over his shoulder. "A hundred and thirty-two heads, my own gun, walking alone last October. Not bad, eh? Ten hours of it and then the night bell till dawn. I'm seventy-nine and don't feel it."

He spoke boastingly but obviously without exaggeration.

They went into a small overcrowded dining room whose red-and-gold paper was almost hidden behind execrable sporting oils and yet more cases of wild fowl. The old doctor looked less extraordinary in these surroundings. He stood on the hearth rug, so much a part of his own world that it was his visitor who felt himself the oddity. His host stared at him with professional interest and Campion, who wondered what he was thinking, was suddenly enlightened.

"Can you fight?"

The younger man was surprised to find himself nettled.

"I'll take on anyone of my weight," he said.

"Ha! Go through the war?"

"Only the last six months. I was born in nineteen hundred."

"Good!" The last word was spoken with tremendous emphasis, and there was a pause. Dr. Bouverie looked sad. "I was considered old even then," he said regretfully.

The woman returned with the decanter and glasses.

"George is waiting, sir."

"Very well. You can go to bed now."

"Yes, sir." There was no expression at all in her voice.

Campion sipped his drink and thought of Chloe Pye, Sutane and the newspapers. He supposed he had driven the old man five miles at the most. It seemed a little space to separate such different worlds.

"Now these roses"—the doctor set down his glass—"they're extraordinary. There's not a rose to touch 'em for exhibition, unless it's the old Frau Karl Druschki. They've got the body. That's the important thing in an exhibition rose—body."

He led his guest through a drawing room which was chilly in spite of the heat of the night and appeared from the fleeting glimpse Campion got of it to be literally in rags.

The conservatory was a magnificent sight, however. It was overcrowded but the show of begonias and gloxinias was astonishing. A tall thin depressed figure in a felt hat and a raincoat awaited them with a hurricane lantern.

"Ready, George?" the doctor sounded as if he were going into battle.

"Yes, sir."

They came out into a dark garden which felt and smelled like a paradise but which was, unfortunately, completely invisible. The roses were found, golden-yellow blossoms fading into apricot on long, carefully disbudded stems. Little white canvas hoods on stakes protected them from the weather.

The two old men, the doctor and the gardener, pored over them like mothers. Their enthusiasm was both tender and devout. The doctor put his blunt fingers under a blossom and tilted it gently.

"Isn't she lovely?" he said softly. "Good night, my little dear."

He rearranged the canvas hat.

"You won't see a better rose than that in the county," he boasted.

As they walked back to the dark house Campion took his courage in his hands.

"I suppose it was hitting her head on the road that really killed that woman?" he said.

"Yes, the skull was fractured. You noticed that, did you?" The old doctor sounded pleased. "What I don't see is how she came to fall, don't you know, unless she threw herself over. That's a matter which must be cleared up, because of the inquest. I—ah—I didn't notice any reek of alcohol."

"No, she wasn't drunk," said Campion slowly. "Not technically."

To his surprise the old man followed his thought.

"Hysterical type?" he enquired.

Campion saw his chance. "There's not a great deal of difference between hysteria and what is usually called temperament, don't you think?" he said.

The old man was silent. He was considering.

"I haven't had much experience of temperament," he said at last, admitting it as though it were a fault. "I attended an opera singer once, close on fifty years ago. She was insane. I didn't like that bathing dress this evening. Had she been walking about like that all day? We're forty miles from the sea."

Campion launched into a careful explanation. He did his best to convey Chloe Pye in elementary terms. She was vain, he said; hard-working, physically active, and anxious to appear younger than she was.

"So you see," he finished, "she might easily have climbed the parapet and waved to Sutane, who was looking at the road and did not see her."

"Yes." The old man sounded interested. "Yes. I see that. But if she was sufficiently active to get up there, and was, as you say, practically an acrobat, why should she have fallen?"

It was a reasonable argument but without inspiration. Campion felt sure he must be on the Bench.

"Something may have frightened her," he said lamely. "Her foot may have slipped on the crushed stems."

"But there were no crushed stems," said Dr. Bouverie. "I looked for them. Still, I thank you for your information. The woman isn't so incomprehensible to me now. I shall go over her carefully in the morning. I may find something to account for sudden faintness, or something like that. It's been extremely civil of you. Come and see my roses in the daylight."

He conducted his guest to the door and Campion, stumbling against something in the dark, felt a warm muzzle in his hand. The dog had made no sound from the beginning and he realised suddenly that the two servants had been the same—silent, utterly obedient, and yet friendly and content.

His host stood on the porch, the lamp raised.

"Good night!" he shouted. "Good night!"

Campion drove slowly back to White Walls. The clouds had shifted and the starlight shed a faint radiance on the wide flat fields about him. It was eerily quiet and very much the country. He felt he was travelling back a hundred years.

In the lane he found the doctor's car parked at the side to await the chauffeur's ministrations in the early morning. He drew up and, getting out, raised the bonnet of the Fiat. He found the main lead from the distributor to the coil and connected it again. When he touched the starter the engine turned over obediently.

He got back into the Lagonda and went on. As he saw the graceful white house rising up against the sky he hesitated for a moment, half inclined to turn back and make for London.

A few hours before he had fully intended to pass quietly out of the lives of the two Sutanes as speedily as possible. He never remembered feeling such curious mental alarm and the experience had not been pleasant. Now, however, a situation had arisen which made his presence necessary, a situation wherein to leave was to run away from something more concrete, and therefore less terrible but more important, than his own emotions.

Mr. Campion was not a medical man, but his experience of violent death was considerable. Dr. Bouverie, he knew, had seen many car accidents in the last twenty years, so many that he was used to them, and that therefore there was a real chance that a certain vital and obvious fact might escape him.

What Campion had noticed when he had first bent over the body of Chloe Pye, and what he had taken great pains to assure himself had so far escaped the doctor, was the remarkable absence of blood in the road.

Since blood does not circulate once the heart which pumps it has stopped, it seemed to Mr. Campion that there were a hundred chances to one that Chloe Pye had been dead for something under fifteen minutes when her body had left the bridge. In that case, of course, she had neither fallen nor jumped from it.

As he drove into the yard he wondered how she had been killed and who had thrown her under the Bentley. He also wondered if she had deserved to die.

What it did not occur to him to consider was his own unprecedented behaviour in the matter.

Chapter 5

The hall door stood open and a wide shaft of yellow light zigzagged down the shallow steps to the drive. An atmosphere of excitement, of catastrophe of the more bearable kind, enveloped the whole building. It floated out into the night with the sound of hurrying footsteps on the polished stairs and escaped from the windows with scattered voices and half-heard scraps of conversation.

Campion paused at the foot of the steps, his thin, loosely knit figure casting a long shadow across the path. The sky was clearing rapidly and a battered moon appeared hanging low over the elm avenue on the other side of the lane. It was quite light in the garden. Over on the lawn the deck chair which Uncle William had set up that morning for Chloe Pye looked like a small dark boat on a moonlit sea.

A thought occurred to Campion and he turned down around the side of the house, taking the path to the lake. As he passed the french windows of the lounge he heard Sutane's voice, sharp with nerves, answering somebody.

"My dear chap, how should I know? I've no experience of the woman."

"All right, all right, don't go off the deep end." Poyser sounded exasperated. "I only thought we ought to make up our minds."

Mr. Campion walked quietly away. It always happened, he reflected. As soon as a violent death occurred there was always some authoritative soul on hand to come forward with the inevitable "plan of campaign," entirely disregarding the fact that there has arisen the one situation which is still taken seriously by the community at large.

Love or money can conceal every other disturbing occurrence to be met with in civil life, but sudden death is inviolate. A body is the one thing that cannot be explained away.

As he walked alone between the yew hedges it occurred to him that in an age when all the deepest emotions can be successfully laughed out of existence by any decently educated person, the sanctity and importance of sudden death was a comforting and salutary thing, a last little rock, as it were, in the shifty sands of one's own standards and desires.

He came out of the shelter of the hedge and walked down an incline to the wide stone margin of the water. The little lake was really no more than a large kidney-shaped pond formed by widening the natural bed of a small brook which ran through the grounds. A past owner had planted willows round the stone pavement and the Sutanes had contributed a bathing pavilion.

He found what he was looking for immediately. On the east bank, in front of the pavilion, there was a wide paved platform about twenty feet square, and upon it stood the small black gramophone, the lid still raised.

In the daylight the place had an overgrown, partially neglected air which was not unattractive. Sutane was not extraordinarily wealthy and two good men and a boy provided all the labour he could reasonably afford for the grounds. In the moonlight, however, all the old formal glory conceived by the original designers was magically restored and Campion made his way to the gramophone through a world of ordered grandeur as visionary as any other ghost of the past.

He stood for some little time at the foot of the low step to the platform and looked at the surface closely. It was as smooth and dry as tarmac and about as informative.

Having convinced himself on this point, he approached the gramophone and squatted down on his heels beside it. The record had played until the automatic stop had silenced it. Campion read the title, " 'Étude,' Vowis," a silly little piece of experimental trivia barely worth recording. If Chloe Pye had danced to that formless bagatelle he took off his hat to her.

He glanced into the record case and saw that two discs were missing. Looking round for the second, he found it lying on its grey envelope in the patch of shadow cast by the gramophone lid. Its discovery interested him considerably. It was cracked, not in a clean break, but in small pieces, as though a heavy foot had been planted directly upon it. The label was still legible, and he made it out with the aid of his torch. It was Falla's "Love, the Magician," Part 1. Part 2 was presumably on the other side, therefore, and an idea occurred to him. Using a handkerchief to protect his fingers, he raised the record still on the machine. As he had suspected, the third and final part of the Falla piece was on the underside. He raised his eyebrows. Trivial pieces like the "Étude" were frequently used, he knew, as fill-ups when a serious work did not divide into an even number of records, but if Miss Pye had been dancing to the Falla, which was a reasonable thing to do, he wondered why she had played through the "Étude" at all, and where she had been when the automatic stop had silenced its delicate inanities.

He sat back on his heels and looked about him for the other thing he had come to find. A glance told him that his second quest was not to be so simple as the first had been. Scarlet silk, so evident in sunlight, is apt to melt into a black shadow in the tricksy light of the moon. However, Chloe Pye had been wearing a red silk wrap-round skirt to her ankles last time he had seen her alive, and she had certainly not been wearing it as she lay so tragically mangled on the grass verge in the lane. He wondered when and where she had lost it.

It was at this point in his investigations, as he sat silent in moonlight so bright that it seemed strange that it should not be warm, that he first noticed that he was not alone in the garden. Something was moving over the dry wiry grass under the oaks behind the pavilion. He thought it was a dog at first, padding backwards and forwards beneath the trees, until a certain rhythmic regularity in the sounds made him change his mind.

Not wishing to be discovered examining the gramophone, he rose cautiously and stepped onto the clipped turf of the path. The shadow of the pavilion sheltered him and he stood there quietly staring in front of him.

Just behind the bathing house there was a natural clearance between the trees. A wide strip of mossy grass which had been allowed to grow wild ran down to the ivy-grown relics of an artificial ruin. This structure had never been an unqualified success, even in its Georgian heyday, and it now remained a record of the failure of an uninspired British workman to reproduce the half-remembered majesty which his employer had seen upon the Grand Tour. The movement came from the shadow below this ruin, and between Campion and itself the moonlight lay in patches upon the grass, making the turf look like the spread-out skin of some enormous piebald animal.

As Campion watched he could hear the steps distinctly, a slow measured rustling in the darkness.

It occurred to him with something of a shock that it must be two o'clock in the morning at least. The very lateness of the hour seemed to excuse an open investigation and he was just about to walk out of his refuge when a light wind sprang up in the trees, swinging the shadows like clothes on a line.

Mr. Campion stood perfectly still. Among the shadows he had seen a figure. As he stared it emerged into the light. It was a girl and she so startled him that he did not recognise her immediately. She was dressed in a flimsy nightgown with some sort of chiffon coat with floating sleeves over it, and she was dancing.

Compared with the professional standard of Sutane and Slippers her display was painfully amateur. Her movements were not particularly graceful and were without design. But there was an intensity of feeling, an urge for self-expression, which was primitive and impressive.

She was intent upon her dance, which appeared to have some half-considered ritual as a motif. Campion watched her running backwards and forwards, bowing and wheeling, her arms now above her head, now shoulder-high. He recognised Eve Sutane and was unaccountably relieved. Out here in the warm night air, her draperies fluttering round her and her body taut with emotion, she was a very different creature from the sullen, dull-eyed girl of the morning.

He remembered that she was probably about seventeen. In common with all good neo-Georgians, he had done his share of reading on the one great study of that barren age and knew a little about the psychology of sex. It occurred to him irrelevantly that whereas a Victorian would have seen in this display either an exhibition of sweet, spiritual sensibility or a girl catching her death of cold, he himself received a confused and un-comfortable impression of sap-risings, undiscovered desires and primitive exhibitionism.

He was considering which aspect was really the most satisfactory in the long run when the unusual circumstances attending this particular mani-festation of youth returned to his mind with a shock. He wondered if she could possibly not have heard of Chloe Pye's death, and, walking round behind the pavilion, he coughed discreetly.

She came sweeping past him as he wandered down the path. At first she evidently intended to ignore him but changed her mind and re-turned. She looked almost beautiful in her excitement. Her eyes were shining and her mouth, wide and sensitive like her brother's, twisted into a smile whenever she forgot to control it.

"What are you doing here? I thought you'd gone to the doctor's."

Her manner was gauche to the point of brusqueness.

Campion eyed her quizzically.

"He was an exhausting old gentleman. I thought I'd cool off before going in."

"Have you been down here long?"

"No," he lied politely. "I've just arrived. Why?"

She laughed and he could not tell if she was merely relieved or really was as exultant as she sounded.

"We don't like sneaking, snoopy people," she said. "We hate them. Good night."

Turning from him, she ran on down the path, happiness in every spring of her body and in the tread of her bare white feet.

Campion made certain that she had gone into the house before he returned to the clearing. There he found Chloe Pye's red silk skirt spread out like a prayer mat. Eve had been dancing upon it.

Chapter 6

"CHLOE PYE DIES TRAGICALLY

"BRILLIANT YOUNG DANCER MEETS WITH FATAL MISHAP

"At a little after ten o'clock this evening Miss Chloe Pye, who only last night had made a successful return to the London stage in The Buffer at the Argosy Theatre, fell to her death beneath the wheels of an on-coming motorcar. The accident happened at the country estate of Mr. Jimmy Sutane, where she had been spending the week-end. Mr. Sutane, *who was driving the car when the fatal incident occurred, is prostrated with shock.*

"And I don't see we can say any more than that, do you? It gives it to them in one. Of course it'll bring them down on us like a cloud of hornets. Still, they'd come anyway."

Dick Poyser looked up from the bureau in the living room and spoke with his fountain pen hovering. Sock, who was lounging behind him, his hands in his pockets, shrugged his shoulders restlessly.

"You can cross out 'The Buffer at the Argosy Theatre,'" he said. "They won't print that. Oh, all right, old man, all right. I'll have it roneo'd and take it round if it'll please you. Some of 'em may even use it. But we're not going to get away with this easily, believe me."

Poyser threw down his pen, letting the ink splatter over the finished page.

"Who in blazes said we were?" he demanded, his voice shrill with irritation. "When you've been in this business as long as I have you'll know that if you give a journalist a bit of copy all ready to send down the chances are he'll use it, or at least a bit of it, rather than take the trouble of working the sentences out for himself. You can't dictate to 'em, but you can sometimes persuade 'em, if they don't know you're doing it.

"Besides," he added with great seriousness, "it's all a question of time."

"You're telling me," said Sock grimly as he took up the written sheet.

"Oh, for God's sake!" said Sutane.

He was sitting in an armchair over a fire which Miss Finbrough was coaxing to life. Linda stood forlornly behind his chair and Uncle William sat blinking quietly in a corner, his round pink face a little bluish and his podgy hands folded on his stomach.

The two men by the bureau gave up their wrangling instantly.

"You go to bed, Jimmy," said Poyser. "You've got to keep fit, old man."

Sock looked up, his young face lightened by a wry smile.

"The whole outfit depends on you, James," he said regretfully.

"I'll take him up," murmured Miss Finbrough as though she had been speaking of a child.

Sutane looked round at them all, a flicker of genuine amusement appearing on his sad, intelligent face.

"What d'you think I am?" he said. "Go away, Finny. I'm perfectly capable of looking after myself. I'm not mental. I may be a dancer of genius, I may make a few thousands a year, I may have just killed Chloe Pye, poor girl, but I'm not a goddam kid. Oh, hullo, Campion, how did you get on with the doctor?"

It was astonishing how his pleasant nervous voice could take on such authority. They were all quiet as Campion came in.

The thin young man smiled at them faintly and gave a guarded account of his visit.

"He's not an unattractive old boy," he said finally, trying to sound reassuring. "It was the bathing dress that got him down. Once I'd put it to him that we were all perfectly normal but busy people he began to be much more tractable. He'll perform an autopsy, of course. I—er—I don't think he's quite so set on suicide as he was."

"Good man," said Sutane. "Good man. I appreciate that, Campion. Sock told me about the car. That was amusing. I shouldn't have thought of it on the spur of the moment. You'll have to stay and see us through, you know."

"What's that? What's that?"

Poyser was interested and, much to Mr. Campion's embarrassment, his little subterfuge was explained in detail. He stood by, looking at them all uncomfortably while they discussed the mechanics of the move with schoolboyish satisfaction. It occurred to him then what a pack of children they were, all of them. Their enthusiasm, their eagerness to escape from the main shocking reality, their tendency to make everything more bearable by dramatising it; it was the very stuff of youth.

He glanced at Linda. She alone had reacted to the tragedy in a way he fully understood. As she stood behind Sutane's chair, her arms hanging limply at her sides and her face pallid, she looked exhausted, ready to sleep on her feet.

Sock went out into the hall and came back in a disreputable leather coat. He was as brisk as if he had only just risen.

"Well, I'll get going then," he said. "I'll trot round and see everybody I can find. We can't possibly keep it quiet. We all know that, don't we? But I'll put in a delicate word here and there and I'll come down in the morning and meet the boys when they turn up. You go to bed, Jimmy. Leave it all to us."

He went out and Sutane turned in his chair and glanced at his wife.

"Mercer had better put up these two," he said. "Where is he?"

"I left him in the little music room," said Uncle William, coming to life with a jerk. "I'll go and find him."

He padded across the room and came back with the composer. Mercer glanced round gravely.

"I knew I couldn't do anything," he said, "so I hung about in there to be out of the way. Was that right? What happened? Police gone away?"

"Yes." Dick Poyser closed the bureau. "Yes. They'll be back in the morning. There'll be an inquest. You'll have to attend that, Jimmy. Would you like to cut out the show for a day or so? Let Konrad take it."

Sutane frowned. "What do you think . . ." he began unhappily.

Linda interrupted. "It's three o'clock in the morning," she said. "He must sleep. Talk tomorrow."

Miss Finbrough sniffed.

"There's a lot to be said for that," she put in so sharply that Campion looked at her. She was resentful, he noticed, and it occurred to him that she did not like any other woman to give a thought to Sutane's physical well-being, a province which she evidently thought entirely her own.

"Where is Konrad?" Campion enquired.

"Oh, he went to bed." Poyser laughed as he spoke. "Konnie has to have his sleep, whoever gets killed. He's got his rally to think of."

Linda turned to Mercer.

"I wondered if you'd put up Uncle William and Mr. Campion?" she said. "They didn't intend to stay, you see, and there isn't a room ready."

"Yes. I'd like that." Mercer spoke as though the suggestion had been put forward as a measure to spare him any loneliness. "We'll push off fairly soon, shall we? Getting late."

"Good idea," agreed Uncle William. "Think better in the morning." He took Linda's hand and held it. "A terrible thing, my dear," he said. "A terrible thing. But we're here, you know, Campion and I. Do anything we can. You can rely on us. Try to sleep and forget all about it until the morning. Things never seem so bad in the morning. I've noticed that all my life."

It was not an inspired speech but its intention was unmistakable. Linda smiled at him gratefully.

"You're a dear," she said. "Good night."

Mercer looked round him.

"I had a coat . . ." he began. "No, that's right, I didn't. I'd better take one out of the cloakroom, hadn't I, Jimmy? It gets damned cold at this time of night."

He went out to pick up the borrowed garment and Poyser giggled. Like many very small men he had a curious rattling laugh with a gurgle in it which is usually associated with childhood.

"What a bloke!" he murmured. "Well, I shall sleep for a couple of hours and go up in the dawn."

Uncle William touched Campion's sleeve.

"Come on, my boy," he said. "Pick up our host in the hall, don't you know."

The three men did not talk as they strode through the dark garden, but when they crossed the bridge Mercer halted and demanded to be shown the scene of the accident. Campion glanced at him curiously. He made an odd figure in the half-light, his top-heavy shoulders straining the seams of Sutane's overcoat; while his attitude towards the affair, which was that of a disinterested but privileged spectator, was disconcerting.

"It must have been suicide," he pronounced judicially when Campion had given him the bare facts. "I shan't say so, of course, if they don't want it known, but any fool can see it must have been intentional. An extraordinary thing for a woman to do. Fancy going to a stranger's house for the week-end and calmly breaking her neck there, making trouble and inconvenience for everyone. Still, I'm not surprised. I thought she was definitely queer in the living room this morning."

He moved on and they followed him willingly. It was chilly in the early dawn and Uncle William's teeth were chattering, while Mr. Campion, for private reasons, had no desire to talk about Chloe Pye's death.

Mercer drawled on. His articulation was maddeningly bad and he appeared to be thinking aloud.

"The woman wasn't even a dancer," he said. "I saw her once. No talent at all. Poyser told me she was thundering awful on Saturday night. Why did Jimmy put her in the show? Do you know?"

He did not seem to expect an answer but went mumbling on until they came through an immense kitchen garden to his house on the edge of the estate.

Campion was aware of a long narrow brick front silhouetted against the sky, and then Mercer kicked open the door and they passed through a stone-flagged, oak-beamed hall into a vast studio or music room which took up at least half of the entire building.

Campion's first impression of that extraordinary room was of incongruity; his second, of extravagance. A remarkable wireless set took up the whole of one wall. It was an extraordinary contraption which looked as if it might have been designed by Heath Robinson in the first place and afterwards allowed to grow, in Virginia-creeper fashion, over everything which happened to lie in its path.

A huge concert Steinway took up the centre of the floor and there was one superb armchair.

The rest of the room was pure chaos. Piles of dusty papers lurked in every corner, books lay about in wild disorder, and the exquisite Cantonese shawl which covered the wall above the fireplace was dirty and had been badly scorched.

Mercer moved a heap of papers and wireless parts from a side table and produced a tray with a tantalus and glasses from beneath them.

"Help yourselves. I don't drink at night," he said and threw himself into the armchair, only to get out of it again at once. "This damned coat is tight," he said, peeling it off and throwing it on the floor as if he had a grievance against it. "I hate tight clothes."

Uncle William helped himself to a stiff drink and insisted on mixing one for Mr. Campion. They stood leaning on the mantelshelf while Mercer lounged in the chair and regarded them, his light eyes sombre.

"It happens very soon—death, I mean," he said solemnly. "There was a woman we didn't know and didn't particularly want to know. She was crude and noisy and blasted ugly, and now she's dead. Where's she gone?"

Uncle William coughed into his glass and his plump pink face was embarrassed.

"Mustn't be morbid, my boy," he said. "Very sad and all that. Shockin'. Got to face it."

Mercer looked surprised.

"Good God, you don't believe all that, do you?" he said with a superiority which was somehow adolescent but none the less irritating because of that. "Sad . . . shocking . . . they're just words. I was thinking as we came along tonight how extraordinary it was that she should have gone so quickly. You'd think some of her would remain. That awful teetering laugh, for instance. I mean, you'd think the things that made her the highly coloured piece she was would disappear one at a time at least, not all go out bang, like turning out a switch. It's a curious thing, that. I never noticed it before."

Uncle William stared at him as if he suspected his sanity.

"My dear feller, get to bed," he said. "You're shaken up. We all are."

"Shaken up?" Mercer was indignant. "I'm onto an idea. I'm not shaken up. Why should I be? I didn't even know the woman and if I had I probably shouldn't have liked her. Her death doesn't affect me at all. It's nothing to do with me. It's nothing to do with any of us. I think Jimmy's making too much fuss about it. After all, she only fell under his car. He couldn't help hitting her. Good heavens, there's nothing morbid about me! I was only thinking of the facts of the case. This morning she was a howling nuisance about the house, so I couldn't help noticing her peculiarities. Now all that has just gone. Where to? There's an idea in it. See what I mean? It's a concrete idea. You could work it into a number, even. 'Out in the dark, where my arms cannot hold you.' See the sort of thing. That's how these songs get written. Something occurs to one and starts a train of thought."

"I should like to go to bed," said Uncle William heavily.

Mercer frowned. "I think you're right," he said regretfully. "One must sleep. It's a frightful waste of time. A stupidly arranged business. Why not let us live half the time and keep it light always instead of this mucking about, going to bed and getting up again and shaving. It's waste."

Campion eyed him narrowly, but there was no trace of affectation in his heavy dark face. He was obviously perfectly sincere. The belief in an omnipotent intelligence which his argument implied was so unexpected and out of character that Campion was at a loss to account for it until the simple truth dawned upon him. Mercer did not think at all in the accepted sense of the word. Ideas occurred to him and engendered other ideas. But the process which linked any two of them was a dark procession taking place in some subconscious part of the brain.

That his efforts at constructive thought were childish was made apparent by his next remark.

"There's no really good rhyme to 'hold you' except 'enfold you,' is there?" he said. "It's a rotten language. I must get Peter Dill onto the lyric. I think I may do that song. It's got possibilities, all that 'where are you' business, 'so near and yet so far away.'"

"That fellow's insane," said Uncle William as the door of the large bedroom which they were to share closed behind them some minutes later. "Hope the sheets are aired."

There were three beds in the large old-fashioned room, and he opened them all solemnly before giving a considered opinion on the two best. Mercer had indicated the door of their room casually as they came up-stairs and it was Uncle William who had demanded and finally obtained pyjamas for them both.

He sat up in the bed he had chosen, his white curls brushed upward and his face as pink and shining as a newly bathed cherub's, and sniffed.

"Money," he said as though he detected its odour. "Lots of money but no decent spendin'. Feller probably never considers his bank book one way or another. Your bed comfortable?"

"Very," said Campion absently. "It's a patent of some sort."

"Most likely." Uncle William did not sound approving. "These wealthy, careless fellers get all kinds of things wished on 'em. Salesmen come round to the door."

"Not with beds, surely?"

"With anythin'." The old man spoke with the unanswerable conviction of one who knows. "They get at the servants if they can't find anyone better. There are servants here, I suppose?"

"Sure to be." Campion spoke mechanically, his mind occupied by the delicate problem of Chloe Pye's death and his own attitude concerning it. He had never withheld vital information before and his sudden de-cision to depart from his usual impartiality bothered him considerably. After all, a woman had been killed, and presumably by one of the people with whom he had spent the day. It was a situation commanding thought.

Uncle William was in talkative mood, however.

"There may not be any servants. You never know with a feller like Mercer," he remarked. "D'you know what I think about him, Campion? He's the kind of feller who ought to be hangin' round sleepin' on peo-ple's floors, pickin' up scraps of comfort, lookin' after himself like a Lon-don pigeon, but, by means of a trick, don't you know, by means of a trick he's made a fortune out of those footlin' songs of his and it's put the feller out of gear. I've met men like him before, but never one with money."

Mr. Campion, whose attention had been captured only midway through this harangue, looked up.

"I think you're right," he agreed. "He hasn't got much to spend his money on except himself."

"Exactly." Uncle William was becoming excited. "And he's a chap who doesn't want much. He's always thinkin' about gettin' his own way and of course he gets it. He's not a feller who wants diamonds."

"Diamonds?"

"Well, elephants, then. Figure of speech."

"Oh, I see." Mr. Campion remained thoughtful. "His songs are very successful," he said.

"Sensuous twaddle," declared Uncle William with forthright disgust. "I'm not musical but I know rubbish when I hear it. Still, it seems to go down. Anythin' too silly to be said can be sung. A German feller pointed that out."

Campion shook his head.

"All Mercer's stuff has something," he said. "They're not merely rot for rot's sake. There's genuine feeling there, however horribly expressed. That's what makes some of those songs so unbearably embarrassing."

Uncle William brightened.

"Like a common feller tellin' you his troubles and shockin' you because they remind you of your own sacred thoughts about some magnificent little woman?" he said unexpectedly. "I've noticed that, you know, but never brought myself to mention it. Oh, well, we're all snobs at heart."

The discovery seemed to please him. He chuckled.

"The extraordinary thing is that the feller knows nothin' about women," he went on. "It's a joke in the theatre, you know. Sutane's known him since he first started writin'. Never been in love in his life. Never even bought a woman a meal. Treats 'em gently but isn't interested in 'em, as though they were pet rabbits or something. Must get it all out of his own head. I remember my cousin Andrew—the one who made all the trouble—telling me a long rigmarole all about that one evening. 'Wish fulfilment,' he called it; never forgotten the word. It sounded unhealthy to me and I told him so. But since I've come out into the world, as it were, I've noticed there's something in it. Mercer's a thoughtless chap. Quite extraordinarily selfish. There must be several bedrooms in this house, but he lumps us in here together because he's too lazy to point out another."

Campion did not reply. Uncle William turned off the light over his bed and settled himself. But he was still not inclined to sleep.

"Suicide or accident," he murmured, adhering to his philosophical vein, which was new to Campion. "What does it matter? Don't want to be hard but I feel she's better dead. Age wouldn't suit her book at all, would it?"

Campion remained silent but his companion was not to be quelled.

"Campion . . ." His voice sounded insistent in the greyness.

"Yes?"

"We've landed ourselves among a funny crowd, my boy, haven't we? A damned curious bandarloggy lot. Nothin' like Cambridge."

Campion relinquished his own thoughts regretfully.

"Bandarloggy?" he enquired.

"Indian," explained Uncle William. "Means the 'monkey people.' Got it out of the Jungle Books," he added modestly. "Got all my India for my memoirs out of the Jungle Books and *Around the World in Eighty Days*. Tried *Kim* but couldn't get along with it. Funny thing about those memoirs, Campion. If I'd done the decent thing and stuck to the truth no one would have read 'em. As it was, they laughed at me and I made a small fortune. I'm not a chump, you know. I can see how that happened. Better be a clown than a pompous old fool. Mother wouldn't have realised that, though, and she was a clever woman, God rest her soul. I stumbled on it and it made me. I say, shall I have to go to the inquest on Miss Pye? Haven't attended an inquest since that silly affair of Andrew's. Don't know if I want to."

Campion stirred. "Where were you all the evening?"

"Me?" Uncle William laughed. "I was all right. No use sounding like a policeman. I didn't see the woman after dinner. I'm no witness. I was in the little music room behind the dining room, listening to Mercer. I don't mind his strumming when there's no words. It's these fellers bleating out their vulgar private thoughts who make me uncomfortable."

Campion raised himself on one elbow.

"You were listening to Mercer play all the evening, from after dinner till when?"

"Until Linda came in looking like a ghost and told us all about the accident."

"I see. Where was Konrad?"

"That little runt?" The old man was contemptuous. "He says he left Miss Pye by the lake and came upstairs to his bedroom, which is over the room we were using. He lay there with the window open, listenin' —or so he says."

He turned over and hunched the clothes round him.

"Don't wish to be unkind," he said over his shoulder, "but if I was a woman one look at that feller would make me want to cut my throat."

Chapter 7

Sutane lay on his stomach on a felt-covered table basking in the ultraviolet rays of the lamp which Miss Finbrough tended as though it had been a sacred fire.

He was leaning on his elbows, and his face, which was turned towards the assembled gathering, wore a gloomy and introspective expression.

The room was large and very light, and the pink Empire chintz curtains swayed lazily in the summer air. Outside, the treetops were green and gold, and small puffs of white cloud sailed by in an infinite sky.

Uncle William, a trifle embarrassed by the unconventional aspects of this morning audience, sat on the window ledge with Campion lounging at his side. Sock Petrie leant back in a big basket chair. His eyes were hollow with lack of sleep but he watched Sutane unswervingly.

Mercer sat in an armchair also, his hands folded in his lap. He looked profoundly bored.

Benny Konrad was the only other person in the room. Clad in shorts and a sweater, he was lying on his back upon the floor, raising one leg after the other with monotonous regularity. The silence had lasted some minutes and now the only sound was his deep breathing—one, two, three, in; one, two, three, out; one two three, in—and so on, it seemed, forever. His petulant young face was red from his exertions and one strand of his soft yellow hair lay damply on a forehead as clear and modelled as a girl's.

"Too hot," said Sutane suddenly, and Miss Finbrough laid a scarlet hand upon his skin.

"Nearly over now," she murmured soothingly. "I'll go on to your legs. Two more minutes."

"Inquest this afternoon at the pub, then," Sock remarked. "That cuts out the *Swing Over* rehearsal for you, James, but I don't see how it can be helped. They'll keep to the chorus, I suppose. What was Maisie like yesterday?"

Sutane frowned. Miss Finbrough had discarded her lamp and was exploring the small of his back with fingers like little steel hammers.

"Oh, all right, you know, all right." He spoke without enthusiasm.

"I thought she was frightful," said Konrad brightly. "Up—down, up—down, up—down . . ."

Sock gave him a long speculative glance.

"Comfort Konrad," he said gravely. "It suits you. You ought to adopt it. You've got a distinct streak of the Puritan, haven't you, Konnie?"

"I don't know, I'm sure." Konrad spoke carelessly but there was a dissatisfied expression on his face, and he looked like a girl who is not quite certain if she has been complimented or attacked. He went on with his exercises.

"The Press is friendly, then?" Sutane was clearly unaware that he had asked the question three times already.

"They're just as they always are, bless 'em." Sock spread out his long, unexpectedly fine hands. "More interested than usual, of course. It's a funny thing," he added with conscious naïveté, "that I should have spent the best part of my life getting you into the news and the last few months keeping you out of it."

Sutane allowed a brief grin to twist his mouth.

"Yes, it's a two-edged sword," he said and put his head down on his arms because Miss Finbrough had decided to ministrate to his neck muscles.

Suddenly, however, he looked up, shrugging away from her vigorous fingers.

"Oh, I got an invitation card," he said, "last night. I forgot all about it. It's in the inside pocket of my jacket, Sock, old boy. In the bedroom next door, if you don't mind."

Sock grimaced as he got up.

"You shouldn't have gone," he said. "It doesn't seem so frightfully important now, though. Who did you get it from?"

"Councillor Baynes of Merton Road." Sutane mimicked the arch refinement of his erstwhile guest. "He was just delighted to oblige. Oh, dear me, yes indeed. Just delighted. He kept everything, every scrap of paper that ever came into the house, and if I'd just wait a moment he was sure he could produce the ticket. Yes, there it was, just as it came to him, envelope and all. Oh, dear, dear, dear, wasn't that lucky? Such a pleasant afternoon. Such a distinguished house. Could he ask me to wait and see Mrs. B.? She was just changing her dress."

It was a flawless caricature, as broad as it was cruel. The councillor was re-created before their eyes. Almost they saw his moustache quiver.

Everyone laughed except Konrad, who protested primly that unconscious vulgarity was too depressing.

When Sock returned with the invitation card Sutane left his couch to join the group round the publicity man, and Campion caught a glimpse of Miss Finbrough's face over his shoulder. She was furious. Her bright blue eyes were hard and her lips compressed. Sutane ignored her.

"Look, Campion," he insisted. "Does it tell you anything at all?"

The young man in the horn-rimmed spectacles eyed the proffered papers dubiously. Neither the card nor the envelope was in any way remarkable. They were both of the type somewhat mysteriously called "cream laid," and either could have been purchased from any stationer's in the kingdom. The blanks on the printed "At Home" card had been filled in by hand in green ink and the calligraphy was a fair specimen of the standard hand taught in the schools of some years ago. It was round, flowing and astonishingly devoid of character. The printed R.S.V.P. had been cancelled with a single stroke and the postmark on the envelope was the familiar but unhelpful Central London stamp.

"I'm afraid there's only the handwriting," he said at last. "The odd thing is it doesn't seem to be disguised at all. No one recognises it, of course?"

"No one I know," said Sock decisively. "I know several people who write rather like it but none exact."

Konrad giggled. "It's a woman's," he said. "One of your pretty ladies is turning nasty, Sutane."

Jimmy turned and regarded him coldly for a moment, and presently Konrad got down to his exercises again, his face hot and his eyes sulky.

Sock continued to study the card.

"The green ink does make me think of a woman. I don't know why," he admitted. "Although the whole silly trick was a bit feminine, wasn't it? Know anyone who writes like this, James?"

Although Sutane was nude, save for a face towel, his dignity was unshaken.

"If I did I should be talking to the girl," he said stiffly.

"If she was alive," murmured Konrad from the floor.

The words shot glibly from his tongue, almost, it seemed, by accident. He became pale with alarm as soon as he had spoken and went on with his training at redoubled speed.

"What the hell do you mean by that?" Sock swung round upon him, outraged. "Chloe's handwriting was like Chinese algebra—you know that as well as I do. What are you getting at?"

Konrad did not answer. The colour had returned to his face. He appeared to be deaf as he swung backwards and forwards.

"Have you seen Chloe's handwriting or not?" Sock persisted.

"Perhaps I wasn't talking about Chloe Pye," Benny Konrad muttered without looking at his persecutor.

"Who else then?" Sock was inclined to shout. "Sit up and stop dithering. Sit up, damn you!"

The slender figure on the floor came slowly and gracefully upright, his bare legs spread out in front of him. He looked meek and a trifle hurt and had adopted a sort of maidenly dignity which was infuriating.

"Well?"

"What were you hinting at?"

"I wasn't hinting at anything." Konrad wriggled. "I'm not that kind of person. I wish you'd let me get on with my work, Petrie. I've got to keep right, you know."

"Keep right!" Sock gurled over the words. "Look here, Konnie, what did you imply just now when you suggested that the woman who wrote these invitations might be dead?"

Konrad bridled. "I'm not going to sit here and be shouted at," he said. "I didn't imply anything. A remark came into my head and I let it out."

"Through the blowhole!" The untidy young man was beside himself. "You ought to have your head tied up inside a little blue silk rubber bag. Can't you control your tongue at all?"

Konrad closed his eyes.

"I know you don't mean it," he said, "but you're doing me a lot of harm. I've got a serious responsibility tonight. I must keep my nerves cool. It's not so easy to step into a big part at a moment's notice when one's been thoroughly upset already, even if one has been understudying for months, ruining one's reputation in obscurity. You wouldn't understand it, but there's an emotional strain."

Sock opened his mouth but he was forestalled by Sutane, who had paused in the act of climbing onto the massage table again. He turned and they had a momentary impression of his intense irritation. His face was not expressive but the muscles of his lean torso flexed and a flood of colour spread over his chest and up his neck to the cheeks.

"No need to excite yourself, my dear chap," he said. "I'm not deserting you tonight."

"What?" Konrad forgot his dignity. His face puckered and he sat up in an unconsciously theatrical pose, his knees drawn up under him. "You're not going on tonight, Sutane?" he said, his voice unsteady in his helpless disappointment. "You can't! Poyser said . . ."

Sock picked him up by the back of his neck and landed him neatly on his feet. Sutane had become very white but he climbed onto the bench and signalled to Miss Finbrough to begin work again. Konrad was trembling violently under Sock's hand.

"Poyser said . . ." he began again.

Sock glowered at him.

"Think of something else," he advised in a dangerously level tone. "James has told you he's made up his mind to go on with the show and it's very decent of him."

There were tears in Konrad's eyes, and his mouth grew red and ugly as he struggled to control it.

"But I'd understood that I was to rehearse this afternoon," he stammered.

"This afternoon you'll stand up in the coroner's court and explain why you left Chloe at the lake. You were the last person to see her alive. You know that, I suppose?"

"Yes, I do. I've told the superintendent all about it once this morning. I put on a couple of records for her and I began to dance myself, but she was sarcastic, frightfully offensive and jealous, and so naturally I left her and came in. I lay on my bed and listened to Mercer playing downstairs. I knew I should have to stay for the inquest. That's what was worrying me."

Sock showed his teeth in an unamused smile.

"Now you needn't worry any more," he said. "You've told the superintendent, have you? Did he believe you?"

Konrad blinked. "Of course he did. Why ever shouldn't he? I told him

I wasn't going to stay putting on records for a woman who was rude when I wanted to dance myself and he quite understood."

"What records did you play?" put in Mr. Campion from his corner.

"Delius' 'Summer Night on the River,'" said Konrad promptly. "It wasn't at all suitable for dancing and I told her so. It was then that she was so rude to me. So I told her that if she wanted to stand about looking like a sentimental crane she could jolly well wind up her own gramophone. As I came away she put on something else—a piece of Falla, I think."

"I see. You went straight into the house then and up to your room?"

"Yes."

"Anyone see you?"

"I passed Hughes in the hall."

"How long did you stay in your room?"

"Until I heard all the rumpus downstairs. It was about an hour and a half, I suppose. I came along to find Mrs. Sutane phoning for the police."

Campion nodded. "All this time you were listening to Mr. Mercer playing in the small music room beneath you?"

"Yes, of course I was. I've told the police this once."

Campion would have soothed his irritation but Mercer forestalled him. He turned in his chair and eyed Mr. Konrad thoughtfully, as if an idea had occurred to him.

"What did I play?"

Konrad stiffened and his manner became wary.

"Your new tune," he said promptly.

"Yes, I did in the beginning. What else?"

Konrad hesitated. "Odds and ends of stuff, mostly. Old tunes of your own and a lot of beginnings of melodies. Nothing outstanding. The kitchen wireless set was bleating away as well."

Mercer laughed. It was an explosive, uncharacteristic sound which made Campion realise with surprise that he had never heard him laugh before.

"Good enough," he said. "Bear him out, Uncle William?"

"Eh?" Mr. Faraday looked thoughtful. "Yes, I do. Not musical myself, of course, but it sounded very nice, don't you know. Couldn't actually identify the tunes by name. Never could. But very melodious, attractive-sounding stuff. Can't be more explicit. Wish I could."

Sock looked down at Konrad. There was a puzzled expression on his weary face.

"In fact, Mercer played just what you'd expect him to," he said. "One of his typical recitals. Thinking out loud on the piano."

"Well, I can't help that, can I?" Konrad's golden head was thrown back defiantly. "I don't know what it matters. I didn't see the accident, if that's what you mean. I only know what everybody knows and what Sutane will find out if he insists on going on in *The Buffer* this evening. He killed Chloe Pye, he ran over her, and he murdered her."

Sock hit him. The blow caught him just under the jawbone, lifted him an inch or so off the ground, and sent him flat on his back on the carpet. Campion and Uncle William reached Petrie at the same moment and Mercer edged his chair a little farther away from the fracas. Konrad tottered to his feet. He was livid and quite speechless with rage and pain. But his histrionic gift had not deserted him. With his eyes closed and his face tragic he took three staggering steps forward and would have fallen into a more graceful position, his golden head pillowed on his arm, had not interference come from a most unexpected quarter.

Miss Finbrough left her position behind the massage table and swooped down upon him like a Valkyrie. Her plump plain face was a glistening crimson into which her light brows and lashes had entirely disappeared. She took Konrad by the soft part of the arm and her metal-hard fingers touched his bone.

"You dirty venomous little beast!" she said and shook him.

Surprise and pain startled the young man out of his histrionics. He opened his eyes and stared at her.

"Don't you dare . . ." he said, and the ridiculous words were embarrassing in his mouth. "You're trying to protect him too, are you? You're all trying to protect him and make him think he can go roaring round the roads killing people without getting into trouble for it, just because he's got his name in lights outside a theatre. You'll soon find you're wrong. He murdered that woman. Her blood is on his head. Thousands of helpless cyclists are killed every year by people like him who drive cars as though they're on a railway track."

His final pronouncement came by way of an anticlimax. Mercer emitted a shrill crow of delight and even Sock smiled. Miss Finbrough gripped her captive afresh.

"Be quiet!" she said. "You've done enough harm as it is. Think what he's gone through already. He's overworked, tired, exhausted——"

"Finny, shut up." Sutane bounded to his feet. He stood draped in his towel, cold, irritable and infinitely more intelligent than either of them. "Oh, dear God, what a pack of apes!" he said. "What is this?—a nightmare in rehearsal? Pull yourselves together, for heaven's sake. Konrad, I don't know what you're doing in my dressing room at all. Get out. And as for you, Finny, my dear good girl, stick to your damned job, do."

Miss Finbrough released her quivering victim. She stood for a moment looking at Sutane, a plain middle-aged woman, very red and hot with unaccustomed emotion.

"I'm sorry, Mr. Sutane," she said meekly and turned away. As she stumbled towards the door a sob, which embarrassed them all because it was so genuine and at the same time so hideous, escaped her.

Konrad glanced after her and shook himself. He was still quivering.

"I'm sorry if I've been rude, Sutane," he said with a touch of bravado, "but I feel these things. Other people do too," he added.

"Exit line," said Sock.

Konrad picked up his sweater and walked over to the door. On the threshold he paused.

"You can end my engagement whenever you like," he said. "But I still maintain that from a humane point of view Chloe Pye was murdered."

There was a moment's silence after the door had closed. Mercer moved at last.

"Suppose she was?" he said.

They all stared at him but he was looking at Sutane, and his eyes were questioning and amused.

The spell was broken by the arrival of Hughes, who announced somewhat surprisingly that Dr. Bouverie was below and would be glad if he might have a word with Mr. Campion.

Chapter 8

When Mr. Campion followed Hughes downstairs he descended into a small world of chaos.

White Walls normally contained an excitable household whose everyday balance was only maintained by the nicest of adjustments, so that this morning, when the proverbial monkey wrench had landed squarely in the heart of the brittle machinery, the very building seemed in danger of disruption and all its people to suffer in some degree from mild confusional insanity.

On reaching the hall the butler looked about him helplessly. At the front door a flustered parlourmaid was coping inadequately with a persistent young man who carried a camera, while in the alcove beneath the stairs Linda Sutane was talking to someone on the telephone, her soft deep voice sounding strained and pathetic.

Of Dr. Bouverie there was no trace.

"He wanted to see you most particularly, sir." Hughes seemed put out. "He was here a moment ago." Even while he spoke his glance wandered anxiously to the front door, where the maid was weakening.

At that moment the whole house heard the doctor's voice on the floor above. The old man was bellowing and apparently with rage.

"Ah, of course," said Hughes with relief. "It slipped my mind, sir. He'll be up with Miss Sarah. I forgot." He glanced down the hall again and quivered. The unwelcome caller was almost in the house. "Would you mind going up to him, sir? I think I really ought . . ."

The finish of the sentence was lost as the impulse proved too strong for him, and he bore down upon the intruder like a bulldog who has burst his collar.

Mr. Campion went upstairs again and guided by the doctor's voice, which had now sunk to a menacing rumble, turned a corner in the upper hall and came upon the fiery old gentleman. He was absorbed in conversation with the nurse Campion had seen on the evening before.

"Bring the maid to me," shouted the doctor. "Don't stand there like an imbecile. Bring the maid to me—and the dog, don't you know."

The woman hesitated. She was elderly and in figure what is somewhat obscurely called "comfortable." Her face was plain and sensible but there was a particularly obstinate gleam in her brown eyes which reminded Mr. Campion vividly of certain important personalities of his own early youth.

"The child is afraid," she began for what was all too evidently the third or fourth time.

Dr. Bouverie's jowls quivered and swelled.

"Do as you're told, woman."

She gave him a single defiant glare and strode off, her starched apron crackling.

The old man turned and peered at Campion.

"Morning. I'd like to see you in a moment," he said and glanced over his shoulder into the room upon whose threshold he stood. He made a vast imposing figure in his loose clothes. His wide collar was cut to lie almost flat, so that his many chins should not be discommoded, and there was a cluster of Little Dorrit rosebuds in his buttonhole.

"Where's the mother? D'you know?" he demanded. "Telephoning? Ridiculous. Perhaps you can help me. Come in here, will you?"

Campion followed him into a large white room furnished as a nursery. Superimposed upon the original modern décor, with its gaily painted screens and educational pictures, were evidences of an older school of thought: a chair in hideous brown wicker, an ancient fireguard and an extraordinary quantity of airing laundry.

Dr. Bouverie pointed to a low bedstead beneath the window on the far side of the room.

"The child's under that," he said. "Don't want to drag her out, don't you know, and if I pull the bed I may hurt her. Raise it gently. Take the foot, will you?"

Campion did as he was told and together they lifted the cot onto the middle of the linoleum. Sarah Sutane crouched in the angle of the wall. She was kneeling, her plump arms over her head and the soles of her little round feet completely visible beneath the arc of her many petticoats. Dr. Bouverie walked over to her.

"Where did the brute bite you?" he enquired conversationally.

Sarah quivered but did not stir, and when he stooped down and picked her up she remained rigid, so that he carried her, still in her original kneeling position, to the bed.

"There's nothing to be frightened of now." The old man was not un-kind but not unduly sympathetic. "We must see the abrasion, don't you know. It simply wants a little lukewarm water on it. Dog bite is not dangerous. You won't go mad or any rubbish of that sort. Where did he catch you?"

Mr. Campion suddenly felt very young himself. That half-contemptuous tone which yet carried such absolute conviction reminded him of a time long ago when he had first heard it, and the thought "That's how God talks" had come to him with the awful certainty of truth.

Sarah relaxed cautiously and peered at them through a tangled mass of tear-wet hair. She was very white and her jaws were set rigidly. There was a scratch on the inside of her upper arm and the doctor looked at it with professional interest.

"That all he gave you?" he enquired.

A commotion behind them silenced any reply the child might have made. The nurse reappeared, angry and sullen, and with her came a bright-faced country girl in an untidy uniform. The maid's round eyes were shining with excitement as she carried a little black-and-white mongrel terrier by the scruff of its thin neck. Her manner suggested both triumph and daring. Dr. Bouverie surveyed the trio.

"Put the dog down, don't you know."

"It might fly at her, sir." The maid spoke brightly, almost, it seemed, hopefully.

"Put it down."

Sarah gulped and the nurse could restrain herself no longer.

"She's frightened, poor lamb," she said. "Hark at her. Put the dangerous thing outside the door. You're frightening her to death, sir. She'll have a convulsion."

There seemed to be a certain amount of truth in her prophecy. Sarah was sitting upright on the bed, her eyes fixed on the dog and her face working horribly. Dr. Bouverie took her wrist in his hand and his eye-brows rose, yet, as the maid turned to the door, he shouted at her with irritable obstinacy: "Put the dog down."

Unwillingly and with considerable dramatic effect the girl set the dog on the floor and darted backwards. The terrier remained crouching, his eyes bright and frightened. Dr. Bouverie picked him up and ran his hands over the trembling body.

"Not a very fierce little dog," he said. "Now, you, little girl"—he looked at Sarah—"why did he bite you?"

The maid stepped forward, eager to talk.

"They were running in the field, sir, and he leapt at her," she said breathlessly. "The dog's shut up when Miss Bellew's Dane is here and he's always very fierce when he's first let out. Miss Sarah began to scream so I ran up to hold him off." She swelled at the recollection of her own bravery. "Then I saw he'd bitten her so I shouted for Nurse."

Mr. Campion cleared his throat and ventured a question at the risk of annoying the doctor.

"Did you tell her they'd have the dog destroyed?" he enquired.

The girl started and stared at him as though he had exhibited supernatural powers.

"Well, yes, sir, I did," she said after a pause. "I wanted to comfort her," she added hastily. "I told her that Mr. Spooner, the groom, would shoot him."

Dr. Bouverie looked at Campion and laughed abruptly.

"That's the end of that mystery," he said. "Here, little girl, here's your dog." He threw the animal onto the bed, despite the nurse's scream, and the child seized it, hugging it with a passionate affection which only a dog could possibly appreciate. The colour surged into her face and her eyes grew heavy. The terrier licked her eagerly.

Dr. Bouverie brushed the palms of his plump hands together.

"Put her to bed," he said. "Give her a hot-water bottle and a cup of milk cocoa. I'll send her a sedative. Somebody had better call down at my house for it. Keep the dog where it is."

"But the bite, Doctor . . ." The nurse was irritable.

"Paint it with iodine, my good woman. It's only a scratch. They were playing and he caught her. She's suffering from shock. This very silly little girl here told her that she was going to lose her pet and that it was going to be shot, so naturally she was frightened. She is very fond of him."

Sarah and the dog remained clasped in each other's arms. It was not a sentimental picture but rather a terrible one. The child's agony of affection was piteous.

The little maidservant hovered, indignant to discover her heroism and forethought so cruelly repaid. Dr. Bouverie regarded her.

"Are you a Mudd?" he enquired.

"Yes, sir. From Rose Green."

"Thought I recognised the shape of your skull." The old man seemed pleased. "You be off about your work and don't get hysterical. All your family are fools. You noticed there was a bit of excitement in the house and you thought you'd stir up a little more. Isn't that it?"

"No, sir." Miss Mudd was scarlet.

"Don't lie." Dr. Bouverie had adopted his God voice again. "Be off. Never interfere."

The nurse followed them out of the room, protesting.

"Sarah can't sleep with the dog, sir."

"Why not?"

"He may have fleas."

The old man looked down at her. "Then wash him," he said. "There are worse things than fleas. Listen to me. That's a very lonely, overimaginative little girl in there, and if you take her dog away she'll lie awake and see him standing waiting to be shot. She'll hear the bang and she'll see him bleed and she'll see his little dead body as clearly as if you'd killed him in front of her eyes. Cruelty, my good woman, is a very relative thing. That child is suffering from shock and it may interest you to know that more people die of shock than from any other disease. Go and cover them up. Keep them warm."

"If you say so, Doctor." The woman was still indignant but impressed in spite of herself.

The old man grunted at her in an Olympian fashion and would have passed on had not a thought occurred to him.

"Give the dog some warm milk," he said. "It's a nice little dog."

As they went down the stairs he glanced at Campion.

"Lucky guess of yours," he said and made the word sound a compliment.

Linda was still at the telephone as they passed through the hall. She sounded almost hysterical, Campion thought, and checked an impulse to go uninvited to her assistance.

"But of course," he heard her say. "Of course. You must come here. Anything we can do we will. Oh, it *has* been a shock for you. I know. I do realise that, of course."

Dr. Bouverie touched Campion's sleeve and led him out into the sunlight. On the step he paused, drawing in deep breaths of summer air through his small nose. He looked like some great animal, Campion thought; a bison, perhaps.

"I don't like nerves," he said. "Rolling pasture, beautiful trees, pretty flowers, birds—all respectable things, don't you know. Decent. Solid. I sometimes feel we should all be better off if we didn't think. All this intensive cultivation of the mind is bad. We're not constructed for it. Human machine won't stand up to it. Walk with me on that grass over there. I want to talk to you. Now about that poor woman who died last night; do you know if she was in the hands of a medical man?"

Campion considered.

"I'm not sure," he said, "but I should hardly think so. She's only just back from a two-year colonial tour, you know. I'll find out. Sutane's the man to ask."

"Wait a moment." The old man spoke hastily. "I don't think I'll make any definite enquiries, don't you know. That's the business of the coroner. I only wondered if you'd noticed anything about her yourself or if you had heard she'd suffered at all—coughs, choking attacks, spasms of holding the breath."

Mr. Campion's pale eyes became shrewd behind his spectacles.

"No," he said cautiously. "I should hardly think so. She was a profes-

sional dancer, don't you see. Still, one of the great men discovered these
clinical disturbances are not always present in every case. Who was it?
Morgan?"

Dr. Bouverie paused in his stride.

"You're a very extraordinary young man. Studied medicine?"

"Purely from the forensic point of view," Mr. Campion explained modestly. "When you mentioned those symptoms I naturally thought of *status
lymphaticus*. You found that at the P.M., I suppose?"

"I did. I don't know if there's any harm in telling you. Most interesting
case."

Dr. Bouverie paused after he had spoken. Campion remained encouragingly silent and the old doctor eyed him.

"Consider myself a good judge of character," he remarked unexpectedly. "You've been very civil to me and I'm inclined to trust you, don't
you know. Rely on your discretion?"

"Yes, I think you may, sir." Campion did not smile.

"Good." Dr. Bouverie looked every inch the eminent Victorian he was.
"As a matter of fact, I'd like to talk it over with an intelligent man who
knew the poor woman. The mischief is we don't know much about *status
lymphaticus*. I'm afraid that must be faced. We know that if the thymus
persists after a certain age—five, isn't it?—a certain state results. The trouble is that this state seems to vary with each patient. Now this woman,
don't you see, had adenoids and tonsils removed at some time, probably
in childhood, so there's nothing to help us there. I opened her up, don't
you know, and I found the thymus considerably enlarged—considerably.
The heart was not actually constricted but the aorta was narrower than
is usual and the heart itself was a little undeveloped, so you see this
makes a different problem of it."

Mr. Campion felt his steps growing heavier and was exasperated with
himself. It came to him suddenly that he did not want the truth to come
out. He did not want this pompous but likeable old personage to put
his blunt finger on the point that was sticking out a mile. He did not
want the Sutane ménage to become disorganised by the tremendous emotional and physical upheaval of a murder enquiry, not because of Uncle
William and his success, not because of Sutane and his career, but because
of Linda, who in thirty hours had become a personality of altogether unreasonable importance in his own life.

Having faced this, he felt better.

Dr. Bouverie was talking again.

"I refreshed my memory on the subject this morning," he said. "The
experts seem to be still quarrelling about it. No one knows what the
weight of the thymus in a normal healthy body ought to be. But the
fact remains that when one gets a sudden death from insufficient causes
it very often is this overdevelopment. I've had several cases in my time.

One poor fellow died under chloroform having his teeth out, I remember, and a child up at Birley stuck its head through its crib rails and died apparently by act of God. Then down on the Lower Green a man got his brother by the throat in a quarrel and the fellow died in his hands, but not from strangulation. We were all very puzzled at the time. In all these cases the thymus was very much enlarged."

He cleared his throat and it occurred to Campion that he was enjoying his own lecture.

"To go back to this poor wretched woman," said Dr. Bouverie. "Looking at her last night we both noticed the skull fracture caused by the fall. There was a Pond fracture of the vault with an extended fissure to the base, by the way. The head injuries would have killed her in an hour or so had she not been dead already."

Campion took a deep breath. It was coming, then.

"She was not killed by the car?" he said dully.

"I don't think so." Dr. Bouverie was pleased with himself. "She died from fright, you know. Fright acting on the *status lymphaticus*. As she stood waving to Mr. Sutane she felt faint, overbalanced, and the shock killed her. When she reached the ground she was dead."

Campion stared at the old man and controlled an insane desire to laugh with relief. It took him some seconds to realise what had happened, but gradually it dawned upon him. Dr. Bouverie was a man of simple and direct thought. From the beginning he had been confronted by a problem of accident or suicide. At first he had accepted the actual injuries made by the car as the cause of death, so that he was not concerned with that aspect of the case. The question which had bothered him to the exclusion of all others was why Chloe Pye had ever left the bridge. Now his discovery of the enlarged thymus had provided him with an explanation and he had accepted it. The simple fact that Chloe Pye's heart must, in this hypothesis, have ceased to pump less than five seconds before her head and rib cage were crushed and that bleeding would in that case have been copious had still miraculously escaped his attention. Campion felt like the child at the party who tries not to watch the conspicuously placed thimble in the old nursery game. He tried to remember Chloe Pye as she had appeared on the night before; he saw again her torn bathing suit and her lacerated chest where the tire had crushed and ripped it. There should have been blood there, quantities of blood, not merely the superficial bleeding of the smaller veins.

The doctor's discovery, however, explained the real cause of death. Campion wondered who it was who had so frightened Chloe Pye that she had died. No great strength would have been needed to kill her, perhaps even no strength at all. The thought of the man in the doctor's story who had taken his brother by the throat only to feel him die in his hands returned to his mind. He wanted to leave the old man before the question which rose to his lips escaped him. Were there any slight bruises on her neck, on her shoulders?

He was saved from the indiscretion by the appearance of Sutane, who came striding across the lawn towards them, a loose silk dressing gown flapping round his angular form. He was eager and inquisitive and the force of his personality swept over them in a wave of which they were physically and uncomfortably aware. In his intensity of need he reminded Campion of the luckless Sarah, and it was evident that he had the same effect upon the doctor, for the old man spoke of the child at once.

"Purely shock, Mr. Sutane. The incident was quite sufficient to account for it."

The younger man stared at him as if he were demented.

"Shock?" he said. "Good heavens, the car passed over her!"

Dr. Bouverie stiffened and his old eyes were severe.

"I'm talking of your daughter, sir," he said.

Sutane blinked and they were aware of his mental effort as he tore his mind away from the one subject to the other. It was the most striking thing about the man—this extraordinary vividness of the unspoken expression of his thoughts.

"Sarah?" he said, not without interest. "What's the matter with her?"

Dr. Bouverie froze. Campion felt his contempt and he regarded the two of them helplessly. He knew that the doctor could never conceive a situation in which a man might love his child and yet have literally no time in which to think of her, while Sutane would never realise that a world existed in which time for thought was not only unrationed but as free and bountiful as to have no value at all.

"Your little daughter is being well looked after. A maid frightened her. She thought she was going to lose her dog." The doctor spoke coldly and with active dislike for the monument of human selfishness which he thought he saw before him.

Sutane listened to him, his head on one side, and quite evidently thought him a little mad.

"Has she found the dog now?"

"Yes. They're both being looked after, I'm happy to say."

Sutane passed a weary hand over his forehead.

"My God," he said.

Glancing at Dr. Bouverie's expression, Campion was reminded of an old gentleman of his acquaintance who used to recount how he walked round the house of a despised contemporary and "mentally spat." Dr. Bouverie was mentally spitting now. Campion changed the conversation.

"Sutane," he said, "do you know if Chloe Pye suffered from semi-choking or fainting fits at any time?"

The doctor coughed warningly, but his eyes were interested. So was Sutane. He looked at them both sharply.

"I never heard of it," he said. "I didn't know her at all, you see."

Dr. Bouverie glowered. "But she was staying in your house . . ."

The faint colour came into Sutane's face.

"I did not know her," he said quickly. "Until she joined the cast of *The Buffer* I had never met her, except casually at parties." In his anxiety to sound convincing he adopted an intensity which defeated his object. "She was a virtual stranger to me."

The doctor was put out by the underlying antagonism in the voice.

"You'll tell that to the coroner," he said.

Sutane paused in his stride. "Naturally," he said and, turning on his heel, he walked swiftly and angrily away.

As he conducted the doctor to his car Campion remembered Chloe Pye sitting on Sock's knee in the morning room and heard afresh her squeaky protest: "Jimmy and I are old friends."

Chapter 9

"There are times, my dear feller," said Uncle William, "when the whole world gets out of gear and tumbles helter-skelter about one's ears, makin' one feel damnably uncomfortable and at a loose end. At those times there's only one thing to do about it, and that's to light a good cigar, take a glass in one's hand, and wait until one sees a ray of light shinin' at one through the gloom. That's been my rule all through my life and it's never failed me yet. Sit down, my boy, and I'll get the drinks."

Looking more bearlike than ever in his old gentleman's suit of brown-and-beige-striped flannel, he waved Mr. Campion to a chair by the fire-place in the small music room and went to a cupboard in the bottom of the bookcase.

"Dear people," he observed as he surveyed a half decanter of scotch whisky which he found there. "Fancy rememberin' me at a time like this. This is my own supply. When I first came down here last year Jimmy pointed the cupboard out to me and told me he'd given orders that a decanter and glasses should always be kept there so that I could get a drink whenever I liked without havin' to fidget round for it. That's what I mean about these people, Campion. They're dear good souls, kind, thoughtful and intelligent, who make a feller feel he's livin' at home. A better home than some I've known," he added thoughtfully. "Poor Mother! No sense of comfort as we know it today. Still, a very grand old woman, Campion. Here's to her. God bless her."

Campion drank a silent toast to Great-aunt Caroline and wished she were still alive without actually desiring her awe-inspiring presence in the moment's dilemma. Uncle William continued.

"Sutane, Konrad and Sock at the inquest, Linda up with the child, Eve driving Mercer to Birley, and that Finbrough woman safely out of the way," he said with satisfaction. "We're alone in peace to think a bit."

"What happened to Slippers Bellew?" Campion enquired.

"Oh, she left. Sensible girl." Uncle William's bright blue eyes applauded her intelligence. "As soon as the news came last night Sock bundled her into her little car and she drove off down the lane, going the other way to avoid the trouble. Not as callous as it sounds. As Sock pointed out, she's not a woman; she's a performing animal with a reputation. He told her that she couldn't do anything to help and might have to carry the show if Sutane dropped out for a night or so. She's not quite what you'd expect from an actress. Lives entirely by schedule. So much sleep, so much exercise, so much work. Gives an entirely different impression from the stage."

He shook his head with mild regret and settled himself opposite Campion.

"Hate carrying tales," he remarked, cocking an eye at the younger man. "Don't like it. Never did. That's the mischief of a rumpus of this sort. People takin' other people in corners and chatterin'. Can't get away from it. Bound to occur. Very funny scene in here just before lunch while you were talkin' to the doctor in the garden."

"Oh?" Campion was encouraging and Uncle William nodded.

"Very funny scene," he repeated. "Made me think. May be nothin' in it. Still, I thought I'd repeat it as I'm not sure I wasn't meant to. I came down here after you left the bedroom—saw no point in watchin' Sutane dress—and had just settled myself when Konrad came sidlin' in lookin' for me. Didn't encourage him. Can't stand the feller. It was he who insisted on talkin'. Said didn't I think it funny Chloe Pye, of all people, dyin'. I answered him. I said I didn't see it was any more peculiar that she should die than anybody else. In fact, I made it pretty plain to him that I could spare the woman. Never have believed in false sentiment, Campion. She was devilish awful alive, and the place is quieter without her playin' the hussy in every room one went into. No point in refusin' to admit that. Well, we beat about the bush for a bit and then he came out with the tale he was determined to tell me. I pooh-poohed it at the time, of course, but it had its points of interest."

He paused and tucked his small fat feet round the legs of his chair.

"There was a bit of mystery about the way the woman got into the show. You know that?" he began slowly. "Sutane just announced it one day and in she came. Well, there's nothin' in that. He may have liked her dancin', although you know my views. However, this little runt Konrad says he was sittin' in the theatre at the rehearsal of a new scene and

Sutane was a couple of rows in front of him, watchin' the show, not knowin' Konrad was there. The feller was eavesdroppin'; got to face it. The woman, Chloe Pye, came along in the dark and sat down next to Sutane. Konrad said he didn't like to move and so had to sit and listen."

Uncle William snorted by way of comment.

"Well, apparently Miss Pye started talkin' about some telephone messages she'd had from Sutane, and Konrad repeated her words. May not be accurate, of course. Still, tell you for what it's worth. The little twip says she said, 'Darlin' '—she used to talk like that, it means nothin'—'darlin', don't be a fool. Your wife has asked me down and I'm comin'.' The next thing Konrad heard—and he must have sat there with his ears flappin'—was Sutane sayin', 'I don't want you down there, Chloe. I've done all I'm goin' to do and I won't have you in my house.' "

Uncle William paused, drank deeply, and blew his nose.

"Monstrous thing, this listenin' and repeatin', bandyin' words to and fro, probably all wrong," he rumbled unhappily. "But this next bit is interestin' if true. Konrad says that Chloe Pye—and what a hussy, Campion, forcin' herself on a feller when told point-blank she wasn't wanted! No hintin', mind you; told point-blank—Konrad says that Chloe Pye said, 'How are you goin' to stop me, my lamb?' and Sutane replied straight from the shoulder, like the dear feller he is, 'I don't know. But if you try to break up my home I'll stop you, if I have to strangle you.' "

He sat back in his chair and surveyed Campion with unblinking eyes.

"The cat's out of the bag," he said. "I've repeated the story. Felt I ought to. Mind you, may be all a pack of lies. Still, it's a funny tale to invent and Jimmy told me himself that he didn't want the woman here, but she froze onto Linda one day behind the scenes and the unsuspectin' girl parted up with an invitation. What I feel is, Campion, it's not the sort of gossip for Konrad to go round repeatin', is it? That's why I couldn't find it in my heart to blame Eve."

"Eve?" enquired Mr. Campion, temporarily out of his depth.

Uncle William's pink face darkened.

"Was comin' to her," he mumbled. "She was just outside that window over there sittin' in a deck chair. Overheard Konrad talkin' to me. More listenin'."

"Did she say anything?"

"The scene I referred to took place," said Uncle William briefly. "I left 'em. Seemed best. When people are hurlin' abuse there's always the chance of one of 'em confusin' the issue and thinkin' you've said somethin' yourself. I came away."

They sat in silence for some minutes. It was cool and dark in the small north room. Outside, the garden was sparkling in the afternoon sun.

Mr. Campion considered Benny Konrad.

"I've heard several references to a 'rally,' " he said. "What's that?"

"Konrad's Speedo Club." Uncle William spoke contemptuously. "One of these publicity notions these fellers have to get up to. You ought to have heard of it, Campion. The feller's the high priest of the bicycle. Ludicrous sort of idea."

Dim recollections of Press paragraphs floated into Mr. Campion's mind. Uncle William prompted him.

"Konrad had a very successful dance act some years ago with a bicycle and lent his name to some sort of advertising stunt which was illustrated. Pictures of him everywhere with a certain firm's machine. One thing led to another, as these things do, and a club was formed with Konrad as president. He presents prizes and attends races in France. That sort of thing. There was quite a large membership once, I believe, composed of a lot of enthusiastic young fellers who used to come and see him act and applaud. The trouble is, he's not good. Can't carry a show alone. After his failure in *Wheels within Wheels* he was lookin' for a shop, as we call it, and was devilish glad to take Sutane's understudy with a couple of unimportant numbers in my show, *The Buffer*. However, he still works hard at his publicity. This rally is the important day in the club's year. It's a small body now but very enthusiastic. They see him as the hero of their hobby, a sort of prince—poor misguided souls."

He leant forward and placed a stubby forefinger on Campion's knee.

"Konrad's the sort of chap who's got all the paraphernalia for success except the essential talent," he said earnestly. "He's like a feller in a fine tail coat without the chest to fill it out."

"What do they do at this rally?" Campion was still interested.

"Ride from a pub in London to a pub in Essex, and finish at a pub somewhere else for a meal and speeches. Takes place next Sunday week."

Uncle William poured himself another drink.

"I'm goin' to have a brief nap. These are stirrin' times. Think about what I've told you, Campion. Jimmy's a good feller. Can't have him covered with contumely, especially from the mouth of a little tick. Think it over, my boy."

Campion rose to his feet.

"I will," he promised and his lean face was thoughtful.

He had a very clear recollection of Sutane's appearance at the window on the evening before and his subsequent behaviour at the scene of the accident, and an uncomfortable doubt assailed him.

Leaving Uncle William reposing in an armchair, his short legs crossed at the ankles and his face composed for philosophical contemplation, Campion went out into the vast hall, on whose stone squares the sunlight laid long shimmering fingers from the front door. The house was placid and quiet in the drowsy afternoon.

He remained looking out into the garden for some minutes and did not hear Linda come down until her foot touched the stone behind him.

She looked white and tired, and the angle of her jaw seemed sharper and smaller than he had noticed it before.

"She's asleep," she said. "Poor darlings! They look like a coloured plate in a Christmas supplement. Rufe is a good little chap. He woke when I moved but he didn't stir. He's very fond of her."

"And how's Nurse?" enquired Mr. Campion.

She laughed and her eyes met his. Campion looked away from her and across the lawn to the trees beyond.

"We'd better use both rooms for tea," she said. "There'll be a lot of us."

He followed her into the drawing room unwillingly and helped her to roll back the folding doors which separated it from the breakfast room.

"They're bringing Mrs. Pole back with them, and her son." Linda sounded weary. "She's Chloe Pye's sister-in-law. Her husband is abroad and she's the nearest relative available. She seems very much upset." She sighed and he glanced at her.

"Difficult?"

"I'm rather afraid she may be. She kept me on the phone for nearly three quarters of an hour this morning. It's ghastly, isn't it? I can't feel it's a death somehow. It's a filthy thing to say, but it's more like a new production."

She accepted the cigarette he offered her and sat down in the window, while he remained standing before her.

"If you had some sleep now it would be a good thing," he said, feeling slightly silly. "I mean, you've had a tremendous strain in the last twenty-four hours—this business and the child."

She looked up and surprised him by her expression.

"I did care about the child," she said. "I do love her. I'm not careless. I do do all I can. I'd let her go, even, if I thought she'd be all right. But she's so young, so terribly young. Poor, poor baby."

She glanced out of the window. She was not crying but her mouth was not perfectly controlled. In her need she was disarming and he forgot the suffocating and novel self-consciousness which she had begun to engender in him.

"That's quite obvious, you know," he said gently.

"Is it?"

"I think so."

She smiled at him in a grateful, watery fashion which unaccountably turned his heart over, reminding him inconsequentially and, therefore, irritatingly of its exact position in his body.

"I couldn't get to see the doctor because of Mrs. Pole," she explained earnestly. "There's such a lot of that sort of thing. I haven't got any definite work but I never seem to be able to be on hand at the right moment. It seems absurd to talk about the house, with an army of servants, but in a place like this, with crowds of people rushing in and out perpetually, all of them without warning, there's a lot of managing to be done. Servants don't expect to have to think, you know. If you can give them a curriculum they can carry it out, but when you can't you've got to think for each of them whenever thought is required. And, anyway, they're alternatively overworked and bored stiff. Then there are little odd things like arrangements, trains to be met, and people to entertain when the others aren't actually needing them. I don't neglect Sarah, honestly I don't. I'm with her every spare second I have. I'm not much good, though. It's so difficult to get your mind to work like a child's, and if it doesn't the child's either bored or puzzled. She's so lonely."

She paused for breath and, catching sight of his face, seemed to remember for the first time that he was a comparative stranger.

"I'm sorry," she said with a certain youthful stiffness. "I've been so exasperated all day because I couldn't see Doctor Bouverie about Sarah. It was all so ridiculously unjust that it's been rankling and you were about so I threw it all at your head. I'm so sorry."

Campion sought in his mind for some suitable rejoinder at once graceful and pacifying. It did not present itself to him, however, and instead he made the observation uppermost in his mind, stating it baldly and without art. "You're lonely yourself, aren't you?" he said.

The girl shot him a single comprehending glance.

"You're clever," she said. "Much cleverer than I thought. That sounds rude. I don't mean it to be. . . . Eve and Mercer should be back soon. It's awfully good of her to drive him about."

He accepted her clumsy change in the conversation politely and watched her profile against the window. She went on, talking a trifle hurriedly.

"They went in to Birley to get some music-manuscript paper. No one in the world but Mercer would insist that he wanted manuscript paper at a time like this. Nothing ruffles him. His man was out, so I'm afraid Eve was forced into offering to drive him. He doesn't touch the car himself. They'll all be back soon. It will be an accident verdict, won't it? Sock said you'd fixed everything."

"I did nothing," said Campion, rather too truthfully, he thought. "But yes, I think it'll be accident."

Linda nodded. "Why should she take her life?" she said. "Poor girl! I thought she seemed so pleased with herself. And she was very much *en grande tenue*. It seems so extraordinary."

"*En grande tenue?*"

She looked a little embarrassed.

"In full regalia, sexually speaking," she said. "Sort of energy people put on, or put out rather, when they're hunting. You know what I mean. Some people do it subconsciously the whole time and some just adopt it when they have someone particularly in mind. It's one of those things you notice instinctively."

Mr. Campion raised his eyebrows.

"Chloe Pye was in full regalia, was she?"

"Yes, I think so." Her quiet voice was thoughtful. "I wondered who she was interested in. Sock, I imagined. Lots of women like Sock very much. He looks as if he could do with cherishing. Not exactly dirty; unbrushed, if you see what I mean."

Campion grinned.

"That would hardly do for Chloe Pye, would it?" he suggested.

"I don't know." Linda eyed him gravely. "I only met her once before she came down here. I was alone in Jimmy's dressing room one day last week and Sock brought her in to see me. She said she'd like a week-end in the country and I offered her a tentative invitation which she seized. Jimmy was rather upset when he heard of it and wanted me to put her off, but I didn't like to because it would have been so rude. I wish to God I had."

She paused. "Perhaps it was an accident," she said at last, but her voice carried no conviction. "It's all very horrible and frightening."

"Frightening?"

She looked up at him and he caught a fleeting expression in her eyes which jolted him.

"I talk too much to you," she said. "It's a gift of yours, making people talk, because you understand what they say, you know."

Campion sat down.

"I'm quite trustworthy," he said briefly. "Why are you afraid?"

She hesitated and suddenly turned to him.

"Have you ever had rats in the house?" she demanded unexpectedly. "If you get mice they're just a nuisance, like flies or too many old magazines, but once you get rats you're aware of an evil, unseen intelligence which is working against you in your own house. It's an inexplicable feeling if you haven't experienced it, but if you have you'll know what I mean. It's the 'enemies about' sensation. That's what I've got now. There was something wrong about that woman's death, and it came on top of a lot of wrong things."

She remained looking at him, curled up on the window seat. Her gold skin was warm against the dark satin of her dress and her small face was alive and intelligent. She was chic, compact, very much a definite person, and it dawned upon Campion that he was in love with her and that he would never again be completely comfortable in her presence.

She was quite right about the situation at White Walls. There were enemies about, and if he deserted her now it would be a desertion indeed. He did not take his eyes from her face but he ceased to see her. The discovery he had just made was not an overwhelmingly astonishing one, for it had been knocking at the door of his mind ever since he had first seen her. He found it shocking, however, not because she was Sutane's wife and Sarah's mother, and therefore not for his pursuing, but because a phenomenon which he had hitherto believed to be more than half an old wives' tale had been at last revealed to him as a fact instead of a fashion. He knew that he had come down to White Walls in a normal state of mind, and yet within an hour an outside force had conquered and possessed him.

"You're looking at me as though I'd done something blasphemous," said Linda Sutane.

Campion stiffened as though she had boxed his ears. Presently he grinned at her. His eyes were dancing and the long creases down his cheeks had deepened. He looked suddenly very much younger and very much alive.

"Fair comment," he said lightly and added, "the cruelest observation you could possibly have made."

She stared at him curiously for a moment and he saw a certain timidity creep into her expression which delighted and invigorated him even while it appalled him.

Linda shook her head, an involuntary childish gesture to shake away a thought.

"Perhaps it's all imagination," she said.

"Perhaps it is," he agreed. "Whatever it is, I'll see it through."

She put out her hand.

"I don't think it is," she said. "Do you?"

He got up and walked aimlessly down the room.

"No," he said, looking down at the empty fireplace. "I know damn well it isn't."

Hughes startled them both and looked a little bewildered himself when he came in an instant afterwards.

"Mrs. Paul Geodrake, madam," he murmured. "I told her you were out, but she caught sight of you through the window. She told me to tell you she was sure you would spare her a moment. She's in the dining room. I had no other place to take her." He glanced reproachfully at the open double doors.

"Who is she? Do we know her?" Linda seemed surprised.

Hughes sank his voice confidentially.

"She lives in the Old House on the lower road, madam. You were out when she called originally and so was she when you returned cards."

Linda drew back.

"I can't see her now, because the others will be here at any moment."

"Her husband's father, old Mr. Geodrake, was friendly with your late uncle, ma'am." Hughes seemed hurt. "She said only for a moment. She's a rather determined lady."

Linda capitulated and he went off satisfied.

Mrs. Paul Geodrake came into the room as if it were a fortress she had stormed. She was a fresh-faced, red-haired woman in the mid-thirties, smartly if not tastefully dressed, and possessed of a voice of power and unpleasantness unequalled by anything else Campion had ever heard. It occurred to him at once that the fashion for well-dressed stridence was out of date. Also he wished that she were less determinedly vivacious.

She swooped upon Linda, her hand outstretched.

"I had to come," she said, her bright intelligent eyes fixed searchingly on the other woman's face. "I've been sitting at home thinking of you and I suddenly made up my mind to run up and tell you you're not to worry. After all, we're next-door neighbours, aren't we?"

Linda looked at her blankly. A lesser soul would have been silenced by that expression of frank bewilderment, but Mrs. Geodrake was of stern stuff. She looked at her small hostess with a compassion that was not altogether untinged with satisfaction.

"You poor child," she said. "It's been frightful for you, of course. The village is full of it. They get things so exaggerated, don't they? And they will talk."

Linda said nothing. She had not spoken since her visitor's arrival, and Mrs. Geodrake, taking pity on her gaucherie, helped her out.

"Aren't you going to introduce me?" she said, dropping her voice a tone or so and eyeing Campion with a frankly appraising air which he found disconcerting.

Linda performed the ceremony politely and Mrs. Geodrake repeated the name, doubtless committing it carefully to memory.

"Not your husband?" she said and shot an arch twinkle at the other woman.

"No," said Linda.

"He's at the inquest, of course," said Mrs. Geodrake, aware of but not in the least disconcerted by the absence of conversational support. "My dear, do you know old Pleyell, the coroner? A perfect sweetie. Awfully stiff, of course, but quite a darling. You'll love him. He'll see you through and do the decent thing. Frightfully unfortunate for you—only your second year here. Who did you have? Doctor Bouverie, wasn't it? Such a charming old character, isn't he? How is your little girl? I heard in the village a dog bit her. Children never ought to have dogs. They're so frightfully cruel to them, don't you think? I'm dying to have a borzoi, but my husband doesn't like them. Do you have to obey your husband, Mrs. Sutane? I cut the word out of our marriage service, but it hasn't made any difference."

She laughed and they joined her politely if rather breathlessly. Campion had the uncomfortable feeling that he ought to do something to stop her and wished it were his own house.

Mrs. Geodrake opened her bag and produced a cigarette case.

"I'll smoke my own, if you don't mind. I sing," she said with a brief artificial smile as Linda produced the box somewhat belatedly from the mantelshelf. "Tell me, was she a great friend of yours, this girl who was killed?"

The concern in her voice was so superficial that it reached the cipher point.

"No," said Linda helplessly. "I'd never met her before."

"Oh, I see. A friend of your husband's. How interesting!"

The bright eyes suddenly reminded Mr. Campion of those of his old friend, Superintendent Stanislaus Oates.

"No, no." Linda was forced on to the defensive now. "She was simply appearing in his show, so I asked her down, don't you see?"

"Oh, a business friend?" Mrs. Geodrake filed the hard-won fact for future reference. "How terribly awkward for you. Still, it's so much better than someone you knew well and rather liked. Do tell me, how did she come to be nude? The village is too intrigued. The policeman's blushing all over, my dear. Were you having a nudist party?"

They both stared at her blankly, but before their honest astonishment could turn to irritation they saw something wistful behind her shrewd, hard eyes. Campion found himself thinking of the original Miss Hoyden of the play, not the tempestuous vulgarian which generations of exuberant actresses have made of her, but the author's own overhealthy and tragically unentertained piece whose energetic imagination fashioned from the half-heard gossip from the gay world a life of idyllic licence and excitement which only the freshest spirit and the strongest constitution could possibly survive for a couple of days. The stage, Bohemia, parties, romance; Mrs. Geodrake evidently saw them all as synonyms.

He stole a glance at Linda. She still looked a little bewildered.

"Oh, no," she said. "She'd been rehearsing down by the lake. She wasn't nude. She was in a bathing dress for dancing, you see."

"Alone?"

Mrs. Geodrake seemed disappointed.

"Yes, quite alone."

The sound of voices floated in from the hall and Linda got up with determination.

"It was very kind of you to come," she said and held out her hand.

"Not at all. I felt I had to." Mrs. Geodrake ignored the hand and turned towards the door with expectant interest. "Is this your husband coming?" she said. "He'll know about the verdict, won't he? I'm dying to hear it, aren't you?"

She smiled at them disarmingly as she spoke, and it occurred to the indignant Mr. Campion that the "superb self-possession" ideal extolled by the novelists of the last generation had been a serious mistake. Linda's hand dropped to her side and the door opened and Mercer looked in.

He caught sight of Mrs. Geodrake, did not recognise her, stared at her, and went out again promptly without a word, passing Sutane in the doorway.

Chapter 10

"Death by misadventure." Sutane glanced across the room and spoke without relief. He looked pale and preoccupied and appeared to be imparting the information without considering it. Even Mrs. Geodrake, who had risen, her eyes eager and ingratiating, made no attempt to speak to him.

He came into the room, glanced at the visitor casually, as at a stranger in a hotel lounge, and, planting his back to the fireplace, waited, with his heavy-lidded eyes on the open door.

Hughes and the parlourmaid, who had entered through the breakfast room, were busy with tea trays and occasional tables. Apart from the gentle clatter they made there was no other sound in the room.

Mrs. Geodrake sat down again.

Outside in the hall someone giggled nervously. It was a particularly inane sound, not at all unusual in itself; rather, startlingly familiar; but in the precincts of White Walls it was an anachronism.

"This way, Mrs. Pole." Konrad's voice came in to them, gentle and insincere. They entered together, the man consciously graceful, bending slightly from the waist, his feet carefully placed at each step, his golden head bent, and the woman self-conscious, triumphant, enjoying herself with all the energy of an amateur actress in the leading tragic role of a play for charity.

She was small and plump and not so much clothed as looped and festooned in black. Black chiffon hung from her hat, from her shoulders, and from her black-gloved hand. From her flat pointed shoes to the crown of her toque she dripped mourning in its most prosaic form.

Beside such a determined display of funeral Konrad's curling yellow hair looked flippant and in bad taste.

Behind them walked a large sulky youth in a black suit a trifle too small for his puppy-fat body. He was painfully ill at ease and with the earnest idiocy of adolescence was covering it with baleful fury. His face, neck and hands were all very red and prominent. Sock wandered beside him, looking both exhausted and alarmed. Eve and Mercer came last, the man unwillingly.

Konrad glanced at Linda more to ascertain her exact position than to convey any message.

"Mrs. Pole," he said softly. "This is Mrs. Sutane."

Chloe Pye's sister-in-law raised her veil and her nervous laugh echoed through the room unhappily.

"Pleased to meet you," she said. "Isn't it awful?" She giggled again with unfortunate effect.

The two women shook hands and Linda conducted her visitor to a seat near the tea tray.

Mrs. Pole gave up the unsatisfactory notion of hitching her veil over her ears like an inverted yashmak, an expedient which both blinded and embarrassed her, and pushed it up over her hat, revealing a round determined face and red-rimmed blue eyes.

She was a great talker, a little out of her depth at the moment but clinging bravely to her unusual prominence and displaying from time to time glimpses of that obstinacy of purpose which was her chief characteristic.

Mrs. Geodrake was temporarily forgotten. She sat gracefully on a small settee in the middle of the room, her intelligent eyes alight with interest and an amusement which was only too clearly unsympathetic. She was a member of the audience who had got in to the play and was frankly and unself-consciously enjoying it.

Mrs. Pole looked about her.

"Where's Bobby?" she said sharply.

"Here, Mother." Robert Pole shouldered his way towards her through what he obviously took to be a hostile crowd. He was introduced to Linda and shook hands with her, scowling.

Mrs. Pole accepted tea and sandwiches and her son took up a protective position behind her chair. Konrad rose to the occasion gallantly. He ran about with cups and plates and cream jugs, posturing and gesturing as if he were actually on the stage.

Chloe Pye's sister-in-law had a loud voice with an accent which would not have been noticeable if she had not made capricious attempts to counteract it at unexpected moments.

"I'm thankful for a cup of tea," she said. "Poor clever Chloe . . ." She gulped and used her handkerchief. "It's been such a shock. We all went to see her on Saturday night, you know. Dad—that's my husband—was away on business, so we took my neighbour and I'm sure I talked about Chloe all the way home. I never thought I'd find her like this. Have you seen her, Mrs. Sutane? My dear . . ." She lowered her voice and imparted some gruesome details. "She was so pretty, too, wasn't she, for her age? You'd have thought sometimes, from the stage, she was nothing but a young girl. It was a terrible strain on her, though. You could see it if you looked into her face. Now she's gone. I'm going to take her home. Dad would wish it. I've seen the undertaker."

Mrs. Geodrake moved a little closer. "It must have been a terrible blow to you," she began invitingly.

The other woman looked at her gratefully and set down her cup.

"Oh, terrible!" she agreed. "Did you know her? She was so talented, even from a girl. We used to think she was a genius." She gave her little high-pitched giggle again.

Mrs. Geodrake's intrusion into the conversation focussed general attention upon her. Sutane looked at her as though he had never seen her before that particular moment, as perhaps he had not. He turned an enquiring glance upon his wife.

However, Mrs. Geodrake, who seemed to be able to see all round her, glanced up before Linda could speak.

"I wondered when you were going to notice me, Mr. Sutane," she said, smiling at him archly. "I'm Jean Geodrake. I live next door to you. I came in this afternoon to sympathise with your wife."

There was silence while she spoke and Sutane, who was no more proof against a direct and smiling glance than any other man, looked puzzled without being put out.

"About the accident," amplified the lady. "Frightful for you all. In your house, I mean."

Mrs. Pole sniffed reproachfully and burst into embarrassing tears. Mrs. Geodrake rose to the situation.

"Oh, of course, you're a relative, aren't you?" she said, turning round upon the other woman. "An aunt?"

"Sister-in-law," snapped Mrs. Pole, a dangerous light in her blue eyes. "More like a sister," she added defiantly.

"She didn't come to see us much." The words were blurted out a full tone more loudly than their utterer had intended and Robert Pole's face became a violent crimson. He stood lowering defensively.

Mrs. Pole turned on her son.

"She did, you wicked boy," she exploded. "Didn't we all go up to her new flat? Didn't I put up her curtains? What are you talking about? She was very fond of us. I'm sure Dad, her brother, worshipped her. Why, we were all so pleased when she got on."

Mrs. Geodrake's smile was sweetly diabolical.

"I'm sure you were," she murmured. "She wasn't born to the stage then?"

Linda intervened with quiet determination.

"You must have had a dreadful day, Mrs. Pole," she said. "Would you care to come upstairs and take off your things?"

"No, thank you." The visitor was roused. The glance she bestowed on Mrs. Geodrake intimated clearly that she was standing no nonsense from any condescending bit of a countrywoman, however many airs she gave herself. She thanked Mrs. Sutane, who no doubt meant well, but she could easily take care of herself—her with her great grief.

"Chloe's father was quite a wealthy man," she said with dignity, her red eyes on Mrs. Geodrake's eager face. "He had her taught dancing from when she was a baby. I've heard Dad, my husband, say that she used to look a little queen in her white dresses. When she was old enough she joined a troupe of properly looked-after children and danced in panto-mime. Later on she struck out for herself. None of us ever thought we'd sit in a coroner's court and hear a jury foreman say they'd brought the verdict in of death by misadventure because of insufficient evidence."

Both Linda and Mr. Campion looked at Sock abruptly. He nodded and turned his head away with a weary gesture.

Mrs. Pole was still talking. Her manner was a curious mixture of dignity and defiance, and the essential strength of character of the woman was apparent.

"None of us ever thought we'd learn when it was too late that she was seriously ill, poor girl, that her glands had overgrown and almost any little shock might kill her. If we had we might have been more charitable and understood a lot of her funny little ways."

Linda sat down beside her.

"I didn't know she was ill," she said.

"Oh, yes! When they operated on her after she was dead, poor girl, they found all this out. It's been a terrible shock to me to hear it all for the first time in an open court. It seems her glands . . ." Mrs. Pole's voice died away into a modest murmuring as she embarked on a subject which she considered her particular province.

Sutane turned away from her with relief and looked again at Mrs. Geodrake, who was still smiling with ill-suppressed mischief in her eyes.

"Why haven't we seen you before?" he enquired politely. "We're not often here, of course—or at least I'm not—but how extraordinary we should have missed you altogether."

He had turned on the full force of his charm and the woman opened before it, became human, if still a trifle girlish.

"Oh, but I've seen you," she said. "All of you. One notices people in the country. There are so few people who are faintly interesting. I've seen you all—you and Mrs. Sutane and your sister and your little girl. I've seen you too," she added, flashing her teeth at Konrad. "I nearly spoke to you last night. You didn't notice me."

She spoke archly and evidently without intentional dramatic effect, but everyone in the room, with the exception of Mrs. Pole and her son, paused abruptly, as though a stone had been thrown amongst them. Mrs. Pole's lowered voice whispered on.

". . . she was large as a child, inclined to put on weight. It worried her very much. She took things . . ."

No one was listening to her. Although no one looked at him directly, general attention was concentrated upon Konrad. He was standing before Mrs. Geodrake, a cup of tea in his hand. One knee was a little bent and his head was slightly on one side. It was one of his most elegantly careless poses.

"I don't think you did," he said.

The woman was blissfully unaware of the sensation she was making. Her loud voice ran happily on.

"Oh, but I did," she said. "In the lane about—when was it?—ten o'clock."

Konrad laughed. He sounded rattled.

"Not guilty, dear lady. It wasn't me."

"Oh, but it was," she insisted, glad to be in the limelight. "I passed the end of the lane. Our house is on the lower road and I was going down to the pillar box. I glanced down the lane, desperately curious to see some of you, and I caught sight of you at once. What am I doing? Dropping bricks? Don't tell me you were going *courting*, as the village says. Now look here, just to prove to you that I'm right I'll tell you what you had on. A yellow pullover and nice clean white flannels. Am I right?"

She glanced round at the rest of the room enquiringly. Her instinct had selected Konrad as an unpopular figure and she was teasing him in an innocent if misguided effort to ingratiate herself with the other men.

Konrad drew back from her as if she had stung him, and his expression became sullen. When he did not speak at all Sutane stepped in to save the silence.

"Quite right, Mrs. Geodrake. He's indicted. Tell me, what do you do with yourself down here all day?"

His quiet affable question relieved the situation, but as the visitor plunged into a tedious recital of her daily round, with an accent on its undeniable dullness, his dark eyes rested upon Konrad speculatively.

Eve and Sock watched him, also, and Campion was interested.

The hero of the Speedo Club retired to the hearth and took up a languid position against it. He looked profoundly uncomfortable.

Halfway through Mrs. Geodrake's recital Mrs. Pole suddenly became aware that she had lost her audience. She put down her cup, wiped her fingers on her wet handkerchief and began drawing on her skinny black kid gloves.

"We shall have the funeral from our house," she said to Linda, but in a tone clearly intended to bring the whole room to order. "I've given your husband the address and the flowers had better be sent there. It will save a lot of trouble in the long run. I quite realise there'll be a lot of publicity, but I'm prepared to put up with that. She was a very popular girl and it's only natural her friends on both sides of the footlights should want to come and pay their respects. You can trust me to see that it's all done nicely. I must be off now because I've got to call at the stationer's before seven and buy the cards. They ought to be put in the post at once. Oh, dear, oh, dear, it is a shock!"

Her feelings overcame her again and she rubbed her red eyes.

"I can't help it," she said to Linda, her voice breaking. "She was all alone in the world, you see, in spite of—well—of everything."

The thought which had only just escaped expression seemed to embarrass her and, as was evidently the habit in her family, she combatted it with a burst of vigorous self-justification.

"After all, she was an actress in her way," she said angrily. "Everyone knows actresses are different to other people. They have more temptation, for one thing. Men flatter them and give them presents and they have to be nice because it's part of their work. She was a good girl, I'm sure— at least her family always thought so, and now's the time to be charitable if ever, when the poor soul's lying dead."

This perfunctory dismissal of what had been both Chloe Pye's lifework and chief publicity plank had the ruthlessness of a pronouncement of time itself and the more sensitive of them shivered a little. Arch, inviting Chloe Pye was dead indeed. It was like the drawer closing on a last year's hat.

"I've chosen Friday because of the matinees on Saturday," said Mrs. Pole, rising. "I'll see her solicitor tomorrow. And Bobby, you go up and get her cases. We may as well take them along. I expect they'll give me the key of her two rooms. She was always short, poor girl. There's her jewellery, of course. You'll hear about that from the lawyer."

She laid a moist hand on Linda's arm.

"You mustn't mind me being practical, Mrs. Sutane," she said. "It's a time for practical people. That's why I'm glad, in a way, I'm here and not Dad. He'd just sit still and suffer. So would we all if we could, but those of us who've always had to do the dirty work know that's no use when there's things to be seen to. Go along, Bobby. Don't stand there gaping."

Sock took the young man out of the room and Mrs. Pole wiped her eyes again, preparatory to retiring from human ken behind her monstrous veil.

"You've all been very kind, I'll say that," she said in the tone of one conveying an unexpected compliment. "There's no hard feeling, Mr. Sutane. You couldn't have pulled up in time and if you had it wouldn't have been any use. She was dead already. The old doctor made that clear. He's a friend of yours, I suppose?"

"No, not at all. We hadn't met him before. His partner attends the servants and we have our own man in town." Linda refuted the implied accusation guiltily.

Mrs. Pole, who now looked like some monstrous black toadstool, nodded.

"He seemed a nice honest old chap," she said. "Is that Bobby down with the bags? How are we going to get to the station from here?"

"My man's waiting with the car." Sutane came forward resolutely.

She shook hands all round, very nearly speechless with an emotion which appeared to be quite genuine.

"You'll all get cards," she said from the doorway. "Give me any names and addresses you can think of. Good night and God bless you all."

Sock and her son escorted her to the waiting car. When the purr of the engine had died away down the drive Mrs. Geodrake rose to go, albeit somewhat reluctantly.

"I'm so glad to have made friends with you all at last," she said with an honesty which was unanswerable. "I hope you'll all come and see us as soon as you've got over all this. So trying for you! Good-bye, Mrs. Sutane, good-bye."

She glanced brightly at Konrad, who avoided her.

"I'm sure there's a mystery about you," she said happily. "I'm sure you had some secret reason for not wanting to be seen in the lane. Say we're friends."

She held out her hand and he took it grudgingly.

Sutane laughed. To the woman who did not know him it was a natural and delightful sound, but to the others, who were familiar with his moods, it was a danger signal.

"Let's get this straight," he said. "It was pretty dark, wasn't it?"

"No, not very. He's a distinctive person, you know." Mrs. Geodrake was only too delighted to continue the discussion. "I saw him quite distinctly as I came back from the post. I was on the lower road and he was in the mouth of the lane."

Konrad stared at her, violent colour replacing his pallor.

"It wasn't me," he said thickly. "That's all I can say. You're mistaken. Some other evening perhaps."

"No, it was last night." Mrs. Geodrake was laughingly insistent. "I won't be bullied. I'm a good witness. What were you up to, you naughty person?"

Konrad began to shake a little and seemed to be about to speak. Sutane took the visitor gently by the elbow.

"Charming of you to have called on us at last," he murmured and directed her gracefully out into the hall.

With their going the room remained in silence for a moment and Konrad, with his head down, strode for the doorway. Eve stepped in front of him. She looked very young with her dark hair standing out round her face and her eyes vivid.

"What were you doing?" she demanded. "Were you creeping about watching?"

Konrad paused. The direct attack seemed to give him just the resistance necessary for him to compose himself. He laughed easily and Campion remembered suddenly that he was an actor.

"The good woman is potty, my dear," he said. "I was not in the lane last night. She saw me some other time and is trying to make herself interesting. There's no point in you getting so excited about nothing. I've got to go and change now. Don't be childish."

He was very convincing and she stepped aside, allowing him to pass her.

Looking back on the scene afterwards, Campion wondered whether, if she had been less precipitate then, the other deaths would have occurred.

Chapter 11

Mercer's attack upon Mrs. Pole was all the more startling because of its singular unfairness and because it came from such an unexpected source.

"What a woman!" he said. "What an unmitigated, incredible, utterly loathsome piece of vulgar female muck! Didn't you want to vomit every moment she was in the room? Don't you hope the car'll crash while she's wallowing in unaccustomed luxury and she'll break her revolting and scaly neck?"

The rest of the gathering regarded him with mild astonishment, a reaction which he appeared to resent intensely. His dark-skinned face became suffused with blood and his light eyes were honest in their hatred.

"You think what you like," he said, planting his slightly unwieldy body on the arm of a chair. "But—I mean to say, did you listen to her? Did you see her?—that awful mourning! That filthy unctuous weeping, with one predatory eye on anything her blasted relation might conceivably have left! Can't you see her going over old clothes, turning out linen baskets, opening up old portmanteaus, trying on dirty half-worn rags that wouldn't fit her, grovelling under beds, searching down the sides of upholstered chairs?"

"My dear!" Linda sounded shocked. "She was all right. A bit ordinary, perhaps."

"Ordinary! My God, if I thought that I'd cut my throat." He laughed derisively and appeared for the moment to have transferred his sudden dislike to his hostess. Linda coloured.

"You're so intolerant," she complained. "She means well and, anyway, she's got to be herself."

"That's what disgusts me," said Mercer in the tone of one settling an argument finally. "I wonder if she's told the undertaker to preserve the bathing dress. Well-darned, it might suit little Evelyn—one never knows."

"Don't, please, dear! You're disgusting." Linda turned her head away.

"It was very kind of her to take Chloe's things. It saves me from sending them on afterwards."

"I wonder if she's got everything. There was a handbag somewhere about."

"Yes. I saw that." Eve spoke languidly. So far she had taken no part in the discussion but had watched the scene with scornful amusement. "It was on the piano in the breakfast room."

"Was it? I'll get it." Mercer heaved himself to his feet. "There's probably the return half of her rail ticket in there. We don't want to lose that." He flung the words at them contemptuously and went into the other room, leaving everyone with the sense of personal insult all the deeper because it was so utterly undeserved.

There was an ominous silence for some little time and presently he came back with the red kerchief and Chloe's book.

"No bag," he said. "Sure she had one?"

"Of course she had one. Besides, I saw it." Eve spoke briskly. "It must be there. It's one of those fold-over things, white with a gilt snap."

They all drifted into the other room and the search began in that curious desultory fashion typical of a mass activity of which the majority does not quite approve.

Mercer alone was eager. His sudden and violent dislike of Mrs. Pole seemed to have given him an unwonted energy. He searched as a child might, looking in the most unlikely places and leaving chaos in his wake. Eve and Linda came behind him, tidying.

"It's not here." He made the announcement as if he were stating a highly suspicious and significant circumstance. "Where is it? If she had a bag it hasn't vanished into space. It hasn't burst. Where is it? Call the servants."

"It doesn't matter. It'll turn up." Linda spoke hastily. "It may even have been packed with her other things."

Mercer thrust his hands into his pockets.

"I think it ought to be found," he said obstinately. "That woman would suggest anything. It may even have a bob or two in it. That'd worry her. That'd give her something to squawk about. I'll ring the bell."

"Oh, please don't." Linda put out a hand involuntarily and as Sutane came swinging in, with Sock behind him, she looked at him with appeal.

"Chloe's handbag?" Sutane stood glancing about him, a certain caution in his manner suddenly becoming apparent. "Yes, that's right, Mercer, we ought to find it. Eve, look in the other room and when you've got it bring it to me."

The search began again, with Mercer leaning on the piano, irritable and impatient.

"We've been all over this room," he said bitterly. "It's been moved. Call the servants."

Sutane pressed a bell at once and when Hughes arrived questioned him brusquely. The nervous vigour of the man was astonishingly evident and Mr. Campion watched the performance with growing interest. Hughes bridled at his employer's tone and went off to find the parlourmaid responsible for the room.

The girl who came was startled but informative. The bag had been on the piano that morning and she thought she had seen it there when she had come to tidy up the newspapers during lunch. It was a white bag. She had not moved it.

With his pale face pink with indignation, Hughes reaffirmed that he had not moved it either, and condescended to make enquiries in the kitchen, although he was certain that no other servant had been into the room all day. He went off, his feathers ruffled.

"It's because it's a handbag, dear," explained Linda in response to Sutane's raised eyebrows. "It suggests money, you see. He's insulted."

"Damn fool," said Sock unhelpfully. "Well, it's gone anyway. You hang on to it when you find it, Linda. I shouldn't—shouldn't open it."

"That's all very well." Mercer was querulous. "It was on there and now it's gone. Who moved it? Has the nurse been in here, or the kid? Where is it?"

Linda gaped at them.

"You're all very excited," she said. "What does it matter? This is absurd."

"What's absurd, my dear lady?" Konrad came bustling in, resplendent in a dinner jacket. His cleanliness and general air of satisfaction seemed to add to Sutane's growing savagery.

"Someone's taken a handbag," he said without preamble. "A white handbag with a gilt clasp. It belonged to Chloe Pye. Have you seen it?"

Konrad smiled.

"Yes, I think so," he said. "A little suède pochette, was it? I'll get it."

He went out of the room, Mercer at his heels.

They were back almost immediately, Konrad passing the composer on the stairs as he came down again.

"This is it, isn't it?" he said brightly, turning the small scented bag over in his hands. "Has the sorrowing sister-in-law phoned for it?"

Sutane took it from him and hesitated, his fingers on the flap. Campion intercepted the glance he shot at Sock and was further enlightened.

"Where was it, Konnie?"

"On the table in the upper hall. I noticed it as I came down just now." The young man was nonchalant and clearly very pleased with himself.

"That's a lie. I saw him coming out of his room with it—or at least I heard him shut his door, which is the same thing." Mercer's eyes were snapping with excitement.

Konrad looked him up and down.

"You're mistaken," he said coolly. "I picked it up off the table outside my door. Why the anxiety?"

Mercer shrugged his shoulders.

"Why did you take it upstairs to your room?" he said. "I've been pretty bored with all this business so far, but now I'm beginning to be interested. I've never liked you, Konrad. You've always seemed to me to be a fishy little person. And now it's dawning on me that you're damned fishy. You were the last man to see Chloe alive. You were creeping about in the lane just before she died, and now you're hiding her handbag."

"I say, old boy"—Sock laid a hand on his arm—"you're a bit forthright, aren't you? Forget it, Konrad. The general excitement's getting the lad down."

Mercer wrenched himself away and went over to the piano, on whose polished top Sutane had shaken the contents of the bag. He stood looking at the small roll of notes, the lipstick, the compendium and the black moiré cardcase. There was also a small amount of loose change and a tube of aspirin tablets.

Sutane showed him the bag was empty.

With Squire Mercer the stimulating effect of Mrs. Pole still persisted. He stood by the piano, presenting a back view to the rest of the room. His hands remained in his trouser pockets so that his jacket was runkled over his heavy buttocks and his short legs looked springy and alert. His shoulders were enormous and his untidy head on its short neck was bent a little. He seemed to be enjoying his unusual burst of energy.

Presently he opened the cardcase, which, however, yielded nothing but its legitimate contents. He turned on Konrad.

"What did you take out of here?" he demanded. "It's no good bleating at me like a tenth-rate stage parson. You've pinched something. What was it?"

Mr. Campion, who had attended many family quarrels in his time, was puzzled. Mercer was behaving in a typically irresponsible fashion, but neither Sock nor Sutane showed the least inclination to curb him. Both of them stood looking at Konrad fixedly, and Eve, too, kept her angry eyes on the young man.

Konrad was very pale and Campion, glancing at his petulant face, was suddenly aware that his eyes were venomous.

"I told you I didn't open the thing," he said, his voice squeaky with passion. "If I had it wouldn't be any affair of yours, Mercer, so keep out of this. I know how you all feel about me and I don't care, I tell you, I don't care. But I'll make you all pay for it in the end. This is a warning. I may hold my tongue for a day or two until my rally's over, but after that you can look out, all of you—and I mean that."

He remained glaring at them, a weak, spiteful, but, in the circum-

stances, extremely comic figure. Yet no one, Mr. Campion was interested
to note, seemed in the least amused by him.

Konrad hesitated. He was beside himself with fury and, although aware
that his exit line had been spoken, yet could not tear himself away from
the stage.

"You've always hated me," he repeated feebly and added with inspira-
tional triteness, "now you're darned well going to be sorry."

He turned and went out, slamming the door behind him.

Sock listened.

"Uncle Vanya has fallen downstairs," he remarked pleasantly if inac-
curately. But there was no smile on his lips and his eyes were solemn.

Mercer turned back to the piano.

"Now all this muck can go to that ghastly woman," he said, laughing
as he shovelled the odds and ends back in the bag again.

Sutane glanced at him and then at Sock and finally eyed Campion
speculatively. The hall door slammed, a phenomenon in itself since in
summer it was always kept open. Linda flushed.

"We can't let him go like this," she said. "He's a visitor here. Besides,
it's so incredibly silly."

She hurried out of the room and Sutane stood looking down at the toes
of his shoes and whistling idly. Presently he took two or three little dancing steps, keeping his feet within an inch or two of their original position.
The occupation appeared to absorb him. Mercer watched and Sock put
his arm round Eve, who did not appear to notice or resent the familiarity.
Nobody spoke.

Hughes came in, still pink and very much on his dignity.

"Mr. Konrad has just gone off in his car, sir, but he appears to have
left his bicycle, the silver-plated one. It's in the cloakroom."

"Who the hell cares?" said Sock briefly, while Sutane turned on the
servant the full force of his personality behind the outburst.

"It doesn't matter," he said. "Don't stand there goggling. It doesn't
matter. It doesn't matter in the least. Go away."

Hughes looked aghast. He opened his mouth to speak, changed his
mind, and went out, closing the door softly but firmly behind him. Sutane
began to whistle again. The atmosphere of the room had become oppressive. Eve threw off Sock's arm and, leaning across the piano top, began
to play with the bag. With her sombre eyes and vivid, unhappy face she
looked like an incarnation of the brooding spirit of the gathering.

"He's done that so that he can come down again and pick it up," she
said thoughtfully. "Gutless little tick, isn't he?"

No one answered her, but her voice broke the spell of silence.

"I shall take Finny up to town tonight," Sutane remarked, looking up.
"Henry needs guidance. Tell her to get her hat on, will you, Sock? Then
I must go. What's the matter, Linda?"

The girl had come in quietly but her expression had betrayed her.

"Hughes is going," she said blankly. "He waylaid me in the hall. He seems to think that things are too difficult, and he's going tonight. He says he's ill. What did you say to him?"

"Nothing, absolutely nothing." Sutane was exasperated.

"My God, these people ought to be on the stage! Still, it doesn't matter, does it? The maids can carry on."

She stood watching him helplessly and he turned to the door.

"I must go. Dinner when we come back, then. Finny's coming up with me. I may bring Dick Poyser back tonight and I want Campion and Uncle William to stay here if they will. I don't think there's anything else. I'm rather glad Hughes is going. He doesn't really suit us."

His last words were delivered over his shoulder as he went out. Linda turned away and Campion, who had developed a keen understanding where she was concerned, realised some of the sense of despair which descends upon a housewife when the mainstay of her staff deserts her in a time of upheaval. An idea occurred to him.

"I've got a man," he said. "Not a very polished soul, I'm afraid, but he'd do anything you told him and he'd tide you over the next day or so until you can get someone suitable. Shall I get him down?"

Her relief was so heartfelt that he was seized by momentary misgivings. Magersfontein Lugg was not everybody's idea of the perfect butler, and in his impulse to be of service to her Campion had not stopped to visualise that lush personality in the Sutane household. However, it was done. Linda had seized the suggestion.

"I'll go and fetch him," he said gallantly.

"Oh, no, don't you go. Jimmy said you weren't to. Can't you phone him?" Her anxiety made her appeal unexpectedly vehement and he smiled at her.

"I don't think so. Lugg's a good chap, but it's a major operation to shift him. Rather like transporting an elephant. We'll be back tonight."

He hurried out of the room before she could speak again and dropped in on Uncle William, who was still napping, the empty decanter at his side.

"Keep an eye on the ladies? Certainly, my boy," he said, blinking rosily. "Must have overslept. I'm gettin' old. Terrible thought. You seem pleased with yourself." He stretched out his plump toes like a cat and hiccuped discreetly. "What d'you want me to do? Only got to command."

Campion considered. "If you have a chance, talk to Eve," he said. "Find out where she's been all her life, what she's interested in and what her ambitions are. If she cares to talk about her childhood encourage it."

"Eve, eh?" Uncle William's bright blue eyes were interested. "A sulky little miss if ever I saw one. Don't understand these new young women. Too much below the surface for my taste."

He got up.

"Don't like women who sit about brooding," he said. "Never did. Still, I'll do what I can. Anything in particular you'd like to know?"

"No. But 1920 is the crucial year."

"The child was hardly born!" Uncle William objected.

"I know. But she may be able to tell you about the family," said Mr. Campion, and as he went out to find the Lagonda he thought it very significant that the only thing that Benny Konrad should have taken from Chloe Pye's handbag, since he himself had examined it early that morning, should have been a cheap silver wrist watch with a broken strap. The watch had interested him when he had looked at it because of the inscription on the inside of the case:

> C. FROM J.
> ALWAYS
> 1920

Chapter 12

Ex-Inspector Blest set his glass on Mr. Campion's desk and reached for a cigarette from the silver box beside it. The study in the Bottle Street flat was warm and quiet. Outside, the blue dusk was beginning to fall over the city and from Piccadilly the quiet snoring of the traffic came soothingly up to them.

The ex-inspector was a large sandy man with raw red ears and boundless good nature lurking shyly behind a defensive bluster. At the moment his pride was in the process of slow recovery.

"I don't mind working with you or even for you," he said. "I didn't care for him going over my head. That's all. He's a queer sort of chap, isn't he? I don't really like him. Too 'I'm-so-busy-get-out-of-my-light.' If he's overworked why doesn't he take a job his own size? I've got no time for blokes who are too busy to live. I was going round to see him when you phoned me. What's he done now? Run over one of his own actresses? Reading between the lines, it sounded like suicide to me. What was her trouble? Love again? Why these women keep killing themselves for love I don't know. Have you ever noticed the only men who ever kill themselves for love are farm labourers? It's a fact. You watch the newspapers. It's having such a long time to brood, I suppose. Well, here's to you."

He took up his glass again and Mr. Campion, venturing to assume their reconciliation complete, came gently to the matter in hand.

"So it was a charwoman," he began. "What variety? Pail, brush, flat cap and curlpapers, or just somebody's nice old aunt in her shopping second best?"

"The last, I'm afraid." Blest was despondent. "The kids at the messenger office remember that the flowers were brought in by an old woman. When I pressed them they said she might have been a char, but whether she had on a brown raincoat or a black artificial fur they do not know. One kid says he remembers a large safety pin showing but more he can't say. The chap at the desk can't remember anything at all. Not very helpful, is it? That's about all I've done and there's been more work in it than you'd think. I had to find the right office first."

He surveyed his feet without affection.

"Mr. Campion," he said suddenly, "I don't want you to be offended, but I've had an idea. Do you think there's a chance this fellow Sutane is having us on a string? I mean, it's not going to turn into a publicity stunt on us, is it? You're sure there is something up?"

Campion sat looking in front of him, his lean face unusually grave. In his mind's eye he saw Chloe Pye lying by the side of the lane, the dreadful irregularity of the line of her head and the tear across her breast, and he remembered her sitting on Sock's knee, her haggard face alight with a vivacity which must in youth have been so very charming.

"Oh, Lord, yes, there's something up," he said. "Don't worry about that."

"Something serious?" Blest cocked a curious eye at him and he pulled himself up guiltily.

"Sutane *is* being persecuted," he said. "There *is* a campaign going on against him. I've told you about the uninvited party. That was genuine. There are other things too. Some I don't follow at all. But from a first look round I think the cause of the trouble is fairly evident. There's a small-part man in the show called Benny Konrad. He's the fellow you want."

"Konrad? I've seen him. Really! Well, now, I shouldn't be surprised." Blest wagged his head and looked worldly. "Very likely. He's a dancer, too, of sorts, isn't he? Now you come to mention it, this is the type of thing they get up to, those little chaps. Petty. Got a mean streak in 'em. Anything to go on?"

"Not much. What I have I'll give you." Mr. Campion was speaking cautiously. "I know he's insanely jealous of Sutane. He was going to take the leading part tonight, and when he was disappointed he practically wept. Then yesterday evening he was seen down the end of the lane that leads from the house. He swore he hadn't been there with quite unnecessary vehemence. That was just after the party, you see, and I happened to notice that just after dinner he went upstairs and came down wearing a key chain. This evening I drove out onto the lower road on my trip up here and I found what I thought I should. There's an A.A. phone box on the road about a hundred yards from the mouth of the lane. He must have sneaked out to phone, not wishing to use the one in the house. It's not much, I know, but it's a little lead. He's got an accomplice."

The ex-inspector frowned. "It could be," he agreed. "It's a foothold anyway. What's his idea? Just spite or has he got any plan?"

Mr. Campion studied his fingernails.

"I've got an unpleasant mind," he said, "but it occurs to me that if Sutane has a nervous breakdown Konrad is his understudy. If a man's overworked there's nothing like a spot of persecution to send him over the edge. This fellow may feel he's being kept under by Sutane."

"Huh!" Blest sounded pleased. "That's a help, I won't deny it," he said. "I'll get hold of the brightest kid from the bureau and take him round to have a look at this fellow's char—or not?"

"Yes, do, only be careful. Don't start the hare running. I don't think you'll find it as simple as that, either. Konrad lives in a service flat at Marble Arch."

Mr. Campion was in his most diffident mood. He had no wish to teach his grandmother to suck eggs and all but said so in as many words.

"I fancy he has a friend, you know," he went on at last. "Some earnest soul about his own age, or a little older, who burns to see the lad succeed. This is probably his handwriting."

Blest took the invitation card that Councillor Baynes had so thoughtfully preserved and his red face brightened.

"Full of ideas, aren't you?" he said appreciatively. "Got his address?"

Campion shook his head.

"No. I don't even know if he exists. But if Konrad is responsible for these little attacks on Sutane—and I think he must be, you know—then he obviously has an accomplice, if only to write these invitations."

He paused and went on consideringly.

"The man I have in mind is youngish, overinterested in Konrad's career, and a silly hysterical type generally. The city's full of them. It may take you a bit of time to find the man you want, but Konrad is a man who goes in for fans. I should look up the secretary of this Speedo Club he sponsors."

The ex-inspector rose. His enthusiasm had revived.

"That's about it," he said, tucking the card into his wallet. "I'm grateful to you, I admit it. This accomplice is taking shape before my eyes. We'll get him, although the chances are Sutane won't prosecute. These private clients never do."

He sighed for the great days of his professional career and looked about for his hat.

"If I can get a tie-up between the accomplice and the char, then between Konrad and the accomplice, we're sitting pretty," he remarked.

Campion leant across the desk. His eyes were narrowed and he seemed absorbed in the blotting paper beneath his hand. Looking at him, the ex-inspector considered privately that he looked less of an ass than he had ever seen him. There was an unusual purposefulness in his bent shoulders and in the poise of his lowered head.

"I say, Blest"—he spoke with studied casualness—"I don't know if all this stuff is sound. It's just my honest opinion at the moment and you're very welcome to it. In return I want every scrap of information you can collect about these people, however irrelevant it may seem. And as a favour to me, don't let anyone suspect you're working on them."

"Oh?" Blest's interest was revived again and he paused encouragingly. "Anything you say," he added after a moment or so. "Anything you say."

Still Campion did not confide and the detective applied a gentle pressure.

"Spotted anything big?" he enquired wistfully, something of an elderly Golden Labrador in his expression.

Campion looked up and laughed.

"Rats in the house," he said. "There's something going on there. Quite a lot I don't understand at all."

Somewhat to his surprise the ex-policeman understood him instantly.

"That's a way of putting it," he said appreciatively. "Rats in the house. Lumme, you don't half know when you've got 'em, do you? We had a flat in the city once. Lock the doors, bung up every hole with glass, and yet you couldn't even turn round without feeling something dirty that didn't like you was watching the back of your neck. Rats in the house! You'll be going down again then?"

"Yes, I think so." Campion spoke soberly and Blest laid an unexpectedly fatherly hand on his shoulder.

"Take a tip from an old pro and don't feel it personally," he said. "That's always the trouble with us. We come up against nice people, people we can understand and enjoy a drink with, and then out comes the dirty linen and it gets us down if we aren't careful. Once we start thinking about right and wrong and extenuating circumstances we're sunk. Take it from me."

He drew back, a little embarrassed by his own homily.

"Hullo?" he said.

"Front-door latch. Lugg coming in."

Campion glanced across the room.

"He was out gallivanting when I arrived. He didn't expect me before the morning."

Blest chuckled. "You'll get the sack from that chap one of these days," he said. "Quite the aged family retainer now, isn't he? What does he weigh?"

"Seventeen stones and eight pounds, and proud of it. I'd recognise your little pipe anywhere, Inspector Smart," observed a sad, thick voice from the hallway. "Don't go before I hang me coat up. I'd like a look at your face again. Just to look at it."

The last words were followed by a minor disturbance which shook the walls a little, and Mr. Lugg billowed grandly into the room, his large white face wearing an unusually friendly expression.

"'Ullo," he said, eyeing his employer with truculent nonchalance. "I thought you was stayin' till Tuesday. Got yourself mixed up in a suicide now, I see. People lay theirselves open to somethink when they ask you down for a week-end, don't they? 'E's a 'arbinger of catastrophe," he added, smiling at Blest. "Take 'im to the pictures and someone's took ill behind yer."

Campion eyed him bitterly.

"He's a conscious clown," he said. "The life and soul of his pub in the mews. Well, I can rely on you then, Blest, can I?"

"You can. And thank you." The ex-inspector shook hands. "So long, Dirigible," he added, prodding the newcomer. "Don't ask me. Look it up."

He went over to the door, but Lugg was before him, his short arms stiff at the sides of his black coat.

"This way, sir, if you please," he said with dignity. "Mind the rug or you'll break your neck. Good day, sir . . . and next time you come 'ere 'ave some gloves so I can give 'em to you like a Christian. So long."

He closed the hall door and it was some little time before he returned, coatless and undoing his winged collar.

"That's better," he remarked, regarding the strip of starched linen. "That won't do again. I use one every time I go out nowadays. I was askin' my friends about laundries. Ours doesn't seem any worse than most, if that's any comfort to you."

He opened a drawer in the bureau and looked thoughtfully at its contents.

"We'll 'ave to buy some new collars," he said. "What do you feel like for supper? I'm 'aving me old tinned 'errings. Per'aps you'd better run out to your club."

Campion got up. "You pack," he said. "I've lent you."

The ponderous form in the vast black trousers and the tight white shirt remained bent over the open drawer. There was a moment of uncomprehending silence.

"Wot?" said Mr. Lugg at last.

"I've lent you. You're to be Mrs. Sutane's butler—God help her—for a day or so, until she can get another man."

Mr. Lugg straightened his back and surveyed his employer with steady dignity. His small black eyes were cold and unfriendly.

"You're barmy," he said. "I'm no butler. I'm a gent's 'elp."

"Well, then, learn a new trade." Campion took out his wallet and studied the card he had taken from it. "I'm going out now and when I come back I want my things packed for a week and yours too. Not in the same bag. Have them at the foot of the stairs and be waiting yourself. We're going down to the country tonight."

"Country?" echoed Lugg in a voice of mutiny. "Butler in the country? You're snuffing round another crime, I suppose? I wish you'd drop this private narking of yours. You're getting old for it, for one thing. It's not smart any more. It's old-fashioned and, in most people's opinion, rather low. I'm sorry to 'ave to tell yer like this but that's 'ow I see it. My friends think you're very vulgar to allow ourselves to get mixed up with crime. Crime's gorn back to its proper place—the gutter—and I for one am glad of it."

He was silent for a moment or so and evidently decided on the other tack.

"I was goin' to suggest we travel, you and me," he said.

"Travel?" Campion was temporarily detracted from his own hasty preparations.

"Mr. Watson's gent is goin' on a sea trip on 'is yacht," murmured Mr. Lugg with crafty casualness. "A very refined type of person one meets, he says, and the motion of the boat is not disturbin' after the first day or so."

His employer regarded him with distaste.

"You make my flesh crawl," he said earnestly. "When you were a ticket-of-leave man——"

" 'Ere—'old 'ard!" Mr. Lugg became both human and reproachful. "Be a gent! Some things we don't bring up if we're decent. I'll do anything you ask me in reason, you know that, but I don't 'ave to be blackmailed into it. I'm glad to see you do look a bit ashamed. You had ought to."

"I was going to say that in those days I found you infinitely more attractive," said Campion, gathering up the shreds of his dignity.

"More shame on you, then." Lugg was not suppressed. "I've bettered myself, my lad, and don't you forget it. What's this noo silly idea of yours now? I'm to take a job as a butler and keep me eyes peeled, I suppose? That's not very nice in itself, is it?—getting into people's houses and nosin' about. It's a low, mean sort of trick *and* an old one. Still, I'll do it for you. I'll be obligin'. I'm to be a detective."

"You're to be a butler," said Campion coldly. "An ordinary butler. You're to do your work and to give satisfaction. And, believe me, you won't have time for anything else. Now, for heaven's sake, shut up and get on with the packing."

He moved towards the door. Mr. Lugg sat down heavily.

"It's madness," he said. "You've never seen a real butler: I 'ave. You're lakes! Where am I goin'?"

"White Walls, where I've been staying. It's a big house with a lot of people in it. The Sutanes own it. Jimmy Sutane, the dancer."

"Oh, the Sutanes . . ." said Mr. Lugg, and his small black eyes became crafty. "There's somethin' chick about the stage," he added unexpectedly. "Per'aps I'll come after all. I don't mind what I do so long as it's not common. Right you are, I'll pack. It'll mean wearin' a coat all day, I suppose?"

"It will. And it'll mean keeping your mouth shut." Campion's tone was final. Lugg sighed.

"All right, Cocky," he said. "I'll do you credit. Where are you orf to now?"

Campion glanced at the card in his hand.

"To call upon a lady."

"Reely?" Lugg was sarcastic. "Give 'er my love."

"I can't," said Mr. Campion. "She's dead."

Lugg guffawed. "Take 'er some flahs then, smarty," he said. "And stay out fer a bit. I've got to 'ave my meal before I pack."

Chapter 13

The warm air, foetid with the vapours from the canal, came gustily down the wide road, bringing with it a cloud of stinging dust and the rustle of paper and prematurely fallen leaves on the pavement.

Through the vase-shaped pillars of the balustrade the gleam of grey-and-gold water was visible, and below, on the towpath, a horse plodded, its feet heavy on the clay.

The tall houses, their stained sides and chipped stucco hidden in the lamplit half-light, rose up with all their original Georgian symmetry, and only the brightly lighted scenes within their many uncurtained windows betrayed their descent in the social scale of an unfaithful city. It was all very quiet and homely and forgotten.

Campion found the number he sought and pressed open the elegant but unpainted gate. The hall door under the square porch with the pillars stood open and a single dusty bulb within cast a grudging light upon worn dark oilcloth and patched, buff-painted walls.

The lower windows were in darkness, but from somewhere far above a wireless set whimpered, its programme maddeningly just out of earshot.

Campion pulled the bell and at the far end of the hall, at the foot of a short flight of stairs, a square of bright light appeared, only to vanish again immediately. He waited, and after a time the door opened once more and crisp footsteps came hurrying towards him.

The woman was not entirely unexpected, in type at any rate. She was small and brisk, her hair elaborately dressed in an old-fashioned style and her silk dress enlivened at neck and elbows with little bits of white lace. Mr. Campion took his courage in his hands and threw away his discretion.

"It's about Miss Pye," he said. "Could I have a word or two with you?"

He was lucky. He knew it the moment he had spoken. She came out to look up at him, and the light from the street lamp opposite the gate fell upon her face, showing it to be small and shrewd, with bright eyes and a turned-up nose which had been much admired in the nineties.

"Why, yes," she said, glancing behind her with a gesture of a conspirator. "Come along to my kitchen. We shan't be disturbed there."

She took his sleeve and pulled him after her, her skirts rustling as she hurried.

"There," she said as they came into a neat little room, bright in spite of its utilitarianism. "Sit down and make yourself comfortable. It's not very swanky but it's cosy and clean."

She had a pretty laugh with a catch of real gaiety in it, and her friendliness contained the whole art of the hostess.

"I don't know who you are," she said, smiling at him, "but you seem a nice boy. Did you know Chloe? Poor girl, what a finish! And she thought she was on velvet. . . . Have a drop of stout? It's all I've got in the house at the moment. . . . Nonsense! You will. Of course you will."

She bustled over to the dresser and, looking at her in the uncompromising light, he judged her to be about sixty, but alert and very pleased with herself and not, at heart, much older than she had ever been.

The panel over the shelf above the range was papered with stage photographs, and as she turned with the glasses she caught him looking at them.

"There I am, on the left," she said. "The one with the saucy little bow. Don't pretend you've heard of me, because you haven't. You were in crawlers when I was kicking my heels about. Renee Roper, that's the name. Don't worry—I never came to the West End. I did my dirty work on tour. Now what's all this about Chloe, poor girl? You were a boy friend, I suppose?"

Mr. Campion hesitated.

"Well, not exactly. I knew her very slightly, as a matter of fact. But I was interested in her and I wanted to know more about her."

"She doesn't owe you money?"

Her intelligent eyes became suddenly hard and he hastened to reassure her.

"Oh, no," he said. "Nothing like that. Frankly, I've got no business to come to you at all. But the fact is she had something I wanted to know about and——"

"Don't tell me any more." The woman leaned across the table to pat his arm. "I understand. All her things are going to those terrible relations. And you've got a wife. So if there was a letter or two from you lying around it might be very awkward. Don't go into it, my boy. You're not the first good-looking youngster who's come to me in the same sort of trouble, I can tell you. I'll take you up to her room in a moment and you can have a look round. I can't do it for a minute or two, so finish your drink. Don't you say a word to anybody, mind, because if that woman Pole got to hear of it I'd never have a moment's peace."

Mr. Campion looked embarrassed. It was hardly the story he would have thought of himself, but in view of all the circumstances it seemed cavalier to refute it.

Renee Roper mistook his silence.

"They'll be there if they're not destroyed," she said and added, a practical touch overlaying her good humour, "if I know Chloe they will be there. I won't say a word against her now she's gone, poor thing, but we weren't exactly old pals. She rented my little box room at the top of the house when she was away and usually when she was in London she took my first-floor duo. Very nice it is. Practically a bathroom as well."

"Have you known her long, Mrs. ——?"

"Miss," she corrected him and sat smiling, her eyes bright. "They never married me, duck," she said, and her laugh was gurgling and happy as a child's. "Oh, dear me, those were the days. Let's see, I've known Chloe on and off for ten or eleven years and I haven't known her well. She wasn't my type. She was all right, though, and you probably knew the best side of her."

Mr. Campion looked interested but unintelligent, and she surveyed him quizzically.

"Men tired of her very quickly," she said and there was a question in her tone to which he did not respond so that she went on hastily. "She had plenty of boys, I'll say that, but they saw through her after a week or two. I am a cat! I don't really mean that. Yes, I do, though. Be honest, Renee. She was spiteful and mean and a sight too possessive for my taste. I'll say it even if she is dead, poor, poor thing. Mind you," she added, refilling her glass after a sharp glance to see that her visitor was still well supplied, "while they were in love with her they'd give her the top brick off the chimney. While it lasted she was the ace all right."

Mr. Campion was leading up to a few delicate questions concerning the identity of his supposed rivals, but he was forestalled. Miss Roper was safely embarked on a flood of gossip.

Chloe Pye had favoured wealthy men friends, it seemed, especially in her latter years. Since she had mainly appeared in vaudeville she had not been thrown in close contact with her own profession and had acquired most of her admirers from what was, in Miss Roper's frank opinion, the wrong side of the footlights.

"She was proud when she was up and frantic when she was down," she summed up. "There's plenty like her and they're not all on the stage. When she had a place in the West End, and she did from time to time, she'd be as starchy as you please when she called round to fetch something from the box room, but she was very different when she first came home from abroad, broke to the wide. Before she got a shop at the Argosy she was very nervy."

She nodded to emphasise her point, and her small face, which was still cheeky in spite of her age, wore a serious confidential expression.

"That's a fact," she said.

Cautious footsteps on the linoleum-covered stairs outside caught her attention and she sprang up.

"There's that woman down at last," she announced. "Wait a moment."

She trotted out, her elaborately dressed head held high and her dress rustling consequentially.

There was much whispering outside in the hall, and presently she came back alone. She was smiling.

"They're having a time at the theatre," she said. "They've been nervy there for some time and now this looks like a real bit of bad luck. Actors are a superstitious lot. That woman was from the Argosy. She brought back a lot of Chloe Pye's things from her dressing room. Between you and me, I think the management's had a taste or two of Chloe's relations and doesn't want 'em nosing around backstage. This girl said she'd take the stuff up so I gave her the keys. That's why you had to wait."

Mr. Campion's eyes grew blank.

"From the theatre?" he enquired, relapsing for a moment into the protective inanity of his early youth. "An actress?"

Miss Roper chuckled.

"No, ducky," she said. "Not every woman employed round a theatre is an actress, by a long chalk. I don't know what this girl's job is but you can take it from me she's not an actress. A little boiled cart horse, that's what she looks like. A secretary or something, on the theatre-management side, perhaps. She told me her name—Finlay, or Finborough, or something. Well now, are you coming up to find those little billets-doux of yours?"

He followed her quick light footsteps up the stairs to the big square room which, with the little bedroom behind it, took up the whole of the first floor. It was much the kind of room he would have expected; bright with chintz and dusty hangings. It had a three-piece suite arranged round the fireplace, and over the mantel was an ill-drawn sketch of Chloe in costume, carefully framed and signed with a flourish.

The other pictures varied between the sentimentally lewd and the illustrated Scotch joke variety wherein Glengarried dogs take the place of figures. There were no books and a small writing table with drawers was the only sign of mental activity.

The landlady sniffed.

"Soon gets musty, doesn't it?" she said cheerfully. "Like to open a window for me?"

While he did so she went over to the desk.

"Hullo!" she said. "You're not the first, my boy. The girl from the theatre has done a bit of looking round, too. See, the drawers aren't quite closed and someone's been through them pretty quickly."

She displayed the tousled contents of the top drawer with growing amusement.

"They were all tidy when I brought her laundry up this afternoon," she said, "and I happen to know because I took a peep. I don't mind telling you I was looking to see if there was any loose cash about. She owed me a week or so and I thought I'd like to be sure it was there before me and that sister-in-law of hers came to high words. There wasn't a halfpenny, of course. Not that I'd have taken it. At least I don't think I would. Certainly not more than I was owed. Although God knows I've given her plenty in her time. Here, I wonder if she's been up in the box room, too? I gave her the key. Come on."

The visitor had been in the box room. After careful consideration of the two tin trunks of old letters, programmes and picture postcards which were up there, Miss Roper pronounced her opinion that the woman had gone through them with a "quick tooth comb."

"What d'you know about that?" she said, her eyes widening and a mischievous smile hovering at the corners of her lips. "Some people have got a nerve, haven't they? I wonder what she was after, the cat. . . . Doing a kindness for one of the fellows in the company, I'll bet!"

She chuckled hugely.

"You're not the only one, ducky. There's dozens of you! Well, now, what about these letters of yours? That Pole woman will go all through this lot. It'll broaden her mind for her perhaps."

The notion seemed to delight her, and Campion, who realised that his work had already been done for him by Miss Finbrough, sought about for some plausible way out of the situation.

"I don't think I need bother," he said. "My—er—what I was looking for evidently isn't here."

Her quick eyes took in his expression and once more she gave her own explanation to his words.

"Oh, you were a *real* writer, were you?" she said. "I know . . . great piles of stuff all on the same sort of writing pad. Reams and reams of it! I know. That's the kind that gets destroyed, my boy. No girl wants to take round a pantechnicon. You needn't have worried. It's the little dangerous half sheets that get kept. Who's going to wade through a life story every time they want cheering up? Well, now that your mind's at rest, come on. Let's go down."

As they descended through the great shadowy house, whose elegance was departed forever, she went on to talk about the accident.

"One of the Brock brothers, on my second floor, said it sounded like suicide to him from the papers," she remarked. "The jury didn't have enough to go on, or something. But if there's one thing I am sure of, it wasn't that. Chloe never killed herself. She was far too conceited, if you know what I mean. Besides, I ask you! There she was safe in a nice long run, starred and everything. She had never done so well for herself ——never! If you ask me, she had a nice fat pull with that management, because she was going off. That's got to be faced. She wasn't the nice little girl you knew, you know. She was forty-two to my certain knowledge. It didn't sound to you like suicide, did it?"

"It wasn't," he assured her absently. "I was down there at the time."

"Really?" She pounced on the admission. "You saw the accident? Well, that is a mercy. You're just the boy I want. I wonder if I could ask you to have a few words with one of my lodgers? It'd be a Christian act and help me a lot. I'm worried out of my mind about him. A word from someone who actually *saw* it might make all the difference."

Mr. Campion hesitated, but to refuse her would have been more than churlish. She dragged him into the kitchen again.

"You sit down and have a drink and I'll fetch him," she said, forcing him into a chair. "He's only a boy, just down from college. Oxford or Cambridge—I forget which. And of course he's writing a play and renting my attic. I think he's got a little money but he says he gets the right atmosphere here, and so I do what I can for him. It's probably a dreadful play. You can tell it's old-fashioned by the mere fact that he wants to write it in an attic. I tell him that, but you know what these college kids are—I don't know what they teach 'em at those places; they just seem to keep 'em a steady thirty years behind the times, as far as I can see— but I want you to talk to him because Chloe got at him. I won't say what I think of her for doing it. She was old enough to be his auntie. He thinks she was I don't know what, and this has bowled him clean over, poor kid. He won't eat and he can't sleep. He's half enjoying it, mind you, but it's not good for him. He's got it into his head that she committed suicide and he's to blame."

She laughed but her face softened.

"Aren't they wonderful at that age? If you told him he was too sure of himself by half he'd either not believe you or cut his throat. Just see him and tell him it was an ordinary accident. Be a dear—to please me."

She went out before he could protest, even had he wished to do so, but put her head round the door again to whisper an admonition.

"Don't laugh at him. He's very unhappy. He's only been in love once before and she was a girl in a shop who reminded him of the Dame sans

Mercy. From what he's told me, she was more like Ophelia. Anaemic, anyway."

She disappeared again and was gone for some considerable time. Campion stood by the kitchen table and thought about Miss Finbrough and the one person in the world for whom she would have come on so questionable an errand. He wondered what she had found in her brief search.

Miss Roper's returning footsteps recalled him to the matter in hand. The door opened and she came hurrying in, her face pink and motherly.

"Here's Mr. Peter Brome to see you," she said briskly. "I know you'll like to have a chat."

Campion glanced over her head at the young man who came so unwillingly into the brightly lit room. He was very young and very handsome in the downy, small-boy fashion of his kind. At the moment his face was unnaturally grave and he conveyed the impression that he was holding himself with particular care, as if his grief was some great overfull pitcher which he was carrying and which any jolt must spill. It gave him a curious clumsy and unsteady air, embarrassing both to himself and to those about him. He wore an old tweed sports jacket which hung limply on wide flat shoulders, and the highly polished pipe which he gripped, as though it were both his mainstay and his passport, was unfilled.

He towered over Miss Roper, who was clearly delighted with him, and addressed Mr. Campion in a naturally deep voice which an effort towards maturity had rendered positively sepulchral.

"How do you do?" he said. "I don't know your name." The baldness of the statement seemed to worry him and he added, "Not that it matters," and blushed violently at the ungraciousness of his own words.

In view of the delicacy of his mission Mr. Campion gave his second-best name and they shook hands solemnly. There fraternisation came to an abrupt stop. Peter Brome moved stiffly and purposefully across the kitchen until he came to the wall, where he turned round and took up a position too nonchalant to be real and barely safely balanced.

Miss Roper looked at Campion appealingly.

"Tell him about the accident," she commanded. "He wants to know."

"No. No, please!" Peter Brome's gesture was unwieldy but emphatic, and his deep voice was quite expressionless. He looked desperately uncomfortable and Mr. Campion felt very old.

"Come out and have a drink," he suggested.

Mr. Brome's embarrassment increased beyond dignity's endurance point.

"You ought to have a drink with me," he said and his grave and unhappy eyes met Campion's own.

"My dear fellow, let's have several drinks," persisted Mr. Campion, resenting the one-foot-in-the-grave sensation which was stealing over him.

"You'd better not hang about or they'll be shut," put in Miss Roper with practical cheerfulness. "Off you go. If I don't see you again then, my boy, good-bye and good luck. I'm pleased to have met you. Not a word to Mrs. You-Know-Who and you can trust little Renee. Good-bye, my dears. Don't fall in the canal coming home."

She bundled them out into the soft warm night and waved to them as they reached the gate.

Mr. Campion and his hatless companion walked down the paper-strewn pavement, the wind behind them.

Peter Brome shook back his locks, which were more untidy than strictly Byronic, and looked up at the sky, tattered by the dark irregularities of the housetops. Campion wondered uncharitably if he knew the lamplight was shining on his magnificent profile and decided in all honesty that probably he did not.

"Quite a dear old thing," remarked the young man abruptly, "but frightfully embarrassing. Some sort of frustrated mother complex."

Campion, who thought for a moment that he was talking about Chloe Pye, was saved from an impossible *gaffe* by his companion's next remark.

"She insisted that I come down to see you. I feel I'm imposing on you frightfully, but when—when a thing happens that's utterly senseless and ghastly one's natural morbid inquisitiveness wants to know how, even if—if the reason why is simply incomprehensible, don't you think?"

The long speech had unsettled him and the pitcher was rocking dangerously. Mr. Campion spoke hastily.

"It really was an accident," he said.

"I wish I could believe that." Peter Brome implied his polite rejection of the theory. "I don't know why I'm talking to you about it. I don't mean to be rude, of course. But if you'd known her as I did. God, the dreadful unreasonableness of it! The appalling unbearable *waste!* She was a wonderful person."

His voice wavered and was silent, and the face he lifted to the London stars was angry and, in its extraordinary beauty, rather terrible.

With the weight of his thirty-six years heavy on his shoulders, Mr. Campion reflected that high tragedy was a right thing and man could justly exult in it, but low tragedy, with its horrible undercurrent of derisive laughter, was deadly stuff indeed.

His desire to kick his companion was tempered by the suspicion that the impulse had its root in envy.

They reached the Spiked Lion, a rather regrettable little hostelry of the refined back-street variety, in silence.

As Peter Brome struggled with the etiquette of drink-buying for a perfect stranger to whom one is in imminent danger of unburdening one's soul, his solemnity returned and he stuck rigidly to his somewhat bigoted idea of small talk, firing abrupt and disconnected questions at his acquaintance and being careful not to betray from his expression that he had understood any word of the replies.

The other drinkers at the bar were known to each other and were inclined to resent the intrusion of strangers, so Campion's visit was not prolonged. They drank their two modest half pints each and, honour and hospitality both being satisfied, came out into the night again.

Feeling that he might now decently return to his own troubles, Mr. Campion was about to take his leave when he was disarmed.

"I'd like to talk to you about her," said Peter Brome. "Half my life has suddenly gone, you see. I didn't know her people and I shall never see or hear of her again. It really is like a door shutting."

It dawned upon Mr. Campion just in time that a clear and vivid word picture of Chloe Pye as she had really been would not help Mr. Brome in his present loneliness. Campion suppressed it, therefore.

"I'd like to walk down to the canal, if you don't mind. There's a bridge there. We can look over it."

Peter Brome stated his desire meekly but with a childlike confidence that it would be gratified, and they walked on over the dry, deserted pavements to the shining and mildly odorous water.

"I suppose if I told you that I'd like to chuck myself in there you'd think I was a fool?" said Mr. Brome, not altogether unexpectedly as they took up their positions against the greasy stucco balustrade and looked down at the froth and leaves in the sluggish stream.

"My dear chap, you'd die of diphtheria, not drowning," said Campion involuntarily, and his companion broke out into sudden happy laughter.

"I am a fool," he said despondently, his amusement vanishing as soon as it had come. "God, I ought to be shot!—clowning and posturing about when she's gone. 'Chloe's a Nymph in flowery groves, A Nereid in the streams.' That's D'Urfey. But the Cartwright one is the best. She was a year or two older than me, you know.

> " 'Chloe, why wish you that your years
> Would backward run, till they meet mine?
> That perfect likeness, which endears
> Things unto things, might us combine? . . .
> So, by this, I as well may be
> Too old for you as you for me.'

I was tremendously pleased when I found it. I thought it was a sort of omen. And now . . ."

He braced himself against the stucco and stretched, as if the vigorous physical effort relieved him of some of his intolerable burden of sorrow.

"Was—was she frightfully cut about?" he demanded gruffly and settled himself with a grim stoicism, all the more difficult because it was conscious and he disliked himself for it, to hear the worst.

Mr. Campion felt out of his depth. He was shocked to discover that he could not remember if a horror was better balm than an anticlimax. He compromised, as many have done before him, by giving a faithful but not highly coloured account of the whole tragedy.

Peter Brome listened in silence, his face very white and young in the lamplight.

"Thank you," he said at last. "Thank you. You've practically convinced me. I was so afraid it was suicide, you see."

"Why? She was very happy at the theatre."

"Oh, yes, at the theatre." Peter Brome's tone expressed his contempt for those material matters which are such an anxiety and yet such a comfort to those who grow wearied of their own emotions. "It was her life that was so difficult. We were in love." He met the other man's eyes squarely, as though defying him to show any amusement.

Mr. Campion was grave, however. He was not too old to know that love in any of its tricksy forms was not negligible.

"I wanted her to marry me," Peter Brome continued with dignity, "but she always said no, putting up all kinds of ridiculous suggestions—the little difference in age and that sort of thing."

"How old are you?" enquired Campion helplessly.

"Twenty-two. Quite old enough to know my own mind, God knows. Well, when these objections of hers went on I began to realise that there was something else she hadn't told me, because she did love me. Otherwise she wouldn't—oh, well, I know she did. We were going on the river last Sunday. We'd fixed it up and were both looking forward to it rather seriously. So when she told me she'd got to go away for the week-end I was pretty fed up and we had our first serious quarrel."

He paused and his eyes were anguished as the enormity of his tragedy overcame him. He pulled himself up and went on.

"Well, it seemed to upset her as much as it did me. We made friends again and it all came out. She was married, you see, and the fellow had found her again after they'd parted for some years and naturally he'd found out his mistake and wanted her back. She was going down to see him to try to make him give her a divorce. She wouldn't tell me his name. I swore I'd never mention it to a soul but it doesn't matter now. She was brokenhearted and so was I. The next thing I heard this had happened."

Campion did not speak.

He stood with his hands on the balustrade, his shoulders a little bent.

Seen through sophisticated eyes, Chloe's story took on a very different flavour from the straight tale of young love in difficulties which he had just heard. As he stood looking at the water a company of little circumstances ranged themselves in his mind and slipped quietly into a neat pattern.

Sutane making a place for Chloe in the show in spite of all opposition; Sutane sitting in the dark stalls, ordering Chloe not to accept his wife's invitation; Sutane insisting to the doctor that Chloe was a stranger to him; Chloe sitting on Sock's knee, referring to Sutane as an old friend; the little watch with its inscription; and finally, providing the key to the whole, Miss Finbrough searching through the dead Chloe's papers with reckless haste.

His pale eyes grew hard behind his spectacles, and he was barely aware of Peter Brome's deep young voice sounding earnestly at his side.

"You probably disapprove of divorce. Forgive me, but you've forgotten what love's like. It's tremendous. It's the only thing that matters. You're helpless. It's quite unreasonable. There's so absolutely nothing you can do. It suffocates you."

Mr. Campion, who had been growing rapidly more human in the past few days, experienced a desire to fly screaming from this awful ghost of dead summers who murmured such emotional truth and intellectual fallacy so unjustly in his ear. One cry of protest alone escaped him.

"You haven't a monopoly on tragedy, you know," he said, but unconsciously he made his tone light and friendly, "not you twenty-two-year-olds."

Peter Brome was misled by the gentleness, which he mistook for toleration.

"No, but we're new to it," he said. "It can't be worse. If it were, people would be dying from it every day. Nothing can be worse than this. It's inconceivable. Why, it's so frightful it almost goes the whole circle. It's a horrible thing to say, but it's nearly—nearly rather *fine*, it's so exquisitely hurtful."

Mr. Campion thought of Linda, of Sarah, of Chloe as the daylight saw her, of Sutane, and lastly of himself. He took Mr. Brome's hand and shook it warmly.

"Good-bye," he said abruptly. "She died very quickly and without any pain at all. It *is* rather fine when you think of it. Good-bye."

He hurried away, his long thin shadow jolting and flapping down the lamplit road.

Mr. Brome remained on his bridge with his tragedy, which was as sad and lovely and remote as the stars above his tousled head.

Chapter 14

On the following morning Mr. Campion sat long over his breakfast, his thin body practically submerged in the plush billows of a crimson settle.

At that hour the club dining room was hushed with that particular variety of breathy peace sacred to the sober business of facing the world again.

The heavy curtains, corded and swathed with Victorian generosity round the vast windows, seemed to resent the strong sunlight which burnished their fringes and strove to disclose the intimacies of their weave, so that the great room was made misty by the little war between light and shadow.

The warmth, the comfort and the general air of friendly privacy soothed Campion and made him feel sensible and secure in mind. From his present sanctuary the events and emotions of the previous evening seemed to have had a dreamlike quality, but without the happy illogicality which makes most dreams so pleasant in retrospect.

Peter Brome had led him into Pirandello's world and today only the common facts remained, and these were as important and as unpleasant from one angle as another.

On reflection he was glad that he had telephoned to Linda excusing himself and had sent the protesting Lugg to White Walls alone. "Young George," the garage mechanic who sometimes obliged him by driving the car, had superintended the transportation and had delivered his report upon it, recording that the lady herself had come to the front door to receive her temporary butler and that Mr. Lugg had been the perfect gent throughout. Young George was of the opinion that Lugg would be okay if he kept it up. Campion devoutly hoped he might. As he sat looking over his paper at the dust particles in the beam of light from the nearest window he went over every detail of his conversation with Linda. He remembered it with surprising clarity. He heard again her quick, disappointed protest and his own apology and hasty insistence that there was work on the case to do in town. He remembered the pause which had followed it and afterwards her polite but unconvinced acceptance and her genuine gratitude for Lugg.

He had rehearsed the whole incident from the first sound of her voice to his own final good-bye before he checked himself and stared blankly and unhappily before him. He had no doubt that his bittersweet preoccupation with her would wear off in a little while, but now the unreasonableness, the thundering idiocy, of the whole phenomenon still exasperated him.

For the first time the pity of it occurred to him; the sudden realisation left him startled and angry. In common with most other unembittered mortals, he cherished a secret belief that the mental, emotional and physical female equivalent of himself did somewhere exist, so that to discover it and find it unattainable was an elementary form of tragedy none the less painful because it was a hackneyed tale. Moreover, he was also faced by the disturbing reflection that the chance of any such miracle occurring twice in the lifetime of a man of his own peculiar and lonely temperament was remote.

The situation shocked him, and he found himself resenting it bitterly. Since he was not of an age to enjoy it, the prospect of becoming involved in a bona fide tragedy revolted him and he took temporary refuge behind a time-honoured shield and denied the existence of the attraction.

He looked down at the newspaper and read the report on the inquest on Chloe Pye, which was recorded in full. Since no publicity given to the dead woman could now conceivably be considered advantageous to her, the journalistic conscience had found itself soothed, and this and a dearth of other news had combined to make a double column of the story in the cheaper press. Optimism had made Sutane careless. It had been an open verdict, not "misadventure" as he had said. The jury had returned "death from shock, accelerated by a state of *status lymphaticus*" but had also recorded that there was no evidence to show if the dead woman had fallen from the bridge by accident or design. Sutane's part in the car accident immediately after Miss Pye's death had been very fully reported by the newspapers and there were several references to his recent ill luck in the gossip columns. It was not a satisfactory story and one which left an unpleasant impression on the mind. The fact that Chloe had been in a bathing dress at the time of her death was mentioned everywhere, but without explanation, and the whole history of fast cars, house parties and hinted suicide suggested wild doings which money and prestige had hushed up. The whole thing was most unfortunate. The public, who hero-worshipped Sutane, had no objection to him enjoying himself but could only be expected to resent any hint that he was relying on their hero-worship to get away with something which would spell disaster to any private member of that public itself.

Campion set down the paper and forced himself to look at his own problem coldly and to consider the miserable discovery which had led to his decision to disappear unobtrusively from the affair and from the society of the Sutanes.

Regarded dispassionately, it resolved itself to a simple enough question. If you are violently and unreasonably attracted to a married woman, to discover immediately afterwards that to the best of your belief her husband has killed, either by accident or design, a previous wife, in order, presumably, to retain his present ménage intact, do you involve yourself further in the situation, denouncing him for his crime and walking off with the lady?

"No, you don't," said Campion aloud, and with such a wealth of feeling that the club servant who had approached him on silent feet stepped back in astonishment.

The message proved to be a summons from Ex-Inspector Blest, who had called at the flat in the hope of catching Campion before he started for the country and had been redirected by a caretaker to the Junior Greys. Campion went to the telephone unwillingly, but Blest was in a tenacious mood and would have none of his excuses.

"What on earth are you playing at?" he demanded, his tone aggrieved and suspicious. "Why the high and mighty all of a sudden? Stubbed your toe on your own dignity? I want you, Mr. Campion. I want you to take sights. I'd like your opinion, I would really. It was your idea in a way. Listen . . . I've found him."

"The accomplice?" Campion betrayed an unwilling interest.

"I don't know yet. One thing at a time." Blest was irritated. "I've found the secretary of the bike club. His name is Howard, and he works in a wholesale chemist's in the Hampstead Road. I met him last night. He'll be at the Three Eagles in the Euston Road about twelve. I'll get him going and you drop in casually about half past. I want you to look at him. What's the matter with you? On to something else?"

Campion, who was finding himself unduly jumpy, disliked the quick curiosity in the last question and capitulated.

"Half after noon, then," Blest repeated. "Don't put on your best clothes, you know. It's not exactly a palace. So long. I'm relying on you."

He rang off, and at twelve twenty-five Campion descended from a bus in the Tottenham Court Road and walked down towards Euston.

The young man deep in conversation with Blest in a corner of the Three Eagles was disappointing. Considered as an accomplice of the elegant Konrad, he was unlikely to the point of being absurd. He was a large, carelessly dressed person with a very clean neck and collar and very dirty fingernails. His face was raw from exposure to the wind and conveyed somehow that it was cast from an inferior design on which no time or thought had been expended, while the fact that his head was almost shaved to the crown, where a limp, greasy layer of thick hair lay like a roof, did not improve his appearance.

He had a loud, aggressive voice with considerable force of character behind it, and at the moment he was riding his hobbyhorse hard.

"It's the game, that's what matters to me," he was saying, conscious of the virtue in the statement but none the less sincere for all that. "It's all honorary with me, you know. I don't take a penny of the club funds, and wouldn't, not if they asked me. It's the road I like. You see things awheel. Get to know the country you was born in. You come into your rightful heritage, that's what I say. Besides, it's so cheap! A chap like me can afford it."

"I agree with you," said Blest heartily and, catching sight of Campion, introduced him as a Mr. Jenkyn. "Haven't seen you about lately," he added mendaciously. "Mr. Howard here is secretary of the Speedo Club —cycling. Heard of it?"

Mr. Howard paused to remark on his pleasure at meeting Mr. Jenkyn and hurried on with his confidences to Blest.

"Even the name's amateurish," he went on, taking up his harangue at the point where he had left it. "See what I mean? Speedo. . . . It's a slang word, isn't it? To my mind that strikes the note of the whole outfit —not quite the article. If we was a proper club we could affiliate ourselves to one of the big outfits, and there's benefits in that. Records and championships and that sort of thing, with decent prizes to compensate you for your trouble. As I was saying to some of the chaps last Saturday, what are we now? What *are* we? A blasted publicity organisation for a chap who isn't a real enthusiast. If he was a real wheel lover it would be different. If he was keen on the game any one of us would be pleased and proud to do him a bit of good. But when he comes down by train and gets tired out by a thirty-five-mile spin, then you're apt to ask yourself, aren't you?"

"You certainly are," agreed the ex-inspector. "You'd like to change things a bit, I daresay?"

Mr. Howard drank deeply from his tankard and his small green eyes narrowed.

"I could resign, myself, and join one of the big clubs," he said, "but then I shouldn't be a secretary—not for years, anyway—and I like organising. It satisfies you if you've got it in you. Besides, if you can see the way to work really difficult things like runs and club dinners and sight-seeing tours and you haven't got the authority, it gets on your nerves to see someone else doing it badly."

He spoke feelingly, and Blest nodded his complete agreement.

Stimulated by a second pint Mr. Howard spoke again.

"If we called ourselves by a proper name—the Merton Road C.C. or something like that—and got rid of our stage associations we could be one of the finest, smartest little clubs in London," he said with sad conviction. "As it is, what happens? Where are we going? Our real tiptop liners are leaving us for clubs with more scope, while a handful of older members who like to get round the stage door run this bloke's publicity stunts for him. They get free passes for the show—we all do, I admit that—but I'm a cyclist. I like fresh air and the road under me."

He paused and refused the cigarette Campion offered him, explaining that smoking was bad for his wind.

"They've given him a presentation machine," he said in a burst of confidence which he obviously considered indiscreet but was unable to control. "Silver-plated and all slap up. I did the collecting because I was asked to and I'm good at collecting. I've got the gift. I like it. But I don't approve of it. I think a silver-plated bike is silly. I think if the other clubs get to hear of it they'll laugh at us—and rightly so. That's the kind of thing that irks you. If you're a first-class man awheel, well up to any amateur standard, you don't want to feel that every other user of the road privately feels that your club is nothing but a pack of pansies on bicycles. It's degrading—degradating. I'll get my own way in the end but it's taking time. There's a lot of snobbery to fight. There's a posh flavour about anything connected with the stage, and some of the silly beggars fall for it. I'm very nice to Konrad when I see him, though I don't like him personally. In the finish he'll drop out of sight and we'll get on with making a first-class job of the club."

At this point Mr. Campion bought another round and the conversation became general. Mr. Howard was consumed by his enthusiasm for his chosen sport, however, and returned to it almost at once.

"He's useful in a way, of course," he admitted. "He's got influence. An article like this, now, needed writing, you know. It was time it was said."

He pulled a folded evening paper from his coat pocket. It was the first of the fuller editions and contained a short topical article on the magazine page with the heading: "Murder on the Roads. A Cyclist's View. By Benny Konrad, President of the Speedo Cycle Club."

Blest skimmed through it, with Campion reading over his shoulder. It was a bright little essay written with deliberate intolerance and printed to provoke correspondence. Cyclists were briefly mentioned, but the danger of the speeding motorist was the main argument.

"It's come at a good moment," said Mr. Howard, replacing the paper in his pocket. "There's thousands of us chaps on the road, every one of us with our lives in our hands. These motorists just kill us. They can't see us half the time. This article could have been much stronger, but I don't suppose the editor would stand for it. He's got to think of his advertisers. Still, it's come after that business in the paper yesterday where Jimmy Sutane ran down some poor girl and killed her. Did you see the bit? Konrad is in the same show as Sutane and their names are linked together. I expect that's why he wrote this and the paper, noticing the connection, printed it. That's how they work these things. Anything topical. That's the motto of the newspapers."

They finished their beer and went out into the sunlight, where they parted from Mr. Howard. Blest glanced after his jaunty figure and sniffed.

"Well, that's not *him*," he said, "is it?"

Mr. Campion agreed. "No," he said thoughtfully. "No, that's not the accomplice. A trying lad in his own way, no doubt, but not a dirty little tick. There's nothing underhand about our Mr. Howard. Konrad doesn't seem to be too popular with him, does he?"

The ex-inspector grunted.

"If you ask me, young Mr. Konrad won't be too popular in other quarters this afternoon," he said. "He's employed by Mr. Sutane, isn't he? What the hell does he think he's playing at, coming out with an article like that? He couldn't have written it in the time, of course. That's something they've had by them. But he must have authorised the use of his name. They probably read it to him over the telephone."

Campion frowned. "I don't think there's much in that," he said with more hope than conviction. "After all, there's very little actual connection . . ."

"Don't you believe it!" Blest interrupted him. "That's an example of the association of ideas. There's whole campaigns of advertising run on that principle. You know and I know that Sutane has done nothing reprehensible and there's no mention of his name in that article. But who reads a newspaper accurately?—one in a hundred. The average half-interested person sees one day that Sutane has been in an accident in which a woman has been killed, and the next day he sees 'Murder on the Road' by Benny Konrad. The name 'Konrad' makes him think of the name 'Sutane' and the last thing he heard in connection with it. The two ideas are put together in his own mind. It's child's play. I had it all explained to me once."

"He'd hardly dare do it deliberately," said Campion slowly.

"Maybe not." Blest was vigorous. "But whatever it was, it wasn't tactful. If you ask me, Master Konrad is shouting for trouble and I shouldn't be at all surprised if he got it."

Campion looked at him aghast, a certain little chain of incidents returning to his mind.

"Oh, no," he said vehemently. "No."

Blest cocked an eye at him.

"You've got something up your sleeve," he said. "I've noticed it all the morning. But don't trouble to tell me. I shall know sooner or later. This is only the beginning of this business. I can feel it in my bones."

Mr. Campion sighed and his lean face looked suddenly drawn.

"You're wrong," he said but added heavily after a pause, "or at least I hope to God you are."

Chapter 15

My dear Campion——[Uncle William's cramped hand fluttered crazily over the page.]

Since your rather extraordinary desertion I have stuck to my post, gathering up such odd scraps of information as have come my way. I have no doubt that you know what you are up to and have some very good reason for going off in this remarkable manner. I shall be glad to hear it when we meet in the near future. Let me say now that I have absolute faith in you, as I have always had, and I am perfectly sure that you are well equipped to bring to a satisfactory solution all the little difficulties with which we now find ourselves beset.

This house is not a very happy harbour at the moment, I am afraid. Konrad's bicycle is still in the cloakroom, I noticed this morning, so I suppose we still have a visit from him hanging over our heads. This depresses Linda, I fancy, for she seems a little less her usual laughing self.

Eve is a curious girl. I used at one time to have a light sure hand with a woman, but I confess I can make but little of her. She has some secret; I am sure of it. Such long hours alone, brooding, are not natural in a girl of her age. In 1920 (you will remember you asked me to enquire particularly into that date) she was one year old and lived with her dear mother in Poole, while Jimmy was away on the Continent. Afterwards she was sent to a convent school in the West Country, her mother dying when she was eight. From that time the good nuns looked after her until two years ago, when her brother conceded to her request that she might attend an art school in London. She has finished there and now there is some talk of her continuing her studies in Paris. From what I remember of that city it seems hardly the place to send a young girl to alone, but I have no doubt it is greatly changed. The war saddened but purified. A pity if true in the case of Paris, but there you are.

To return to the girl. Her lassitude puzzles me. At seventeen one should be up and doing, straining at the leash, the blood boiling in the veins, but she is not really anxious to continue her art work and speaks of it without great enthusiasm. I shall hammer away at her, gently of course, but at the moment she remains an enigma.

Jimmy returns here each day and is growing rapidly more and more distraught before my eyes. Sometimes I feel it is only his work and his indomitable courage which keep him going at all. Young Petrie flits in and out in a newer car, his own having gone to perdition long past its time, and Richard Poyser, a type I cannot bring myself wholly to trust, has visited us once. He was here to lunch and seemed very excited over a foolish article which some wretched newspaper fellow persuaded young Konrad to set his name to. I read it and confess I saw nothing to it, but both Poyser and Jimmy seemed to think it unfortunate. Of course, one is apt to forget that Art is a hard taskmaster and when a man like Jimmy is suffering from overstrain "how easy is a bush supposed a bear," as my immortal namesake says.

Squire Mercer, with typical callousness and what I think I may allow myself to call damned selfishness, has flown to Paris to attend some function but is expected to return before the end of the week, if not in time for the funeral.

The only happy people here are the child and your man Lugg. He is shaping as well as can be expected and appears to have become devoted to little Sarah, whom he insists upon calling "the young mistress," an appellation which seems to afford them both great pleasure. I fancy I detect a note of derision in it at times, but she seems to have grown very fond of him in this short time, which speaks well for the kindness of his heart, a virtue which, in my opinion, must much more than outweigh any other shortcomings.

In spite of the noise they make between them as they practise opening doors to visitors, answering bells and so on, I think that Linda is very glad of him. He certainly provides a touch of gaiety in an otherwise sad, unhappy house.

I hope to see you at the funeral of Chloe Pye. (What a trial to others that woman must have been in her life, and now in death she retains the same character. De mortuis!)

I shall come to Town with Jimmy. The relative, who seems a very ordinary sort of person (I think you met her), has shown an almost morbid anxiety to have everyone connected with the woman's death and her work represented at her funeral. Jimmy is naturally anxious to give no offence and I understand that he and all the male principals in My Show, as well as those of us present at the house party, will follow the coffin to its last resting place. I am particularly anxious that you should do your duty and appear. The arrangement is that we shall follow the hearse to the cemetery and afterwards return to the house for a few minutes. I did protest at the latter suggestion, which seems unnecessary, for it is not, thank God, as though we were near relatives, but the good Mrs. Pole seems adamant and Jimmy is bent on humouring her, a very wise move taken by and large. I hope to see you, therefore, at 101 Portalington Road, tomorrow, Friday, at five minutes to two o'clock. Do not disappoint us. I have sung your praises so loudly to Jimmy that I feel I have a personal responsibility.

With kind regards, my dear boy,

Believe me, ever yours,
WILLIAM R. FARADAY.

P.S. Have just opened this letter again after a turn round the garden, during which I made a somewhat strange discovery. I fear it may lead to nothing more interesting than some pretty yokel idyll, but I report it for what it is worth. Deviating from my usual route round the flower beds and the lake I took a path through the plantation. There are some very fine trees here and the sight of them reminded me of my boyhood's bird's-nesting days. Although a little late in the season, I determined to try my luck and see if my eye had lost its cunning. Rather foolish you will think, no doubt, but it was lucky in a way that the notion came to me, for I soon discovered a this-year's mavis nest just within reach of my hand in the crutch of a young elm. I put my fingers in and drew

*out a screw of paper, of all things! It was a sheet of plain white note
and the words upon it were scrawled in pencil in a hand so hurried I
could not hope to recognise it instantly even had it been known to me,
which I do not think it was. I copied out the message in my notebook
and I now send you the page for what it is worth. I left the note where
it was, not liking to take it, but I have the calligraphy pretty well photographed in my mind and you can rely on me to look out for it.*

W.F.

The enclosure consisted of the memorandum leaf from a pocket diary,
and the message, written in Uncle William's flurried pencil, was brief
but quite remarkably to the point. On the back of the page he had scribbled an explanatory note: *Found Thursday, mid-afternoon, in bird's nest
in crutch of tree, quarter of a mile inside the White Walls boundary
(rough estimate).*

The message consisted of a single line, poignant even in that shaking
stylised hand.

I love you. I love you. Oh, I love you.

Chapter 16

The small room with the bay window and the clean hard stuffed furniture
was heavy with the smell of flowers. The sweet cloying scent hung over
the whole house, half hiding those other smells—cooking from the kitchen,
camphor, floor stain, and the miserable, mean odour of damp handkerchiefs. Petals lay on the imitation parquet in the dining room, on the
imitation Chinese carpet in the parlour, and on the imitation Persian
runner in the hall. They lay, too, on the narrow staircase down whose
sleek red steps the elaborate casket with the silver-plated handles had
come swaying dangerously less than an hour before.

It was over. Chloe Pye had gone. The hideous yellow earth in the cemetery had opened and taken her in. The crowd, attracted by her name,
her profession, the manner of her dying and the eminence of her mourners, had gone shuffling off again, stumbling over unnamed graves or pausing idly to read the inscriptions on the more ostentatious headstones.

Campion stood in a corner of the parlour fireplace, bending his head
a little to one side to avoid the shaded tassel of a hanging candleholder.
The room was packed to bursting point, as were the other two downstairs
rooms, but there was no murmur of conversation to alleviate the sense
of physical discomfort, and the sombre, dark-suited throng stood miser-

ably in a dreadful intimacy, shoulders to breasts and stomachs to backs, their voices hushed and husky and self-conscious.

Outside, in the sunlit suburban street, a few people still waited. They were curious; but silent and well-mannered because of the nature of the occasion. The great moment when the procession, with black horses, silver trimmings and a glass-sided hearse topped with flowers and old-fashioned black plumes like folded sweeps' brushes, had set out at a snail's pace, was a thing of the past. Mrs. Pole's first essay at pageantry was over, but there still remained a few well-known mourners to be seen again.

The houses over the road had blinds drawn as a mark of respect in all the rooms below stairs, but behind the net half curtains of the bedroom windows bright inquisitive eyes peeped out eagerly, and from the house on the left came sudden flashes as the afternoon sun caught the lenses of a pair of opera glasses.

A scrawny maid with a black armlet on a black dress, assisted by a perspiring waiter hired from the nearest restaurant, struggled through the crowd with trays on which there were goblets of bright crimson port and dull yellow sherry. As they approached one they would each mutter an imperfectly comprehended formula concerning whisky and soda on the dining-room sideboard "if any gentleman would care for it."

Sutane stood on the hearth rug, outwardly at ease. The bones of his head were unusually apparent, but his blank dark eyes regarded the crush in front of him steadily, if sombrely. There was no way of telling if he was thinking at all.

Uncle William was held in the crush on the other side of the room. Campion caught a glimpse between two black hats of his indecorous pink face and gaily blue eyes. He was not attempting to move because to do so he would have to pass through the small open circle surrounding Mrs. Pole, her son and a solid daughter, fat and self-conscious in a hideous black suit but sticking to her mother's side gallantly with the stoic heroism of adolescence.

Mrs. Pole was triumphant and deeply happy but she played her part still, never allowing the satisfaction which filled her so exquisitely to show sufficiently to mar the perfection of her presentation of patient and dignified grief.

It was at the moment when physical discomfort and mental unease seemed to have reached their ultimate pitch that the woman with the glass in her hand came burrowing through the crowd towards Sutane. She stood just in front of him and looked up with a little sly, secretive movement of her head which brought her face just below his own. It was an indescribable gesture, arch and yet ashamed, and it was not at all pleasant.

Campion glanced down at her and experienced that little sense of shock that is part disgust and part irritation at oneself for being disgusted.

She was white and bloated in the face and poor and bent in the body. Her loose black coat was not very clean, and yet the small eye veil on her hat was arranged by fingers which had known deftness. Her eyes were greasy and shiftless, and there was an ominous twitch at one side of her mouth.

"Well, Jimmy," she said, "don't you know me?"

Sutane stared at her, and at his side Campion caught some of his horrified surprise.

"Eva," he said.

The woman laughed and raised her glass to him. She would be drunk again in a very little while.

"Little Eva herself," she said. "Come to see the last of the poor old girl for old times' sake. Things had changed, hadn't they, for her and me—and you too, old boy. You're doing very well for yourself, aren't you? West End manager and everything . . ."

She had not raised her voice, but because she was the only person in the room who seemed to have something definite to say to anyone everybody listened automatically. She became aware of the silence and turned on them with a swing that was just a little too sudden. Those immediately behind her looked uncomfortable and began to talk hurriedly to each other. The woman returned to Sutane.

A little later in the day she would be grotesque and disgusting, with exaggerated movements and blurred, drivelling speech, but now there was only the promise of these things. She came a little closer.

"I suppose you couldn't use a bright little soubrette who knows the ropes?" she murmured and smiled with sudden bitterness when she saw his involuntary expression. "That's all right, Jimmy boy, I'm only kidding. I couldn't walk across a stage these days. I've gone to hell. You can see that, can't you?"

She laughed again and seemed on the brink of further confidence. Sutane interrupted her. He was as nearly flurried as Campion had ever seen him.

"Where are you living now?"

"With my old mama—old Emma, you remember her." She was easily diverted and ran on in the same confidential way, as though she were telling secrets. "We're in a slum in Kensington. You've forgotten that kind of life. D'you remember you and Chloe and me and Charles on the boat going over? That was a good time—years ago."

She paused and Campion kept his eyes studiously on the wall opposite him because he knew that Sutane was looking at his face. The woman continued.

"Poor old Chloe! I never thought she'd beat me to it. I'm the one who ought to be in my grave. I'm not safe out alone nowadays. I shouldn't be here if someone hadn't brought me along. He's a nice boy to look up her old pal and bring me along to see the last of her. He's going to take me back too. He's got to or I shan't get back. There he is, over there. Little Benny Konrad. I'd never seen him before. Nice of him, wasn't it?"

Her weak, indeterminate voice trailed away and she laid a flabby hand in a tight discoloured kid glove on Sutane's wrist.

"So long, old boy," she said and gave him once again her odd, bleary smile with the nauseating dash of coquetry in it. "We'll have a drink to the old days sometime perhaps?"

The remark was barely a question, but amid the bitterness and defeat in her voice a little flame of hope quivered and died and she smiled to herself. She went away, the crowd parting for her as she blundered towards Konrad.

Sutane rattled the money in his pockets, glanced sharply at Campion, who did not look at him, and prepared to make the initial effort towards escape.

"Campion, we'd better go," he said softly. "Come on."

Mr. Campion followed him with a curious unwillingness. As they approached Mrs. Pole there was a momentary diversion. The maid reappeared in the doorway holding a florist's envelope above the heads of the visitors. It was a sensible enough precaution, since the crowd was very thick, but it gave her entry an air of triumph which was incongruous. She reached her mistress as Sutane and Campion came up and they overheard her breathless message.

"Boy just brought these, ma'am. Said order bid delayed. Would you please excuse?"

Mrs. Pole took the frail package and tore it open in a ponderous irrevocable fashion which she seemed to find compatible with her tragic role. A large bunch of purple violets fell out on to the floor and the daughter stooped to retrieve them, blushing painfully. Mrs. Pole discovered a card in the debris of the envelope and read from it aloud.

"*Chloe from Peter—'That perfect likeness.'*"

The quotation puzzled her and she repeated it, turning the card over as if she expected to find a clue to its meaning upon the other side. Frustrated, she shrugged her plump black shoulders and dismissed the mystery.

"Somebody who knew her, no doubt," she said. "She had a lot of friends. What a pity these came so late, or they might have gone with the others. Put them in water for me, Joannie. If I have time I'll take them down to the grave tomorrow. What a lot of flowers she's had! Wherever she is, I'm sure she's pleased. Must you go, Mr. Sutane? It was very kind of you to come. I know she would have liked to have seen you all here. Poor, poor girl!"

Sutane shook hands with her and murmured a few eminently suitable words. Campion, who was not without grace himself, admired his elegant and comforting ease.

As they struggled out of the door the daughter of the house panted behind them, clutching Peter Brome's bouquet.

They had passed the straggling group of sight-seers outside the iron gate, had seen them nudge each other and stare at Sutane with studiously blank faces, and they were halfway down the broad hot road to the taxi rank before Uncle William caught them up. He was blowing gently and still flourished a crisp white handkerchief as he appeared between them.

"Don't blame you for forgettin' me," he said. "Distressin' experience. Glad to get out myself. Terrible situation if grief was genuine, but more bearable than this. Not so embarrassin'. Haven't felt so damnably indecent since I was a child at the same sort of function—better class, of course."

The final observation was in the nature of an aside, a placatory offering to some past relative, no doubt.

Sutane did not speak at once. He was striding along, his head thrust forward and his hands in his pockets. His face was sombre and Campion was very much aware of his thoughts.

"Ghastly," he said suddenly. "Ghastly. It didn't even make you wish you were dead. We'll take that cab over there. Campion, I want you. Don't clear off."

He spoke with his old nervous authority which it was only possible to disobey and not to ignore. Mr. Campion climbed into the cab after Uncle William, feeling that he was making a great mistake.

As they settled down Uncle William produced an old-fashioned cigar case and solemnly presented them each with a half corona.

"This is the time for a risky story," he remarked unexpectedly. "Must get back to normal. Pity I can't keep the things in my head. Still, we can wash our hands of that affair now. That's over. Done our part. Done it well. Goin' to take you both to my club. Won't take a refusal. Don't often make use of it but it's still there. The one place you can get a drink at this hour."

It was a difficult journey back to the city. Campion was anxious to escape and yet strangely loath to make a definite move towards that end. Sutane was silent and moody, and Uncle William alone appeared to have a practical aim in view.

They went to his club finally, which was in Northumberland Avenue— an extraordinary institution which seemed at first glimpse to be a cross between a cathedral and the old Café Royal. In a dark corner of the lounge they sat sipping whisky and soda, conversing only very occasionally and then in whispers.

Sutane left to telephone to the theatre where *Swing Over* was in production, and before he went he looked at his host meaningly.

"He's got it into his head you're goin' to run away," murmured Uncle William. "Bundle of nerves, poor feller. Glad you turned up. Never doubted you would, after my letter. Pathetic business. Had to square up and face it. The silly woman brought us a lot of trouble. Thought she would the first time I saw her. What did you think of my enclosure?"

"From the bird's nest?"

Uncle William nodded, his pink face serious.

"Yes. Rum go. Startled me, don't mind admittin' it. May be nothin' but it struck me. Voice in one's ear, as it were. Out there alone in the woods . . . nothin' about but greenery and sunny air. Touch of the romantic in my nature, you know. Always has been."

In response to this final confidence Mr. Campion kept silent. There seemed to be nothing he could say. The old man put down his glass.

"Been thinkin' about it," he said. "Prepared myself to find it was a servant-girl romance. Thought I'd thrash it out just the same in case it wasn't. It's still there. Had another look at it this mornin', but the writin' is nothin' to go by. Badly formed, scribbled in pencil, might be woman's, might be man's. It's not Linda's."

Mr. Campion sat up with a start.

"Of course not."

Uncle William's bright blue eyes grew wide and he shot the younger man an unexpectedly shrewd glance.

"Nothin's impossible," he said. "Got to be prepared for everythin' in this world; that's my experience. I examined her hand very carefully and it's a peculiar sort of calligraphy. You'd know it anywhere. Squarish stuff. Well, not bein' able to take the note away, thus raisin' the alarm, I put my brains to it, Campion. These are my deductions. First of all from the matter. You remember the phrase?—good. Well, from the matter, it's either a very young man or a woman. Women in love will write anythin'. Known it to my cost. Great argument against teachin' women to hold a pen at all. Men are more cautious. Inherent in 'em. Boys are different again. When love seizes a boy it makes a silly young jackass of him. Follow my argument, Campion?"

"Perfectly. The tree was right in the grounds, you say?"

Uncle William sighed.

"See I'm too long-winded for you," he said regretfully. "Had it all worked out. Long and the short of it is, think it's Eve. She's the age."

"Eve? Who to?"

"That's the point." Uncle William wagged his head. "Shall have to keep my eye on the tree."

He paused and his bright eyes were contemplative and kindly.

"Poor little girl," he said. "May have nothin' to do with the business we're investigatin' at all, except that it accounts for noises in the garden at night and footprints in the mornin'. Still, we'll respect her secret."

Mr. Campion considered Eve Sutane.

"Sock," he said aloud. "Even Konrad."

"Girl's demented if she's writin' love notes to Konrad. Loses my sympathy." Uncle William's whisper was hearty. "May be anyone. Secret love affair is very attractive at that age. Maybe there's a feller among the neighbours. Can't rule out anyone—grooms, gardeners, anyone. . . . I remember my sister Julia, the stout one—you met her over that dreadful affair of Andrew's—yes, well, she, you know . . . oh, dear me, yes! There was a great row about it at the time. Cried herself ill, poor girl. I was packed off back to school; never got the full story. Mothers were more like mothers in those days."

His voice rumbled and died.

"Leave this to me," he whispered as a nearby old gentleman glowered at him. "If it's important I'll ferret it out. If it isn't, I can keep my mouth shut, I hope. Delicate affair, best in my hands."

He looked down at his plump bear's paws and folded them. Campion smiled.

"You and Blest can manage this thing between you," he said. "I've got to go now. Sorry I haven't been of any more use."

Uncle William took him by the sleeve.

"No, my boy," he said solemnly. "Believe I've got a glimmer of your difficulty, but a soldier can't desert his post, a lawyer can't desert his client, a gentleman's got to meet his engagements. Speakin' like man to man now, you understand. Old stuff, I know. Made a lot of fun of these days but still holds good. Jimmy here is a decent feller in trouble. Don't know what it is but feel it just the same. More trouble than I thought. Think of him. Decent feller. Bein' worried. Frightened. Driven perhaps to doin' things he wouldn't normally think of doin'. Your commission is to get him out of it. Put things straight for everyone. Speakin' personally, there's my show to think of. If anythin' happens to Jimmy I go back to Cambridge and retirement . . . a damned dull life for a man who's tasted a bit of the real thing for the first time at sixty. But I'm not harpin' on that. I'm thinkin' of everyone and I'm thinkin' most of you. Dear decent feller. Remind me amazin'ly of myself as a young man. Don't let yourself down, my boy. Ah! There's Sutane . . ."

Chapter 17

At nine o'clock at night Campion and Sutane were still together and still acutely embarrassed by each other's presence. It had been an uncomfortable evening. Uncle William had watched over Campion and what he considered was Campion's duty with all the faithful obstinacy of a bobtail sheep dog and had only consented to go when the departure of the last train for Birley became imminent.

He left them in the Savoy grill and padded off, pausing in the doorway to cast an admonishing glance at his older friend. Sutane's eyes, which were dark without being bright, narrowed and a faint smile passed over his crooked mouth.

"Lovable old boy," he observed. "The ass *par excellence*."

Campion nodded absently. The moment which he had seen approaching all day with relentless, unhurried pace had now arrived. He wished he had not been so abominably weak but had made his escape immediately after the funeral.

He did not want to hear Sutane's confession. He did not want to pledge his word to a secrecy upon which he had already decided. It was all over as far as he was concerned. Chloe Pye was safely buried and he did not want to know definitely how she had died.

Sutane glanced at his wrist.

"I want to go down to the theatre if you don't mind," he said. "I didn't play on the day of the funeral. It seemed to be the sort of gesture that was expected of me. It gives me an opportunity to see what Konrad makes of the show. He won't have the wheel turning, of course. We didn't want him to make a fool of himself or break an ankle."

The final remark, a very human touch of weakness which had escaped him in spite of himself, embarrassed him as soon as he had made it. He laughed and his unhappy, intelligent eyes were apologetic. Campion experienced a warm wave of liking for him, which he resented, feeling it exasperatingly unfair.

They went to the theatre, postponing the evil moment for yet another twenty minutes. Konrad was on the stage when they stepped into the back of a box. He and Slippers were in the midst of the "Leave it to Me" number in the first act. The house was friendly and well fed, but disappointed to miss Sutane, and so much mass regret made a cool, heavy atmosphere in the great auditorium.

Campion watched Konrad with interest. He was technically sound, skilful and eminently satisfactory to look at, but his exhibition was not inspired. No personality came out over the footlights to grip the attention of the silent watching throng and force its sympathy. There was no ecstasy. The irresistible and final appeal was not there. The magic had departed. There was no light in the lantern.

Slippers was her flaming self, but her small light was not fed and strengthened by her partner. Rather he took from her, revealing the frail quality of her little gift.

The man at Campion's elbow sighed. It was an expressive sound, mainly of regret but containing a definite underlying hint of satisfaction.

"It's not there," he said softly. "I knew it. He knows it, poor beast."

The roar as the curtain descended drowned his voice. It did not come from the stalls or the circle, both of which gave a kindly if not enthusiastic hand, but from the pit and gallery, which seemed to be at least partially inhabited by a deliriously excited throng. The noise was prodigious and it went on too long. Slippers and Konrad took two calls. Konrad was shy and boyish before the curtain. His smile of gratified surprise was modest and ingenuous. The stalls gave him an extra hand because of it.

As Sutane glanced up at the dark gallery a glimmer from the stage caught his face. He looked worried but not annoyed.

"That damned claque again," he said. "How very silly of him. He can't afford it, you know."

They stayed to watch the curtain rise again on the Alexandra Palace scene, with the chorus in high boots and roller skates assisting Rosamund Bream and Dennis Fuller to enact a travestied version of the now famous "Leg-o'-Mutton Escapade" from Uncle William's memoirs.

During the garter business, that piece of inverted humour amusing to the audience only because it was funny to them that their fathers should have considered it funny, Sutane touched Campion's sleeve and they went backstage.

There were a few surprised nods of recognition as they passed down the corridor, but no one stopped the great man, and when he closed his dressing-room door behind them his mood had not altered.

"Look here," he said, motioning his visitor to a chair and glancing round for a cigarette box to offer him, "I owe you a sort of explanation."

"No," said Campion with a firmness which surprised himself. "No, I don't think so. I've been afraid you were going to come out with something, but frankly I don't think it's necessary."

He paused abruptly.

The other man was staring at him. Since meeting Sutane in private life Campion had almost forgotten his better-known stage personality, but now he was forcefully reminded of it.

Here in the theatre Sutane was his remarkable, magical self again. Once more he seemed a little larger than life, with all his many physical peculiarities exaggerated and his restless, powerful spirit pressed down into the dangerous confinement of packed explosive.

"My dear chap," he said, "you've *got* to listen to me."

He swept aside some of the miscellany on the dressing table and perched himself on the cleared space. One foot rested on the seat of the chair and he kept his long, expressive hands free to emphasise his words.

"When I said I'd never met Chloe Pye before she came into *The Buffer* I was lying," he said abruptly.

It occurred to Campion irrelevantly that the dramatic intensity of the words was not lessened by his histrionic skill.

"I lied to the doctor. I lied on oath in the coroner's court. I knew her very well sixteen or seventeen years ago."

"Yes." Campion could not bring himself to express surprise. His apathy seemed to irritate the other man, but in some curious professional capacity, and Sutane hurried on, his words clipped and his tone sharp and impersonal.

"You guessed that, of course. You heard that wretched woman talking to me this afternoon. Konrad dug her up to satisfy some dreadful complex of his own. She was appalling, I know it—horrible! She made me crawl. I hadn't seen her for fifteen years. When I knew her she was a jolly little creature, very full of pep, shrewd and able to take care of herself. Today —did you see her? She was like a disintegrating corpse. I met Chloe in Paris in 1920, or '21, I forget which."

Campion stirred and with an effort threw off the oppressive spell of the stronger personality.

"It doesn't matter," he said, glancing up into the other man's face. "I don't want to know. I'm not interested."

Sutane sat very still. He was snubbed and hurt. His pained astonishment had a childlike quality which was endearing.

"I lived with the woman," he shouted suddenly. "I lived with her for two years. I was her partner in a vaudeville act. We toured Canada and the States."

Campion relaxed. Into his pale eyes behind the big spectacles there crept a new and cautious expression. It was not happening as he had foreseen. The miracle had occurred. Sutane was not confessing. Sutane was not trusting him. The discovery came in a blessed wave of relief. The man was, mercifully, still not his friend.

"Yes?" he enquired gently.

Sutane settled down. "I knew you'd listen. I wanted to tell you. Well, we broke up finally—you know how these things happen. Chloe ceased to be the brilliant star I was bobbing along behind. I grew tired of being 'and partner' on the bills. We split. She went off to the eastern States alone and I came back and built up a career. When she came home again we did not meet. I saw her name about and doubtless she saw mine. But vaudeville doesn't mix much with revue, and we never ran into each other. She had no need of my help, even if I could have given her any. She had her own methods of getting along. There were several affairs from what one hears. She had a few in my time."

Now that he had captured his audience and was safely embarked upon his story he seemed to derive a certain amount of enjoyment from the telling. He regarded the other man quizzically. Perched upon the table, he looked like some thin, attractive monkey, his eyes sad and clever and disillusioned like an ape's.

"Four weeks ago she turned up here and wanted a shop," he went on slowly. "You saw the sort of woman she was. She was vain and crazy to appease her vanity. All her life she had relied on her sex to get her by and now she was beginning to find it hadn't anything like its old power. That's the devil of it, Campion! It goes so quickly. One day it's there and the next day it's gone. The wretched women can't bring themselves to realise it. When Chloe came to me what she really wanted was reassuring. To herself she blamed a change in the times, manners, type of man—anything but the obvious truth. She chose me to come to because I had once loved her and because I was in a position to give her a job."

"Why did you give it to her?"

Sutane looked down at his feet.

"God knows," he said and sounded as though he meant it.

There was a pause, but he went on again after a little while, his voice resonant and youthful in his eagerness to get the story out.

"I told her I was happily married, and I thought she was convinced and that any damned silly attempt upon me was ruled out. She seemed very sensible. I hadn't realised her full trouble then and thought she was merely hard up. Anyway, I took her on. There was a sort of excuse for it. We were justified in having an added attraction for the three-hundredth performance and the receipts could stand it easily. She jumped at it, of course, and almost at once I regretted the decision. I remembered all the things I'd forgotten about her—her energy, her constant nattering at one, and her incredible vanity."

He broke off and looked at Campion shyly.

"If you're nervy already that sort of relentless pursuit gets under your skin, doesn't it? Besides, she was so appallingly general, if you see what I mean. She had become impossible. I didn't want her at White Walls, for instance, and I told her so. Yet she came just the same. You suddenly find you're at the mercy of a woman like that. There's nothing you can do, short of hitting her. After she was dead I thought I'd risk keeping quiet about our old association. We'd never appeared together in England and no one knew about us, as far as I know, save for a few old-timers like Eva who had dropped out of sight. If there had been any serious public enquiry into her suicide I should have to have spoken. As it was, there seemed no point in it. I used a different name in the early days —La Verne or something equally footling—and I have never used the story of that tour in my publicity because I was not very proud of it. Chloe wasn't a big enough name, and, of course, there was the private side of it."

He spread out his hands in a gesture of finality and looked at Campion inquisitively.

"Why were you so anxious for her not to come to White Walls?"

The other man put the question hesitantly, disliking himself for disguising it.

Unexpectedly, Sutane was ashamed. He sat looking at his feet again, wriggling them inside his shoes.

"Linda thinks I'm the most remarkable and magnificent person in the world," he said simply. "I was afraid Chloe might come out with some tasteless revelation in front of her. She might have done that easily, you know. She had just that kind of insanity. Linda terrified her, fortunately."

Since Campion did not speak but sat with a perfectly expressionless face, he continued hastily.

"Linda is not an ignorant, foolish little nincompoop. Don't think that. I was considering myself, not her. God! Would you like to introduce some of your old loves to your new ones?"

Campion pulled himself together. He got up and spoke carelessly.

"Look here, Sutane," he said, "I understand. It's all quite clear to me and it's over. I shall respect your confidence, of course. In my opinion you took an appalling risk in denying any past acquaintance with Chloe, but, as you say, it didn't matter, as it turned out. Now, I've finished. Blest is looking after your other trouble and he'll solve it for you in a day or so. Quite by chance I think I was able to put him onto the right line, but that's really no credit to me. He'll get you proof and between you you'll be able to clear it up for all time. It's a job for a professional and he's doing it very well."

He smiled. "I think I'll fade away," he said.

Sutane did not speak. Now that he had finished his performance and was off stage again, as it were, his moroseness had returned and he sat limply, his joints relaxed, looking like a resting marionette.

Campion had collected his hat before his host glanced up. Sutane did not smile.

"You don't understand, old boy," he said. "I'm an important person —so damned important I'm terrified whenever I think of it. Three hundred people in this theatre are dependent on me. With Konrad dancing, the show wouldn't last a week. There's not another star in London who could carry it. It depends on me. Then there's White Walls. Gardeners, Campion. Maids—Linda—Sarah—Eve—Sock—Poyser—old Finny—the nurse —they're all dependent on me. On my *feet*. Every time I look at my feet I feel sick with apprehension. Every time I look at this damned great theatre I go cold with terror. White Walls turns my stomach over. I'm frightened of it. They're all directly or indirectly supported and held up by me, and I'm an ordinary poor little bloke who has nothing—God help him—but his feet and his reputation. Nothing must go wrong with me, Campion. I've got nothing to fall back on. A businessman has his organisation and his firm, but I've got nothing. I'm doing it alone. Now do you understand?"

There was no art in this appeal. It came out unadorned with all the poignancy of truth.

"I've got no money. The whole ridiculous organisation takes every ha'penny I make, and I make something fabulous. I go bobbing along with my coattails flapping, like Eliza on the ice. If I was run over by a bus I shouldn't care—it would be over. I shouldn't see the crash. But if I get driven into a breakdown, if I once lose my nerve . . . I'm terrified, I tell you. Terrified!"

He got off the dressing table and solemnly executed an intricate little dancing step. His lean body in the dark morning clothes, which he had not changed since the funeral, trembled in the air. The ecstatic movement, so indescribable and so satisfying, was there. The sight of him was amusing, stimulating and aesthetically comforting.

"That's all," he said, his long face puckered. "That's all I've got, and it depends on my mind, which is being attacked. That's all it is and it supports a mountain. It's a dizzy cathedral balancing on a joke. If there's anything in your power that you can do to help me you've got to do it. Can't you see that? You've got to be on my side."

It was an extraordinary appeal, utterly unanswerable. Campion kept his hat in his hand, but he did not go.

After a while they went down the corridor and into Konrad's dressing room, where an anaemic young man was helping the understudy into a suit of white tails. Konrad was delighted with himself. Made up for the lights, his face was indecently pretty.

"Hallo, Jimmy," he said, "how am I doing? Going down all right?"

"Sounds so. Haven't seen you yet." The unnecessary lie tripped out so naturally that even Campion believed it for a moment. Sutane went on.

"It was charitable of you to dig out Eva this afternoon."

Konrad bent closer to the mirror, before which he had seated himself.

"Oh, did you know her?" he said casually. "One likes to do what one can at such a time. Chloe's dresser told me they had been great friends, so I looked her up. Frightful case. Positively puts one off gin, my dears. Oh, by the way, I wanted to see you, Jimmy. I'm calling in at White Walls for my precious bicycle on Sunday morning. The club is meeting at Boarbridge, just down your line, for lunch. I simply couldn't face a thirty-mile run before eating. I mean, it's inhuman. So I thought I'd come down to Birley in the morning, take a cab up to your place, change, collect my machine and ride down to the station, taking the local train for the odd fifteen miles. The boys will think I've come from London and be on the station to meet me. Sock can bring my case back to town, can't he? It's all arranged."

"It sounds like it." Sutane was annoyed and Campion reflected that it was queer that few things should be more irritating than the elaborate arrangements of others which involve, however slightly, one's own house. Konrad flushed.

"Well, it was all arranged when I was down there last week-end," he said.

"Was it? Who with?"

"You, I think. I told someone. It must have been you." Konrad turned a face towards them which was scarlet under the grease. "If you're going to be childish, throw the bicycle out of the gate and I'll change behind a hedge," he said and giggled.

Sutane flushed.

"You made no arrangement with me," he persisted obstinately. "But it doesn't matter in the least. There'll be a room at your disposal on Sunday morning."

Konrad rose. He made no attempt at thanks.

"I have nowhere to keep the bicycle in town," he said petulantly. "I live in a service flat, as you very well know, and the fools won't let me bring it into the theatre. If I leave it down at the garage it may get tarnished. It's silver-plated."

The callboy interrupted Sutane's comment, which was rude, and Konrad resumed his mood of excited triumph.

"I must fly," he said quite unnecessarily. "Sweet of you both to have dropped in to wish me luck."

The door closed behind him and Sutane glanced round the room with distaste.

"Blast the bicycle," he said briefly. "Little ass. Did you hear him getting at me? It's an unwritten law in the theatre that one never watches one's understudy work, you know. He forgets I'm the producer as well."

He did not leave but wandered round the small apartment, conveying contemptuous dislike for all that it contained. The dresser kept out of his way as far as possible in the confined space and watched him with an oblique and respectful eye.

Konrad's personality as displayed in dressing-room adornment tended towards the sentimental and old-maidish. His many mascots included a small model of the Discus Thrower and a child's stuffed white dog with a blue bow round its neck. A number of photographs, many of himself, adorned the walls, and there was also a poster of the ill-fated show in which he had starred. A small hanging bookcase below the grating of a window contained an incense burner and half a dozen volumes as well as a box of very expensive Cyprian cigarettes.

Sutane took down one of the dusty books and opened it. From where he stood Campion could see that it was verse. The dancer glanced at the flyleaf and his face changed. He was suddenly deeply and quietly angry, and the bone at the angle of his jaw showed white through the skin. He handed the volume to Campion, who read the inscription.

In friendship. B. 1934.

The words were written in green ink and the handwriting was uncomfortably familiar.

"Where's that invitation card?" Sutane's tone was ominously casual.

"Blest has it," said Campion.

Sutane put the book under his arm. Outside the door he glanced at the other man.

"I'll see Blest tomorrow. We'll go, shall we?"

He made no comment on the discovery, which was curious since there was so much that might have been said. Campion was surprised until he saw his deep, weary eyes in the gleam of a wall light. Then he saw that he was consumed with anger and was holding it down only with extreme difficulty.

They parted at the stage door. Sutane smiled and shook hands.

"If Blest fails I shall still rely on you, my dear fellow," he said.

As Mr. Campion walked away down the dark side street to the avenue vivid with lights and roofed with summer stars he was appalled to find that he did not care if Sutane's suspicion concerning the inscription and the invitation card was well founded.

Hitherto he had been an observer only in the many dramas which he had investigated, and that circumstance had given him an unfounded sense of superiority. Tonight he felt cold and disillusioned; no longer shocked but frankly despairing to find himself both so human and so miserably unhappy.

Chapter 18

The rumour appeared in London somewhere about teatime on what afterwards proved to be the closest Sunday of the year.

It ran through the lazy crowds in the park, sped along the broad dusty streets, dived underground with the tube trains, was carried to the suburbs on a thousand plump red buses, growing and changing as it travelled, trickled into clubs, houses and teashops, mounted a million stairs to flats and rooftops, and waved its coloured tongues in every idle ear.

It was not a definite story at any one time; rather, a series of unsubstantiated statements ranging the whole way from the frankly electrifying to the merely sad. Its effect was gently unsettling, producing in the public mind a vague sensation of excitement only faintly tinged with alarm, as though it had been an unexplained bump in the night or the just incomprehensible shouts of newsboys in far-off streets.

It came from one of the great railway termini where trains were thought to have been delayed for anything between one and twenty hours. Because it was a Sunday the usual channels of news were stopped, but the bus conductors, who can generally be relied upon to know most things, had a wild story about unidentified enemy aircraft reducing the garrison town of Colchester to smouldering ruin.

In the Corner House in Coventry Street the waitresses had a theory that it was not enemy aircraft at all but two Air Force bombers who had come to grief in a built-up area while carrying out secret practice on the South Coast, and an enterprising newspaper vendor in Oxford Circus chalked "Pit Explosion: Many Dead" on an empty board and actually sold a quantity of leftover morning papers before his fraud was discovered.

As the evening wore on the scattered theories became less diverse and the scene of the disaster, whatever it was, became fixed as a railway station on an eastern line. The words "air raid" persisted, however, even after the more general term "explosion" had become frequent, and it was not until the running news bulletins in lights above the rooftops in Trafalgar Square and in Oxford Street came out with the gist of the story that the town settled down to take in the piquant and rather horribly risible truth.

Mr. Campion had gone away on Saturday to Kepesake in Suffolk and had spent a soothing week-end in that remote village, where London and European news is not heard at all until it becomes stale, or discussed until it becomes history. He heard nothing of the sensation, therefore, until he sank down into the corner of a compartment in the London train at Ipswich station on Monday morning and opened the paper which he had caught up in his flight past the bookstall. Then it was presented to him baldly and with as much detail as could be gathered in the mysterious circumstances.

Above and beside a quarter-page photograph of what appeared to be, at first sight, the snow-covered relics of a serious fire, the headlines were briefly informative.

HOME COUNTY STATION OUTRAGE.
FIFTEEN DEAD AND INJURED.

MYSTERY EXPLOSION.
WELL-KNOWN DANCER AMONG KILLED.

Mr. Campion's startled glance travelled hastily down the column, where, as usual, the portentous young voice of the *Morning Telegram* did its best to disguise its natural featherbrained exuberance with heavy dramatics.

Three people met their death yesterday morning in what may well prove to be one of the most extraordinary and perhaps far-reaching accidents of modern times. Twelve others lie in the Boarbridge cottage hospital injured, some of them gravely so. At the moment the cause of

the accident is unknown, but Scotland Yard officials (called in by Lieutenant Colonel Percy Beller, chief constable for the district) are understood to believe that high explosives were instrumental in causing the
disaster.

Among the three persons who lost their lives was thirty-two-year-old
Benny Konrad, the London revue star, who had travelled to Boarbridge
to meet members of a cycling club of which he was the president. Richard
Duke, who was also killed, was a member of the cycling party. The third
person to die was a porter.

Having given what it felt was the main story, the *Telegram*, in accordance with its custom, began again in fuller style.

*Late yesterday morning, when the twelve-three from Birley had just
pulled out and the slow up train from Yarmouth, laden with summer
travellers, was in the station, the quiet little country junction of Boarbridge was visited by an explosion so sudden and terrible that Mr. Harold
Phipps, the stationmaster, tells me that he has seen nothing like it since
the War.*

*At the time, unfortunately, the down platform was crowded with visi-
tors. Some forty members of a cycling club had foregathered there to
welcome their president, Mr. Benny Konrad, the revue star, who had come
from London to take part in an annual celebration outing.*

*Mr. Konrad, who was in cycling kit, wheeling his machine, a new gift
from the club, was laughing and chatting with his friends when there
was a sudden deafening explosion and the quiet station was reduced to a
shambles of groaning men and women.*

*The glass in the roof with which the platforms are sheltered was shat-
tered, as were many of the windows of the stationary train, and a number
of the injuries were caused by splintered glass.*

*Two hand trucks of milk cans were being drawn by a porter at the
time of the accident, and in the panic after the explosion these became
strewn upon the line, adding considerably to the general confusion.*

*Doctors were rushed to the scene and the two small waiting rooms were
turned into temporary casualty stations. Trains on the line were held up
for nearly an hour.*

*Tonight the cause of the disaster is still a complete mystery. The theory
held by some that an infernal machine had been dropped by a passing
aircraft has now been generally abandoned, although the stationmaster
still stoutly adheres to that view. No one in the thriving little market town
of Boarbridge noticed any aeroplane in the vicinity during the morning.*

*Railway officials are silent. The regulations regarding the conveyance
of dangerous goods are very strict, but it is just possible that a parcel containing explosive matter may have escaped the vigilance of the
authorities.*

The mystery is deepened by the fact that Mr. Phipps insists that both platforms were clear of goods parcels at the time of the accident, and the senior porter, Mr. Edward Smith, who is prostrate from severe shock and superficial burns, assured me when I visited him in his cottage in Station Lane that he took nothing from the goods van of the down train save Mr. Konrad's bicycle, which was collected by its owner immediately on arrival.

In the circumstances the County Police made an instant decision to ask the official help of Scotland Yard experts, and last night Inspector Yeo of the Central Branch of the C.I.D. travelled to Boarbridge, bringing with him Major Owen Bloom and Mr. T. P. Culvert, both of the War Office research department.

Last night it was understood that the accident is not thought to have been political in inspiration, but that possibility is not yet wholly ruled out.

The dead are: Benjamin Evelyn Konrad, thirty-two, dancer and revue star, Flat 17, Burnup House, W. 1; Richard Edwin Duke, nineteen, 2, Bellows Court Road, S.E. 21; Frederick Stiff, forty-three (porter), Queen's Cottages, Layer Road, Boarbridge.

The list of the injured followed and made appalling reading. Five women, three children and seven men had received wounds of varying gravity, most of which could be accounted for by flying glass from the roof or carriage windows.

Mr. Campion put down the paper and stared blankly at the grey upholstery in front of him.

The whole story seemed so utterly incredible that he read it through again carefully before he could attempt to assimilate it. He glanced at the other paper, which the fat man in the corner was holding between himself and the world, and there also he caught a glimpse of the same story, so that his first wild notion that the *Telegram* had gone mad and invented the tale in a fit of wanton idiocy was brushed aside as it deserved.

Gradually he accustomed himself to the facts. Konrad was dead, startlingly dead, blown to hell with his ridiculous bicycle and two other unfortunate mortals. Konrad, who until this moment had figured in his mind as a busy little self-seeker blithely scattering trouble broadcast in an attempt to achieve his own dubious ends, had been wiped out by an accident. Of all the forty million to whom the disaster might have occurred it had overtaken only three, and one of those had been Konrad. As a piece of irony he felt it surpassed itself. He did not take his eyes from the paper all the way to London.

A small paragraph tucked away at the foot of the news story recorded that Konrad's was the second violent death to occur in the cast of *The*

Buffer within a fortnight, and mentioned as a coincidence that he had been present among the guests at Sutane's house when Chloe Pye had met her tragic end.

Campion was still startled and shocked when he arrived at Liverpool Street. He took a cab to the Junior Greys and was hesitating in the lounge, trying to decide if his strong impulse to phone Sutane was a wise one or the reverse, when he received a message from Scotland Yard.

The note said briefly that Superintendent Stanislaus Oates would be glad if Mr. Campion would make it convenient to call upon him at three o'clock that afternoon.

In the ordinary way Campion was not a wavering or unduly apprehensive spirit, but he spent the half hour before lunch and the hour after it in a restless, nervy mood which all but demoralised him.

At five minutes to three he was walking down a long bare corridor which smelt vaguely of disinfectant behind a helmetless constable and a moment or so later had stepped forward to shake hands with the dour figure who had risen to greet him.

His recent promotion had no more altered Superintendent Stanislaus Oates than had any of the previous steps in his career. He remained at heart the eager, solemn young countryman whose concentration and tenacity had first earned the commendation of a rural inspector nearly thirty-four years before.

He was not an unfriendly man, but even Campion, who probably knew him better than anyone outside the force itself, was never in danger of permitting familiarity to grow into amicable contempt.

The superintendent stood for a moment, his shoulders stooping and his pepper-and-salt head bent over the blotter on his desk.

"Ah, Campion," he said. "Sit down, will you, mate?"

The form of address was a relic of his Dorset days. All through his thirty-four years' slow ascent through the service he had carefully suppressed it, but now that he had attained the peak and promise of his career he brought it out occasionally, a minor laxity permissible in one of his eminence.

"Been away?"

"Yes. To Kepesake. I spent the week-end with Guffy Randall and his wife. Do you mind?"

"No. When did you go?"

"Saturday morning."

"You're staying at your club?"

"Yes."

"Lugg's away?"

"Yes."

"Where?"

"White Walls, near Birley. Jimmy Sutane's house. Why?"

Campion leant back in the visitor's chair. He knew that his forehead was damp and wondered at himself. Presently he took out a handkerchief and sat looking at it.

The superintendent seated himself and rested his elbows on the desk. He had a sad, bony face and very interested grey eyes.

"What do you know about Benny Konrad?"

Suddenly Mr. Campion felt more at ease.

"Very little," he said cheerfully. "I've been acting as honorary adviser to Blest on a private investigation which seemed to be leading towards him. That's all. You've seen Blest, I suppose?"

The policeman's country eyes flickered with a brief smile.

"Yes. We've seen Blest. Saw him last night. He looked us up."

Mr. Campion thought he had begun to understand, and the sneaking, unnameable fear which had been nibbling at the back of his mind all the morning was allayed.

"You're consulting me, I take it?" he said brightly. "It's a great honour. I appreciate it."

Oates laughed, a dry little explosive sound expressing friendliness and good humour but no amusement. He was singularly seldom amused.

"I'm questioning you in pursuance of my duties," he explained laboriously. "What was Konrad up to? Do you know?"

"Up to?" Campion echoed him blankly. "My dear man, why are we playing detectives? Come down to earth. You've seen Blest and so you know all Blest knows. I can't tell you any more, old boy. That's all there is to it. Konrad had been playing the fool around the theatre and he was on the verge of being found out. That's the lot."

"Ah!" The superintendent seemed partially satisfied. "You've heard about the way he was killed?"

"I've seen the papers. It seems to have been a nasty accident."

"Oh, it was." Oates was genuinely moved. "I went down myself last night and took a look at the place. Then I went on to the hospital and the mortuary. It was fearful. The mess was terrible. Women cut about with glass, you know, doctors digging splinters as long as my fingers out of them. The men who were killed were in a frightful condition. Konrad had a piece of metal blown clean through his head. It had dug a furrow you could put your wrist into clean through the top of his scalp. And the poor porter chap! I won't make you uncomfortable with a description. They got a steel nut out of his stomach."

His pleasant dry voice ceased but he kept his eyes on Campion's own.

"It was fearful," he repeated. "I'm not a squeamish man myself but the sight of that milk and blood and glass everywhere upset me; it made me feel sick. A very extraordinary and dreadful thing altogether," he finished with a touch of prim severity.

Campion had remained silent throughout the harangue, his face growing more and more grave as his earlier apprehension returned.

"I don't quite see where all this is leading," he began cautiously. "I'm completely in the dark. I mean, the cause of the explosion had nothing to do with Konrad, surely?"

"I'm not so sure." The superintendent wagged his distinguished head. "I'm not so sure at all. I don't know if I ought to tell you, but the opinion here at the moment is that someone threw a bomb at the little blighter."

For the second time that day Mr. Campion experienced that rarest of the emotions—genuine astonishment.

"No . . ." he said at last. "I don't believe it. It's incredible."

"Ah, you think so?" Oates seemed disappointed. He looked down at his desk. "Major Bloom is coming along in fifteen minutes or so. He's been at work on the evidence all day. I'm hoping he'll have some definite information for us. So far we've been working on the few hints he could give us last night. From the first look round he told Yeo that in his opinion there was no doubt that the explosion originated roughly on the spot where Konrad was standing. They can tell you that, you know, these fellows, from the general direction of the damage. It's very ingenious how they work it all out. There's no guessing. It's all very scientific. Yeo was particularly impressed."

"But . . ." began Mr. Campion and was silent. "A bomb?" he said at last. "What sort of a bomb?"

"That's what I'm waiting to find out," explained the superintendent severely. "Something very efficacious. I'd like you to have seen that station, my lad. I wouldn't have gone down there myself in the ordinary way, but Yeo and I are friends and the county police sounded so excited on the phone that I couldn't resist taking a peep. Yeo's coming up at four for a conference. He's been interviewing people down there all day."

In spite of his seriousness there was still a touch of the schoolboy about Oates, a certain naïve excitement which betrayed him every now and again. His work still fascinated him.

"Now look here, Campion," he said, "you knew Konrad. Would you say he might have any secret political activities? We don't get many bomb outrages over here, you know, and when we do they're nearly always political or the efforts of lunatics—usually an unhealthy combination of the two. What would you say, now? Let's have your frank opinion."

He spoke coaxingly and Mr. Campion was frankly sorry not to be able to oblige him.

"I'd say 'no,'" he said. "I can't help it, but I would, definitely. He wasn't a friend of mine, of course—I didn't know him well—but no, no, I really couldn't see him mixed up with politics of any sort. What an absolutely unbelievable thing to happen!"

Oates leant back in his chair.

"Mr. Campion," he began with unusual formality, "I've known you for a long time and we've done a bit of work together. If you're going to be in this affair I'd like you to work for us. I'm not saying that I don't trust you, now. Don't think that. But I want all the facts from you, and if you're working for me then I know you won't be working for anyone else behind my back. Consider yourself an expert called in on the case, just as the major is."

Having known the superintendent for fifteen years, Campion was able to appreciate the effort such a decision had cost that logical and conventional policeman. He was properly impressed.

"My dear chap, anything you like," he said lightly. "You know all I know at the moment. I was called in by Jimmy Sutane to help Blest in uncovering a sort of persecution campaign. I thought I saw Konrad was at the bottom of it and I tipped Blest on to him. Then I rather lost interest and faded away. From what I saw of Konrad he certainly did not strike me as a likely candidate for public assassination. The only feasible explanation that occurs to me offhand is that your bomb thrower was demented and mistook him for somebody else."

"Who else did he look like in a vest and cycling shorts?" demanded Oates with practical curiosity.

Campion shrugged his shoulders. Words were beyond him.

"Mr. Sutane was at his own house surrounded by his family twenty miles away when the explosion occurred," observed the superintendent sadly. "We can be fairly sure who was on the down side of the station where Konrad stood, but some of the travellers on the up line may have escaped us."

Mr. Campion blinked.

"Didn't anyone see someone throw the thing?"

"No. No one's come forward. Yeo's working on that now." Oates leant across the desk and his unexpectedly youthful eyes were indignant. "Can you imagine any living person doing it, Campion?" he demanded. "Scattering death or disfiguration among a crowd of innocent, helpless bodies on a country railway station? The man's either hopelessly insane or a— a bad, dangerous fellow. We'll have to lay our hands on him. There's no two ways about it."

Campion smiled faintly at the "bad, dangerous fellow." The superintendent's maidenly restraint was typical of him and bore no relation to the depths of his feelings. Stanislaus Oates had spent much of his life in the pursuit of murderers and had invariably delivered them into the hands of the public hangman with serene satisfaction whenever he had the opportunity. There were very few greys, in his view; only varying depths of black. He had once expressed a certain sympathy for Crippen, but only because the little doctor had permitted himself to succumb to temptation. Once Belle Elmore was dead, Crippen was already half hanged, and very properly so too in the gentle Oates's opinion. Yet Crippen, Campion remembered, had been "a poor weak scoundrel." The "bad, dangerous fellow" was evidently in a different class altogether.

Oates was not without softness, however, although he reserved his sympathy always for the right side.

"There's a young woman maybe going to lose a leg and a lad of eighteen with his face cut to ribbons in the hospital. If it had been a train accident I'd have been simply very sorry, but when it's wanton, deliberate wickedness it makes me spiteful. It's a fact, now. We'll have to get this fellow."

Campion glanced up.

"The authorities are clamouring, too, I suppose?" he ventured.

Oates smiled. "Yes, they're nattering," he said cheerfully. "But they'll have to wait for us. We can't go worrying our heads about them when there's work to be done."

His bland superiority was superb. Campion felt curiously comforted. In a world of conflicting loyalties it was a relief to find someone who could really put his finger, if only to his own satisfaction, on the exact spot where right ends and wrong begins.

The superintendent took a large flat watch from his waistcoat pocket and considered it.

"Time for the major," he said. "Now I'm trusting you, mate. I don't have to ask anyone's permission. I'm the superintendent of the Central Department of the C.I.D. and I can have what help I think fit. I want you to sit in that corner over there. You've been working on Konrad and you can work some more."

Mr. Campion went over to the small hard chair obediently. There had never been any ceremony between them, and Oates's sublime conviction that an invitation to work for the police was the highest honour man could hope to receive was unanswerable. He sat down.

Major Bloom was ushered in almost immediately and Mr. Culvert, his assistant, came with him. The major was tall and heavy, with lumbering movements and eyes which peered shortsightedly from behind truly terrible steel-rimmed glasses. He shook hands with nervous affability and betrayed a pleasant Midland voice.

Mr. Culvert, his assistant, hovered round him deferentially. He was a small, neat young man, precise to the point of primness. His quiet, cultured voice contrasted with his chief's burr, as did his ease and self-assurance. Yet no one could have confused the master with the apprentice. Mr. Culvert only too evidently considered that he was out in charge of his god, a fragile, breakable deity who was to be protected and placated in every way. They made an odd, knowledgeable pair.

The major sat down in the visitor's chair, smiled nervously at Oates, and fumbled in the leather brief case which Mr. Culvert held open for him. He found the notebook for which he was searching at last and looked up with a sigh.

"We've hardly begun yet, of course," he said with a nervous giggle. "This is going to take some time. You do realise that, don't you? I know you people are always in such a hurry. I haven't prepared any sort of statement and I haven't had time to go into the analysis of the metal at all, but there are just one or two points that may be of interest to you at the moment."

Oates thanked him gravely.

"Make it simple," he said.

The major blinked. "I don't think I follow you . . ."

"Make it simple, sir. I'm not very up in chemistry. Let's just have the straight tale first."

"Oh, yes, I see. I see. Of course." The expert seemed alarmed, and he glanced at his assistant helplessly. Mr. Culvert coughed.

"First of all, the superintendent should know that you're satisfied it was a grenade, sir," he murmured.

Oates nodded. "Oh, ah, it was, was it? Well, we feared so. An amateur grenade would you say, sir?"

"Well, no, you know. It's a funny thing, but I don't think it was." The major got up and walked down the room; his shyness dropped from him and his voice rose with sudden authority. "I can't be certain, but as far as I can see the explosive was either amatol or tetrol. That's as near as we shall ever get. Tetrol. Tetramethylaniline, you know. I think it was that. That's by the damage and the action on the cast-iron casing. One of the doctors gave me a most valuable specimen of the casing, taken from the porter's chest. We can say that for certain, can't we, Culvert?"

"I think so, sir."

"Amatol . . ." The superintendent was making notes. "Where would that come from, now? Could an amateur obtain it?"

"I don't know. I suppose he could. It's very usual stuff. The wholesalers have it." The expert appeared to resent the interruption. "However, what I'm trying to tell you is that it didn't look like amateur work to me. The casing was grooved inside, you see. It wasn't one of your petrol cans, or the dreadful tea-caddy things that we get sometimes. As far as we can tell at the moment from the evidence we've received, it was a very decent, well-constructed grenade, not at all unlike a Mills bomb but rather more powerful."

"How much more powerful?" Oates sat up with frank interest.

"My dear good man, how can I possibly tell you? A Mills bomb, now, holds about three ounces of explosive. I think in this case you might multiply that by anything up to four. That's on the damage. Don't run away with the idea that the grenade used was four times as large as a Mills bomb. That's not what I'm saying at all. It might have been any size. It depends on the casing and on the filling. And don't ask me how big it was or what shape it was because I can't possibly tell you and no one on earth except the men who made it and placed it can."

He paused and eyed them with frank, weak blue eyes.

"I'm working now on the scraps of metal which we've been able to collect, you understand, and, while I think of it, there are some pieces embedded in the platform. I'd like those. Every tiny piece is of value to me. You never know . . . I may, with luck, be able to tell where the iron came from. The country of origin, I mean."

He stopped, seemed suddenly to become aware of the unfamiliar surroundings, and sat down abruptly.

Oates remained quiet for a moment, digesting his astonishing information.

"How do these things go off?" he enquired at last. "Can you tell me that, sir?"

The major permitted himself one of his unhappy little giggles.

"There are nine-and-sixty ways," he murmured, "but in this particular case I think there really must have been the usual cap and detonator. This isn't evidence, you understand. This is simply my present opinion. It was something very like a Mills bomb; I really can say that."

Oates sat looking at him, his head a little on one side.

"You mean someone must have pulled a pin out before throwing it?"

The major seemed to hesitate on the brink of a confidence but thought better of it and remained cautious.

"Something like that. A pin, or a switch, or a screw."

"I see." Oates seemed only fairly satisfied, and after an enquiring glance at his chief Mr. Culvert broke in to remind the superintendent in his prim, deferential way that the investigations were at a very elementary stage.

The major rose again and heaved himself over to the desk, where he made a rough sketch on the superintendent's clean blotting paper.

"You take an iron casing filled with explosives and projectiles," he said, breathing gustily on Oates's bent head. "Into that you introduce a tube of thin perforated metal, which is roughly hourglass in shape, narrow in the middle. Inside the tube you put a striker, which is held in place by a rod, with an arm on the end of it. The rod is connected with the switch or screw on the outside of the casing. Now above the striker you put a little spring, so that when the rod is turned the arm slips aside and the striker plunges down, being guided by the construction in the hourglass, onto a small anvil. The anvil is formed by the base of the hourglass. On the anvil is the cap and detonator, probably fulminate of mercury. Understand what I'm telling you?"

"Yes, I think so." Oates was blinking. "And this is what was used?"

The major shrugged his shoulders.

"That's what I can't tell you. I'll never be able to tell you. But I think so. Something very simple, but professional work. I may have something more to say later on. It's a rather interesting point, but I don't like to commit myself at the moment. All I'll admit now is that it was a grenade and it was professionally made."

"Ah!" said the superintendent and was silent.

A young constable knocked and put a polished face inside the door. "Chief Inspector Yeo, sir."

The superintendent looked up with a grin.

"Hallo, Freddie," he said. "Glad to see you. Come in. We've got some nice bad news for you here, my lad."

Chapter 19

Chief Detective Inspector Yeo came in briskly. He was square and efficient, with a solid bullethead and an insignificant, almost comical face. His snub nose and round eyes had been a serious disadvantage to him all his life, undermining his dignity and earning him friends rather than admirers. Even Oates, who had the utmost respect for his quite extraordinary ability, was inclined to sympathise with him whenever he saw him.

At the moment he was very tired and his plump face was drawn.

The superintendent performed the introduction briefly. He ignored Yeo's sharp glance of enquiry and offered no explanation for Mr. Campion's presence.

"You wouldn't have had time to prepare any sort of report, of course?" Oates was inclined to put the question mischievously. "You're just off the train, aren't you? Anything new?"

Yeo shook his head.

"Nothing," he said gloomily. "Plenty of negative evidence. However, my men are still slogging away at it and the local people are very helpful but they've got their hands full. One rather wretched thing happened. The porter's wife chucked herself into the local millpool this morning. She was left with two little kids. Couldn't face life without her husband and all that. She was a bit crazy, of course; demented by the shock, probably. They got her out, but it was no good. Makes you feel a bit sick, don't it? It's a nasty, callous business. No sense in it."

He wiped his forehead and his thick short neck with a vast handkerchief and looked glum.

The superintendent made no comment on the extraneous tragedy so briefly recorded but his face grew very hard, and Mr. Campion, who was sitting quietly in his corner, was reminded that Oates was a countryman who had come from just such another village with just such another mill-pool, and more than probably with just such another porter.

The superintendent plunged into business.

"Major Bloom holds the view that the grenade was professional work. Does that help at all?"

"Professional?" Yeo looked at the major blankly. "That's a funny thing. It must have been in a parcel lying around. Someone's hiding some little technical offence against the railway. Must be."

He spoke hopefully but without great conviction.

"We've made fifty-four interviews and taken thirty-nine statements," he went on slowly, "and at the moment if I heard you gentlemen had decided it was a thunderbolt I should be convinced and thankful. It's an extraordinary thing, but no one admits to having seen anyone throw anything at any time, and they're nearly all strangers to each other, so it can't be conspiracy."

The major, who had been listening with interest, leant across the arm of his chair.

"Could you give me a good eyewitness report of the two or three minutes before the explosion?" he enquired.

Yeo grimaced.

"I can, sir, but I'm afraid you'll find it very ordinary. There doesn't seem to have been much to see. There's one young chap who gives the down platform view very clearly."

He opened a battered attaché case and took out a sheaf of typewritten sheets.

"I'll read it to you. Here he is. Joseph Harold Biggins, 17 years of age, 32, Christchurch Road, N.E. 38. He was one of the cyclists and he's in the cottage hospital with half the skin flayed off his chest, poor chap. I won't bother you with all the preliminary stuff, about how he got to Boarbridge and so on. This is what he says about the actual thing."

He cleared his throat and began to read in expressionless police-court tones.

" 'When the train pulled out of the station Mr. Konrad, our president, who we had come to meet, was standing about halfway down the platform holding his bicycle. We advanced to meet him and, as our secretary had been detained outside the booking hall, I and Duke went forward in front of the others. Mr. Konrad was in cycling costume and seemed very pleased to see us. He smiled as we came up and said, "Hallo, boys, here I am," or something like that. I cannot swear to the exact words.

" 'There was a bit of a pause because of shyness on the part of the members, and to make everybody comfortable Mr. Konrad indicated the bicycle he was holding, which was a present from the club, and said: "Is she not a beauty? She runs like a bird." He then turned the bike sideways, showed off the drop handlebars with the special grips, pretended to switch the lamp on and off, etcetera. That is the last I remember.

" 'There was a sort of roar and I remember falling. When I came to I was in great pain and Duke was lying over me. I did not realise he was dead until I saw his face.' "

The inspector ceased abruptly.

"A terrible business," he said. "All the statements are like that. Just horror coming out of the blue, you might say. One woman in the up train said she saw Konrad and the bicycle shoot into the air, but the porter with the milk cans was between her and him and he staggered forward, you know, pulling the whole thing on top of him. The sight of all the churns toppling over onto the line in a shower of glass from the roof seems to have sent everything else out of her mind. The thing couldn't have been *in* a milk can, could it? I don't know much about these things, but it seems to me . . ."

He broke off questioningly. The two experts, who had been exchanging glances, were on the verge of speech. Mr. Culvert appeared to be urging his chief to make some sort of confidence and the major suddenly capitulated.

"I wanted to be more sure, d'you see," he began in his soft homely accent, "because, frankly, the idea is so—so *peculiar*. But in view of that first statement made by the young boy I think we really might consider the evidence of the fragments of glass and the bicycle, even at this dangerously early stage."

Both policemen and Mr. Campion regarded him with polite bewilderment.

"What glass?" demanded the superintendent.

Yeo was interested.

"You're referring to the little chunks of thick glass taken from Duke's body?" he said. "I wondered about that myself. What's on your mind, sir?"

Although he had decided to confide, the major was still very guarded.

"You must understand that I'm not giving you evidence," he said. "There's still an enormous amount of work to be done before I could consider the case for the bicycle lamp to be absolutely watertight. There are certain comparisons we'll have to make, or a clever counsel could make us look like a pack of idiots. These legal fellows, you know, are very difficult."

"We haven't got that far," murmured the superintendent dryly. "We don't know if we're going to have to make an arrest at all. You people may have to go to war or something. It may be a political business, clean out of our province."

The inspector, however, had heard remarkable words.

"The bicycle lamp?" he said.

"Yes. Yes. As far as we can see, though I really don't like to commit myself." The major was excited. "The grenade was inside the bicycle lamp —where the dry battery should have been. Some of these lamps turn on with a screw, you know, and my own personal theory—which isn't evidence —is that the man with the bicycle exploded the grenade when he turned on, or attempted to turn on, the lamp. That explains all the facts, you see: the state of the bicycle, which was injured in a most significant fashion; the tiny pieces of thick lens glass in the one man's body; the general direction of the damage; the fact that nothing appears to have been thrown; the . . ."

He broke off. No one but Mr. Culvert was making any pretence of listening to him. The two policemen were staring at each other, speculation in their eyes, while Campion had frozen and sat staring rigidly in front of him, his mind leaping from one appalling conjecture to the next.

"He brought it with him!" said Yeo. "God Almighty, he brought it with him!"

"You'll have to trace the original lamp and find me a similar one for comparison with my fragments," put in the major, who appeared to be completely blind to the sensation he was creating. "That's most important if it comes into court. That woman in the train too. You spoke of her just now. She must have seen the explosion itself. If one of us was to question her she might remember a great many little details which seemed to her unimportant at the time, and we may get a lot of stuff to help us to establish absolute proof. You see, I'm thinking that there was probably a very short time fuse—say two or three seconds—fitted to the thing. That would have made it considerably safer to handle, and he could have moved the bicycle, or spoken even, actually after he'd ignited the fuse by turning on the lamp. As far as we know, he made no attempt to save himself.

"I haven't gathered all the circumstances yet. What was he doing? Making a protest of some sort?"

His final words percolated through the superintendent's preoccupation. Oates looked up slowly.

"He had no idea what he was doing," he said. "That's certain. He was ignorant. He didn't know it was there."

Yeo rose to his feet.

"But all those people?" he began, his round eyes wide and shocked.

As the obvious truth dawned upon him the colour rushed into his face.

"It was a mistake!" he ejaculated. "It was a mistake. It ought not to have happened there. It ought to have happened on a lonely road somewhere. It's a mistake. It's a murder gone wrong!"

He remained for a moment bewildered by his own discovery and then, as another thought occurred to him, he swooped down upon his brief case.

"Oates," he said unsteadily, "it's all here. That bicycle was given to Konrad by the cycle club. The collection was taken and delivery made by the secretary. His name is Howard. I've got his statement somewhere. He didn't like Konrad. That has emerged in several statements. It struck me at the time. He wasn't present on the station at the time of the explosion and—this is the point—he works in a wholesale chemist's. I've just remembered it."

Mr. Campion rose from his chair in the corner and came quietly forward. His voice was heavy and impersonal and he stood limply, as though the weight of his own body had suddenly become oppressive to him.

"I'm afraid that's no good," he said, unaware of the chief inspector's startled glance. "Konrad was given that bicycle weeks ago. You'll have plenty of proof that he's been all over it with the excitement of a woman examining a new handbag. But he had not seen it for five days before he collected it on Sunday morning and hurried down to Birley station on it to catch the slow down train for Boarbridge. During that five days it had been standing in the cloakroom at White Walls."

"Where's that?" The inspector put the question sharply.

Oates answered for Campion.

"Jimmy Sutane's country house. He's the actor chap Blest was telling you about. Remember?"

Chapter 20

"Mr. Campion . . ."

The chief inspector set down his modest glass of Bass and leant confidentially across the coarse linen tablecloth.

"When Mr. Sutane phoned you last night and you spoke to him, what did you say?"

It was late in the day for lunch and Bonini's stuffy upper room was practically deserted. They had that corner by the window which gives into Old Compton Street to themselves and Yeo's gentle murmur carried no farther than the ear for which it was intended.

Campion, who was looking a little leaner and, in the inspector's opinion, a good deal more intelligent than his usual, casually elegant self, blinked thoughtfully as the explanation of the hasty and pressing invitation was revealed to him. He glanced at Yeo, sitting square and absurd before him, and was inclined to like him very much.

Their acquaintance was of long standing and each man knew the other well by repute, but this was the first occasion on which they had had actual dealings.

"He wanted me to go down there," said Campion truthfully.

"Why didn't you go? You don't mind a few questions, do you?" Yeo was smiling affably but his manner betrayed caution, for, as a valued expert and the C.I.D. "super's" personal friend, Mr. Campion merited careful handling.

"I thought I'd keep out of it."

"Quite. Quite. I can understand that."

The inspector was satisfied only in part. He tried another line.

"It's an A case," he observed. "We're out to get him. I saw our chief constable and the assistant commissioner this morning. I've got the whole force behind me and I can have anyone I like to call on. The case is to get real preference. The man we're after is *dangerous*, you see, Mr. Campion. I mean, you could call him antisocial, couldn't you? If he's a private person with facilities for tapping stuff which is nothing more or less than war material, and doesn't mind who he does in, well, I mean to say, he *must* be stopped!"

His earnestness widened his eyes and shortened his nose until he looked like a comedian in the midst of his act.

"He must," he repeated. "We've got to get him. That woman with the injured leg is in danger. If she dies there'll be four persons killed, eleven injured, and no one knows how much damage."

Campion smiled crookedly.

"My dear chap," he said, "don't think for a moment that I don't agree with you. I do. The whole nature of the thing is so preposterous that I don't think any sane man could argue with you about it. Whatever the circumstances turn out to be, nothing could ever excuse or extenuate such an incredible piece of stupid wickedness. When you get your man you'll have to hang him. I do see that."

Yeo shot him a relieved but still puzzled glance.

"Both Oates and I knew you were sound," he said naïvely, "but frankly we were wondering if you weren't holding something back—something that might put us on to a *motive*, for instance."

Campion did not respond, and the detective continued after a brief pause.

"You've had time to get to know all that lot down there, and they're a funny crowd. I can't help thinking that if there had been anything a bit fishy going on beforehand you'd have noticed it. Something that might have led up to this, I mean. We're at a great disadvantage coming in only after the event, with the newspapers printing all they can find the instant after they find it. There was that actress woman who died down there . . . did she fall or did she jump? No one knows and it doesn't really matter. Still, it was a funny thing to happen, all the same. I don't like coincidences. It's silly to pretend they don't occur, but I don't like them."

Mr. Campion raised his eyes from his plate.

"You're concentrating on White Walls?"

"Well, yes, in the main." Yeo lowered his tone and scowled at the plump Bonini, who was bearing down upon them with hostly affability. The restaurateur altered his course, affronted, and the inspector, having satisfied himself that he was not overheard, went on with his story.

"It's four days now and we've been working steadily, with a certain amount of results, of course. As soon as you came out with your piece of information about the bicycle—which saved us quite a bit of time, by the way—I checked up on it and found you were right. Konrad had received the bicycle on the second, nearly a fortnight before the rally, and I found quite a number of people at the theatre, and in other places, who had actually seen the lamp alight. Bit by bit we narrowed it down to the time when he took it to Mr. Sutane's house. There's a chauffeur there—a decent, sensible chap . . . I don't know if you know him? He's one of these gadgety lads who was very taken by the bicycle. He swears that on the first Sunday Mr. Konrad had it down there he, the chauffeur, made a complete examination of it and was particularly impressed by the lamp, which he described to me as 'super.' He was able to give me complete specifications and these tallied exactly with those I got from the firm which supplied the machine."

He paused and Campion nodded his comprehension and approval. The inspector lit a cigarette.

"Well," he said, "we've covered the lamp all right until the time Konrad left the bicycle in the cloakroom at the house. He went up to town on the Monday by car. On the following Sunday he came back in a cab with very little time to spare. The evidence is that he rushed up to the room which had been prepared for him, hurried into cycling kit, leaving his other clothes strewn about for someone else to pack—your man, Mr. Lugg, was very chatty on that question, by the way—and tore down to the cloakroom, where he snatched his bicycle and rushed off on it, catching the train at Birley by the skin of his teeth. No one noticed the lamp at the time.

"Mr. Lugg says he saw the bicycle standing in the cloakroom all the week, but he never thought to examine it. If you ask me, he was lucky. It's a natural thing to do, isn't it?—switch on a lamp."

"But the grenade couldn't have been there long." Campion was aghast. "Think of the danger. There's a child in the house. Anything might have happened."

Yeo shook his head knowingly.

"It all depends who put it there," he said. "If you ask me, the man who did this job wasn't the imaginative type. He's straightforward and ingenious; that's how I see him. Single-track mind. He argued that Konrad would ride that bicycle until it grew dark, and then he'd switch on his light and sit there with his head over the lamp until it blew up and killed him. Looked at like that, it seems foolproof, doesn't it?"

Campion considered the problem unwillingly.

"It must have been put there on the last morning. Probably the whole lamp was changed and a similar one substituted. Now I think of it, it must have happened like that."

"You're right." Yeo was pleased and he beamed upon his guest as at a promising pupil. "Major Bloom has had a bit more to say. He's now prepared to swear that the explosive was in the lamp all right, but the minute fragments of lamp which remain are not consistent with them being part of the actual one supplied with the bicycle, the specifications of which we have from the chauffeur and from the firm which sold it.

"So you see, as far as we know for certain, someone changed the lamp after Mr. Konrad left on the Monday and before he took the bike away on the following Sunday. I agree with you the substitution probably took place towards the end of the time, but we can't prove it, can we? That leaves us with everybody who came and went in that house for the best part of six days—and believe me there's a crowd of them."

Campion hesitated.

"What about *after* he left the house?" he suggested dubiously.

"Impossible. I've checked the time he left the door with the time he came flying into Birley station. He could only just have done it. The bicycle was thrown into the guard's van and the guard remembers sitting near it the whole journey. He nearly fainted when I told him about the grenade. I had to laugh—couldn't help myself."

Yeo grinned at the recollection but frowned again and sighed as the problem presented itself once more.

"If we could get on to the motive we'd have a definite lead," he said, eyeing Campion meaningly. "As far as I can gather from the people down there, no one liked Konrad but his sudden death is the last thing any of them wanted."

Still Mr. Campion refused to be drawn. He sat back in his chair, his face grave and friendly, but he made no suggestion.

Yeo, who was a man of infinite patience, continued the attack.

"You know the family and the immediate circle, so I needn't reintroduce them," he said. "There's an old man called William Faraday staying there. He was mixed up in that Cambridge case some years ago, wasn't he? You met him then. He's a friend of yours. He admits he had no time for Konrad, but he was the author of the show Konrad was appearing in and he's drawing big money for the first time in his life. Even if he were the type to go to the length of procuring the grenade and fixing it up, I can't see what he could possibly gain by Konrad's death, and the scandal might be definitely detrimental to his pocket. The same goes for Mr. Sutane, the composer Mr. Mercer, and the manager Mr. Poyser, who was in the house over the Saturday. Then there's Mr. Petrie, the secretary and publicity fellow; his job depends on Sutane's success, and he's not too flush for cash. The servants are out of it, as far as I can see, and the women don't appeal to me as suspects. Either the wife or the sister could conceivably have done it, but I'm hanged if I see why they should. Konrad doesn't seem to have gone in for love affairs and, apart from that consideration, the same main deterrents apply equally to them as to the men."

He shook his head.

"People don't go murdering for nothing unless they're homicidal maniacs. This is the work of a reasonable but callous mentality with a blind spot. Someone who wanted the chap to die and wanted him to go away and die, and didn't much care where. That's how I see him. But why he should do it at all I do not know."

There was silence between them for some time. Mr. Campion found he was doing his best not to think at all.

The chief inspector leant across and prodded his arm with a blunt forefinger.

"Faraday's a friend of yours but the others aren't," he said. "You went to White Walls for the first time less than a fortnight ago?"

Campion grinned.

"It seems longer."

"I'll lay it does. They've had a packet down there." Yeo's eyes were bright and still friendly. "Blest has done well. I've had everything out with him, of course. Oates and I have gone over that persecution story from A to Z. That's how you got into the business in the first place. We know all about that and we've taken it into consideration. But however irritated Mr. Sutane was, he'd hardly go killing Konrad when he could sack him, would he? Or he might have lost his temper and socked the fellow, but he wouldn't go messing about with explosives and delayed-action methods. Besides, there wasn't the time. Blest told Mr. Sutane his suspicions on the Saturday after he had located the accomplice, and Konrad met his death on the Sunday. That grenade had to be obtained."

Campion roused himself with an effort.

"Where did it come from?"

"We don't know yet. Major Bloom's still working on it."

For the first time throughout the interview Yeo showed signs of his normal reticence.

"I seem to be doing all the talking," he remarked. "What about you saying a few words?"

"I've been agreeing with you." Campion spoke carefully. "Everything you've said I've thought myself. I'm in the dark. The crime has astonished me. It's not the kind of thing I could ever imagine emanating from that house. But if it has, then I'm sorry but I don't want to be near it."

Yeo shrugged his shoulders.

"That's where you have the advantage over us professionals," he said acidly. "I can't choose myself. I've never known you like this, Mr. Campion. You're usually so keen. If I was asked, do you know what I'd say? If I didn't know you were a comparative stranger to these people I'd say personal feelings were involved. Yet Faraday's the only friend you've got in the bunch and, frankly, I can't for the life of me see how he can be in it."

"Look here, Inspector, if I thought I could help you put your hands on the man you want I'd do it." Campion's voice was unexpectedly strained. "You must believe that. But I can't. I do not know. I cannot think of anyone with any motive who could conceivably have done such an appalling, such a stupid, thing. You say Blest found the accomplice? Who was he? May I know? It's a point of professional interest to me."

"You can see him if you like." Yeo was the soul of affability. His reputation for tenacity had not been lightly won. "I'm going to look him up after this. Who do you think it was? Beaut Siegfried, of all people."

"No, really?" It seemed to Campion that he had not heard that florid name since his childhood. "The dancing master?"

"The old haybag himself," agreed Yeo disrespectfully. "He's ballet master now, by the way. Regular old pressed rose. Blest got him to admit he wrote those invitations. Don't ask me how. I don't want to know. I'd get kicked out of the force if I used some of the methods these private chaps employ. Blest was never more than a divisional inspector, you know. He was a bit too hot for anything. Anyway, he managed old Beaut. Mr. Siegfried wrote to Mr. Sutane a nice little letter of apology for 'what was, perhaps, an only too unfortunate practical joke.' Sutane has accepted the apology, Blest says. It was about all he could do in the circumstances. It was a silly trick, enough to make anybody wild.

"But not *murdering* wild," he added after a pause and cocked his head at Campion like a terrier at a mousehole.

In the end Mr. Campion accompanied the inspector to the studio in Cavendish Square, accepting the honour in the spirit of good fellowship which he was no less anxious than the police to maintain. After years of the closest and most friendly co-operation with the authorities he felt his present position on the fence very keenly, and his resentment at the combination of circumstances which had forced him to take it up grew deep.

As they came across the fine square in the warm odoriferous London afternoon Yeo coughed.

"This is just a little friendly chat. You're my unofficial sergeant for the time being. There's been so many infringements of the regulations already where this chap is concerned that I don't think another matters very much. You'll have to lie out of it if you ever see him again. He knows me. We've had one or two little chats in our time."

As they climbed the shallow steps to the graceful Georgian doorway another thought occurred to him.

"He's a bit of a sketch," he said. "Thinks he's the School of Scandal, or something."

Beaut Siegfried interviewed them in his beautiful studio. He was a thin, elderly man on whom old affectations hung like faded garlands. His court breeches and silk stockings betrayed ageing, sharp-boned legs, and the shoulders beneath his long-skirted velvet coat were bent and weak. He had fine white hands and was childishly proud of them, letting them drop into careless, graceful poses whenever he remembered. His face beneath his fluffy hair, which was still brown and still curly, was the face of the traditional withered spinster, prim, lined and spiteful, the eyes slightly prominent and disconcertingly blank.

When they were shown in he was posing with a fiddle, a shaft of sunlight from a high window falling on his bent head. He laid the instrument down with a little sigh as they appeared and advanced across the polished floor to meet them.

"My dear Chief Inspector," he said, "this is a pleasure. I am free, too. None of my dear boys and girls will be here till six. They still come to me, you see, and I teach them to move their beautiful bodies with the true grace. But they won't be here till six o'clock and so I was able to have you shown in at once. A glass of amontillado? Just a little one? In my crystal glasses."

Yeo refused and sat down uninvited, motioning Mr. Campion to do likewise.

Siegfried remained posed in front of them, the light playing on his hair and on the soft folds of his coat. There was an irregular board in the floor, Mr. Campion noticed, to show him just where to stand if this effect was to be satisfactorily attained.

Yeo regarded his host blandly and with a certain satisfaction, as at a peculiar pet.

"I came to talk to you about Konrad," he said. "I thought you might be able to help me."

"Konrad?" Siegfried threw a white hand over his eyes. "I can't think of it," he said. "I sent some roses but I can't think of it. Don't ask me to. He had such a gift, such a spirit! To die so young!"

He had a curious soft voice with a crack in it and a refinement of accent which was oddly not at all unpleasant. Campion found himself wondering what on earth he had been like at school.

Yeo's round eyes were amused.

"Do you know of anyone who didn't like him?" he enquired baldly.

"Oh." The dancing master dropped his hand and his sharp, withered face became startlingly inquisitive. "Oh. Why do you ask me that?"

"Because I thought you might know," explained Yeo stolidly. "He was a star pupil of yours or something, wasn't he?"

"Well"—Siegfried was flattered—"I taught him all I knew. His poise, his grace, his divine spirit, was all mine. But his modern technique . . . No, I don't think I can lay claim to that. I used to scold him sometimes for leaving the classical school of sheer beauty for the intricacies of the terrible new rhythm."

"Anyway, you knew him," Yeo persisted. "Had he any enemies?"

Siegfried hesitated, his mouth narrowed and pursed and his eyes growing spiteful.

"There were people who were jealous of him," he said primly.

Yeo waited patiently until with a shrug of his bent shoulders, which proclaimed as clearly as if he had spoken that he was throwing off restraint, Siegfried took the plunge.

"It may be slander," he said. "I don't know, I'm sure; the law's so ridiculous. But I do think someone ought to be told. I'll let you know in confidence, Inspector, but I'm not going to be badgered afterwards. The poor boy was *persecuted*."

It seemed extraordinary that one wizened old creature could hold so much living forceful venom.

"Sutane," he said. "That man Sutane. He's not a dancer. He's an acrobat and the mob have made a god of him. He's got no soul, no poetry, no spirit at all, and when he saw Benny he was jealous of him. He's dogged the boy. He's forced him into his shows and kept him out of sight all because he simply *daren't* let him appear."

He forgot the shaft of sunlight and came a little closer, thrusting his face into the inspector's own and bubbling a little at the lips in his excitement.

"Benny's been here and *cried* to me," he insisted. "If Benny had a good entrance Sutane took it away. If there was an opportunity for costume Sutane disallowed it. If Benny got an ovation Sutane sneered at him. The boy was simply a mass of nerves after a month or two of Sutane. I don't know what happened at the end. I can't read the newspapers. They're disgusting. But whatever it was, Sutane was morally responsible. There, now I've told you. My conscience is clear. But do understand I *won't be worried*. I won't make a statement and I certainly won't go into court. I've got my boys and girls to think of. I teach them to be artists in the true sense of the word and I won't be hindered."

"Konrad never complained to you of anyone except Sutane?"

Yeo was stolidly impervious to the gibbering face so near his own.

"No. No one but Sutane." The old man stood biting his thin lips, his prominent eyes starting and vindictive. "Sutane was killing him in spirit, stifling him and devitalising him. But I don't want to hear anything more about it. It upsets me. The tragedy has happened and the poor boy is dead."

He walked back to the great Italian chest in the corner and picked up his violin. Yeo took his leave.

They were shown to the door by a respectable elderly charwoman who fitted the messenger boy's description of the woman who had despatched the garlic bouquet.

As they came away they heard the quavering strains of a little air of Puccini's rendered atrociously.

Yeo walked along in silence for some minutes.

"There's nothing there," he said at last. "I saw it at once. You can see how that monkey business round the theatre came to happen, can't you? Konrad was eaten alive with jealousy, transposed it in his mind, as they all do, and he and Siegfried egged each other on until they had to break out into action or burst."

Campion nodded. The action had been typical, he reflected; little sporadic eruptions of weakness, petty, absurd and infuriating.

Yeo laughed.

"The old devil wasn't mentioning his brush with Blest, was he?" he said. "You'd think an experience like that would teach him to keep his mouth shut, but I thought it wouldn't. He is an old woman and no mistake! Oates can't stay in the room with him, but he makes me laugh. There's nothing vicious about him. He's just a bundle of old fancy dress and always has been. Why don't you accept Mr. Sutane's invitation and go down to White Walls, Mr. Campion?"

The suddenness of the question had its desired effect and took Campion off his guard.

"Because I don't want to," he said.

Yeo sighed.

"Think it over," he advised. "You could be very useful to us on the inside like that. See here, these are my last words. You don't think Mr. Sutane is the man we want and I can't see why on earth he should be, any more than anyone else. It's to his interest to have the thing cleared up quickly, because we're going to keep at it if it takes us from now until eternity, and we'll ruin him before we've finished. We can't help ourselves. So whose hospitality will you be abusing? Think it over . . ."

Mr. Campion walked about London for nearly four hours. The complete privacy of a sojourn among four million total strangers was comforting and the exercise soothed him.

As he came up the quiet, dignified street to the Junior Greys the evening sun picked out the colours at the windows of the solid grey-white buildings and the air was pleasant and full of the quiet laughter of a London after work. He began to feel free again. The gnawing, shameful preoccupation with Linda which had been at first amusing and then shocking and finally downright terrifying was now battened down, banished, part to some far-off corner of his mind and part to a spot somewhere at the base of his diaphragm.

He felt responsible again and his own mind's master.

There was a message waiting for him with the club porter. It was brief and mysterious, without being particularly disturbing. The caretaker at Bottle Street had phoned to ask if he would call in at the flat the moment he returned. Because it was so near, barely three streets away, he went round at once and hurried up the familiar staircase, fumbling in his pocket for his key.

As he came to the foot of the final flight he paused abruptly, his new-found peace scattered as the battens were burst upward and all the mental and emotional confusion of the past ten days took possession of him once again.

Linda Sutane, who had been seated on the topmost stair just outside his door, rose wearily to her feet and came down to meet him.

Chapter 21

As Campion stood balancing his lean body, his heels on the curb and his shoulders braced against the high mantelshelf, he looked at the girl seated in his wing chair and made the disturbing discovery that the progress of an affair of the heart does not cease at the point where the two parties are separated, resuming its course when they meet again, but rather continues its relentless progress slowly and inexorably all the time, whether the participants are together or apart.

Linda Sutane looked smaller than he had remembered her. Her black suit with the pleated white collar was a Lelong, and the hat perched on her sleek hair gave her a new air of sophistication which he liked and found somehow comforting.

She had followed him into the flat without speaking and had seated herself without glancing about her. Her silence had demoralised him and he stood looking at her, his hands in his pockets, wishing that she would speak and put the ridiculously disturbing meeting on some concrete basis of reality at least. At the moment he felt he was suffering from an hallucination with the added disadvantage of knowing very well that it was not one.

She glanced up at him and he saw that her small face was white and stiff and her honey-coloured eyes dark with worry.

His heart contracted suddenly and painfully, and this, the final emotional straw, turned the wheel right over and he felt gloriously and freely angry with her. The whole monstrous imposition of love confronted him and he boiled at it.

"Well," he said spitefully, "this is very nice of you."

She drew back into the chair and tucked her feet up under her so that it contained her entirely.

"Uncle William thought you would come to help us if I asked you myself, so I came to find you."

She spoke with an unusual ingenuousness, and he saw that she was ill at ease and received an unworthy satisfaction from the discovery.

"But, my dear lady," he said, "if there was anything I could do, believe me, I should be wandering round your delightful garden, badgering your servants, leaping about from flower bed to flower bed with a reading glass, and generally behaving like the complete house-trained private tec. But as it is, I really don't see how I can impose myself upon you. What can I do?"

She stared at him.

"You've changed," she said.

The suddenness of the direct attack defeated, or rather deflated, him. He fumbled for a cigarette case and offered it to her. She shook her head in refusal but did not take her glance from his face. She looked hurt and puzzled and reminded him irritatingly of Sarah.

"We're in dreadful trouble," she said. "The police come every day. Do you know about it? What they think about Konrad?"

"Roughly, yes."

"Yet you won't do anything?"

For what was probably the first time in his life Campion ceased to think during an interview. There are occasions when the intellect retires gracefully from a situation entirely beyond its decorous control and leaves all the other complicated machinery of the mind to muddle through on its own.

Since he was a highly bred product of a highly civilised strain, his natural instincts were offset by other man-implanted cultures and taboos, and the result of the war between them was to make him, if inwardly wretched, outwardly a trifle insane.

"My dear," he said, "I'll hold the whole blithering universe up for you. I'll stop the whole dizzy juggernaut of British police procedure for you if you want me to. I'm all-powerful. I'll wave a little wand and we'll find it all isn't true."

For a moment she wavered maddeningly between anger and tears and finally crept further into the depths of the chair, to sit looking out at him like a wren in a nest.

"How is Lugg?" said Campion. "And Uncle William? And the helpful Mercer? Sock, too, and Poyser and Miss Finbrough? You all have my most sincere sympathy and if I were a first-class magician I'd put the clock back a month or so, say to the beginning of May, with the greatest of pleasure for you. As it is, however, I'm not the man you thought me. God bless my soul, I'm not the fairy queen after all."

He was concentrating on making her angry. It seemed to have become the only important thing in life.

"I'm a cad at heart," he said cheerfully. "I can't work the oracle and miracles are beyond me. You see, there are quite a number of other powerful spells at work—the porter's wife, for instance."

He was very much alive now and laughing. The vacuity had vanished from his face, leaving it lean and pleasant. He had taken off his spectacles and his pale long-sighted eyes were darker and sharper than before.

Linda nodded to him gravely as if he had imparted a secret to her which she had already known.

"Come down with me now," she said and held out her hand to him.

He looked at the hand, shooting it a sharp quick glance which took in everything there was to notice about it: its shape, its texture, and the very faint blue veins under the golden skin. A colt in the field looks in the same way at the skip of feed held out to entice it.

He turned abruptly and went over to the cocktail cabinet.

"Let us drink and discuss this," he said. "A White Lady?"

He was a long time over his preparations and she watched his thin, muscular back and the short fine hairs at the base of his skull.

"The rats are right in the house now," she said in a small quiet voice behind him. "We shall have to see them soon. It's like being besieged by ghosts. Jimmy's insane with worry and everybody's different. I thought it was only in the house but now I'm beginning to find the whole world's like it. I thought you'd like to help."

"I would," he assured her lightly. "If I could, I'd come beetling down like a homing chipmunk. You see, it's the size of the thing which discourages me so. Have you noticed that about murder? It goes by compound interest. Two are twice as bad as one and three are three times as bad as two. I may run round and muck about with the insides of motor-cars in a little case of dubious suicide, but when I see such a quantity of carnage I know when I'm beaten. I knew a mongrel whippet once called Addlepate. He'd take on any bull pup singlehanded but he gave one look at the bull-pup ring at a country show and raised his eyebrows and walked away. I sympathised with him. I'm like that myself. Your cocktail, lady."

She took the glass and set it down untasted. He found her bewildered expression unbearable and so he did not look at her.

"If you found out the truth and told, I wouldn't blame you," she said.

"I don't know. It might be a howling cad's trick to tell. Things like that sometimes happen," he said and laughed.

She turned her face into the upholstery of the chair and he paused abruptly and stared at her, his eyes wretched. There was a long silence and in it he was acutely aware that he was in his own familiar room and that she was in it, too, and no right thing there.

He took the handkerchief from his breast pocket and dropped it lightly onto her hand.

The movement roused her and she took it up and looked at it.

"You're very hard," she said. "I didn't realise that. Incredibly hard."

"Solid rock," he agreed. "Granite. Beneath the superstratum of mud you come to stone. The ghastly monotony is relieved here and there by occasional fossilised fish."

"Oh, well, it's been very—very interesting," she said and climbed out of the chair.

She smiled at him, her brown eyes shining.

He did not echo it. His face was pinched and grey.

"Did you come by car, or may I take you to the station?"

She moved close to him and looked up at him, her face working.

"I'm frightened," she said. "That's really why I came. I don't know what's going to happen next. I'm alone down there with them all and I'm physically frightened. Don't you see?"

Mr. Campion stood staring down at her with his arms hanging limply at his sides. Presently he lifted his chin and looked over her head. His expression was blank and introspective.

"All right," he said with sudden brisk decision. "We'll go now. This is my full responsibility, remember. It's nothing to do with you at all. Both your husband and the police have asked me to make an investigation and I'll try to do it. That's all. But I'm afraid . . ."

He broke off and she prompted him.

"What?"

"Afraid the time may come when you will think I'm a pretty low-down sort of tick, Linda my sweet," said Mr. Campion gravely.

Chapter 22

"Ease it," said Mr. Lugg through the door. "Put yer back into it. Ee-ease it. Don't git excited and don't be frightened. I'm 'ere. I'll let you out if you can't do it, but come on—try. Don't be a little wet."

The long corridor which ran from east to west throughout the whole top floor of White Walls was silent save for his earnest injunctions, and Mr. Campion, who had been looking for him ever since his own arrival, was confronted by a monstrous back view of that vast familiar form.

"Steady—steady now! I can 'ear it goin'."

The white arc of a bald head appeared over a much greater arc of broad-cloth tail coat, like an up-ended crescent moon, as its owner applied a great ear to the panels of a door. There was a grunt of regret.

"Lorst it. . . . Never mind. Try again. You'll never do it if you don't try. Take the pin out. 'As it lost its shape? Wot? Well, *square*, you snufflin' little chump! I showed you. Got it? Now then, in she goes. Quietly!—quietly! You don't want to rouse the 'ouse. 'Ere she goes—'ere she goes. . . . That's it. Now then . . .'"

The ominous scratching at the door lock ceased as with a triumphant click the bolt shot back and the door slid quietly open, to reveal a flushed and excited Sarah with a bent hairpin in her hand.

"Done it!" she screamed, dancing round the old man like a demented puppy. "Done it! Done it! Done it!"

"Shut up." Lugg let out a friendly blow at the side of her head which would have felled an ox and mercifully missed its half-hearted objective. "Don't bawl the place down. You'll get us ticked orf again. No need to go orf like a gin palace on a Saturday, even if you can pick a lock with anyone twice yer size. Now, there's something useful I've learnt yer, only don't advertise it. That's the kind of trick you want to keep under yer 'at —see? 'Ullo . . ."

The final utterance was in the nature of a warning. They both stiffened and Mr. Lugg's beady bright eyes rested coldly upon the thin form at the far end of the corridor.

Campion came forward.

"Lugg, what are you doing?"

"Amusin' the child." Lugg was truculent and casual. "I'm a nursemaid now. Didn't they tell you?" He looked down at his pupil and winked. "Run along now, Miss Sarah," he said with travestied formality. "Nuss will no doubt be a-searchin' of for you. You do not want to cause her any anxiety? I thought not. We will continue our 'obby later on. Go on, get out. Beat it, there's a good kid."

Sarah squeezed his hand and slipped the hairpin into his coat pocket.

"Thank you, Mr. Lugg," she said with rehearsed dignity. "That was most int'resting."

She walked off sedately, only breaking into uncontrollable giggles when the newcomer had been safely passed. Campion waited until she was out of earshot and spent the time surveying his only real responsibility with a chilly interest guaranteed to inspire shame.

"You think you're a damn fine sort of a fellow, I suppose?" he said at last. "A sort of ministering Boy Scout, bringing a little dusty sunshine to a misunderstood child?"

Lugg sniffed to convey that he was not impressed.

"I'm very fond of my fellow creatures," he said. "Besides, you never know when a simple little wrinkle like that might come in useful. Every kid ought to learn 'ow to pick a lock. She's a helpless noisy little bit. She's bound to come up against it sometime in 'er life. I'm preparin' of 'er for it. I'm doin' 'er a bit of good. You lay orf. I like 'er. She's all right."

"She reminds you of yourself when you were a child, no doubt?" enquired Mr. Campion affably.

Lugg looked down over a highly coloured career to some distant hotbed in the slums of Canning Town.

"No," he said seriously. "Not reely. She's simple to what I was. It's the bringin' up what does it. Well, you've turned up at last, 'ave you? About time too. I've 'ad a room ready for you for a week. Come on. I'll show it to you now you are 'ere."

He waddled down the corridor with Campion behind him.

"There you are," he said, flinging open the door of the chamber immediately above the small music room. "Mr. Benjamin Konrad's late apartment. The last gentleman 'oo slept in 'ere was blown to Buenos Aires. 'Ope you'll be comfortable."

Campion walked through the chintz-hung room and stood looking out over the wide garden, misty in the twilight.

"Well?" he enquired over his shoulder. "Noticed anything of value about this business?"

"No. I'm keepin' right out of it." Lugg heaved a leather suitcase onto the bedspread and began to pitch out its contents. "You didn't think to bring me a shirt or two, I don't suppose?" he said. "I'm right away from civilisation down 'ere, you know."

"No, I didn't. Leave those things alone. Pull yourself together. You can't have been going about in a trance. You must have noticed something. What have you been doing?"

"What I was asked—bein' a butler." Lugg sounded smugly satisfied. "You lent me to the lady as a butler and a butler I've bin. It's not my line but I've made a job of it and in a way I've quite enjoyed it. The servants are well under my thumb and in my spare time I do my best to amuse the kid, 'oo I like. Give me a year or two with that kid and I'll make somethink of 'er. She's got the makin's of a first-class little tough. I'm very strict, you know. No swearin'. Nothin' unladylike. She's give me a few tips too. If there's somethink I don't know and don't like to lower meself by askin' the servants, I mention it to 'er and, if she don't know either, she gits it out the nurse. It's mutual.

"Oh, we've 'ad the police 'ere—I can see by yer face that's all your interested in. There's a sergeant stayin' at the pub down the road now, as far as I know, but I've not let a pack of flatties bother me."

He seemed to regard the final statement as a sign of virtue.

"That was what you told me, wasn't it?"

Campion sighed. "Quite," he said. "Oh, by the way, perhaps I ought to have mentioned it; if there is a fire while you are here you will act—temporarily, of course—as a fireman. And if the river at the bottom of the garden overflows and floods the lower story you should become for a brief hour or so a boatman, conveying members of the household to safety as best you can."

Lugg was silent for a moment.

"You're not quite yourself, are you?" he said at last. "Anythin' up? Fun's fun, but no need to be spiteful. This is a mad'ouse, you know. If I was the inspector I'd arrest the lot, give 'em good food and attention fer a month, and 'ang the one 'oo was still crackers at the end of the time."

Having delivered himself of this dictum, he returned to the suitcase.

"Serve the boss right for allowin' the bike in the 'ouse," he remarked over his shoulder. "I see by the papers they suspect the lamp now. I thought there must be somethink like that by the way they was carryin' on about the machine. I ban newspapers in the kitchen. I tell 'em I've got the inside stuff and everythin' they want to know they must take from me. I 'ad to do somethin' like that or they'd all be leavin', and I don't want the blarsted 'ousework of a place this size on me 'ands."

He paused and glanced sharply towards the door just before someone knocked.

"Come in, Mr. Faraday," he called out and added as he opened the door with all the dignity of a better-trained man, "I knoo it was you, sir. 'Eard you breathin'. 'Ere is Mr. Campion—at last."

A subdued and almost pallid Uncle William came padding softly into the room.

"My dear boy," he said with genuine emotion. "My dear boy."

Lugg bristled and his small and bright black eyes contained a gleam of jealousy.

"Wot 'o, the fatted calf," he murmured derisively.

Uncle William, who was slow of perception, did not see the allusion instantly and appeared to think some personal insult was intended. He swung round with parade-ground severity.

"I'll trouble you to control your tongue, my man. Get out. I want to speak to your master."

The fat man by the bedside dropped the sponge bag he had taken from the case and stood staring, his huge face dark with indignation.

"Be off with you," insisted Uncle William with more vigour than impressiveness.

Lugg looked at Campion and, receiving no hint of encouragement, moved ponderously towards the door.

When it was actually closing behind him and he had not been recalled, he paused and put his head in again.

"If you 'ave not dined, sir, there are a few cold bits on the sideboard in the dinin' room," he said with tremendous dignity, and, having recovered his self-esteem and achieved the last word, he surged off to his own domain below stairs.

In the bedroom Uncle William frowned and cast a worried glance behind him.

"I don't want to hurt the fellow's feelings," he said, "but this is no time to stand on ceremony. What a business, Campion! What a terrible business! You probably know more about it than I do, if the truth were told, but I've watched some of the effects down here. We're livin' in a nightmare, my boy. I've woken up from a nap more than once with my heart in my mouth. One can't forget it even for a moment. It hangs over one's head day and night. Day and night!"

He gobbled a little and wiped his face with one of his stiff white handkerchiefs.

"Just when we thought the worst was over, bar the shoutin', and were quietly gettin' back to normal again, that silly little whippersnapper calls in for his bicycle and rides off on it to meet his death. When I first heard of it on the Sunday night I own I wasn't brokenhearted—except for the other poor souls, of course. Konrad always struck me as a weed and it didn't upset me to hear that he'd gone to the Great Incinerator. But yesterday, when the London police arrived with the local man and started puttin' us through it about the bicycle, it came to me in an overwhelming flash that we were back in the mire again, and well over the ankles this time."

He sat down in a chintz-covered armchair, which was too small to contain his plump sides with comfort, and remained hunched up, looking down at his red leather house slippers.

"The police are confused, shouldn't wonder," he remarked presently. "Last Friday was the funeral of that silly woman who began this run of bad luck, and on the Saturday Jimmy gave up his matinee to put in the best part of a long day on the new show. All the principals came down here on Saturday mornin' and most of 'em stayed the night to go on with the work over Sunday. It's goin' to be a terrible performance, I'm afraid. Didn't like what I saw of it. Still, that's neither here nor there. When Inspector Yeo started askin' me who was in the house at the end of last week I was hard put to it to give him a full answer. I told him he'd never arrive at the truth by the elimination of possible suspects.

"There was a prince here for a night—Friday or Saturday. A Russian feller. Very civil. Seemed to be an old friend of Jimmy's. Knew him in Paris years ago. Kept me awake half the night with tales of wolf shootin'.

"The place has been full of people. I said to the police sergeant it's like lookin' for a tiger in South America. If he's there he's in disguise. And if you accept that, he may be any one of the peculiar-lookin' fellers about."

He paused, blew, and raised a worried plump old face to his friend's.

"We're in the devil of a hole, Campion," he said. "Which of us is it? D'you know?"

He received no answer and bowed his head, so that his misty tonsure, frilled with yellow-white curls, made a sudden and pathetic appearance.

"I can't believe it," he said. "And I'll tell you something, Campion. I'm not an obstinate feller by any means, but there is one possibility—only a faint one, mind; but I'm not a fool, I see it—there's one possibility that I'm shuttin' my eyes to. Come what may, I'm not goin' to believe it. Understand?"

Mr. Campion glanced over the garden again.

"I rather thought you might feel like that," he said.

Uncle William looked up sharply. His bright blue eyes were hunted and shifty.

"Why should . . ." he began but thought better of it. "No point in fruitless discussion," he said. "Feel like a rat in a treadmill once you start thinkin'. Tell you what I've done. I've consulted my heart and made up my mind and I'm stickin' to my decision. It may not be the right way, but battles have been won on it, my boy. If you don't mind we won't mention it again. . . .

"I don't like the girl goin' off like this, do you? What's she up to?"

Campion swung round from the window.

"What girl?"

"Eve. Didn't Linda tell you?" Uncle William seemed put out. "What's Linda holdin' that back for? Thought she'd get you down here safely first, I suppose. Can't tell with a woman. Yes, well, Eve's gone, you know. Went off yesterday afternoon. Got the chauffeur to take her to the station with a small suitcase. The feller said she'd been cryin'. I've been sittin' by the telephone all day, waitin' for her to ring up. Nothin' yet."

Campion stared at him in fascinated silence. Uncle William dropped his eyes.

"Queer, isn't it?" he murmured.

"Very." Campion's tone was sharp. "Do the police know about it?"

"No. No, I don't think they do, as a matter of fact. That is, they don't realise we don't know where she is."

Campion leant back against the window ledge.

"You'll have to explain, you know."

Uncle William shrugged his shoulders and stirred uncomfortably.

"Feel I may be makin' a mountain out of a molehill, don't you know," he observed in a particularly unsuccessful attempt to hide his concern. "I'm gettin' on myself and, realisin' the girl's so young, I'm apt to be a bit of an old woman. Very likely Linda feels much the same and doesn't think it was worth mentionin'."

Mr. Campion thought of that long silent drive through the country lanes and wrenched his mind away from the contemplation of it.

"What happened exactly?" he demanded. "When the chauffeur came home he was questioned, I suppose?"

"Yes, well, we saw him comin' in, don't you know, and asked him where he'd been."

Uncle William managed to sound reluctant without being actually evasive.

"The long and the short of it was that there was a certain amount of general surprise when we heard the girl had gone off without a word. Someone ran up to her room to see if she'd left a note and when we found she hadn't we were all standin' about, worried, and then Jimmy, who was down here after waitin' to see the police, suddenly seemed to remember that he knew about it. He said she'd be back today. The sergeant didn't ask for her this mornin' when he came round, and no one mentioned her bein' away. There's so many people comin' and goin', the police can't keep track of it all unless they come out into the open and keep the house under general arrest."

He drew a deep breath and blinked uneasily.

"I asked Jimmy straight out where she was and he said he thought she was stayin' with a woman friend in Bayswater. Linda knew the name and after Jimmy had gone to town she rang the woman up. But Eve wasn't with her and hadn't been."

His voice trailed away.

Campion digested the somewhat disturbing story.

"Was she in the habit of going off up to town at a moment's notice and staying the night with friends?"

"Not without a word to anyone, my dear fellow." Uncle William sounded shocked. "That's a funny thing for anyone to do. Monstrous in a girl of seventeen or so. I'm worried about her, Campion. She wrote that note I found in the bird's nest all right."

"Oh, she did? Who to?"

"I never found out." He reported the failure regretfully. "Couldn't keep my eyes on the tree all day. It was still there on Saturday. On the Sunday mornin' too. But on Monday I was prowlin' round early, tryin' to get my mind accustomed to the new catastrophe, when I caught a glimpse of someone in the woods ahead of me. I knew it was Eve by her pink dress. Presently she came past with her face screwed up and tears in her eyes and when I said 'Good mornin'' or somethin' equally footlin' she didn't look at me. When I got to the nest it was empty, but there were small fragments of the note scattered over the grass. Shouldn't have noticed them if I hadn't been lookin' for them. They were quite dry and it had showered heavily in the night, so I took it that she'd only just torn the paper up."

For an instant a shy twinkle appeared in his eyes.

"Rather neat work," he murmured. "Don't you think?"

"Very." Campion was properly impressed. "Has Sock been down here?"

"Several times. Run off his feet, poor lad. Don't know when he sleeps.

Extraordinary thing! Have you noticed it, Campion? If a feller's under twenty-seven no one ever thinks he needs rest of any kind. Jimmy's not a hard man but he looks on Sock as a sort of messenger boy on wings. You don't think the girl would run off to Sock, do you? I mean, two young people on their own. No restraint. No curbin'. Monstrous."

Campion passed his hand over his hair.

"Who's in the house now, besides ourselves and Lugg?"

"Only Linda and Miss Finbrough. Jimmy will be down in an hour or two and heaven knows who he'll bring with him. Mercer's at his own cottage, in bed. Poisoned, silly feller."

"Poisoned?"

Uncle William chuckled.

"Caught a cold comin' home on Friday night," he said with malicious amusement. "Serve him right. Ought to have gone to the funeral. Terrible feller to have anythin' the matter with him. There were we, worried, nervous, distraught, and there was he fidgetin' about a cold comin' on. On Sunday I lost my temper with him. I told him to go to bed early and take somethin' hot and keep himself to himself instead of whinin' about the place, doin' nothin' except scatterin' infection. What did the silly feller do then but wait until the last moment, when we were all thunderin' upset, havin' heard of the news of the rumpus on the wircless at nine o'clock, and then go down to the kitchen here to borrow a bottle of ammoniated quinine from the cook. He took it home, wearin' my ulster without a by-your-leave, and sent his man for a spoon. Naturally the feller, not knowin' what was wanted, brought the first one he saw, and Mercer took a tablespoonful in half a tumbler of water. The sensible dose is half to a whole teaspoonful.

"Well, he went to bed, woke up half deaf and blind, and let out a howl for a doctor. I saw the medical man." He smiled at the recollection of the meeting. "He called it cinchonism, and Mercer's still laid up. Better now, though. Saw him today. Told me the cracklin' in his ears was dyin' off a bit. Still, he's very sorry for himself, stupid feller."

Linda did not appear when they went downstairs and Campion was grateful to her for her forbearance. A still-reproachful Lugg brought Uncle William his half decanter and set it down before him without a word. The old man sat looking at the golden-brown liquid in the cut glass for a long time. Campion thought his mind had wandered from it, when he suddenly bounced to his feet.

"Don't think I will," he announced. "Got to keep the mind clear. Don't drink as I used to—nothin' like. Still, can't sit lookin' at it. Put it away in the music room in my cupboard. Come for a turn in the air."

He stowed the whisky away, his plump hands infinitely gentle, and they went out into the warm scented garden. They were still strolling on the lawn when the Bentley's headlights drew great fingers across the dark grass.

Sutane was alone. They saw his slender, rackety figure silhouetted against the beam as he sprang out and came towards them.

"Campion!" he said. "Good man. Knew you wouldn't desert me. Eve back, Uncle William?"

"No." The old man's tone was unwontedly brusque. "Understood you were goin' to find her and tell her to come home at once."

Sutane did not answer immediately, and they had difficulty in keeping up with him. As they ascended the steps to the brightly lit hall Campion glanced at his face and was startled by what he saw there. Every superfluous gramme of flesh had gone, leaving it an oddly vivacious death's-head with the powerful, vigorous nerves almost apparent.

"Oh, yes." Sutane spoke lightly. "That's right. So I was. But the theatre's in such a hysterical state. Two deaths in the cast, you see, and they're a superstitious lot. I forgot all about it."

He glanced at Campion obliquely and his dull, intelligent eyes were smiling and confiding.

"She'll turn up tomorrow, won't she?" he said.

Chapter 23

The sleeping house was bright and a little stuffy in the early morning when Mr. Campion came quietly downstairs at half past six. The brilliant sunshine which even in the country seems so much cleaner at that hour than at any other in the day burst in through the curtains, making little patches of vivid colour on stone floor and carpet, while outside the gilded tops of the trees were dancing in the morning wind.

Campion had surveyed the cloakroom and the hot, sun-bathed lounge with some care before he became conscious of a quiet scuffling in the drawing room and put his head in to find Mr. Lugg and his assistant already at their housework.

Clad in a singlet and a pair of ancient grey-black trousers, a luggage strap about his middle and disreputable carpet slippers upon his bare feet, the temporary butler was dusting the china in the Georgian wall cupboard, while a galvanic little bundle in pyjamas and a red dressing gown scrubbed away with a rubber at the polished parquet floor. They were both engrossed in their work. Sarah's tight pigtails were screwed up on her small round head and her grunts and squeaks betrayed both concentration and considerable effort.

"Go on, git right in the corners. I don't want to 'ave to go over it after you." Lugg spoke over his shoulder as he rubbed a great thumb over the delicate face of a Dresden milkmaid. "Pretty stuff, this," he observed. "Not of great value, you know, and it makes a lot of work. But I like it. Little dolls, that's what these are. Toys reely."

Campion waited with commendable caution until the fragile group was back in its place again before he spoke.

"Good morning," he ventured.

Lugg swung round. "Gawd! You give me a turn," he said reproachfully. "What on earth are you up to now? I 'ave to git up in the dawn to git the work done in comfort and peace, but you needn't. The drawin' room I always see to meself. I don't let a maid touch it. That means gitting up early so that I'm not seen about in me slacks. It lowers yer dignity if you're seen comfortable.

"Go on, git on with it!" he added to his aide, who was listening to the conversation with apprehensive eyes. "'E ain't yer nurse. She 'elps me do the floors because I ain't so nippy on me knees," he explained, returning to Campion. "What's the good of 'er sittin' up in bed waitin' for the 'ouse to wake? Much better make 'erself useful. You ain't tired, are you, chum?"

Sarah shook her head contemptuously, and Campion, realising that his presence was constraining a conversation between two persons whose minds were singularly of an age, left them and went back to his quiet investigations.

He did not find what he was looking for in any of the downstairs rooms, although his search was thorough, but the failure did not seem to depress or even to surprise him, and, as signs of life began to appear in the house, he drifted out into the bright garden.

There his progress was equally slow. He pottered round the terrace and the shrubbery between the kitchen and music-room window, paying special attention to the water butts and the ornamental pool in the rosary. To his left the kitchen garden lay prim and tidy. Its rectangular beds were divided by moss-grown gravel paths and were bordered by fine box hedges nearly two feet high. The mid-season clipping was in progress, and the plump round tops of half the bushes were already replaced by neat square angles.

The gardener whom he met nodded at the half-finished work and regretted that he had not been able to get back to it.

"Friday and half day Sat'day I done that piece," he remarked. "I couldn't get to it Monday and Tuesday, and on Wednesday and Thursday I was down at the lake with the rest of 'em, helping the police."

He cocked an inquisitive eye at Campion, who did not rise to the bait but continued his walk after murmuring a few idle uninformative pleasantries.

He came on Linda as he approached Uncle William's bird's-nest copse.

She came down towards him in a yellow linen frock. Her head was bent and her eyes were dark and preoccupied.

He hailed her hastily, and she looked up at him with a faint air of guilt which delighted him unreasonably.

"I've been for a walk," she said. "I didn't feel like sleeping. It's breakfast time, you know. Come on."

He dropped into step beside her and they walked along between the fine, flamboyant flowers, his tall lean figure towering over her.

"When the police came the other day did they do anything besides ask questions?" he said suddenly.

"Oh, they looked about a bit, you know. I don't know what for." Her voice had a brittle quality and was determinedly light. "They were very secretive. Rather heavily tiptoe, in fact. They borrowed the gardeners to look for something in the lake. When I offered to let them see over the house they jumped at it."

"Why did you do that?" he said curiously. "It was very wise, of course."

She was silent, but as they came across the lawn to the terrace she shivered suddenly.

"I want it to end," she said. "Whatever is coming, I want it to come and be over. D'you know?"

He nodded, reflecting that her complete comprehensibility constituted half her charm for him.

"Did they find anything?"

"No, I don't think so. They'll come back today."

They mounted the terrace and came in through the open windows, to find Uncle William seated at a small oval table which had been set up for the meal. Miss Finbrough was beside him, eating steadily, obviously without thinking what she was doing.

She was directly in front of Campion as he came in and he was startled by the change in her. Her vivid colour, which was perhaps her most salient feature, was still there, but it was no longer the plump and shining redness of rawness and health. Now she was turgid-looking and dry-skinned, red with the redness of sandstone. Her strength seemed to have been drawn into herself, as if the muscles of her body had become knotted and hard.

She blinked at Campion dully and gave him a brief, mechanical smile.

Uncle William put down the *Times*. He had been looking at the small advertisements, which, in common with a great many of that eminent paper's subscribers, he found the most interesting reading of the day.

"Friday," he said. "So it comes round again. Good mornin'. Couldn't sleep. No reflection on your excellent beds, Linda my dear. Can't read the paper. Doesn't seem to have any interest. No sense of humour either; an occasional pun in Greek, nothin' more. It's worry with me; just worry."

He started violently as the door behind him opened and he turned to cast a belligerent glance at the newcomer, who proved to be Mercer in a fine newish suit.

The composer came in noisily, making the door shudder as he threw it to behind him. He still looked pale from his recent misadventure and his eyes were hollow.

"Hello," he said. "Hello, you down again, Campion? God! I feel ill. I'm going to town to see a specialist about this damned cinchonism, Linda. I'll be back tonight. My man's calling for me here, taking me to the station and meeting me off the last train. It's the ten-two, isn't it? I think I'll have some tea."

His complete self-preoccupation came as a relief to them all, if only as a counter-irritant. He threw himself into an armchair and held out a still-quavering hand for the cup Miss Finbrough passed to him.

"I've been deaf!" he shouted to Campion. "My ears have been popping like machine-gun fire. I've been blind and cross-eyed."

"Still, it hasn't killed you," muttered Uncle William, goaded into gentlemanly sarcasm. "Merciful thing."

"It is. Damned lucky." Mercer held the cup to his grey lips. "I had a wretched policeman sitting on my bed all Wednesday, asking me idiotic questions about things he could quite easily have found out from somebody else. I was so ill that I told him what I thought of him, his force, and his stupid great notebook. He didn't come again. It's a poison, you know, cinchona bark. I could have died from it."

Uncle William's forget-me-not eyes looked dangerous and Linda cut in. "You'll be back tonight then, Squire?"

"Yes, probably. I've got some work I want to finish. This damned business has wasted days."

Miss Finbrough seemed to be on the verge of collapse.

"Business?" she said faintly.

"Well, poisoning then." Mercer was happily oblivious of the contretemps. "That little dance thing I was mucking about with turned out very well. I've got something good there. Dill doesn't like my title, 'Pavane for a Dead Dancer.' He wants to try some other idea. These lyric writers think they're little tin gods. He feels it's highbrow or something."

"He probably feels it's in very bad taste, sir," snapped Uncle William, getting the rebuke in adroitly before he could be stopped.

"Bad taste?" The other man was genuinely surprised at first, but afterwards, when he suddenly saw the objection, he defended himself irritably. "Don't be a *perishing* fool," he said with quite unnecessary violence. "All this other affair will be forgotten long before we can get a song out. If you're going to talk poppycock like that it shows you don't understand the public mind any more than the average dirty-nosed child. You, for instance, do you remember what was in the papers six months ago? Of course you don't!"

Uncle William began to simmer. He shared the practically universal belief that the word "public" is opprobrious when applied to almost any other noun and more particularly so when it is allied to the word "mind." He felt himself insulted and was about to say so when a fortunate diversion was caused by the arrival of a soberly clad Lugg, who announced that Mr. Mercer's car was at the door.

The composer got up hastily.

"Is it?" he said. "Good. I don't want to miss that train. Did I leave my coat in here? Are you sitting on it, Linda? No, it must be outside. Find it, Lugg, will you? Good-bye, Linda. I may drop round on you tonight if I'm not too tired when I get in."

He went out with rather more clumsiness than usual, and the girl looked after him.

"He's made himself very ill," she remarked. "Jimmy's terribly worried about him. Quinine is filthy stuff. It makes one feel beastly. Fancy getting all that down him—a whole tablespoonful!"

"Miracle to me he didn't take the whole bottle, the fuss he was makin' over a little cold," said Uncle William unsympathetically. "Wonderful to be so interested in one's ailments. Jimmy ought to snub that feller. Think I'll go up and see Jimmy, by the way. He'll be awake by now. I'd like a word with him."

Miss Finbrough made a sound that was midway between a sob and a hiccup.

"You can't," she said flatly.

"Oh?" The old man turned slowly in his chair to look at her, and as the silence grew the others imitated him until she was in a circle of startled and enquiring eyes.

"Why not, Finny?" There was a hint of sharpness in Linda's tone as she put the question.

"He's not there. He's gone. He went out early in the car. If the police ask for him I was to tell them he'd be at the theatre after eleven o'clock."

Miss Finbrough spoke with a dullness which gave her voice a spurious complacency.

Linda flushed.

"But I haven't seen him," she said. "I didn't even see him last night. Hasn't he left any message for me?"

"He's very worried, Mrs. Sutane." The other woman was reproachful. "He knocked at my door at five this morning and told me to go down and make him some breakfast. I got everything ready and then he wouldn't eat it. He just rushed into the kitchen, swallowed a cup of tea, and then went off in the car."

She began to tremble violently and took out a crumpled handkerchief.

"You'll have to excuse me," she said. "I don't feel well. That's the only message he left."

Even in her agitation the ghost of her dominating personality remained. Somehow it enhanced her weakness. She went out and presently Linda followed her.

Uncle William looked up.

"Remarkable thing," he said. "Convey anythin' to your mind, Campion?"

Campion did not reply. He pottered round the room for a minute or two and then, having convinced himself that the women were safely upstairs and Uncle William lost in his own unhappy thoughts, he went out to the kitchen and borrowed two iron weights from the cook's scales.

In the privacy of the small music room he fitted the four-ounce disc into the eight-ounce one and tied them both in a handkerchief. Then, opening the window wide at the bottom, he stepped back and pitched the white bundle as far as he could into the most thickly shrubbed portion of the garden before him.

It went over the wall into the kitchen garden and he hurried after it, sliding over the low window sill onto the iron-hard turf below. It was not hard to find. The white heap lay between two rows of lettuces. He picked it up and with his eye measured a wide arc with himself at a point on the circumference and the window as the centre.

His line lay through some currant bushes, over a couple of paths and an onion bed, and ended at the wall on one side and a marrow patch at the other.

He made his search carefully, making a width allowance of four yards either way.

The marrow bed yielded nothing save a fine collection of surprising gourds, but at the farther box hedge along the second path he stopped abruptly. It was here that the clipping had ceased and the gardener had paused and laid down his shears at noon on the Saturday before. His barrow and garnering boards were still there by the side of the path.

Campion walked on slowly until his eyes rested upon a dark irregularity in the smooth sharp outlines of the newly clipped shrubs.

When at last he found it he plunged his hand down among the dense springy branches and a sigh escaped him. He slipped his handkerchief off the weights in his pocket and used the cambric to protect his find from his own fingerprints.

The birds sang, and the scent of flowers from the other garden came over the low wall on a breath of sparkling sunlit air as he stood looking down at his discovery.

It was a silver-plated bicycle lamp.

Chapter 24

The clubroom of the Hare and Hounds was overfilled with furniture in spite of its size. The vast table, at which sat Chief Inspector Yeo, Detective Sergeant Inchcape, both of the C.I.D. Central Branch, Chief Inspector Cooling of the county constabulary, and Mr. Albert Campion, private and unwilling investigator, supported, as well as the paraphernalia belonging to these gentlemen, thirty-seven ash trays, each inscribed with varying advertising matter, a polyanthus rosetree in a remarkable pot, a cracked bottle of solidified ink, and a Bible with a red marker.

The rest of the room was in keeping with this centrepiece and contained some very fine connoisseurs' specimens of early camera portraiture.

"He wiped the lamp and simply pitched it out of sight, thinking that no one would remark on it even if it were found. He's been reckoning entirely without the major. We weren't expected to find out how that explosion originated."

Yeo made the pronouncement with a gravity befitting his position as the most authoritative person present, and the local inspector, who was a fine solid man of military smartness, nodded his grave agreement.

Yeo glanced down at the typewritten sheets of notes before him.

"As soon as you turned the lamp in yesterday, Mr. Campion, we saw at once that it was clean-wiped," he said, "and of course we recognised it from the manufacturer's specifications. They are prepared to swear that it is the actual lamp they delivered with the bicycle. Inchcape here reported your evidence about the hedge clipping and I'm inclined to agree with you. The gardener must have found it if it had been there when he cut the box. That fixes the time it entered the hedge as somewhere between twelve noon on the Saturday, and, I think we may presume, ten-fifty on the Sunday morning when Konrad took the bike away. Who was in the house during that time?"

Inspector Cooling sighed.

"Thirty-seven persons off and on," he said sadly. "We've interviewed about half of 'em so far. Well, we'll carry on. It's spadework that does it."

Yeo grimaced.

"There's only the family and Mr. Faraday, not counting Mr. Campion, at the house now, I take it?" he said. "I shall go down there again this afternoon. Sutane has a matinee, of course. He didn't come home at all last night, did he?"

"He stayed at his flat in Great Russell Street, sir. He often does before a matinee." Sergeant Inchcape supplied the information gladly from his meagre store. "They're all at the house with the exception of the young lady, Miss Eve Sutane. She went to town on Wednesday and has not yet returned. Her absence escaped my notice on Thursday, but I learnt of her visit to friends from a maid yesterday, Friday. The explanation given to the household is that her brother thought she needed a little change. Miss Finbrough gave that out."

He paused and sucked his teeth, an appalling habit which he allowed to punctuate his every second remark. It gave him a consequential, self-satisfied manner which was either irritating or amusing, according to the temperament of his hearer.

"Have you got the address?" Yeo enquired. "No. Well, it doesn't matter. I'll pick it up when I go down this afternoon. It's of no importance, but we may as well keep on the careful side."

He glanced at Campion.

"We're still up against the same old snag. There's still no motive," he observed. "We're grateful for the lamp—very grateful—don't think we're not, but that only proves what we knew already, you know. The crime emanated from that house. The lamps were changed there. But who amongst the whole outfit should want to do such a thing is still a mystery. Isn't that so?"

His final question was addressed to his police colleagues, who murmured their agreement and followed his glance to the tall thin man who sat amongst them.

Campion was lounging in his chair, his hands in his pockets and his eyes half closed. He might have forgotten the conference.

"I was saying, Mr. Campion, as you were on the inside you were the one to spot the motive," prompted Yeo. "What are you thinking?"

Campion glanced at him out of the corner of his eye.

" 'There are forty policemen sitting in this room, but I would rather have you, my darling,' " he said.

"Beg your pardon?" Yeo sounded startled.

Campion got up. He was laughing, but without deep amusement.

"It's out of a play," he said. "Sir James Barrie wrote it. It's a sort of fairy story. You wouldn't know it. I'll wander along now, if I may. Should I find any more spare parts I'll ring you. See you this afternoon. I'm doing all I can."

As the door closed behind him the county inspector smiled with unexpected sympathy.

"He feels his position, don't he?" he remarked. "He's a friend down at the house. It's not very nice."

Yeo raised his eyebrows.

"A man can't have friends in our profession," he said with dignity. "Right's right and wrong's wrong. He knows that. He's been to school."

Cooling nodded, not wishing to disagree in any way with the distinguished visitor and most especially so on such an incontrovertible point.

Mr. Campion walked back down the dusty lower road. He passed the

Old House and avoided Mrs. Geodrake, who eyed him wistfully from the front garden, where she was weeding with ostentatious assiduity. He observed the A.A. phone box where Konrad had rung up Beaut Siegfried on the night Chloe Pye had died, and came up through the woods where Uncle William's bird's nest still perched, empty and forgotten.

He made a solitary and somewhat forlorn figure. Even the sight of Lugg, vast and impressive in a cutaway coat and posed ridiculously in a flower bed as he indicated suitable blooms for Sarah to cut for the drawing-room bowl, did not move him to comment.

He felt he was chained to a very slow avalanche. Sooner or later, today or tomorrow, it must gain impetus and roar down in all its inevitable horror, breaking and crushing, defeating and destroying. He could do nothing to impede it. With an effort he might possibly accelerate its present pace, but he did not want to. White Walls lay quiet in the shimmering sunlight. In the beds the blue butterflies flirted brightly with the flowers. The light wind was warm and caressing.

Surely the night, tomorrow night, the next rainy day, surely, surely one of these would be time enough?

But at that moment, of course, he knew nothing of the shabby little coupé drawn up on the verge by the side of the Birley road.

Sock phoned at three o'clock, before Yeo had put in his promised appearance. Lugg brought Campion to the telephone and he took the message and made his inevitable offer.

"I'm at Birley station." Sock's young voice sounded thin over the wire. "I can't get a cab anywhere. Someone pinched my car yesterday. What? Oh, in the usual place at the end of the alley. I was a fool to leave it there, but it's cheaper than a garage. Some ass simply walked off with it. Yes, rather, the new one, blast him!"

"I'll run down for you." Campion sounded friendly. "No, I won't worry the chauffeur. My dear chap, I've got nothing to do. In fifteen minutes, then."

He passed the coupé on his way to the station. White Walls was some way off the beaten track and the nearest way to the railway lay across a belt of meadow land between two main roads. The lanes were in good repair, if not much frequented, and Campion drove fast.

The blue coupé had been parked on the wide grass verge and sat there shabby and forlorn, with its windows closed; it might have been there for ten minutes or ten years, and Campion barely noticed it as he sped past.

Sock came clattering down the station steps as the Lagonda climbed the hill. He was a little more presentable than usual in costume, but his dark youthful face was worn and strained and there was an irritating air of suppressed excitement about him, as though he were conscious of taking a part in strange and important events.

"This is extremely good of you," he said as he sank into the comfort

of the front seat. "I'm lost without a bus of some sort. I had to come
down. I must see Jimmy and the only time to get hold of him these days
is at the week-end. I hope we don't have to take the show off. We'll know
on Monday."

"Oh, is that in the wind?" Campion spoke dully, reflecting that there
is nothing so uninteresting as something which has been all-important for
a long time and is suddenly outclassed. "The publicity's ruined it, I
suppose?"

"It's not the publicity, curiously." Sock seemed surprised himself. "The
bookings haven't fallen off as you'd think. In some parts of the house
they've even improved. It's the cast. The whole place is a mass of hysteria.
I've never seen anything like it. It's the drama in the blood, I suppose.
Three quarters of the chorus passed out after the show last night. We've
all had the hell of a time. The new show is nearly as bad. None of them
have got a hap'orth of ballast. It's only Jimmy who holds 'em all together,
and he looks as if he was going to drop dead at any moment. Have you
seen him lately? He's amazing! Takes such *risks*, Campion . . . I go cold
for him sometimes. But he gets away with 'em by sheer personality."

He sighed and slid further down into the deep upholstery.

"My car going was the last straw," he remarked.

Mr. Campion made sympathetic noises and his passenger chattered on.

"I used to leave the old one in the cul-de-sac near the flat. I've got a
hovel just off Baker Street, you know, and in this fine weather it saves a
garage bill. People are amazingly honest in London, and, as I never left
anything in it, it seemed as safe as houses. Where I made my mistake
was that I forgot the state of the old bus. I did the same thing with my
new secondhand one, and it was all right for a week, but yesterday, just
about four o'clock, I went home to write a bit of copy. It took me a certain
amount of time and I didn't come out until seven. Then I found the
car had gone. The chap who sells papers on the corner saw a man take
it. He just walked over to it, got in and drove off. I told the paper man
what I thought of him, naturally, but he said he didn't like to interfere
in case I'd lent it to a friend. I couldn't really blame him. Still, he gave
the police a description and they're having a look for it. Meanwhile it's
just annoying."

He was silent for some moments as they negotiated the right-angle turn
at the bottom of the hill.

"Jimmy told me you were down here," he said at last. "I saw him yesterday for a moment or two. He's a queer bloke. I don't know anyone I
admire more, but you've got to know how to take him."

He paused. There was clearly something on his mind and Campion
listened to him beating round the subject with a deepening of that new
sense of apprehension which had become habitual with him.

Sock cleared his throat.

"I used to be rather keen on Eve at one time," he remarked a little too casually. "But she went off me and I rather thought our James frowned on the idea, too, so I let it go. She's a sweet kid when you get to know her, and I felt rather sore about it in a vague sort of way. But Jimmy has been damn marvellous to me and I didn't want to muscle in where he didn't want me. After all, I'm not a startling proposition; I know that. I'm only telling you this, by the way, to get over my point about Jimmy.

"A day or two ago he sent for me and gave me a dressing down about the girl. He practically asked me point-blank what I thought I was doing to let her escape my manly clutches and who the hell I thought I was to pass up something pretty good. I practically fainted on the spot. He is a funny chap, isn't he?"

Mr. Campion's face became even more expressionless.

"He probably feels that she may need a spot of supervision," he suggested cautiously. "Elder brothers go all paternal at times. She's not here now, by the way."

"No, I—I thought not." Sock sounded confused. "Besides, she's lost all interest in me, if ever she had any. As a matter of fact, I thought I caught the nasty whiff of 'metal more attractive.' She's been pretty hard hit the last week or two. It's y'uth—y'uth and the balmy summer air—that does it with these 'ere young girls."

"Who's your rival?" Campion's question was hesitant.

"I don't know for certain." Sock shook a wise young head. "I've had a dirty suspicion for some time, but I won't slander the girl, bless her. After all, she ought to draw the line somewhere. I say, Campion! Campion, hold on a minute!"

The last remark was jerked out of him as he swung round in the car and sat staring over his shoulder. Mr. Campion pulled up obligingly.

"What's the matter?"

"Look!" Sock was kneeling up in his seat, his face ludicrous in its astonishment. "Look, I say! That's my bus!"

Campion turned his head and stared at the shabby blue coupé which he had passed on his outward journey. He dropped the car into reverse and ran backward, with Sock hopping on the running board.

"The shape caught my eye and then I saw the number plate," he babbled excitedly. "This is fantastic—incredible! I don't believe it! I bet the ticks have run her dry of oil and seized her up."

He sprang to the ground as they came to a standstill and ran over to the stranded car. For a moment he stood peering in through the window and then without a word wrenched open the door. Campion saw him bending down, his head and shoulders hidden from view in the dark interior.

The next moment a rug came hurtling out and a cry that was not a scream or a shout, but somewhere midway between the two, escaped its owner.

Sock drew back slowly. His face was livid and his young eyes were horror-stricken. He put his hand over his stomach.

Campion sprang from the Lagonda and, pushing past the younger man, peered down into the coupé.

The body lay doubled up on the floor with its legs forced round the controls and its head jammed against the front of the passenger seat. That it was a dead body was painfully apparent. The skull had been battered unmercifully and there was blood on the mat and on the rug.

Mr. Campion, who was hardened to such unpleasant sights, peered down into the small dark face.

"Who is it?" he demanded.

Sock forced himself to look again.

"I don't know," he said at last, his lips shaking. "I don't know. I've never seen the chap before in my life."

Chapter 25

Mr. Campion dozed. The night had gone on, it seemed, for ever. The wooden armchair in which he lay had been designed by a man with definite but erroneous ideas concerning the human form, and he was peculiarly uncomfortable.

It was four o'clock in a scented country dawn, with a world astir in the fields and a light, exciting wind shivering through the leaves.

In the room in which he sat, on the iron mantelshelf below the fly-blown tariff of licenses obtainable from His Majesty's revenue officers, a round tin clock ticked with a shudder a second.

From the local superintendent's office next door came sounds that had gone on all through the night: voices and footsteps, slow country intonations and the brisk, clipped abbreviations of the town, chair legs scraping on wood and solid boot heels clattering on uncarpeted boards.

The phone bell alone was silent, and everyone in the police station, including Mr. Campion, who listened even in his sleep, was waiting for that shrill, familiar alarm.

Dr. Bouverie's old Fiat drew up in the quiet street outside with a roar and a grunt and the tempestuous old gentleman heaved himself out of it, bellowed at his sleep-dazed chauffeur, and plunged into the building, the plaid-lined skirts of his mighty overcoat swinging about him like sails in a storm.

His authoritative voice had a penetrating quality and Campion sat up with a jerk. The new, straightforward, bona fide murder had evidently caught the old man's imagination, and the full force of his astonishing energy had been loosed upon its elucidation with a generous disregard for the hour and his own and everybody else's personal convenience.

"Got down to it at once, don't you know."

The familiar roar percolated through the door panels of the superintendent's room.

"We must get it cleared up. I can't have this sort of thing in my district. I've been working all night. Stopped for a meal at eight o'clock and went back to it. Sweat's been pouring off me. I had to change and bathe before I came over or I'd have been here an hour ago. Young Dean wanted to give up at one o'clock, but I kept him at it and I think we've got it clear now, between us. Superintendent, lend me a man for a moment."

Alone in the small front office on the first floor, Campion stretched his cramped limbs and brought his mind round to face the situation once again. When at last he put his head inside the superintendent's door he was confronted by a spectacle which might have been very funny in any other circumstance.

A group of interested police, with Yeo and Inchcape prominent among them, were watching a remarkable performance which was taking place in the centre of the room. A chair had been placed in the foreground and against it sprawled a youthful constable whose head and shoulders were completely covered by the doctor's greatcoat, while the old man loomed above him, spanner in hand, and demonstrated the method of murder with great dramatic effect.

"The first blow caught him on the vault, Superintendent, just about here."

Dr. Bouverie brought the spanner down none too gently.

"That cracked his skull for him, don't you know. After that the man seems to have gone mad. He beat the poor creature wildly. Lost his own head, I should say. Call it blood lust if you like, but I should be inclined to say terror. Like a trapped horse, don't you know. Kicks itself free, whatever the damage. I'll prepare a full report for you. No time yet. The organs are perfectly healthy—very good indeed. Decent heart, lungs sound, age between forty and fifty, well-nourished, stained hands . . . get up, my man!"

The final remark was addressed to the constable, who was breathing somewhat stertorously beneath the suffocating coat.

The constable scrambled to his feet and emerged grinning; he was very proud of himself.

The doctor dropped the spanner into his side pocket. His pugnacious old face was stern and alive, and his invincible dignity permeated the room. Viewed dispassionately, there was a great deal that was comic about him, but the essence of the man was far from ridiculous. It passed through Mr. Campion's mind that this serio-comic element was the very stuff of tragedy. It was the dreadful reality of disaster which took the fun out of funny things, reminding the brain perpetually that something truly frightful had honestly occurred.

Dr. Bouverie turned his head and caught sight of him. He got up at once and held out his hand.

"Hallo, Campion," he said. "You mixed up in this too? Two corpses within a fortnight and you about each time, yet no possible connection between the two affairs . . . that's an extraordinary coincidence."

The local superintendent, a friendly lump of a man with an old-fashioned police moustache and service boots, caught Campion's eye and winked. He cut in hastily before the younger man could speak to the doctor.

"How long had he been dead, sir?"

Dr. Bouverie returned to the subject with alacrity.

"I've been puzzling over that," he said, his grey eyes as bright as if he had been in the thirties, "and I'm inclined to put it at twenty-four hours as a maximum and twelve as a minimum from the time I first saw the body at four o'clock this afternoon. That is to say, somewhere between four on Friday afternoon and four on Saturday morning. Can't you find a witness who noticed how long the car stood there?"

Inchcape glanced at the superintendent and, receiving his nod of assent, plunged into the question.

"We've been working on that," he said. "We've found a man who is prepared to swear that it was not where we found it when he went down to the Queen's Head at eight-fifteen on Friday night, but he noticed it standing just where it is now when he returned about half past ten. He suspected a courting couple and did not look inside. There's no way of telling if the car was driven after the man was dead, is there?"

"Why not? The man was not moved after he died. I can say that for certain, don't you know."

The old man was fascinated by the puzzle element in the case.

"Oh, yes," he went on. "I can give you clear proof of that. From the way he was lying with his feet round the controls I doubt whether anyone could have driven the machine an inch once he was dead."

Yeo coughed and the local superintendent turned to him deferentially. Campion noticed that the distinguished visitor from Scotland Yard was being received with proper country hospitality. Yeo addressed the doctor.

"You're *sure* he was not moved after death, sir?"

"Perfectly." The old man's magnificent authority was comforting. "As I see it, he was driving the car. His passenger suddenly clapped the rug over his head and set about him. The position of the wounds, all on the left side, and the way the body fell, show that quite clearly."

"I see." Yeo was silent and his comedian's face was thoughtful. "I don't know this part of the country," he began, "but it seems to me that the road to the town from the spot where we found the body is fairly lonely?"

"So it is now," agreed the superintendent. "There's not a house on it until you pass the station turning." He paused. "Suppose the murderer took the last train to Boarbridge?" he said suddenly. "He could walk down to the station without being seen and there is just that one train after nine o'clock. The station opens at six. I'll send a man down to find out if there was a stranger about then. There's an idea there—a good idea."

Dr. Bouverie was quite prepared to take an even more active part in the investigations than he had done already, and they had some difficulty in getting rid of him gracefully. It was only when he proposed routing out his old friend Lieutenant Colonel Beller, the chief constable, who had only just been persuaded to go home to bed, that the alarmed superintendent put his foot down.

"Ah, well, ye see, we're on to something, sir," he said, "and we don't want to hurry it. That all depends on a telephone message from Scotland Yard. Sergeant Cooling, of the Central London Branch, has nipped up to town with the dead man's fingerprints. There's a great likelihood that the dead man is the same fellow who was seen to steal the car up in London. We've just heard the sergeant was able to get hold of the department before it closed and he's keeping them at work on it now. We're all sittin' here waitin' to hear what he's got to tell us."

The vigorous old man was partially satisfied. The assurance that a great many people were losing their sleep in a decent public endeavour to clear up the mystery which had smirched his beloved district comforted him considerably.

"All right, Larkin," he said a little wistfully. "I'll leave it to you, if you prefer it. I'll get back now. What is it? A quarter to five? Yes, well, I shall have a couple of hours' sleep and invite myself to Beller's table for breakfast. We shall be down here about half past eight. Good night. Good night, Campion. Don't forget to come and see my roses when you're passing. Very fine show. Very fine indeed."

He went at last and the tension in the office relaxed considerably. The young constable who had taken part in the demonstration was despatched by the superintendent to make "farmer's tea" and went off to do so amid grunts of approval from the local members of the conference.

The party spirit, which is never far absent when countrymen get together to observe a Londoner, became very apparent when he returned and they sat round sipping the somewhat remarkable beverage, half thick sweet strong tea and half whisky, from immense coarse white cups. Yeo, who had been not unnaturally suspicious of the concoction, expressed sincere gratification at its taste, which reminded Campion of the cheap "flavoured caramels" of his youth, and the excitement which had been growing all the night bubbled up to boiling point.

"I doubt not the superintendent's right he took the down train," remarked Inchcape, the local inspector, giving up all attempts to conceal his pleasant country accent. "Where else would he go? He wouldn't be hanging about the fields, surely?"

The superintendent glanced at Yeo.

"That all depends who it was, don't it?" he said slyly, his own country intonation increasing now that the doctor had gone.

Yeo nodded and his round eyes turned towards Mr. Campion, who avoided his glance.

It was just before five when a sergeant came up from below stairs.

"The young gentleman would like to speak to you, sir," he said. "He's been thinkin', seemingly."

The superintendent gave the word, and he and Yeo exchanged significant glances.

Sock came in looking haggard and exhausted. The pains to which the whole police station had been put to get it into his head that he was not under any sort of arrest, but had merely been invited to stay in the charge room until he remembered why he had not come down by train that afternoon and had merely waited in the booking hall until Campion had come to fetch him, had not been successful.

The evidence of the station officials had been disconcertingly full. A porter had seen Sock walking up the hill that afternoon. A booking-office clerk had seen him phone from the box in the hall and the ticket collector had watched him kicking his heels on the steps until Campion and the Lagonda had arrived.

Sock caught sight of Campion as he came in and appealed to him direct.

"It's a damn silly story. So I have to tell everybody?"

The superintendent intervened tactfully. He had a vast experience of that other half of the world which he so delightfully called "the gentry."

"We're all officers, sir," he began in a fatherly, not to say motherly, fashion, "and we're all working hard to get to the bottom of the mystery. There's not one of us here who can't keep his mouth shut if it be that we're not called upon to know something in the way of duty. Sit down, sir, and tell us how you come to get into the town."

Sock dropped into the chair so lately vacated by the doctor.

"I'm a fool," he said. "I ought to have told you this right away. I would have done only I felt it had nothing whatever to do with the murder and——"

"Ah, you must let us be the judges of that, sir." The superintendent was still parental but firm. "Your car's been stolen in London and you come down to a country place the next day, and the first thing you see on your way from the station is your car with a murdered body in it—well, that's a big coincidence now. We had to check up on your story as a matter of form and we found out you didn't come by train like you said you did. Well, that sets us thinking. We feel we'd like to have a talk to you. You don't want to talk to us and so we say we're very sorry but we'd like you to sit downstairs until you do decide to tell us something. That's fair now. You can't say that isn't fair."

Sock laughed and looked remarkably young again.

"You're perfectly right, Superintendent," he said. "I'm an idiot. I was driven down here by car this afternoon—that is to say, Saturday afternoon; it's Sunday now, isn't it? I left London by train Saturday morning and went to Watford. From there I was driven down here to Birley in a Hillman Minx. I got out at the station because the driver of the car didn't want to go to White Walls. The rest of my original story is perfectly true."

"I see, sir." The superintendent paused long enough for the constable in the corner to complete his shorthand notes. "Now, who was the driver of the Minx? You'll have to tell us that."

Sock sighed helplessly.

"Eve Sutane," he said.

Yeo beamed and Inchcape sat forward.

"The address in Watford where the young lady met you?" murmured the superintendent with the delicacy of a good maître d'hôtel.

Sock hesitated.

"Is this really necessary? I'm betraying a confidence."

"I'm afraid so, sir. What address?"

"St. Andrews. 9, Cordover Road."

"And the name of the occupier?"

"Major and Mrs. Polthurst-Drew. For God's sake, don't drag them into it. Eve's been staying there with the daughter. Her name's Dorothy. Is that enough?"

Yeo leant forward and touched the superintendent's arm and a nod of mutual understanding passed between them. Yeo cleared his throat, and the side of Mr. Campion's mind that was not sick with apprehension noticed with amusement that the country superintendent's velvet-glove technique had impressed the Yard man and he was inclined to pay it the sincerest form of compliment.

"There are just one or two little points I should like to clear up, Mr. Petrie," he began affably. "Why did Miss Sutane hesitate to drive you right up to her own home?"

Sock fidgeted and suddenly capitulated.

"She's very young," he began awkwardly. "She ran away on Wednesday and Jimmy—I mean Mr. Sutane—and I have had the devil of a job looking for her ever since."

His audience took some seconds to digest this information, and when he spoke again Yeo had resumed his familiar sharpness.

"The young lady was missing for three days and no one mentioned it . . . why was that?"

Sock smiled disarmingly. He was at home with brusquerie.

"We'd had a spot of bother already, Inspector," he murmured. "As you know, she's ridiculously young and her brother wanted to keep her out of the newspapers if possible. That was quite natural. I think he said she was staying with friends, and, after all, that did prove to be true. She went to town on Wednesday afternoon and called at the Drury Lane studio of some art-school friends whose name is Scott. They're sisters. While she was there she met the Polthurst-Drew girl, whom she knew, and who asked her down to Watford for a day or so. Mr. Sutane saw the Scotts at once. It was the first place he thought of looking. But they had some barmy idea of shielding their dear little pal from cruel guardians and what not, and like little lunatics they swore they hadn't seen her. It was only Friday night, when we'd tried everywhere else, that I got the idea of going back to the Scotts with a romantic yarn of deserted but undying affection and they coughed up the right address. I went down there this morning and she drove me as far as Birley in Dorothy's car. I was trying to get her to come home, but she wouldn't listen to me. No one knew that there'd been a spot of difference—no one at White Walls, I mean; except Jimmy, of course—so I thought I'd pretend I'd come down from town by train. There you are. I've told you the full strength."

He sighed and lay back in his chair.

"It's a great weight off my mind," he said frankly. "I didn't bash any unknown car thief over the head and you can go through every moment of my time in the last twenty-four hours and prove it."

Yeo nodded gravely. There was a preoccupied expression on his round face.

"You spoke of a difference between Miss Sutane and her brother," he said. "What was that?"

Sock's hesitation was barely noticeable and his reply was glib and convincing.

"I don't know. I don't think it was important. Eve is inclined to be—well—young, you know, and Jimmy is naturally nervy. It was probably something very trivial. It usually is when they have a row. Perhaps he told her she was spending too much or using too much lipstick. . . . I don't know."

"She didn't tell you?"

"She drove me here in silence. I was nearly frozen out of the bus."

The local superintendent smiled indulgently.

"Wouldn't it have been better to tell us all this before?" he murmured.

"We had to hold . . ." he coughed, ". . . ask you to wait, because of your car turning up so strangely."

"I know. That's fantastic! Why should it happen here? It's an incredible coincidence." Sock looked about him earnestly. "It's crazy," he said. "Was there anything in the man's pockets to show who he was?"

No one answered this unprofessional question, but the superintendent, who seemed to have taken an incomprehensible liking to the young man, made a little concession.

"I'll tell you one thing," he said. "It wasn't robbery. He had quite a quantity of money on him. That's not for publication, mind."

"Not robbery?" Sock repeated dully. He shook his head. "I'm all in," he confessed. "My mind doesn't work any more. Can I go now? Coming, Campion?"

The lank figure in the corner roused himself.

"No," he said. "I'm waiting for something. You take the car. Someone will run me down in the morning. Make my apologies, won't you?"

The superintendent glanced up.

"Stay in the district, won't you, sir?" he murmured pleasantly. "Just till we get the address verified. It won't take long. Tomorrow teatime, perhaps. We'll let you know. Meanwhile, we'll have to hold the car."

"Lord, yes! I don't want it. This has put me clean off it." Sock's smile was sickly. "Good night, everybody. I'll do the polite for you, Campion. I'll tell 'em you're not exactly on the tiles. So long."

When he had gone Yeo frowned.

"It seems a straight story," he said. "Why make such a mouthful of it? He knows more about the row than he cares to admit. I'll have to get that out of the girl."

The telephone bell silenced them all. The instrument stood trilling on the superintendent's desk for what seemed a full minute before Yeo leapt upon it and clapped the receiver to his ear. Campion saw his face light up.

"Good man!" Yeo said enthusiastically to the weary Cooling in London. "Oh, good man! Wait a minute." He pulled a pad towards him and wrote from dictation.

As the minutes went by his spirits soared and his comical face became jubilant.

"Beautiful," he said at last. "Just what I wanted. Stay where you are and do the necessary. Oh, he's still there, is he? Give him my compliments and tell him this is my show. Don't put him off. I want the old ferret right on the trail. Yes, righto. I'll ring you later. Don't say I called him a ferret. That's a breach of discipline and you never know. Yes, fine. Good-bye."

He hung up the receiver and sat grinning at them.

"Listen to this. Just listen to this," he said at last without attempting to disguise his delight. "They've got the prints on the files and here's the dope we want."

He began to read from his notes in a steady, monotonous drone.

"'Georg Kummer, alias Kroeger, alias Koetz, thought to be a Pole. About forty-four or forty-five years old. First attracted police notice in this country in January 1928 when he appeared before the Bow Street magistrates on a charge of failure to register as an alien. Papers found to be unsatisfactory. Deported. Reappeared June 1929. Charged with felonious conspiracy in Glasgow and sentenced to six months in the second division in company with four others. Deported. Next heard of in France, following year, in connection with arson charge. No sentence but deported from France. Became mysteriously wealthy during and just after Repudiation of Arms agreement by Severino government. Reappeared in England, 1932, and was apprehended by police after he had been working in a firework factory for three months. Once more deported. Last heard of 1934, when he was acquitted by a Viennese court on a charge of concealing arms and war material. (Foreign information by courtesy of Austrian police, who applied to us for English details concerning him.) Note: This man is known to have been employed by several governments in his capacity as a chemist. He is believed to hold valuable degrees in his subject but has always come to grief through a crooked streak. He is subject to sudden and great changes in his financial condition. During the last two years his headquarters have been in Vienna. Last permanent address: 49, Wien-Strasse 7.'"

Yeo paused and cleared his throat. His eyes were dancing.

"I didn't read the physical description because they've checked it up that end. He's the chap who pinched the car all right. The paper seller described him to a T. Well, there you are. It's what I've had in the back of my mind ever since I saw the stains on his hands. See who he is? He's the man who made that ruddy bomb."

Chapter 26

At six o'clock breakfast arrived from the Red Lion over the way and the superintendent entertained his own inspector and the two distinguished visitors to the meal in his office. Yeo had become a new man since the message from the Records Department. The hunt was up and he was getting into his stride. His good humour had developed a certain vigorousness which might have been almost horrific in a less attractive personality. He sat eating a great plateful of bacon, fried egg, sausage and steak, his round eyes sharp and eager and his stubby fingers crumbling his bread as if he felt it represented an enemy.

"It must have been blackmail," he said. "I knew it as soon as I saw the body and heard the story of Petrie's stolen car. There had to be a connection between the two cases. I'm not prepared to accept a miracle. We're not out of the wood yet, but if this should turn out to be another stroke of chance then I'll resign and go in for conjury."

"When shall we know?" enquired Inchcape, who had been startled into meekness by this sudden turn of events.

"I can't say." Yeo was ready and happy to talk. "Cooling will have gone ahead under our super's direction. The Austrian police may take their time, but I don't think so. Foreigners often seem to be a bit quicker than us," he added naïvely. "We'll find out how long he's been over here and we'll find his lodgings. Once we can take a look at them I think we'll be sitting pretty. My guess is that he's been over here about ten days and when he came he brought that grenade with him."

The local superintendent looked uneasy.

"About the gentleman we're after . . ." he murmured. "Since there were no fingerprints on the car, other than the deceased's and Mr. Petrie's, it shows he wore gloves, don't it? Probably they were ordinary gloves which he didn't trouble to take off. He'd never have wiped the whole car clean, even if he'd thought of it, would he now?"

"The lamp was wiped," said Inchcape with his mouth full. "Still, every kid knows about fingerprints these days."

Yeo looked at Campion.

"We're going to catch this fellow, you know," he observed. "I don't see how we can help ourselves. Did you ever hear of a chap who behaved so silly? There's no subtlety about him at all. He's behaving as if he's a god or something."

"Ah, they're often like that," said the superintendent. "Not insane. Just sort of exalted."

Yeo went on with his harangue, addressing Campion in particular.

"I see a chap who is a sort of great white chief in his own little world," he said meaningly. "A bloke who's used to getting his own way in everything. The people who work for him think he's something a bit bigger than life, and, because they stand for him doing the most amazing things, he thinks he can do the same elsewhere. He wanted to get rid of Konrad, and he must have had a good reason, mind you, or he wouldn't have bothered himself, so what did he do? He thought out a scheme which sounded all right and did what he was in the habit of doing in his business. He called in an expert. The expert delivered the goods and was paid for his trouble. Our man put his stunt into action and it went wrong. Instead of simply killing Konrad he raised little hell and got the police on him hot and strong. He kept his head—or more probably didn't quite

realise what he *had* done—and went on with his own work in his own admiring circle. However, the expert who had delivered the grenade wasn't
barmy. He could read the papers and he knew a good thing when he saw
it. Our man was blackmailed by him. That settled it. Having found a
simple way of getting rid of tiresome people, the man we have in mind
proceeded to get going once again. He borrowed a car, choosing the one
that he knew would be in a certain spot at a certain time. He seems to
have got Kummer to do the pinching and I think how he did it was this.
I think he stood at the end of the street, making the excuse that he was
buying a packet of fags or something, and asked the chemist to bring the
bus down for him. He probably just pointed it out and said: 'Bring it
along, will you, old boy?' or something like that. Then he got in and
they drove out to the most convenient lonely spot he knew, a spot from
which he could either walk home or pick up his own car. Then he made
the other chap pull up for something, threw the rug over his head, and
beat him up with a spanner."

"But why so near home?" protested Inchcape.

"Why chuck the bicycle lamp out into the garden?" retorted Yeo. "Because it never dawned on him that we might be able to prove anything
against him. I've known plenty of men like that. Forty-five per cent of the
criminal classes have that bee in their bonnet. Be careful of your fingerprints and you're okay; that's their motto."

Campion stretched his long legs under the table. He looked haggard
and weary.

"If the murder took place about nine or nine-thirty . . ." he began
and paused.

Yeo was regarding him with a slow, not unsympathetic smile.

"Mr. Sutane wasn't at the theatre after four o'clock on Friday," he
said. "He didn't appear that night. Phil Flannery, his new understudy,
went on. I didn't know that until after you left us yesterday or I'd have
told you. We were going to interview him yesterday evening and then
this broke. I thought it would be best to wait to identify the body."

Campion sat still and Yeo eyed him.

"My case is mainly theory, I know that," said the Yard inspector. "Several points have got to be cleared up before we can make an arrest. That's
why I particularly don't want anyone scared. We want that motive."

Campion hardly heard him. His pale eyes were hard and introspective.
As he sat staring down at the uneaten food congealing horridly on the
coarse plate it dawned upon him painfully that the moment had arrived.
The inevitable hour when he must pay for his return to White Walls was
now at hand.

He got up.

"I'm going back now," he said. "If you'd care to run me down in the
police car, Inspector, I'd like to have a word with you."

Yeo rose with alacrity.

"I'd like to. This last business makes all the difference, don't it?" he remarked as they moved towards the door. "I must say it wasn't in my book at all. I never thought he'd do it again so soon. The quicker we can pull him in the better. We don't want him taking a dislike to someone else."

He coughed. His heavy jocularity had struck the wrong note, even to his own ears.

The telephone delayed them. It was the local sergeant phoning from the station to say that no one at all had joined the late down train on Friday night. The ticket collector remembered the occasion perfectly.

Yeo shrugged his shoulders.

"It was only an idea," he said. "He must have fixed it with a second car somehow. Perhaps they came down in separate buses, as Kummer appeared to be driving the coupé. We'll have to work on that. There's a lot of routine enquiries to be made. We're going to have a busy day. There's the weapon to find yet. That's in a ditch or a furze patch, I'll bet my last dollar. It *would* be. We must find it, of course. The doctor thought it might have been a spanner. Fancy looking over twenty-five square miles of rough country for a spanner . . ."

Campion blinked.

"He may have got rid of it in the same way as he got rid of the bicycle lamp—chucked it away as soon as he had finished with it," he suggested meekly.

Yeo stared at him.

"He might," he said. "Lord! He's a fool, isn't he? I don't think he knows we're on the earth. The boys have been looking all round the car, of course, but I'll make them go over that area with a tooth comb. I'm beginning to hate this chap. He's so insulting."

Inspector Inchcape, who had been listening to the conversation, came to life.

"I'll see to it right away," he said quickly. "You'll be back, won't you, Inspector? Our chief constable, he do like to be in on everything. He's a wonderful particular gentleman. He and the doctor'll be down just after eight, I'll lay a pound."

"I'll be back," Yeo promised. "Are you ready, Mr. Campion?"

They drove out of the quiet little town into the lanes. The sun was climbing swiftly and the light mist over the low-lying meadows promised great heat in the middle day.

When they came to a convenient straight stretch just before the White Walls approach Yeo pulled up.

"Now, Mr. Campion," he said, "I've been waiting to hear from you. I've let you see my position pretty clearly, haven't I? I'm going to get that man. Sooner or later evidence must come in which will get me a warrant.

At the moment I can't stir because the P.P. doesn't like the idea of us holding him on suspicion, and although I can build up a first-rate case I can't substantiate every point until Cooling gets his stuff. What I need is the basic plank, the thing that pins it on to *him* and him only. I want the motive. I shall get him in a day or two, but in the meantime what else is he going to get up to? He's not particular who he makes trouble for, is he? Look at Boarbridge."

Campion shivered a little. He felt cold and strangely dispassionate.

"Yes," he said abruptly and with an authority Yeo had never heard in his voice before. "Yes, you're quite right. Now look here, there's a masseuse at White Walls, a Miss Edna Finbrough. Get her to go down to the station with you. Don't rouse her out of bed now. If you do you'll start the alarm and you must avoid that if you're going to get your man without trouble. When you get this woman down to Birley on some suitable pretext put her through it. She's tough but she's cracking. I've seen that for days."

"What do we want out of her?" Yeo was beginning.

But the thin man who seemed suddenly to have become so dry and impersonal went on without hearing him.

"Tell her you know that she went to a theatrical lodginghouse on the Monday evening after Chloe Pye died. I'll give you the address. She made an excuse to go through Miss Pye's rooms alone and while she was there she ransacked the place for papers. I think she found what she was looking for and took it back to the person who had sent her. That paper was almost certainly destroyed that same night, but she can tell you what was on it, and from her information you will be able to get concrete evidence of the motive you need."

"Do you know what the paper was?"

Campion regarded the policeman coldly. He was very controlled and seemed almost callous about the whole subject.

"I don't, but I can guess. It was a marriage certificate."

Yeo whistled and his face looked like a comic mask.

"A-ah!" he said. "Now you're talking. That's something like."

His companion ignored him.

"I think Konrad got to know about this marriage and was prepared to use his information. That is why he was killed. You may have some difficulty in getting it out of Miss Finbrough, but she knows."

"Like to see her yourself?"

"No." Campion's tone was sharp. "That's a job for the professional police. That's all I can give you. I shall be at the house all day. When you've found out what you can, perhaps you'll let me know? I'll stay on the spot until you make the arrest. I should keep Miss Finbrough out of the way until then. Don't let her communicate with the house."

"Good Lord, no!" Yeo spoke fervently and the glance he shot at Campion was almost affectionate. "This is just what I wanted. If you're right you'll have put him just where he ought to be. I told you you had to come down here."

Campion did not speak and Yeo, whose energy was mounting rather than diminishing after his long night, let in the clutch and roared on down the road.

"I'll be along for the woman about eleven," he said as he set his passenger down at the drive gates. "Don't worry. I'll be discretion itself. If this comes off I'll hand it to you. Did he kill the first woman too?"

Campion shrugged his shoulders.

"I see. It's like that, is it? We'll never prove it anyway." Yeo was grave and he made a little depreciatory grimace. "Nasty business. Hard on the family. Well, we've got enough to go on with, God knows. Once he's inside he may talk. Sometimes they like to—that conceited type. The newspapers are going to have a treat, aren't they? Well, so long, and thank you."

Campion came slowly up the drive and saw the white house, like a lovely ship in full sail, in the blazing morning. As he crossed the lawn a bundle in a gaily striped dressing gown detached itself from a deck chair and came padding towards him. It was Uncle William.

He looked pink and sleepy and pathetic, the wind ruffling his thin curls and his face puckered with weariness and anxiety.

"Been waitin' since the dawn," he mumbled. "Had to. Been prayin', practically. Everythin' all right, my boy? Relyin' utterly on you."

Campion turned away and went into the house.

Chapter 27

At noon, when the garden was sweltering luxuriously in the full heat of the day and the house was peaceful in that odd Sunday quiet which is mysteriously different from the peace of other days, Uncle William let himself into Campion's room and advanced to the end of the bed.

He stood there for some little time, his hands in the pockets of his white trousers and his shoulders bent dejectedly. He looked more bearlike than ever.

"Awake, Campion?"

The man on the bed regarded his old friend steadily. His appearance gave no indication that he had slept at all. His eyes were cold and wakeful and the skin was drawn tightly over the bones of his face.

"Feller came and took Miss Finbrough off to help the police," observed Uncle William presently. "Didn't hear the rights of it. Somethin' about needin' her assistance. As a masseuse, I suppose. Couldn't understand it. So many confusin' things happenin' all round one."

His worried old voice trailed away into silence and he padded over to the window and looked out.

"What's in the wind?" he asked at last.

Mr. Campion sat up in bed. His impersonal, authoritative mood which Yeo had first noticed earlier in the morning still persisted.

To Uncle William, who was a little bewildered by it, he seemed to have suddenly become a stranger.

"Where is everybody?" he demanded.

"Linda's out there." The old man nodded towards the garden. "Sock's gone off in the Bentley, and Jimmy and Slippers are practisin' in the drawin' room with Mercer playin' for them, and in a damned condescendin' fashion, I don't mind tellin' you. Jimmy seems to have to keep up his practisin' all the time. He's workin' himself to death, poor feller. When's this infernal cloud goin' to lift, Campion? Upon my soul, it's a sin to have to think about some things on a day like this. Did the police succeed in findin' out who the ruffian in Sock's car was?"

Once again Mr. Campion ignored his question and asked another.

"Where has Sock gone?"

"To see Eve." Uncle William wandered back from the window. "We all waited up for the boy last night," he explained, his small blue eyes rounding childishly as he made the confidence. "He came in dead-beat, had a word or two with Jimmy, and then they both told us the full story in the drawin' room. He seemed ashamed he'd told the police so much, but, as I said to him, there are times when a man must choose between makin' serious trouble all round and givin' a friend away. Then the conscience is the only guide. I told him I was glad to see he had one, and I flatter myself I spoke to him like a father."

He paused.

"It wasn't as if the girl had done anythin' really wrong, you see," he added, neatly destroying his argument at a stroke. "Sock's attracted to her. He didn't actually say so, but I could see it with half an eye. So that's that. What a time for a lovers' quarrel, Campion! One can't expect women to be considerate, I know, but fancy runnin' off like that without a word when we were all so worried about somethin' else! If the girl wasn't so young I'd call her a hussy. Even so, I didn't see quite why she chose that particular moment to clear out, did you? Sock wasn't quite up to the mark last night and I didn't care to press him. She'd had words with Jimmy, I understood. Don't know what about; do you?"

"Some other man, I think." Campion spoke absently.

"So I gathered. But I didn't see who if it wasn't Sock."

Campion dragged his mind away from the all-engulfing disaster which was so quickly approaching and tried to remember his conversation with

Sock Petrie in the Lagonda before they had passed the shabby blue coupé.

"She went off Sock and had a soulful affair with someone unlikely," he said. "Either Sutane found out about it and put his foot down, or, since that note of hers was left uncollected for so long, perhaps the man faded away on his own account."

"And the poor little girl felt the world had come to an end," cut in Uncle William happily. "That sounds more like the truth to me. It would account for her refusin' to come home. That's it, Campion; depend upon it. A blow at the pride. Known it drive a young girl off her head before now. Poor creature! Who is the whippersnapper? Far too big for his boots. I'm an old man but——"

"No," said Campion and added firmly: "I shouldn't."

The belligerent light died out of Uncle William's eyes, albeit a trifle reluctantly.

"Perhaps not," he said. "I was forgettin'. Make matters worse, of course. Still, it's a pity we don't know who he is," he added wistfully, looking at his plump fists. "Feel I'd like to do somethin' useful, you know. Suspense is gettin' us all under the weather. It's like a storm blowin' up. These dear people are bein' heroic. They're forcin' themselves to carry on. Jimmy looks like a skeleton and Linda's walkin' about like one of those dead workers in Haiti—what-d'ye-call-'em?—zombies."

Campion took hold of himself.

"Oh, yes," he said quietly, "I want to talk to you about Linda. Before she married, where did she live?"

"With her mother, naturally." Uncle William seemed to consider the question superfluous. "The old lady was the sister of the feller who owned this house. She has her little estate down in Devon. Very pretty place, I believe. There's money in that family, you know. Linda goes to stay with her sometimes and takes the child. What d'you want to know for?"

Campion shrugged his shoulders.

"Idle curiosity," he said. "I wondered what her background was, that was all."

The old man was silent for a long time.

"If you're worryin' about all this publicity breakin' Jimmy financially, she's got a home to go to," he said at last, and his eyes, meeting Campion's own, dropped furtively. "I've made up my own mind and I'm stickin' to it," he added with apparent irrelevance. "I told you that in this very room days ago. Linda's taken a fancy to you."

Mr. Campion stiffened.

"I don't think so."

Uncle William became the Man of the World, *circa* 1910. It was his third happiest role, but one which he particularly enjoyed. His blue eyes became shrewd and tolerant.

"When a woman's lonely—nice woman, trustworthy, sensible, capable of controllin' the team she's drivin'—then these harmless little affairs do her good, cheer her up, keep her young," he said surprisingly. "They mean nothin'. She thinks of them as she thinks of the ornaments in her hair. The same with a man. It flatters him and keeps him a boy at heart. As long as they mind their manners and steer clear of sentimentality, it's a good thing. After many years of experience I can honestly say I approve of it. Spice of life, you know. I don't like the dish drenched, but a modicum here and there improves the meal."

Campion sat looking at him and once again Uncle William was conscious of him as a stranger.

"I don't know if that's your view, my boy," he added with hasty capitulation. "Bachelor's view."

Campion laughed.

" 'If you haven't got the temperament, philandering isn't pleasure,' Guv'nor," he said. "That's a quotation from Don Marquis, probably the one philosophic poet of the generation. As far as I remember, he said it apropos of Lancelot and Guinevere, which makes it a very enlightening remark."

Uncle William looked mystified and uncomfortable.

"Spanish feller?" he observed, feeling no doubt that the operative word, which he particularly disliked, had a continental origin. "Sorry I interfered, my boy. One stumbles across things and makes the mistake of rememberin' 'em. Fact is, I keep leapin' on any subject which will take my mind off the trouble. Daresay you do too. Don't care what happens to my show—I'm past that. I'm simply holdin' my breath and prayin' for a bit of peace for myself and my friends. When's it goin' to end? That's what I want to know, Campion. When's it goin' to end? Well, I know you'd tell me if you could. Since you can't I'll go down and potter until lunchtime."

He padded off on plump crimson-shod feet and Campion got up and dressed slowly. He had ceased to consider his own personal part in the heartbreaking and irrevocable business. That problem had been faced and settled in his own flat when Linda had made her final appeal to him.

Since then he had found it possible to consider the miserable programme which circumstance and the unalterable part of his character had laid down for him by going through it steadily with one half of his conscious mind shut down. That there were flaws in this arrangement he discovered only too soon. He found himself doing unexpected things, making unreasonable detours, avoiding meetings, all to save himself the emotional reactions which he would ordinarily have experienced had he not taken his original precaution of mental semianaesthesia.

This morning, for instance, he found that he was dressing himself with extraordinary deliberation and not out of any particular desire for sartorial elegance. When the explanation did occur to him it shocked him. It was not pleasant to find that he was aiming to be late for lunch, so late that he might unobtrusively avoid eating Sutane's food at Sutane's table.

The discovery of this primitive taboo, with its physical reaction which decreed that he should not be hungry in spite of his neglected breakfast, left him both startled and irritated. It was like finding one half of himself suddenly under new management.

He pulled himself together impatiently. Yet when Lugg came surging in half an hour later he was still in his shirt sleeves.

The temporary butler was aggressively cheerful.

"Another corpse yisterday, I 'ear," he remarked, sitting down to rest his feet. "Quite an outin' for you, ain't it? Enjoyin' yerself? There's a bunch o' narks at either end of the lane, by the way. Does that mean anythink or is it just you showin' orf?"

His employer did not turn his head and, receiving no encouragement, Mr. Lugg was silent for a moment or so. When the hush became oppressive to him, however, he made a further attempt at small talk.

"This is life, ain't it?" he observed with relish. "A certain amount o' class but still free and easy. I'm like a duck in water 'ere, you know."

Campion knotted his tie with careful neatness.

"We shall probably both be leaving tonight," he said without looking round. "Don't mention it to anyone. Simply get everything ready."

The fat man did not blink. His small eyes rested on the tall figure silhouetted against the light.

It was a moment of great sadness.

Finally Lugg sighed.

"I knew it," he said heavily. "I felt it comin' on. As soon as I saw you in the passage last week I thought to myself, 'Ullo, I thought. It's a funny thing, ain't it, 'ow you take to a place?" he went on, philosophic resignation in his thick voice. "I'd git sick of it in time, but up till now I've took a pride in the drawin' room and I've bin interested in trainin' my young mate. She's on the three-card trick now. Comin' along a treat. We'll go after she's gone to bed, eh? We don't want a bloomin' cryin' setout. You've made up yer mind to go today? It's a lovely day."

His wistfulness was pathetic and Campion felt sudden sympathy for him.

"I'm afraid so," he murmured. "The party's over. Sorry."

Lugg heaved his mountainous shoulders.

"I'll take me tail coat," he remarked. "I 'ad it sent from the stores on your account. Largest they 'ad. Ten bob extra. It wouldn't fit anybody else. Make them look funny. You might ask all these people to dinner one night and I could wear it then, eh?"

Campion glanced out of the open window at the dancing garden.

"I shouldn't hope for that, Lugg," he said. "Take the coat by all means, if you want it. And now clear out, old boy, will you? I'm not in a chatty mood."

The large man got up obediently and lumbered towards the door.

"Per'aps I'll git 'er perfect this afternoon," he remarked optimistically. "She can't quite git the flip of the card in time with the moody. Oh, well, even the spadgers go back to London when the 'op pickin's over. Git on with yer dressin'. Gong's goin' any minute now."

He went off sadly and ten minutes afterwards Mr. Campion followed him, late for lunch.

Chapter 28

Mr. Campion sat near the house because he wanted to hear the telephone bell when it rang. Tea had been served on the terrace and now the company had split up into little groups. Linda, Sock Petrie and Eve were walking among the flower beds. The young man had brought the sulky, smouldering-eyed girl home just before the meal and Campion had marvelled at her self-possession as she had come swinging in to take her seat amongst them all. She had given no explanation and there had been no hint of apology in her manner; only an impenetrable, youthful defiance, both cool and rigidly polite.

Sock had managed her very well. He had adopted a cheerful superiority, whipping her over dangerous places in the conversation and devoting his whole attention to her.

Sutane and Slippers had rushed out for a cup of tea and rushed back again to the drawing room. They had both slept during the afternoon after their arduous morning's work and had decided to put in another hour to the gramophone, since Mercer had grown tired of accompanying them.

That wearied genius had returned to the grand piano in the morning room and now sat there, strumming his endless improvisations with the double doors closed to shut out the dance music.

Uncle William sat in a corner under the window. The Sunday papers were on his stomach and the decanter was at his side. He invariably refused to drink tea, insisting that it was effeminate or poison to his system, according to the company in which he found himself.

Campion looked out across the flower beds, where the rainbow gladiolas and the second delphinium crop were blazing in the last of the full sunlight, and wondered if the day would ever end. The atmosphere of oppression had grown slowly until it was now unbearable.

They were all aware of it, even Mercer, whose habitual self-absorption had turned him into a silent, inanimate dummy at tea.

Campion had not looked directly at Sutane all day, although he had been acutely conscious of him all the time. The extraordinary nervous force of the dancer's personality had pervaded every room which he entered until the whole house seemed to tingle with him. He had rehearsed with a cold, passionate energy which had called forth comment even from the gentle Slippers Bellew.

Campion was sitting on the low wall of the terrace, his long arms resting on his knees and his head bent, when Linda appeared before him. He had not seen her leave the others and her sandalled feet had made no sound upon the grass.

He looked up at her and preferred not to see the shadows in her eyes.

"How long?" she said.

"Soon." The word escaped him involuntarily. It was the last thing he would have chosen to say, and he rose, angry with himself and a little frightened.

To his relief she did not seem to see its significance.

"I hope so," she said.

As they walked over the turf together it occurred to him that it was for the last time, ever.

They were both silent for a while and when she spoke it was with a directness which startled him.

"Everyone knows except me. Jimmy knows. You know. So, I think, does Eve. You'll stay with me until I know?"

"Yes, I'll stay."

"I shall be sorry when you go," she said.

He did not reply and was grateful to her when he realised that she did not expect him to.

Her next words appalled him.

"When it's all over we shall go to America—Jimmy and Sarah and I and perhaps Uncle William. They like Jimmy over there, you know, and it's a wonderful country, especially for children. American children really have a childhood. Sarah will be wildly happy—nearly as happy as she is now with old Lugg. They're going to write to each other when he goes away, she says. It ought to be a grand correspondence. You were very kind to lend him to me. He's been appreciated."

Campion glanced sharply towards the house, but he was wrong. The phone bell had not rung. He glanced down at the girl and she caught sight of his expression. To his amazement she took hold of his hand and walked along looking down at it.

"It's going to be difficult to say this," she said, "and I probably shouldn't dream of doing it if things were remotely normal. But I like you better than anyone I've ever met. You're not a boy, so you won't go away with your head swelling and your virtue outraged because you think I'm telling you I've fallen in love with you—which I haven't, yet. But I don't think I shall see you again. We shall rush off to the States, for one thing. Anyway, it's in my mind to say this now. I like you because you're the only person I've ever *suddenly* liked who hasn't turned out to be a dreadful error of judgment. I made a fool of myself to you and you understood it. You didn't make love to me when the idea occurred to you and I rather wanted you to. And you've been loyal to our interests when it was obviously very awkward for you to do anything of the kind. Because you began on our side you stuck to us. I thought I'd like to say thank you, that's all. . . . What's the matter? Why are you looking like that?"

Campion turned his hand and took her own in it. He held it very tightly for a long time. It was firm and heart-easing and very hard to have to lose.

When he looked up again he was laughing a little.

"When one kicks over a tea table and smashes everything but the sugar bowl, one may as well pick that up and drop it on the bricks, don't you think?" he said lightly. "That was the phone, my lost, my lovely, one. I've been waiting for it all day."

He left her standing among the rose trees, a puzzled, frightened expression in her eyes.

Before he was halfway across the lawn Lugg came out of the glass door at the back of the hall to summon him.

The hall was empty as he crossed to the table and he paused for a moment before picking up the instrument. His face was blank and he felt breathless.

"Hullo," he said at last.

"Hullo. That you, Campion? Everything all right your end?"

To his surprise he recognised Stanislaus Oates at the other end of the wire. The Central Branch superintendent sounded quietly jubilant.

"Yes," said Campion steadily. "Yes. Quite all right."

"Fine. Are you alone?"

"I think so."

"I understand you. I'm being discreet myself. Country exchange, you know. Congratulations, son. Nice work. We'll be with you. Get that?"

"Where are you?"

"At the local station." Oates laughed self-consciously. "I couldn't keep out of it. I came down with the sergeant and we brought the necessary authorisation. Campion . . ."

"Yes?"

"I think I might tell you this. I'll wrap it up. The woman cracked at once. Yeo phoned us in town before noon. She gave him all he wanted to know. Seemed glad to talk. We went ahead at our end and found the church. It's in Brixton. The date in the register is 1920. Suit your reckoning?"

"Near enough."

"Are you still alone?"

"Yes. Why?"

"I thought you sounded a bit subdued. It's probably the line. Well, that was that. We had plenty for a pull-in on suspicion, but to be on the safe side I called up the P.P. But the publicity still scared him. He said wait. However, I'd hardly put down the phone when the Austrian stuff came through. Campion, it's magnificent! Just what we want. K. was actually under surveillance up to last week. . . . Eh? Oh, concealing arms. I ask you! The Austrians were more than civil. I'll show you the wire. Seven forms of it and all relevant." He chuckled. "You can't help being excited, can you?" he said happily. "It goes on too. I must tell you. Things began to move at once. Last night I sent a routine call to the hotels, and this afternoon, just as we were coming away, we had a reply from a little place in Victoria. We rushed down there and got everything intact. It was all there in K.'s luggage. We got the name again, the ad-dress—everything—all in a tuppenny notebook. It was blackmail all right. Then we hurried down here and found this end busy. The railway people had started remembering things once they had the name. It was a childish trick on Friday. The same trick as Petrie's. The train wasn't used at all. Follow me? We found the spanner too. It belonged to the car, as we thought. The whole thing has dropped together like a puzzle running out. It's open and shut. We've got everything. Pleased with yourself?"

"Howlingly."

"You don't sound it. You've got nothing to worry about. You couldn't have done it more quickly. Yeo's here. He sends his regards and takes back all hard thoughts. He says he misunderstood you, but now that he sees what you were working up to he'll be happy to buy you a beer at the first opportunity. It's such a pretty case, Campion. There's not a flaw in it."

"How long will you be?"

The younger man's voice was very quiet.

"Half an hour at most. We're practically set. I just phoned to warn you and to make sure there was no hitch your end. We can serve the doings at White Walls now, can we?"

"Yes."

"You'll stay there with your eyes glued till we come?"

"I will."

"Right. Half an hour, then. Good-bye."

Campion replaced the receiver and looked down at the polished sur-face of the table, where a light film of summer dust had collected since the morning. A childish inclination to scribble in it assailed him and he wrote the three words which he was trying to keep in the forefront of his mind against the intolerable temptations which besieged him: "The porter's wife."

He regarded the inscription helplessly for some seconds before he rubbed it out with his handkerchief.

As he crossed the hall he kicked something small and round in his stride and stooped to retrieve it. It was a small yellow button with a flower painted on it. He recognised it as one of the six on Linda's yellow dress. He turned it over, hesitated, and finally dropped it into his pocket with a secret, comforted sense of acquisition.

He saw Sutane as soon as he stepped out into the garden again. The dancer was seated on the last step of the terrace outside the morning-room windows. He had his back to Campion, and in the tight black sweater which he had pulled over his white flannels his body looked kite-shaped and angular, like a modern drawing. He sat with his knees pulled up to his chin and his head resting upon them. No other man in a similar position could have appeared so completely comfortable, at peace and at ease.

Far down at the end of the garden Linda was walking with Slippers. Their dresses flickered white and yellow among the leaves. Eve had returned. She was lying in the hammock couch at the far end of the lawn. Her hands were behind her head and her eyes, Campion guessed, were staring with dark resentment at the little skiffs of pink cloud floating so serenely in the painted sky.

Sock had vanished, but the sound of his voice, punctuated by squeals of delight from Sarah, echoed from the kitchen lawn on the west side of the house and indicated that the three-card tricksters had found a suitable mug.

Campion sat down beside Sutane. In the cool depth of the morning room behind them Mercer was still strumming. His new tune, "Pavane for a Dead Dancer," had grown from a motif into a completed thing, and he played it over several times, working a flight of spontaneous conceits into it before skimming off into other phrases, some amusing and others reaching that substratum of banality which has, at least, always the merit of provoking astonishment.

Neither of the two men on the terrace spoke immediately. Sutane sat very still. He had not altered his position save that he had turned his head and now sat watching Campion with his dull black eyes intelligent and questioning.

"Hello," he said softly at last. "Come to make your report?"

Campion regarded him gravely. His own gamut of sensation had been played through. He had heard the whole scale and knew the last thin flat note. He was emotionally finished and was strangely at peace.

Sutane stirred and the familiar bent smile passed over his wide mouth.

"I thought you had."

Campion looked at his own long brown fingers and spoke without taking his eyes from them.

"The police have a copy of Chloe's marriage certificate," he said slowly. "I told them about it. They got it from a church in Brixton. When she came down here and increased her blackmailing demands on her husband he lost his temper with her and . . ."

Sutane stretched himself suddenly.

"Oh, it wasn't so simple as that, my dear fellow," he said, turning over so that he lay on his stomach on the grass, with his elbows resting on the low flat step. "He didn't know he *was* her husband, you see."

Campion stared at him in fascinated resignation and Sutane went on, his pleasant voice playing dreamily with the words.

"She was a strange woman when she was younger. I don't know if you'll know what I mean, but she had that quality of recklessness which is the essence of passion. When the war was first over there was a feel for it. People talk of youngsters *drifting* into a life of good times. They don't know. There was energy, force, ecstasy, put into those good times. There was no drifting about it. We hurled ourselves into them and made them riotous.

"Here and there a particular woman was thrown up out of them like a bubble on the brew. She became not a leader but an embodiment of the spirit of the urge for enjoyment. The old anxiety to fill the day because of the death that was coming tomorrow had become a habit with our immediate elders and we caught it from them, but without their fear. We were young. We weren't tired. We weren't shattered. Our nerves weren't shot to pieces. We were repressed. We'd grown up in a world where there wasn't any fun. And suddenly, just when our blood was rising, it came.

"Chloe was a little older than the rest of us. She was successful and at the height of her looks. She married lightly in a fit of exuberance and a few months after, when she tired of it, she took another man. There was a row. The poor idiot of a husband thought he was in love with her and tried to hold her and she annihilated him by explaining cheerfully as she packed her clothes that he had no possible claim on her. She'd been married before, in the war, she said. Her husband was alive. She must be a bigamist and wasn't it amusing? She was not very sorry and he was not to be silly, not to be *vieux jeu*. It had been a rather jolly experience, she thought."

Sutane's voice ceased and he glanced down the garden to where the two women were still walking.

"The husband was brokenhearted, silly young ass, but he recovered," he added presently.

In the long pause which followed, much that had been dark to Mr.

Campion became suddenly and painfully clear. He saw the garden again as it had been on that twilit evening a fortnight before when Chloe had gone down to the lake to dance to "Love, the Magician."

Sutane was waiting and Campion roused himself to speak.

"I had not seen that," he said.

"How could you?" the dancer murmured. "You never knew the real Chloe."

Campion took up his story again. He was acutely conscious that there was very little time and that there was much that had to be said.

"When she came to London this time she found it impossible to get hold of her husband alone," he began. "He was too busy, too closely surrounded. In despair she forced herself down to his home and begged or cheated him into meeting her in the garden at night. When the moment came and she actually had him before her in a lonely and romantic setting she must have played her trump card immediately. I didn't know how strong it was. She told him she was still his wife. Either her previous marriage had been a fabrication, invented on the spur of the moment when she wanted to be rid of him, or her first husband had died before her second marriage took place."

"There was no first marriage," said Sutane.

Campion felt intolerably weary. His bones were weighing him down and his head ached. He struggled on.

"She was alone, dancing, when he found her that night," he said, "and she must have talked to him with the gramophone still running. The whole interview couldn't have taken long because the last record of the set was still on the machine when I found it that night. I think she simply walked up to him and told him she had lied long ago and could prove it. Something like that?"

He paused questioningly.

Sutane nodded gravely. "Go on," he said.

Campion's precise voice wavered as he took up the tale.

"His first reaction was fear, naturally," he murmured. "Fear and then rage. He caught hold of her by the throat and, before he realised at all what had happened, her knees sagged and he felt her go limp. She was dead. The *status lymphaticus* accounted for that. He didn't know about that then, of course, and he must have been terrified. He only saw that she was suddenly and unaccountably dead and the whole miserable secret must come out, with scandal and ruin in its trail.

"I think the gramophone must have finished about that time, for he turned the record over, not realising that the piece of trivia on the other side was hardly the sort of thing she would ever play. It was a natural thing for him to do. It was a subconscious effort to keep things as they were, you see, an instinctive attempt to delay the moment of disaster.

"After that I fancy he lost his head completely. He picked her up and

carried her as far away from the house as he could. That was unreasoning
instinct too. He was so careless that he left the gramophone running,
trod on a record and dropped her red silk skirt, which had been tied
tightly around her waist, and which he must have loosened in his first
frantic efforts to revive her. The skirt fell on the grass, where someone
else found it and danced on it.

"All this was done madly in his first terror, but when he came to the
bridge his mind began to work again. The car was there and it put an
idea in his head. He pitched her over into the lane and staged the accident. It wasn't murder the first time. That's the whole ghastly pity of it."

Sutane was still lying on the shallow steps, his eyes quiet and without
expression.

"Why hadn't she come out with it before?" he demanded, bitterness
in his voice for the first time. "Why leave her rotten story until now?
Why give the poor beast years of peace and then spring it on him?"

Campion did not look up.

"Money, don't you think?" he suggested gently. "She came back and
found—or thought she found—him rich. She didn't want the man. She
wanted to be bought off."

Sutane laughed. The violent explosive sound echoed over the garden
and startled the birds in the ornamental cherry trees.

"I never saw it, Campion," he said huskily. "I never saw it. It would
have been so easy."

Campion passed his hand over his forehead and found it damp. It was
a mad interview, a conversation in a dream, with nothing solid or static
in the world, only a sense of inexorable disaster coming nearer and nearer
every second.

"Konrad saw him," he said. "Or the husband thought he saw him. Konrad sneaked out about that time to telephone his accomplice and report
the success of his surprise party. The following morning he began to talk
wildly up in the dressing room. Then he appropriated the handbag. Then
he threatened. The husband got frightened. He instigated a search of
Chloe's rooms. The marriage certificate was found and burnt. Chloe was
buried. He felt safe again, or almost safe. There was only Konrad to consider. But Konrad looked dangerous and in the end the husband committed the intolerable, incredible folly of deciding to shut his mouth.

"There was a man called Kummer in Vienna, a brilliant chemist with
a crooked streak, the kind of person a young bohemian in Paris just after
the war might easily have got to know. He was not hard to get hold of
now, for a man with friends among the intelligentsia abroad. Need I go
on?"

Sutane laid the back of his hand over his face. It was ballet rather than
theatre and was oddly expressive.

"Those other people . . ." he said. "Oh, God! Those other people . . ."

The sun had sunk down behind the house and they were in the shadow. Linda and Slippers had passed out of sight. The kitchen lawn was silent, and in her swing couch Eve appeared to be asleep.

In the silence Mercer's little tunes came floating out caressingly, their sentimental meanderings flirting idly with the memory. An older melody than the rest caught Campion's attention. It reminded him vividly of his first arrival at the house. The name of the song slipped up in his mind— "Water-Lily Girl." He remembered Chloe playing it as she sat beside the disgruntled composer, and he saw again her raddled face, with the pale green, overbright eyes, turned archly towards the embarrassed man. He saw the scene clearly: Chloe playing the song all the way through, with obstinate insistence on each sickly phrase. Mercer was playing it like that now, almost as though he were caricaturing it.

As Campion listened to him a further memory returned to his mind. He went back to his undergraduate days and saw himself drinking coffee in a shabby teashop in a Cambridge back street where, behind a thin green curtain, an appalling gramophone ground out the plummy mouthings of a tenth-rate ballad singer.

> *"When the stars are wide awake, Water-Lily Girl,*
> *I'll be waiting by the lake, Water-Lily Girl.*
> *There's a beating heart at stake.*
> *Will you hide and let it break?*
> *For old times' sake—Water-Lily Girl."*

He sat up as the significance of the doggerel sank into his mind. That, then, had been Chloe's invitation to the meeting. There had been no note or hurried word during the flurry of the day, as he had supposed. The arrangement had been made then, under his nose. He understood at last her insistence on the verse of the song.

As the little piece of jigsaw dropped into place his mind jolted. A new thought clamoured at him. Sutane had not been there. Sutane had been out in the hall, rehearsing. He himself had not set eyes on the man before lunch.

As he sat stiffly, his eyes fixed upon the middle distance, his brain seemed suddenly to turn over in his head. It was a definite physical experience and was comparable to the process which takes place when an expected train in the underground station appears from what is apparently the wrong tunnel and the mind slips over and adjusts the phenomenon by turning the universe other side out, substituting in one kaleidoscopic second east for west.

Eve had been in the room that Sunday morning and so had Sock, but Chloe had been playing to Mercer.

Campion stared at the new vista.

Squire Mercer.

Mercer, who never considered anyone except himself, not only as a main rule but down to the smallest and most trivial circumstance. Mercer, who honestly thought himself all-important and, because of his gifts, was tolerated and encouraged by his friends.

Mercer, who had the one type of mind which was sufficiently ingenious and sufficiently devoid of humour to conceive the dreadful and ludicrous bicycle-lamp grenade, a notion quite as laughable and quite as horribly effective as the notorious Mr. Smith's recipe for murdering wife after wife in the cracked baths of second-rate boarding houses.

Mercer, who would not be particularly disturbed by the news that a number of strangers had met with an appalling accident on a railway station, so long as it took place twenty miles out of his sight.

Campion bent forward, his head in his hands. His mind had become very clear. He had the illusion of thinking very slowly.

Mercer had taken an overdose of quinine immediately after hearing on the 8:45 news bulletin the news of the disaster at Boarbridge. He had then developed, or said he had developed, severe cinchonism, which was a peculiar condition inasmuch as any doctor consulted had only the patient's word for the symptoms experienced—blindness, shakiness, headache, congestion of the middle ear. All these things could be simulated very easily by a man who was afraid his nerves might give him away during an awkward interview with the police.

Campion's mind travelled back to the night of Chloe's death. Mercer had been in the little music room with the window open. It was practically Mercer's own room. He certainly used it more often than anyone else. Campion remembered that window. He himself had slid out through it during his experiment with the weights from the kitchen scales. He remembered the hard turf below it and the straight path leading right through the garden to the lake. A man might slip out on to the dark lawn and back through that window a dozen times without being missed.

He thought of Kummer.

Kummer had come to London and had put up at a small hotel in Victoria. It had been assumed that the man had been in England for some time. But there was now the likelihood that he had only just arrived.

If Mercer's cinchonism was fictitious, why should he have gone to London on Friday to see a specialist? Suppose, instead, he had gone to see Kummer? Mercer could not or would not drive a car, but he knew where Sock kept his coupé, parked in the open street.

Suppose Yeo's piece of reconstruction had been the truth and Mercer had indicated the car standing at the end of the cul-de-sac and had asked Kummer to drive him back to his cottage on the White Walls estate. Suppose he had sat beside the man until the convenient moment had arrived and had then whipped the rug over his head and had killed him

CRIME AND MR. CAMPION

with Sock's spanner, battering out his brains with all the frenzied terror
of the man not naturally violent.

The superintendent's cautious conferences on the telephone returned
to his ears. He had spoken of Petrie's trick. Suppose Mercer had pushed
the car onto the verge after Kummer was dead and had then walked back
to Boarbridge station and had waited there for his own chauffeur, who
naturally assumed that he had come down by his ordinary late train.

Mercer had gone to Paris on the Tuesday after Chloe's death, when
the bicycle was already in the house and Konrad had already made his
threat. If to Paris, why not to Vienna, a few hours' flying distance beyond?

The whole series of murders had been so utterly careless. As Yeo had
said, the man responsible was evidently blind to his danger. His crimes
were the crimes of one who was a little god in his own circle. Who then
was the little god of this circle? Not Sutane, who was the worker, the
man who recognised his responsibilities and was secretly appalled by them,
but Mercer, who was cozened, flattered and protected until his opinion
of his own importance lost all touch with reality.

Campion scrambled to his feet.

The significance of Yeo's message through the superintendent had burst
upon him. Yeo now knew the truth and erroneously supposed that he,
Campion, had known it all the time. It was Mercer who had married
Chloe, Mercer who had derived from the very briefness of his association
with her the inspiration for his embarrassingly poignant music. It was
Mercer's name in the tuppenny notebook, Mercer's name in the register at
the Brixton church.

Relief burst over Campion, engulfing him, soothing him, comforting
him with the old magic cry of his childhood—"It isn't true! It isn't true!"
He was free. The load was lifted. Sutane was not the man. Linda—Sarah—
Sock—Eve—the theatre—the house—the lovely excitement of those dancing
feet—they were all miraculously saved on the brink of disaster. He had
been gloriously wrong. It was not true!

He paused. Through the overwhelming flood which lifted him out of
himself he heard the tinkle of the piano and with that sound came a new
recollection, which stopped his heart.

There was an obstacle.

There remained the unanswerable consideration which had struck
Mercer from his list of suspects from the very beginning. Mercer had an
alibi for the hour of Chloe's death.

All that evening he had been playing in the music room and the one
man whose word on such a vital matter Campion would have taken without question had been sitting there listening to him—Uncle William,
faulty but incorruptible, human but honest as the day.

Campion moved slowly across the terrace and stood looking into the
house through the wide french window. In the shadow at the far end

of the morning room he saw the crown of Mercer's untidy black head above the angle of the piano top. His glance travelled forward and he caught his breath.

In the deep armchair, his chubby feet crossed, his hands folded on his paunch, the empty decanter at his side and his crimson face immobile in the sleep of the happily drugged, lay Uncle William human.

A herd of buffalo in the room might conceivably awaken him within the hour, but very little else would disturb that deep and alcoholic peace.

Campion stepped back and turned abruptly at the top of the steps to find Sutane beside him. The dancer's angular and expressive body was relaxed and his arms hung at his sides.

"Keep Eve out of it," he said softly. "They were in the midst of one of those wild, impossible love affairs when it happened, you see. She was so jealous of Chloe at first and then after the woman's death he altered and she couldn't understand it at all, poor little beast. That's why she ran away. She couldn't bear to look at him any more. I hunted for her all over the place. I gave up the show on Friday night to go down and see her, once Sock found out where she was. I got it all out of her then."

He sighed and peered into Campion's face.

"They'd kept it a secret, knowing I wouldn't approve." Campion looked at the other man steadily.

"How long have you known the truth about Mercer?"

Sutane stared at him.

"I saw him," he said. "I thought you knew. My dear fellow, I saw him on the bridge. He pitched her clean under my wheels."

He came a step nearer and his deeply lined face was desperately sincere.

"I didn't dream he'd go on," he said earnestly. "I got hold of the certificate and I burned it because I knew he'd never think of it. But I didn't dream he'd go on. After Boarbridge I had to have you here. I *had* to, Campion! Don't you see, you were my conscience. You had to find him out. But I couldn't direct you. I couldn't give him away. We were together in Paris after the war. I was his only friend and, oh, my dear chap, don't you see, I was the beggar who pinched his wife."

There was a whir of gears at the drive gates and as they glanced up two police cars crackled smoothly over the gravel towards the front door.

In the morning room Mercer was playing his little pavane.

Sutane took a long, slow, infinitely graceful step. In the midst of it he looked up. The crooked smile was on his lips and, surprisingly, his black eyes had tears in them.

"How could I, old boy?" he said.